**International Yearbook
of Educational and Instructional
Technology 1982/83**

International Yearbook of Educational and Instructional Technology 1982/83

Association for Educational and Training Technology

Editor:
C W Osborne
*Middlesex Polytechnic,
Learning Systems Group*

General Editor:
A J Trott
*Bulmershe College,
Reading*

Kogan Page, London/Nichols Publishing Company, New York

First published in Great Britain in 1982 by
Kogan Page Ltd, 120 Pentonville Road, London N1 9JN

Copyright © 1982 Association for Educational
and Training Technology

British Library Cataloguing in Publication Data

International yearbook of educational and
  instructional technology. – 1982-83
  1. Educational technology – Periodicals
  I. Association for Educational and Training
  Technology
  371.3'07'8   LB1028.3

  ISBN 0-85038-550-4
  ISSN 0307-9732

First published in the United States of America in 1982 by
Nichols Publishing Company,
PO Box 96, New York, NY10024

ISBN 0-89397-130-8

Printed and bound in Great Britain by
Robert Hartnoll Ltd,
Bodmin, Cornwall

Contents

Section 4: Directory of Centres of Activity

Section 5: Producers and Distributors of Programmes and Audiovisual Software

Section 6: A Guide to Audiovisual Hardware on the Market

Introduction

The *International Yearbook of Educational and Instructional Technology* is published under the auspices of The Association for Educational and Training Technology, formerly APLET. AETT's international membership includes people with interests in all levels and aspects of education and training, and the *Yearbook* is one of a range of publications by which it seeks to promote communication among these members and all who are interested in the development and applications of educational technology. AETT's activities are fully described on p 10. The Association's regular publications include its journal, *Programmed Learning and Educational Technology*, its bulletin, *Ed Tech News*, the proceedings of the Annual Conference, published under the title *Aspects of Educational Technology*, and this *Yearbook*. Within this range the *Yearbook* attempts to provide a biennial survey of the field at an international level.

The above paragraph also opened the introduction of the last edition of the *Yearbook*, and it is interesting to note how many of Anne Howe's remarks then are still appropriate now. We continue to see the growth of the concept of educational technology as 'the systematic planning, development, management, and evaluation of educational and training systems', wherein is absorbed the more traditional element of educational technology in the form of audiovisual hardware and software. It is also interesting to notice, however, that in some senses the hardware may now be making a partial resurgence: in the last two years we have seen a rapid popularization of the microcomputer, for domestic and for educational use, and also the establishment of the Microelectronics Education Programme (MEP) in the UK. In the same period, CET has carried out and reported on its educational field trials with PRESTEL. Both of these projects receive some coverage in this edition (and it is almost certain that micros will feature even more strongly in future years), and both offer challenge as well as opportunity to the teacher and learner.

The contents

In common with all publications, costs of publishing are rising steeply and the *Yearbook* faces a choice: to become bigger, and cost more; or to seek to control costs by reduction in length. For the present edition we are trying to pursue a middle course, and this has meant making decisions on the prime function of the *Yearbook*. My conclusion is that its greatest value lies in its role as a directory not only of centres of activity, but also of sources of hardware and software, and of information and ideas in the field of educational technology. Such a view has had its consequences, and some readers may consider that the articles section has been too greatly reduced — I would welcome comment on this. More significantly, however, it is important that *Yearbook* entries should be as accurate as possible and up-to-date, and it has been disappointing to note how many institutions or persons failed to supply updated information. In such cases, the present edition repeats the last edition's text (identified by the symbol *) but, unless further information is received prior to the next edition, *such entries will then be deleted* (centres or persons who do not supply updated entries are unlikely to respond to other enquiries). The elimination of such 'dead wood' may offer the *Yearbook* room for expansion in other areas.

On the subject of expansion, I am aware that the *Yearbook* continues to exhibit a strong Anglo-Saxon bias; this is understandable in terms of the history of AETT/APLET but is not necessarily good for the future, and I would welcome more information not only from Third World countries but also from Europe — audiovisual materials, for example, in languages other than English might be of wide interest. Similarly, there is an increasing awareness of how educational technology approaches can be of use to those not in, and not capable of, higher or further education. Mike Freshwater's article indicates one approach to this field; I would be pleased to hear of others. The *Yearbook* can only be as good and relevant as its contents, which have to be supplied by those in the field; I would welcome all, and any, comments and contributions.

Turning to this edition, the first two Sections of the *Yearbook* consist of articles supplied (and perhaps reflect those that failed to appear!), some of which have already been mentioned. It would be inexcusable to omit mention of the death of Jean Piaget whose work has had such a profound influence on educational thinking — a brief tribute appears, courtesy of Professor Lovell. Distance learning and study skills continue to be of interest, and are the subject of articles by Professor Holmberg and Anne Howe respectively. Alex Romiszowski presents an analysis of the factors that may inhibit or prevent successful implementation of a new idea.

Section 3 is 'new' in that it brings together chapters on sources of information and assistance that were previously scattered in different sections of the *Yearbook*. They should now be easier to locate and use.

Section 4 is much as before, subject to what are intended to be some simplifications and some corrections — although no doubt I'll hear in due course of others that have yet to be attended to!

Section 5 is also relatively unchanged, although enlarged. As observed in the preface to the section, it is early yet to incorporate microsoftware but this will undoubtedly form a new category in the next edition. This is a section, incidentally, where advice and information is particularly useful.

Finally there is Section 6. Partly for economy, partly in recognition of the great pace of technological change and yet of the now relatively basic formats in audiovisual hardware, it was decided to dispense with the text relating to each category. Instead, the UK section now resembles that for the USA, but with different categories and with an attempt to identify the major manufacturers of microcomputers.

Acknowledgements

It is really rather invidious in a publication such as the *Yearbook* to single out individuals for special mention when, as indicated above, the outcome can only be as good as the information supplied by countless correspondents — to them my sincere thanks, as indeed to those who supplied articles.

But one must try, and I must thank Middlesex Polytechnic and John Duke for clearing me to take on the editor's role. That said, I must then thank Anne Howe as ex-editor for giving me invaluable support and advice, and also my colleague Rodney Battey for completely overhauling the Bibliography — a massive task. Jill Coates at CET provided valuable assistance (and sympathy), as did Ann Whiting at Unesco in Paris — to them, too, my thanks. Dr Carl Hendershot, as in previous editions, was most helpful in providing American information as well as his article.

The greatest debt, however, must go to two ladies: Katy Carter who, as editor at Kogan Page, never once let me lapse or rest on my laurels, yet never failed to be pleasant and relaxed — I still don't know how she did it! And finally to my wife, Anne, who now knows what it is like to live for three months with a bear with a sore head — and she still speaks to me, which says a great deal for her tolerance.

I'll close with thanks, however, to those correspondents, notably in Australia (but also in South America and India) who, as our letters to them were inadvertently sent by surface mail, did not receive requests for updated information until after the official deadline — but who replied nevertheless. I was particularly touched by the reply that was addressed to 'The Editor, International Yewburk' — I'm still wondering if that was a Freudian slip or just Australian honesty!

Chris Osborne
Learning Systems Group
Middlesex Polytechnic
Bounds Green Road
London N11 2NQ

AETT: Its Activities, Officers and Publications

The Association for Educational and Training Technology (AETT) is an independent, voluntary body which seeks to improve education and training by the study of existing situations, by the systematic application of instructional technology, by the dissemination of information, and by providing opportunities for interested colleagues to hold discussion meetings.

The Association was originally formed in 1962 as the Association for Programmed Learning (PL). Since then, of course, the field originally opened up by the examination of programmed learning and its application has been subsumed under the general name of 'educational technology', and as the scope of the emerging field has widened so has that of the Association. Thus, in 1969 the Association changed its name to APLET — the Association for Programmed Learning and Educational Technology, and in 1979 it adopted the new name 'The Association for Educational and Training Technology'. The new name reflects the broad base of membership of the Association, whose interests in educational technology cover the whole spectrum of its theory and applications in education and training.

AETT has most successfully established links with national and international bodies. Within Britain, combined seminars and projects have been mounted with the Council for Educational Technology for the United Kingdom, with the Universities Council for the Education and Training of Teachers, and with the Network of Programmed Learning Centres. International consultations have been conducted through Unesco, the British Council and the Overseas Development Administration. These organizational links are valuable to the Association and to its individual members, who are able to keep in touch with national and international developments and with recognized experts on all aspects of educational technology.

The Association remains essentially a collection of individuals, many of whom hold posts of responsibility in educational and training establishments throughout the UK and abroad. The main aim of the Association is to promote communication amongst educational technologists and those of various disciplines who are interested in the uses of educational technology. In pursuance of this aim it organizes an annual Conference, which has gained an international reputation. The publication of the Conference proceedings, under the title of *Aspects of Educational Technology,* has provided both the expert and the student with a valuable source of information over the years. The Association's

Journal *PLET (Programmed Learning and Educational Technology)*, published quarterly, provides a forum for research and development in educational technology. The Association also plans to publish from time to time monographs on specific subjects of interest to its members. A full list of publications follows later in this Yearbook, itself an important AETT publication.

In addition to the annual Conference and other events, and its frequent publications, the Association is currently exploring ways in which information about recent innovations in the field of microprocessors might be disseminated; ways to assist research students by the collection and categorizing of previously published papers into subject categories; ways in which the publication of monographs on specific topics might be increased; and ways to help members obtain short-term consultancy work overseas.

By kind permission of the Trustees, the Association has the use of the London premises of the British Life Assurance Trust for Health and Medical Education, situated in Tavistock Square, near Euston and St Pancras main line stations. Personal callers will be made welcome.

International Conference

AETT's annual Conference, known internationally as the ETIC Conference, is held every spring at different educational institutions. The 1982 Conference, on the theme of 'The effectiveness and efficiency obtainable in education and training', will be held at Bulmershe College of Higher Education, Reading, from Monday 5 April to Thursday 8 April (inclusive).

Details of these and other AETT seminars and activities are published in the press, in *EdTech News*, or can be obtained through the Conference Organizers and the AETT office.

AETT membership

There are three classes of membership:

Individual Members: professional educational and training technologists and interested individuals.

Corporate Members: institutions concerned with education and training and organizations and business contributing to educational and training research, development and equipment production and marketing.

Associate Members: of special interest to students of educational technology and to educators and trainers wishing to sample AETT membership, this category is open to new members only and is available for a maximum period of two years. Associate Members receive all benefits except a copy of the yearbook.

Members receive, on joining, the AETT Constitution, Standing Orders and Rules; the AETT Journal *Programmed Learning and Educational Technology*, and *EdTech News* (both quarterly); and the *AETT Yearbook of Educational and Instructional Technology* (biennially). The AETT Membership List is also issued biennially.

Membership benefits include reduced fees at AETT's Annual International Conference, AETT publications at reduced prices, the use of the AETT Information Service and the AETT Register of Educational Technology Consultants. AETT has worldwide contacts and is represented on various official and subject teacher committees. It has close links with other organizations working in the field. For full details, write to:

> The Administrator,
> AETT,
> BLAT Centre,
> BMA House,
> Tavistock Square,
> London WC1.

Officers of the Association, 1981-82

President	Dr Harry Kaye
Vice-Presidents	R E B Budgett
	Dr E M Buter, Amsterdam, The Netherlands
	J Clarke, Dundee College of Education, Scotland
	Professor L R B Elton, University of Surrey, UK
	Dr J F Leedham, OBE, Leicestershire, UK
	Dr P David Mitchell, Concordia University, Montreal, Canada
	Miss M Procter, Inner London Education Authority, UK
Chairman of the Association	J K Sinclair, Central Region Education Authority, Scotland
Chairman of Council	A J Trott, Bulmershe College of Higher Education, Reading, UK
Vice-Chairman of Council	L F Evans, The City University, London
Hon Secretary	E Howarth, Plymouth Polytechnic, Plymouth, UK
Hon Treasurer	J A Davies, Bradford College, Bradford, UK
Administrator	F R Willmore

AETT Council, 1981-82

N E Allen, Engineering Industry Training Board
B S Alloway, Huddersfield Polytechnic
Dr K Bung, Recall Consultants
Dr W D Clarke, BLAT Centre for Health & Medical Education, UK
J A Davies, Bradford College
Dr H I Ellington, Robert Gordon Institute of Technology, Aberdeen
Dr P J Hills, Leicester University

E Howarth, Plymouth Polytechnic
Ms A Howe, Middlesex Polytechnic
R McAleese, University of Aberdeen
N Rushby, Imperial College, London
J K Sinclair, Central Region Education Authority, Scotland
A J Trott, Bulmershe College of Higher Education, Reading
Miss S Ward, BACIE
Sqn Ldr M Ware, RAF School of Education
Q A Whitlock, Sheffield City Polytechnic

AETT publications

General Editor: A J Trott
Yearbook of Educational and Instructional Technology (biennial).
Journal of Programmed Learning and Educational Technology (quarterly).
Educational Technology News (quarterly).
Aspects of Educational Technology Volumes 1 - XV (for full details, see
p 00).
APLET Occasional Publication No 1 *A Systems Approach to Education
& Training*, ed A J Romiszowski.
APLET Occasional Publication No 2 *Videocassettes in Education
& Training*, eds J Leedham and A J Romiszowski.
APLET Occasional Publication No 4 *Selected Microteaching Papers*,
ed A J Trott.
AETT Occasional Publication No 5 *Selected Readings in Computer-based
Learning*, ed N Rushby.
(All the above publications are published by Kogan Page Ltd,
120 Pentonville Road, London N1).
'Problems and Methods in Programmed Learning'. Proceedings of the
Birmingham Programmed Learning Conference 1967, ed M J Tobin.
Published by University of Birmingham.

Section 1: Trends and Readings

Distance Study and Mediated Teaching in a Continental European Context

Börje Holmberg, *Professor of Education, Zentrales Institut fur Fernstudienforschung (ZIFF), FernUniversität, W Germany*

Historical background

Distance education in the form of traditional correspondence study began on the European continent at the end of the nineteenth century. It proved particularly successful in Scandinavia. Hermods was founded in Malmö, Sweden, in 1898. Favourable experiences of correspondence study paved the way for ready acceptance of the various types of mediated study which began to appear in Scandinavia in the middle of this century (Gaddén, 1973). It no doubt contributed to the early interest in programmed instruction, often enough without much consideration of its basis in behaviourist learning theory, the use of audiovisual media, computers and technology generally. Maybe the same could be said about France, which has long had a strong tradition of correspondence education. Its state-owned Centre National de Tele-Enseignement, in 1981 renamed Centre National d'Enseignement par Correspondence, founded in 1939, was and is one of the biggest multi-media distance-teaching institutions in the world. The Netherlands may offer further parallels with its high quality correspondence schools.

In West Germany the opposite tendency seems to be noticeable (although German correspondence schools have been known since the 1980s). Interest in the educational use of media ('Mediendidaktik') seems to have opened the eyes of the establishment to the potential of distance study. In 1967 the Deutsches Institut für Fernstudien was founded at the University of Tübingen for the purpose of developing distance-study courses (largely for the further training of teachers, to be offered to the German states for use as decided on by the latter) and doing research in the field of distance study (Rebel, 1981), and in 1975 the FernUniversität, a state university basing its teaching on distance study, started its work in Hagen, Nordrhein-Westfalen. East Germany on the other hand developed a strong tradition of correspondence education soon after the war, later diluted into a kind of semi-distance study relying heavily on face-to-face consultations and seminars, which is paralleled in other East European countries. Active work in fields of mediated study in general and distance study in particular now occurs all over Europe.

Against this background it should be of some interest to look into the most important recent research and development activities on the European continent.

Theory

Some attempts have been made in Germany to develop a theory of
distance study. These are to some extent related to the general concerns
of mediated learning and its frustrating failure to create a media taxonomy
(Dichanz, 1974) and largely to the concept of educational technology
(Flechsig, 1970). How these are intertwined with distance study is evident
(see, for example, Dohmen, 1970). What separates pure self-study from
distance education is — in Michael Moore's terminology — that distance
education is characterized by a varying amount of dialogue and structure,
whereas study without any (mediated or live) tutor support is an entirely
independent study programme (cf the work of the Russian educationist
Berdichevsky, 1975).

Learning and teaching theories play an important part in the considerations
of mediated learning generally and distance education particularly.
Continental scholars — probably in agreement with most scholars in other
parts of the world — tend to stress that it would be futile to believe that
theories of teaching providing guidelines for action can be deduced with
any certainty from theories of learning. When something has been learnt,
this learning may have been caused by other influences than those of the
teaching. When something has been taught we do not know if something
has been learnt or, in fact, if something has been learnt we do not
automatically know what. Possibly something different from what was
intended by the teaching has been learnt (Loser and Terhart, 1977: 29).
If, in accordance with generally accepted rules, we expect of a theory of
teaching that it should establish functional relationships between the
conditions and the outcomes of teaching and learning and that it should
be expressed in such a way that research data capable of possibly refuting
the theory can be collected, we soon find that these requirements are
not always met. Thus, for instance, Peters' fruitful theory of distance
education as a kind of industrialized learning and teaching pays
comparatively little attention to what above has been called the
functional relationship between the conditions and the outcomes of
teaching and learning. In a systematic comparison with industrial work
Peters points to rationalizing, division of labour, mass production,
mechanizing, automation, planning, organization, controlling and checking
etc as typical of distance education (which here would seem to include
most kinds of mediated teaching). Prescriptive principles are deducible
from his work, but it is probably above all to be seen as an attempt to
mark a clear line of division between distance study and face-to-face
methods (Peters, 1971 and 1973).

Similar limitations apply to a process model developed by Delling
featuring eight dimensions of distance education (society, the student,
the distance, the information carrier, the study aim, the study matter,
the learning result and the supporting organization), by means of which
it should be possible to describe all distance-education processes
(Delling, 1971), and to Graff's cybernetic approaches based on decision

theory which lead to the conclusion that the great problems are 'beyond the calculation' (Graff, 1970).

The present author's theory of distance education as a method of guided didactic conversation implies that the character of good distance education resembles that of a guided conversation aiming at learning and that the presence of the typical traits of such a conversation facilitates learning. This theory both serves the purpose of understanding the character of distance education and is explanatory. On the basis of specified postulates and characteristics of what is regarded as didactic conversation formal hypotheses have been developed which have made empirical testing possible. So far nothing has come to light that could falsify the theory (Holmberg, 1981: 30-2; Holmberg and Schumer, 1980).

A successful and highly illuminating attempt to relate distance learning (and, implicitly, most mediated learning) to current learning and teaching theories has been made by Bååth (Lund University and Hermods, Sweden). He has analysed the following models with a view to finding out to what extent they are applicable to distance study:

- ☐ Skinner's behaviour-control model
- ☐ Rothkopf's model for written instruction
- ☐ Ausubel's organizer model
- ☐ the model of Structural Communication
- ☐ Bruner's discovery-learning model
- ☐ Roger's model for facilitation of learning
- ☐ Gagné's general teaching model.

For each of these models Bååth has investigated its general applicability to distance study, the implications for the development of course material, for non-contiguous two-way communication, for supplementing this two-way communication by face-to-face contacts and related concerns. Bååth has found that all the models investigated are applicable to distance study, that some of them (Skinner, Gagné, Rothkopf, Ausubel, Structural Communication) seem particularly adaptable to distance study in its fairly strictly structured form, that Bruner's more open model and even Roger's model can be applied to distance study, though not without special measures, eg concerning simultaneous non-contiguous communication (telephone, etc) and that demands on distance-study systems which should inspire new developments can be inferred from the models studied (Bååth, 1979).

Methodology

A number of continental studies concerned with the methods applicable to mediated teaching have been made. The one on didactic conversation is of some relevance here. The existence and application of two entirely different teaching methods — on the one hand the presentation of intellectual knowledge as ready-made, ie already discovered and described systems, and on the other hand problem-solving approaches — have been studied by Lehner and Weingartz at the West German FernUniversität (Lehner and Weingartz, 1981).

Weingartz has, on the basis of a consistent view of learning as understanding and problem-solving, provided an in-depth analysis of some distance-study courses from different parts of the world illustrating these differences (Weingartz, 1980), and Lehner has developed a learning theory bearing on this. He describes all learning as problem-solving in the sense that it is composed of making assumptions (ie developing hypotheses) and modifying these as the learning progresses — an application of Popper's epistemological principles of 'conjectures and refutations'. This leads Lehner to what (like Wagenschein and others) he terms a 'genetic learning approach' (Lehner, 1978 and 1979). Starting out from problems instead of from the comprehensive systems constituted from the knowledge amassed through the centuries (for instance, when studying gravitation, asking the questions asked by Aristotle, Galileo etc instead of starting by learning the solutions they found) favours genetic learning. Weingartz's theoretical approach is linked with Lehner's and has led her to study current practice in distance education. To judge from her study, much remains to be done to improve problem-solving learning in distance study, where on the whole the 'ready-made systems' presentation dominates, although guidance in far-reaching problem-solving occurs in some courses.

Students' learning styles are evidently of prime importance in all mediated learning. Two Swedish scholars, Ference Marton and Roger Säljö, have looked into learning styles, somewhat in the spirit of Gordon Pask (Pask, 1976), and have identified deep-learning vs surface-learning habits in the study of printed learning matter. Surface learning endangers the educational outcomes as it leads to priority being given to the external characteristics of the text concerned rather than to its content, to examples rather than to principles of general relevance. Apparently many students are 'capable of using "deep" or "surface" strategies'. What is expected of them in an examination may influence the choice of strategy. Focusing the attention on 'the underlying meaning' can probably be brought about 'by ensuring that the assessment procedures demand deep-level processing' (Marton and Säljö, 1976).

The requirement that university students should get used to differing approaches, considerations and standpoints has caused some interest in possibilities to achieve this aim by suitable course structure in mediated teaching. This is a snag in much distance education. Distance teaching may mean 'teacher centred education, where the media are used as substitutes for the teacher, "telling" students what they ought to know (Ljoså 1977: 71).

For this reason an all-embracing course structure is often too rigid. It is felt only proper that the students should be offered a choice of relevant course units in each individual case. Such an approach leads to each unit or each small set of units being separate and providing a sufficient treatment of a limited, and strictly defined, part of the subject. When that is the case students can build their own curricula from units or sets of units belonging to different courses. This is what in German is called the Baukasten-Prinzip, the principle of the box of bricks (Ehmann, 1976).

This modular principle lends itself to supporting the general autonomy of the students. If each unit or set of units is provided with a kind of product declaration including statements of the objectives, the availability of sufficient numbers of units on related topics will give the individual student a possibility to select his or her own objectives, his or her study method (by weighing distance study, mediated study of other kinds against conventional methods) and, as is normal in mediated study, the pace of study.

Often students must be made to see a complicated picture of a subject with conflicting theories and views, or must learn how to trace facts and arguments from different presentations and to study various sources critically. In such cases a study guide steering and facilitating the study of set or suggested texts is evidently more suitable than a self-contained course in that the study guide causes students to read and/or listen to presentations of various kinds, to compare and criticize them and to try to come to conclusions of their own. This study guide approach is generally practical when the learning is to include part or the whole of the content of various books, papers and other sources of knowledge. This is a subject to which German and Norwegian contributions have been made during the last few years (Holmberg, 1977, Ljoså, 1975, Ljoså and Sandvold, 1979, Weltner, 1977).

The requirements concerning the lucidity of written presentation have been studied in a way relevant to distance education by scholars analysing the use of English and German printed texts. Langer, Schultz von Thun and Tausch have shown, on the basis of German instructional prose, that the accessibility of texts — ie how intelligible ('verständlich') they are — mainly depends on four 'dimensions' of the text characteristics, namely (i) simplicity of sentence structure and vocabulary, (ii) structure and cohesion, (iii) succinctness and relevance, and (iv) additional stimulation. These dimensions are largely independent of one another. Nevertheless, the authors point out that (iii) and (iv) usually influence each other. In the third dimension a medium value (between extreme succinctness, making almost every word important, and long-windedness) seems preferable, whereas the other dimensions denote qualities of positive value for the readability of texts (Langer, Schulz von Thun and Tausch, 1974). Another German study by Groeben, relying more on theoretical considerations than the one referred to, largely supports these conclusions (Groeben, 1972), although a scrutiny by Tergan (1980) indicates that Groeben's comprehensibility concept is not compatible with that of Langer, Schulz von Thun and Tausch.

Learning from texts has been thoroughly studied by a Tübingen research group of cognitive psychologists under Heinz Mandl. Comprehension is regarded as an active and constructive process on the part of the learner and on the basis of this and other approaches stressing reader-text interaction rather than text characteristics as influencing retention and achievement an assessment is made of available research results on readability and text comprehension (Mandl *et al*, 1979). Dabrowski (1976) is concerned with partly the same problem area in his analysis of didactic potentialities in systems of media combinations.

Techniques have been developed to direct students' attention to important issues, to considering and searching for solutions. The use of questions as attention directors along Rothkopf's line to promote 'mathemagenic-positive' behaviour has been criticized. Whereas much research supports it and many agree with Macdonald-Ross (1979) in regarding this as support of common sense, others are rather negative. This would seem to apply to Weingartz, who considers formal text criteria fairly insignificant in relation to the basic text design, which may start out from problems to be solved and thus support problem learning, or may simply present ready-made systems of knowledge for reproductive learning; to Mandl *et al* (see above) and even more to Marton, who fears that all kinds of attention-directors may avert students' interest from the content to the technical aspects of the reading process, thus encouraging surface learning and leading to neglect of deep structure learning (Marton, 1979). The present author is somewhat sceptical on this last point.

Considering arguments for and against inserted questions, it would seem to be important what type of questions are asked. If they merely concern facts, wordings and examples provided in the text, they may certainly encourage what Marton calls surface learning. Questions causing students to think independently, to formulate their thoughts and relate these to the text are not only radically different from the questions attached to the wordings of texts, but would also seem to be verbal instruments to encourage problem learning and deep-structure study as Marton and Säljö define this concept.

On real communication in distance study the most thorough research is to be reported on from Scandinavia. Bååth (1980) has analysed attitudes to and practices of written two-way communication in distance study, and Flinck (1978) has done something similar for telephone tutoring supplementing correspondence study. Both are empirical studies looking into the consequences of various practices.

Some schools of distance education have found it practical to work with a battery of carefully prepared explanatory comments that tutors can use either in the form of appendices to the student's paper when this is returned with handwritten tutor comments, or as sections of typed letters. These sections are sometimes programmed on cards or tape for automatic typing, whereas other sections of the same letter are typed following dictation by the tutor. The experiences of pre-produced tutor comments are favourable (Rekkedal and Ljoså, 1974).

An evident weakness in normal distance study is the delayed feedback given in tutor comments, whether direct and personal or computerized.

Only by telecommunication is immediate feedback in distant two-way communication possible. Students seem to accept and profit from comments and corrections given within seven to ten days after an assignment has been completed, but are usually dissatisfied if the delay is of longer duration. Students on the whole seem highly appreciative of the two-way communication element (Beijer, 1972) and expect full comments on their submitted work within as few days as possible. Completion rates have been shown to correlate with turn-around time (and also with encouraging, 'reminding' letters on the occasions when students have been passive for a period) (Rekkedal, 1973).

Media R and D

Interest in the use of various media adapted to the student bodies concerned and the study objectives aimed at was and is considerable. This applies to the European continent as well as to all other developed parts of the world. The Germans have contributed two new concepts of relevance in our context: *Mediendidaktik*, which is a term for the branch of the educational science concerned with the purposes, conditions and use of media in teaching and learning situations, and *Fernstudium im Medienverbund* as a designation of modern multi-media distance study. Well-known names in German *Mediendidaktik* are, for instance, Günther Dohmen, Horst Dichanz, Helmut Fritsch, and E U Heidt. Dohmen (1973) provides a valuable survey of the media problems (in English). A useful Norwegian contribution of the same type is Handal, 1973 (also in English).

The media use to which the most important contributions seem to have been made concern printed learning material, radio, TV and computers. On the use of the telephone for two-way communication see above under 'Methodology'. Apart from what was said in this previous section on printed presentations a few words should be added on the influence of typography and on a German 'redundancy' theory.

As a supplement to the British research on access structure as developed by Waller, Doerfert's research on graphic presentation in West Germany is of considerable interest. His approach is based on information theory and the so-called redundancy theory developed by von Cube. The formation of 'supersigns' is regarded as particularly important for learning efficiency. Supersigns are comprehensive concepts including 'signs' on a lower level in the way a word is a supersign in relation to the individual letters of which it is composed. According to von Cube, supersign formation is an effective means to bring about 'redundancy' as this concept is understood by him.

Von Cube's theory is based on a cybernetic approach mathematically defining the probability of what a student can foresee. The gist of the redundancy theory can be described as follows: Each study task contains a certain amount of information that is to be absorbed. Each item of prior knowledge and each step on the path of learning leads to a reduction of the amount of information left, and so does the capacity to form supersigns with the inclusion of new knowledge matter in its proper context. To the individual student the task then contains redundant information apart from what remains to be learned. The more that is learned, the smaller the amount of remaining subjective information and the greater the redundancy. Felix von Cube explains all learning processes by means of this theory. The fact that meaningful material is learnt more quickly than meaningless material is explained by the higher statistical redundancy in the meaningful material: thus the amount of information per unit to be learned is lower than in the meaningless material. Similar illustrations are given of conditioning and learning by success (von Cube, 1975).

Doerfert applies this thinking to the use of graphical elements in distance-study courses. The use of structuring keywords in the margins to denote essential concepts in the course presentation has been tried with success: these keywords reproduce the content of the course unit as a kind of abstract and, according to Doerfert, in this way facilitate the formation of supersigns favouring redundancy (Doerfert, 1980). Various typographical measures including the use of italics, underlinings etc which serve the understanding of relations between concepts and other items of a presentation are also seen as facilitators of supersign formation.

Weaving texts and pictures into one integrated lexi-visual presentation including explanatory drawings and text units, panoramic pictures and photographs of details, documentary illustration, etc, has been tried with success. This lexi-visual approach is a result of development work performed in Sweden by Sven Lidman (Lidman, 1979).

In spite of fairly extensive use of radio and TV it would seem to be difficult to find a core of methodological insight about which consensus can be said to have been attained. Probably, a majority of educators have come to the conclusion that TV, apart from its potential for demonstrations, can have a strong motivating influence and that this to some extent also applies to radio.

A case study of some relevance is the Swedish Delta project, an updating course on mathematics for teachers of that subject offered as an integrated TV-radio-correspondence course. Some 52,500 teachers took this course in the early 1970s, 41,300 of whom completed it. A study of the students' (ie the participating teachers') attitudes showed that whereas more than 90 per cent of them found the correspondence and radio parts of the course satisfactory, more than 50 per cent of them reacted negatively to the TV elements, which were found to be neither motivating nor providing good surveys (Holmberg, 1973).

Similar experiences have been had elsewhere. This probably reflects exaggerated expectations as far as the TV element is concerned rather than a rejection of TV as a medium of instruction. Critical students evidently do not want course items presented on TV which can equally well be presented in print, nor do they normally want to hear formal lectures which, if provided in print, they can read in much less time than is required for listening and then consult again and again. However, what suits one target group may not suit another. Dohmen (1971) and Krajnč and Škoberna (1973) (the latter on work in Jugoslavia) report on findings relevant in this context.

For two-way communication between students and their supporting organization with its tutors and counsellors the computer has proved valuable. Whereas on-line systems are so far useful only to a limited extent, ie when study centre or similar facilities with computer terminals like those of the British Open University and the German FernUniversität are available, a most promising generally practicable use of the computer has been developed for application off-line, ie where the students are not in direct contact with computer equipment. The computer usually corrects and comments on replies to multiple-choice questions with carefully selected distractors. In the CADE system (Hermods, Sweden) an optical reader 'corrects' the solutions of the students, after which the computer selects relevant comments and explanations from among a great number of those programmed and stored for the purpose. The computer also checks and refers to the individual students' earlier achievements when parallel or similar problems have been solved. A mistake or unsatisfactory solution of a problem can be, and is, given different comments according to which of the incorrect distractors the student has chosen, ie in relation to the way in which he or she has misunderstood or wrongly combined items. The computer programmes see to it that sometimes even correct replies are commented on to underline something important or to support the motivation of the students. Encouraging and counselling comments based on the total result of students' papers are also provided by the computer. All this is typed out by the computer on to a personal letter addressed to the individual student.

The use of the computer is based on so-called objective assignments of the multiple-choice type which, though regarded with some suspicion, have proved to be acceptable in many cases and to some extent very useful for didactic purposes. Their value varies with the way in which they have been worked out and tried out and particularly with the suitability of the distractors (Bååth and Månsson, 1977).

A computer system which allows the free rendering of replies in the form of numbers has been developed in Germany (LOTSE, FernUniversität). The numbers are 'read' by the computer, not by 'mark-sensing', but by the numbers being produced through markings in columns of numbers provided. Thus there is no choice between different solutions suggested (Wilmersdoerfer, 1979). The students create their own answers (numbers).

Instead of computer use, similar though less sophisticated procedures can be introduced by means of multiple-choice questions, correction by scanning machine and commentaries programmed on tape or cards and typed by an automatic typewriter.

If applied in a suitable way, computer-assisted distance study can evidently be very valuable. In an empirical study, Bååth has found strong indications that computer-assisted versions functioned better 'as far as starting behaviour, completion and attitude toward the tutorial was was concerned' than tutor-marked versions of the same courses. 'These findings are well in accordance with the results obtained from the evaluation of the CADE system' (Bååth, 1979: 29).

A somewhat parallel system is CAVA, developed at the FEoLL in Paderborn, West Germany (Brönstrup, 1979).

The computer is also used in counselling. An application of this kind is to be found in a pre-study advisory system developed at the FernUniversitä⁺ in Germany. In connection with an information booklet a number of questions are asked. The foreseen replies to these, in their various configurations, are commented on by computer through the automatic selection and use of pre-programmed text modules (Fritsch, Küffner and Schuch, 1979).

Various forms and media adaptable to distance study two-way communication have been analysed against the background of German experiences by Valkyser (1981).

Further studies on media in distance study worth referring to are, among others, Wurster, 1979 (a survey) and Fritsch (1978), an examination of the structuring of acoustic learning matter on audio cassettes.

Systems approach

A number of studies which for reasons of space cannot be commented on here concern essential elements of any system for mediated learning, like target group studies, organization, economy, and formative and summative evaluation. As far as distance education in an international context is concerned, I have tried to cover these elements (as well as attempted to present distance education as a system) in my recent book (Holmberg, 1981), on which I have drawn for parts of this presentation. Here should only be added references to a systems approach developed in Norway (Brevkursproduksjon . . . , 1975), a comprehensive Finnish study on the aims and realization of mediated study (Lampikoski and Mantere, 1978) and generally to the presentations of systems and their various components continually appearing in *Epistolodidaktika*, the periodical of the European Home Study Council, in which, incidentally, the systems approach is being analysed by Kurt Graff, a German economist active as a professor of distance study methodology (Graff, 1977 and 1978) and in which the concerns of educational technology have been illuminated in various contributions since 1971.

References

Bååth, J A (1979) *Correspondence Education in the Light of a Number of Contemporary Teaching Models*, LiberHermods, Malmö

Bååth, J A (1980) *Postal Two-way Communication in Correspondence Education*, Gleerup, Lund

Bååth, J A and Månsson, N -O (1977) *CADE — A System for Computer-assisted Distance Education*, Hermods, Malmö

Beijer, E (1972) A study of students' preferences with regard to different models for two-way communication, *Epistolodidaktika*, 1972 (2), 83-90

Berdichevsky, P V (1975) Distance education — guided self-teaching, *Epistolodidaktika*, 1972 (2), 6-11

Brevkursproduksjon i lys av systemtenkning (1975) *Brevskolerådet — Norsk Brevskoleforbund*, NKS, Oslo

Brönstrup, H (1979) Der Korrekturdienst im System CAVA, in Tauber, M J (ed) (1979)

von Cube, F (1975) Der informationstheoretische Ansatz in der Didaktik, in Ruprecht, H, Beckmann, H -K, von Cube, F and Schulz, W (eds) *Modelle grundlegender didaktischer Theorien*, pp 117-54, Schroedel, Hannover

Dabrowski, G (1976) *Didaktische Potenzen in Medienverbundsystemen*, Münster, Diss

Delling, R M (1971) Grundzüge einer Wissenschaft vom Fernstudium, *Epistolodidaktika*, 1971 (1), 14-20

Dichanz, H et al (1974) *Medien im Unterrichtsprozess. Grundlagen, Probleme, Perspektiven*, Juventa, München

Doerfert, F (1980) *Zur Wirksamkeit typografischer und grafischer Elemente in gedruckten Fernstudienmaterialien*, Bericht zum ZIFF-Forschungsprojekt Nr 1.2, FernUniversität, Hagen

Dohmen, G (1970) *Fernstudium im Medienverbund. Entlastung und Reformanstoss für die Hochschulen*, Beltz, Weinheim

Dohmen, G (1973) Media selection and media research, in Granholm, G (ed) (1973)

Dohmen, G (1971) Rundfunk und Fernsehen im Rahmen des Fernstudiums, in Dohmen, G and Peters, O (eds) *Hochschulunterricht im Medienverbund II*, pp 73-80, Quelle and Meyer, Heidelberg

Dohmen, G (ed) (1976) *FIM-Glossar. Informationsbausteine zur Aus- und Fortbildung wissenschaftlicher Mitarbeiter an Fernstudienprojekten*, Deutsches Institut für Fernstudien, Tübingen

Ehmann, C (1976) Baukastenstudium, in Dohmen, G (ed) (1976)

Flechsig, K -H (1970) Begriff und Konzept der Unterrichtstechnologie, in *Audiovisuelle Bildungsmittel in der Schule von morgen*, Institut für Film und Bild, München

Flinck, R (1978) *Correspondence Education Combined with Systematic Telephone Tutoring*, Hermods, Kristianstad

Fritsch, H (1974) *Medien im Hochschulunterricht*, Deutsches Institut für Fernstudien, Tübingen

Fritsch, H (1978) *Zur Strukturierung von akustischem Lehrmaterial auf Tonkassetten*, ZIFF-Papiere 21, FernUniversität, Hagen

Fritsch, H, Küffner, H and Schuch, A (1979) *Entwicklung einer Studieneingangsberatung für Fernstudenten*, FernUniversität, Hagen

Gaddén, G (1973) *Hermods 1898-1973*, Hermods, Malmö

Graff, K (1970) *Voraussetzungen erfolgreichen Fernstudiums*, Dargestellt am Beispiel des schwedischen Fernstudiensystems. Lüdke, Hamburg

Graff, K (1977 and 1978) Der Systemansatz im Fernstudium I - II (with English summaries), *Epistolodidaktika*, 1977 (1), 49-57 and 1978 (1), 9-19

Granholm, G (ed) (1973) *The Selection of Relevant Media/Methods for Defined Educational Purposes within Distance Education*, European Home Study Council, NKI, Oslo

Groeben, N (1972) *Die Verständlichkeit von Unterrichtstexten. Dimensionen und Kriterien rezeptiver Lernstadien*, Aschendorff, Münster

Handal, G (1973) On the selection of relevant media/methods for defined educational purposes, in Granholm, G (ed) (1973)

Heidt, E U (1978) *Instructional Media and the Individual Learner,* Kogan Page, London

Holmberg, B (1973) The Swedish Delta Project — a case study, in Granholm, G (ed) (1973)

Holmberg, B (1977) *Das Leitprogram im Fernstudium,* ZIFF-Papiere 17, FernUniversität, Hagen

Holmberg, B (1981) *Status and Trends of Distance Education,* Kogan Page, London

Holmberg, B and Schümer, R (1980) *Methoden des gelenkten didaktischen Gespräches,* Ergebnisse einer Voruntersuchung, ZIFF-Projekt 2.6, FernUniversität, Hagen

Krajnč, A and Škoberne, F (1973) An empirical insight into the integration of correspondence and audio (radio) education, in Granholm, G (ed) (1973)

Lampikoski, K and Mantere, P (1978) *Final Report of the Distance Education Development Project,* Institute of Marketing, Helsinki

Langer, J, Schulz von Thun, F and Tausch, R (1974) *Verständlichkeit in Schule, Verwaltung, Politik und Wissenschaft,* München, Diss

Lehner, H (1978) *Die Steuerung von Lernprozessen auf der Grundlage einer kognitiven Lerntheorie,* FernUniversität (ZIFF), Hagen

Lehner, H (1979) *Erkenntnis durch Irrtum als Lehrmethode,* Kamp, Bochum

Lehner, H and Weingartz, M (1981) Ready-made and individualised distance study, *ICCE Newsletter,* 11 (1), 7-10

Lidman, S (1979) Towards a more functional picture language, *Epistolodidaktika,* 1979 (1), 21-41

Ljoså, E (1975) Why do we make commentary courses? *The System of Distance Education,* 1, ICCE, 112-18, Hermods, Malmö

Ljoså, E (1977) Course design and media selection — some implications on co-operation between broadcasting, publishing and distance education, *Epistolodidaktika,* 1977 (1), 75-84

Ljoså, E and Sandvold, K E (1979) Hvorfor og hvordan bør vi lage kommentarkurs? *Mellom oss,* 10, NKS, Oslo

Loser, F and Terhart, E (1977) *Theorien des Lehrens,* Klett, Stuttgart

Macdonald-Ross, M (1979) Language in texts: a review of research relevant to the design of curricular materials, in Shulman, L S (ed) *Review of Research in Education 6,* Peacock, Itasca, Ill

Mandl, H, Ballstaedt, S -P, Schnotz, W and Tergan, S -O (1979) *Lernen mit Texten,* DIFF-Forschungsberichte 5, Deutsches Institut für Fernstudien, Tübingen

Mandl, H, Tergan, S -O and Ballstaedt, S -P (1981) *Textverständlichkeit — Textverstehen,* DIFF-Forschungsberichte 12, Deutsches Institut für Fernstudien, Tübingen

Marton, F (1979) *Learning as seen from the learner's point of view,* ZIFF-Papiere 30, FernUniversität, Hagen

Marton, F and Säljö, R (1976) On qualitative differences in learning, *British Journal of Educational Psychology,* 46, 115-27

Moore, M G (1977) *A Model of Independent Study,* ZIFF-Papiere 16, FernUniversität, Hagen

Pask, G (1976) Styles and strategies of learning, *British Journal of Educational Psychology,* 46, 126-48

Peters, O (1971) Theoretical aspects of correspondence instruction, in MacKenzie, O and Christensen, E L (eds) *The Changing World of Correspondence Study,* Pennsylvania State University Press, University Park

Peters, O (1973) *Die didaktische Struktur des Fernunterrichts. Untersuchungen zu einer industrialisierten Form des Lehrens und Lernens,* Beltz, Weinheim

Rebel, K (1981) Nutzungserschliessung — Der dritte Schwerpunkt des DIFF, *Fernstudium aktuell* (DIFF-Journal), 3 (2), 2

Rekkedal, T (1973) *Innsendingsoppgavene i brevundervisningen. Hvilken betydelse har det å reducere omløpstiden?* With an English summary: The written assignments in correspondence education. Effects of reducing turn-round time, NKI, Oslo

Rekkedal, T and Ljoså, E (1974) *Preproduserte laererkommentarer i brevundervisningen*, Brevskolerådet, Forsøksrådet for Skoleverket, NKI-skolen og Norsk Korrespondansedkole, Oslo

Tauber, M J (ed) (1979) *Der Computer als didaktisches und organisatorisches Hilfsmittel des Fernstudiums*, Paderborner Forschungsberichte 8/9, Schroedel/Schöningh, Hannover and Paderborn

Tergan, S -O (1980) *Ist Textverständlichkeit gleich Textverständlichkeit?* Überprüfung der Vergleichbarkeit zweier Verständlichkeitskonzepte, DIFF-Forschungsberichte 7, Deutsches Institut für Fernstudien, Tübingen

Valkyser, H (1981) *Fernstudiensystemkonforme Beratung und Betreuung als didaktische Elemente einer Zweiweg-Kommunikation im Fernstudium — unter besonderer Berücksichtigung bisheriger Erfahrunge an der FernUniversität*, FernUniversität (ZIFF), Hagen

Waller, R (1977) *Typographic Access Structures for Educational Texts*, The Open University (IET), Milton Keynes

Weingartz, M (1980) *Didaktische Merkmale selbstinstruierender Studientexte*, FernUniversität (ZIFF), Hagen

Weltner, K (1977) *Die Unterstützung autonomen Lernens im Fernstudium durch integrierende Leitprogramme*, ZIFF-Papiere 17, FernUniversität, Hagen

Wilmersdoerfer, H (1979) Aufbau eines maschinellen Korrektursystems (CMA) für Einsendeaufgaben der Fernuniversität, in Tauber, M J (ed) (1979)

Wurster, J (1979) *Technische Medien im Studiensystem der Fernuniversität*, FernUniversität (ZFE), Hagen

Basic Skills Analysis – A Tool for Learning Managers

M R Freshwater, *Senior Training Adviser (Skill Development Programme),*
Manpower Services Commission, Training Services Division, Directorate of
Training

1. Introduction

In developing learning experiences the learning manager is often faced with
the problem of tailoring their content to meet the skill development needs
of individuals whilst at the same time providing experiences appropriate
for a group with a variety of ability levels.

This article describes a technique (Basic Skills Analysis) which will help
learning managers to tackle this problem whenever they are devising new
learning experiences or examining and developing existing ones. It also
describes a range of associated techniques (eg skill matrices and profiles)
which form an integrated part of a model for learning management which
emerged through its application.

The paper falls broadly into two parts: a brief description of the Basic
Skills Checklist, followed by a case study which describes the process of
Basic Skills Analysis (BSA) in a Training Workshop (Freshwater, 1980a).

2. The Basic Skills Checklist

BSA has evolved from part of the Manpower Services Commission's
(MSC) Grouping of Skills research programme concerned with the
development of a 'common language' or 'descriptive system' for describing
the similarities and differences between the basic skills needed for jobs.

This 'common language' has been found useful in the following ways: first
as a means for describing the learning process in terms of the basic skills
learned or needed to complete a learning experience successfully, and
second as a means of communicating between the learner, the learning
manager and his colleagues.

The analysis technique was made possible through the development of a
Checklist (Freshwater, 1980b) of basic skill statements which has been
designed and tested in Training Workshops, and other training
arrangements set up under the MSC's Special Programmes Division's
Youth Opportunities Programme (MSC, 1980) for unemployed
school-leavers.

The Checklist has been developed as a simple and quick analytical tool for
examining training activities or products and identifying the basic skills
they contain. This process, it is hoped, will enable learning managers
(supervisors) to design learning experiences and curriculum materials to
provide the widest opportunities for trainee/student skill development.

The Checklist was conceived as a tool with which the learning manager might consider existing or planned learning situations. Skill items were listed in a convenient checklist format so that an activity, task, learning experience or product might be considered in terms of basic skill usage. The Checklist was designed to provide a frame of reference against which the skills used may be examined, and against which more detailed job-specific skill descriptions might be generated. The items listed in the Checklist were produced by drawing on reference material prepared by leading authorities in the field of occupational analysis in Britain, the USA and Canada (Freshwater, 1980b). In the main, the basic skill items it contains were selected to cover capabilities which might be required to carry out tasks performed in a wide range of occupations.

Nearly 400 descriptive statements have been generated and grouped under the skill headings of:

- ☐ Basic calculations (eg add whole number, calculate area)
- ☐ Measurement and drawing (eg measure length, take information from scale drawing)
- ☐ Listening and talking (listen to get information, ask questions)
- ☐ Reading and writing (read letter to get information, write message)
- ☐ Planning and problem-solving (decide methods, identify causes of problem)
- ☐ Practical (cut by sawing, join by glueing).

A typical page of the Checklist produced is shown in Figure 1.

3. Using the Checklist — a Training Workshop case study

In order to explain BSA as a technique I would like to describe in some detail an application of the method in a Training Workshop set up under the Youth Opportunities Programme.

The Workshop was situated in an area with severe job problems for young people. The level of achievements of the trainees was varied and the majority were of low academic attainment. This meant that much of the work had to be tailored to match the capabilities of the individual.

(a) The setting

In setting up a Training Workshop, a learning manager has to attempt to reconcile a variety of factors that will directly affect the nature, scope and effectiveness of the learning experiences, for example:

- ☐ the views of the sponsors, directors, board of management and other agencies
- ☐ the type of training which might be provided to meet local needs
- ☐ the premises available
- ☐ the abilities and interests of the supervisors who can be recruited
- ☐ the number of training places provided
- ☐ the likely nature, strengths and needs of potential trainees

BASIC CALCULATIONS	(1)					
NUMBERS: read or write	1					
WHOLE NOS: add	2					
multiply	2					
subtract	2					
divide	2					
FRACTIONS: add	3					
multiply	3					
subtract	3					
divide	3					
DECIMALS: add	4					
multiply	4					
subtract	4					
divide	4					
MONEY: calcs. in handling	5					
special aid used	5					
MENTAL ARITHMETIC: whole numbers	6					
fractions	6					
decimals	6					
PERCENTAGES: 1st — simple	7					
2nd — rate	7					
3rd — principle	7					
remembered or looked up	7					

6

Figure 1 *A typical page of the Checklist*

☐ the types of machinery and equipment required and the methods which can be used

☐ the amount of finance available to support the Workshop

The training opportunities which can be provided therefore evolve out of the balance struck between these interests, some of which compete with others.

In order to test out the effectiveness of the BSA and the Basic Skills Checklist, a Workshop was selected which was representative of Workshop operations as a whole.

Although a pattern of the content of training opportunities had already been established, the Workshop manager and his staff were anxious to exploit this further for the benefit of their trainees. The manager considered that an analysis of all his Workshop's activities might result in a fuller understanding and provide answers to such questions as:

☐ What basic skills can a trainee learn within each section of the Workshop?

☐ What were the variations in terms of basic skill demands made by different products and learning options offered?

☐ What were the similarities and differences between sections – the types of skills used and demands made of the trainees?

☐ What skills would a trainee need if he or she were to get the best out of a section?

(b) The Checklist in action

The initial analysis of the activities focused on a section which upholstered chairs, where the manager had noted that the work did not generally appeal to trainees. He felt, therefore, that an examination of its activities would be a useful starting point. In addition to giving some guidance as to the type of work which should be brought into the section, the manager was keen to discover what help the analysis might provide in finding ways of reducing the personal workload of the section supervisor.

Once the areas of analysis were established and agreed, more detailed discussions followed with the supervisor.

(i) Deciding what to analyse
The range of work for analysis in the upholstery section was established by selecting categories of activity or products that typically represented the type of work performed, eg:

(a) Cushion-making
(b) Standard office chair renovation
(c) Domestic chair renovation
(d) Specialist furniture – chair renovation.

It was felt that by analysing these broad categories of work, a full picture of work done and skills used on the section would be given.

(ii) Coding the skills used

Having decided the range of products or services to be analysed, discussion centred on how the work carried out in the section could best be represented and how to record what skills might be needed on entry to the section and the work that might be done by the trainees or by the supervisor. It was agreed that it would be most helpful if the skills information could be coded to indicate whether it was needed at the time of entry to the section or whether all trainees used or acquired it. The following codes were developed during the analysis and subsequently found to be generalizable to all sections.

P (Prerequisite)   This code referred to a basic skill that the supervisor considered to be desirable for the trainee to possess on entry to the section. It was appreciated that the code could not be used in a hard-and-fast way. Supervisors would still consider trainees who did not possess all the prerequisite skills. Since the abilities of those without the skills would be limited, methods might have to be simplified, or the more able might have to help the less able.

T (Taught)   This referred to a basic skill that the trainee would be taught, learn or experience in the section. It was recognized that the more practice and the more varied the setting was in which the skill was used, the greater would be the level of competence achieved. Practising a skill in conjunction with other skills would also be important.

O (Optional)   This represented skills that a trainee might optionally be taught, learn or experience in the section. These skills were often carried out by the supervisor himself and by the more able trainees. Supervisors generally tried to get trainees to acquire as many of these skills as possible. The greater the number of trainees who could perform the optional skills, the smaller the workload of the supervisor and the more time he could spend with the less able. In many cases supervisors were aware that to exercise an optional skill, the trainee might need to acquire other more fundamental skills.

S (Supervisor)   This code indicated those skills which could be carried out only by the supervisor. Different types of work required the supervisor to carry out the skill himself because of the complexity of the work or the type of tools or the materials being handled. Other considerations were the effects of cost of error, safety legislation, etc.

(iii) Recording the skills

The skills required in each activity were recorded by going through the

Checklist item by item. This was done with the supervisor in order to
deal with any problems of understanding of Checklist terms as they arose.
Analysis of activities began with the simplest job and increased in
complexity through the range of activities. The first activity — cushion-
making — took 50 minutes, the remainder were completed in about
20 minutes each. The supervisor was able to complete the analysis of
subsequent activities unaided.

(iv) Producing a matrix of the basic skills

Once all the products had been analysed and information recorded on the
Checklist it was extracted from the completed 22-page Checklist, and a
matrix was produced showing the skills used for each product (see part
of Workshop Overall Matrix shown in Figure 2). The matrix lists the
product or activity in the left hand column, and the coded skills
(P, T, O and S) are recorded against the descriptions which are listed at
the head of the sheet. This matrix format enables the skills used to be
studied more concisely. From this information, skill usage can be
examined and skill awareness fostered.

(v) Examining the matrix

The matrix was examined to establish what insight it might give into the
operation of the upholstery section. The findings were discussed with the
supervisor and the Workshop manager and the following points emerged:

(a) A large proportion of the skills needed to do the work were
provided by the supervisor (see O and S on the Workshop Overall
Basic Skills Matrix)
(b) All basic calculation work (whole numbers) was either optional
or was carried out by the supervisor
(c) The matrix indicated that most of the difficult measurement and
marking-out and practical skills were either optional or supervisor tasks
(d) The section could cope with people who could not read or write.
Simple reading only was required, and even this was an optional skill.
This meant that listening/talking skills involved with giving/getting
information and answering/asking questions were desired on entry
(e) The supervisor was doing all the planning work (sorting, fault
diagnosing, method, tool and standard setting and checking). Trainees
were required only optionally to count or solve work problems
(f) An important tactile skill of checking tension in cushions and seat
covers was identified
(g) Prerequisite skills (P) which would need to be established before the
trainee entered the section were identified, eg ability to estimate length
and distance, cut with scissors, check to see that things are level,
square, etc.

In discussing with the upholstery section supervisor the analysis procedure
and the information that was obtained, he commented:

(a) It had made him aware of the wide range of skills which might be
learned in his section

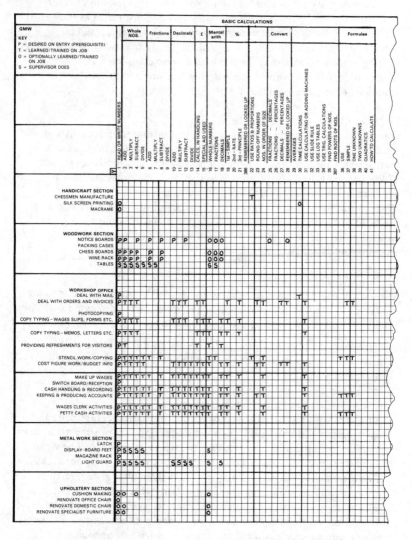

Figure 2 *The Workshop Overall Matrix*

(b) The Checklist had acted as a memory aid

(c) The act of going through the Checklist enabled him to see how the various production stages held together — eg written or verbal instructions can result in calculation, measurement and marking out before using hand tools

(d) It would be useful as a means of communication between supervisors

(e) It had indicated where he might concentrate his instructional effort and how he might alter some of the methods to reduce his personal workload. In particular it had thrown into sharp relief the need to ensure that induction and assessment procedures were designed to identify trainee strengths and needs and to ensure that trainees who entered the section had the necessary skills to make the most of the opportunities offered

(f) It was now apparent that a product was needed which would allow the regular practice of the simpler skills and enable trainees to take up the options involved in the renovation of specialist/antique furniture. (An order was subsequently obtained for re-covering chairs of simple construction.)

(vi) The Overall Basic Skills Matrix of the Workshop
As a result of the useful information gained from the study of the upholstery section, analyses were carried out for each of the remaining sections.

It was established that each section was organized to provide a spread of activities, affording a range of different skills which could be sampled by any of the trainees.

It was found that the technique of identifying the activities or categories of work reflecting the range of jobs within each of the sections was clearly generalizable. The Checklist also proved to be equally appropriate for analysing sections with yearly work cycles or short-term production cycles, as well as for sections providing services.

An example of part of the Overall Basic Skills Matrix is shown in Figure 2. This enables comparisons to be made between the activities of each section. It also illustrates how many of the basic skills are common to the diverse activities of the different sections. This highlights areas where learning might be arranged to allow the transfer of skills to a variety of new situations.

Discussion between the Workshop managers and supervisors on the results of the Overall Basic Skills Matrices revealed that:

(a) Different sections required trainees to possess different skills on entry and, depending on these skills, the complexity and variety of work experience would vary

(b) The handicraft section (seen as a remedial section) was providing only limited support for the trainees in helping them to overcome skills deficiencies. A large proportion of the skills needed to do the work were carried out by the supervisor. Much of the basic calculation work, difficult measurement, marking out and practical skills, were either Optional (O) or Supervisor (S) tasks

(c) The nature of the basic skills sampled in a section was determined by the type of work activity provided, eg:

Office work — provided opportunity for fewer practical skills than other sections but encouraged development in calculations; reading and writing; direct contact with management; supervisors and trainees;

	specialist skills such as keyboard, copying etc, and the close supervision of output
Building and general maintenance	— provided experience in customer and supplier contact; journeys; ladders, team work, specialist skills (associated with plumbing)
Agriculture	— experience involved: contact with and the care of animals; maintenance (which required measurements to be made, a range of tools to be used, manuals to be read, service to be carried out); specialist skills such as tractor and rotavator driving

(d) An activity could be carried out in different ways, eg verbal or written instructions could be given, or drawings and illustrations could be used. Alternative skills could be used to accomplish the same task, eg mark out and measure or use a template. A calculator could be used to overcome basic calculation weakness

(e) Certain skills could be identified as keys to later development, eg:
    reading numbers
    counting
    measuring length of distance
    reading words
    listening to get information etc

(f) There were different ways of supervising a section. The less work carried out by the trainees, the more skills would have to be exercised by the supervisors. The work did not necessarily get done by other trainees

(g) Different trainees on the same section could acquire different skills. This depended on their ability on entry, the work given and the progress made

(h) Different sections made different demands on trainees, eg metal work required no reading or writing skills

(j) Many skills were common to a number of sections and could be sampled in a number of different contexts, eg cutting by sawing could be learnt in woodwork, metalwork, agriculture, building and general maintenance sections. Alternatively other skills were unique to each section, eg: office — keyboard; maintenance — plumbing; agriculture — driving tractor, etc.

(k) Most of the planning, problem solving, costing, standards-setting and checking was done by the supervisor

(l) The Workshop's method of getting things done was predominantly by verbal instruction. Few reading or writing skills were used, other than in the office, and drawings were not commonly used in the manufacture of products

(m) Because the Workshop used few powered machines or equipment, hand tools were employed. These called for other skills to be practised, such as measurement, clamping, marking out, sawing, etc

(n) All the ancillary services which the Workshop required, eg stores,

TRAINEE 'CAN-DO' PROFILE

Things .... can do

(1) **Basic Calculations**

- Can Read and Write Nos ——————————————— ☐

	Whole Nos.	Fractions	Decimals
• Can add ————————————	☐	☐	☐
• Can multiply ————————————	☐	☐	☐
• Can subtract ————————————	☐	☐	☐
• Can divide ————————————	☐	☐	☐

- Can do mental arithmetic ————————————— ☐
- Can use a calculator or adding machine ————————— ☐

(2) **Measurement and Drawings**

	Length or Distance	Weight	Time
• Can use scales or dials to measure ————————	☐	☐	☐

	Metric	Imperial
• Can use units of measurements		
weight ————————————	☐	☐
length or distance ————————	☐	☐
liquid volume ————————	☐	☐

- Can tell the time ————————————— ☐
- Can estimate length or distance ————————— ☐ Can look to ——— ☐
  see if level,
  square or true

- Can read/understand simple map, drawing or diagram ———————————— ☐

(3) **Listening and Talking**

- Can listen attentively to get information ————————— ☐
- Can talk to people do not know very well ————————— ☐
- Can hold a conversation with fellow trainees or supervisor involving:—
  - describing or giving information about something ————— ☐
  - asking questions ——————————————— ☐
  - answering questions ——————————————— ☐
  - explaining something ——————————————— ☐
- Can follow verbal instructions to do simple task/job ————— ☐

(4) **Planning and Problem Solving**

- Can count objects ——————————————— ☐

14   Date ....

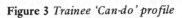

Figure 3 *Trainee 'Can-do' profile*

(continued)

(5) Reading and Writing

- Can read words ⸻ ☐   • Can write words ⸻ ☐
- Can read simple notes, messages or ⸻ ☐
  list of instructions to get information
- Can write simple notes or messages to record information ⸻ ☐
- Can fill in a form giving the correct information ⸻ ☐
- Can follow written instructions on how to do a simple job/task. ⸻ ☐

(6) Practical

- Can use simple every day tools ⸻ ☐
- Can use tools to check that things are level, square or true ⸻ ☐
- Can use scissors to cut ⸻ ☐   • Can use a hammer to drive a nail ⸻ ☐
  along a straight line in cloth or paper.
     • Can use a screw driver ⸻ ☐
- Can saw along a straight line in ⸻ ☐
  wood or metal
- Can use a spanner to tighten or ⸻ ☐   • Can drill a hole in wood or metal ⸻ ☐
  loosen a nut and bolt
- Can use a paint brush ⸻ ☐   • Can glue or stick wood, cloth or ⸻ ☐
  paper
- Can pull, push or lift things ⸻ ☐
- Can use sand paper to smooth ⸻ ☐   • Can clamp things in a vice ⸻ ☐
  wood
- Can use a spade and rake ⸻ ☐

(7) General

- Can use public transport ⸻ ☐
- Can use a dictionary ⸻ ☐
- Can use a telephone ⸻ ☐

Figure 3 *Trainee 'Can-do' profile (continued)*

transport etc, could be viewed as a source for developing additional
basic skills
(o) It was now very clear that by making a variety of products, it was
possible to provide a very varied range of training and work experience.

4. 'Can-do' profile

By means of the Basic Skills Checklist, staff were able to identify skills
that were desirable for trainees to have on entry to each section of the
Workshop. These are shown (P) on the Overall Matrix. From the nine
sections, skills were identified as entry requirements. These skills were
then listed on a 'Can-do' profile (Figure 3), which provides the Workshop
personnel counsellor with a reference for more effectively relating and
matching the abilities of the trainee with the skills required for each
Workshop section during induction and with a focus for 'trainee-centred'
counselling interviews.

(i) Self-assessment technique

Seen as a complementary part of the interview is the introduction of a method of trainee self-assessment. From the list mentioned above, 17 statements have been devised which cover either one or several of the skills. These are incorporated into the profile and are used as a starting point for the formulation of descriptions to be included on ability cards used as part of the self-assessment technique. The skill descriptions are devised to be meaningful to young people and to elicit a quick response.

Trainees must be assured that the cards are not a form of selection and that a place at the Workshop is assured. It must also be stressed that there are no right or wrong answers and that it is important to be honest. The trainee is asked to read through the cards and place them in two piles which represent: (a) those abilities they consider that they possess (their strengths) and (b) those with which they would like to be helped (their needs).

Each card is numbered, and the final results of the assessment should be recorded by the administrator in descending order from the strongest ability or greatest need. Where a trainee considers his/her abilities to be of equal strength the corresponding card numbers should be recorded alongside each other. When this has been done, the administrator will go through the two piles and carefully discuss each ability with the trainee in order to confirm the accuracy of their assessment.

(ii) Placing the trainee

Once the trainee's section preference and job aspirations have been established, a decision about placement can be made. This is achieved by considering the results of the assessment of the LASS tutor, the supervisors and the trainee, and the prerequisite skills needed on entry to a section.

5. 'Has-done' profile

(i) The Section Basic Skills Profile

The Workshop concentrates its efforts in bringing a trainee to a standard of achievement upon which employers can build and developing as many skills as possible. A valuable aid in achieving this aim is the Basic Skills Profile for each section (see Figure 4 for part of a section profile), which indicates the maximum range of skills which can be acquired. This profile can be produced once the overall range of skills used within the Workshop has been identified using the Basic Skills Checklist.

(ii) Monitoring progress and recording achievement

The Section Basic Skills Profile is designed as a tool with which to monitor progress and record achievement. To make trainees fully aware

UPHOLSTERY SECTION			DATE OF ISSUE		SUPERVISOR			
SKILLS TRIED OUT AND ACQUIRED BY:								
Ref No.	Description of Skill	Section Initial Date	LASS Initial Date	Ref No.	Description of Skill	Section Initial Date	LASS Initial Date
	Basic Calculations				**Listening and Talking**		
1	Read and write numbers			1	One to one Conversations		
	Whole Numbers:			3	Informal group discussion (talk)		
				3	Informal group discussion (listen)		
2	Add				Listening and talking to:		
2	Subtract			7	Fellow workers		
	Mental Arithmetic:			7	Supervisor		
6	Whole Numbers			7	Senior to Supervisor		
	Calculations:				Purpose of talking:		
13	Time			9	Describe or give information		
	Measurement and Drawing			9	Tell what to do		
24	Read or use scales and dials			9	Ask questions		
	Measure:			9	Answer questions		
25	Length or distance			10	Explain something		
26	Liquid Volume				Purpose of listening		
	Work with:			13	To get information/directions		
28	Metric Lengths				**Reading and Writing**		
28	Imperial Lengths			16	Read words		
30	Metric liquid volumes			16	Write words		
30	Imperial liquid volumes			16	Read single letter of alphabet		
33	Time: 12 hour clock			16	Write single letters of alphabet		
	Conversions			18	Read completed forms		
34	Metric to imperial			18	Fill in complete forms		
34	By looking up table			19	Read messages		
	Calculations:				Write messages		
35	Perimiter of circle				Manuals and textbooks		
35	Perimeter of other shapes			23	Read		
	Estimate:				Reading: the person		
39	Length or distance			27	Supervisor		
39	Areas				Writing: the person		
41	See if level or square			27	Supervisor		
42	Draw with instruments				Reading: the person		
43	Sketch or draw freehand			28	Work people outside		
45	Take info: scale drawing			28	Other sorts of people		
47	Take info: how parts fit				Purpose of writing		
50	Take info: make from raw material			29	To note statement		

17

Figure 4 *Part of Section Basic Skills Profile for Upholstery*

of the opportunities that a section has to offer, and to encourage them to take an active part in their own basic skill development, they should have access to a copy of the section profile.

Individual progress is recorded by the supervisor on the profile, regularly updating the range of work done and noting the date on which the trainee performed the skill satisfactorily. The recognition of this achievement is signified when, in the opinion of the supervisor, the trainee has reached a level of competence in exercising a basic skill that would be acceptable to an employer.

The profile also makes it possible for Life and Social Skills (LASS) tutors to monitor and record progress. For this reason a second column is added which can be initialled by the LASS tutor when a skill has been developed to a satisfactory standard. It is hoped that the adoption of this system will encourage a more integrated awareness between the Workshop and the LASS Unit on the progress of the individual trainee.

(iii) Skill development

The supervisor plays a key role in developing the potential of the trainee. This is best achieved by the careful sequencing of tasks and gradual allocating of work of increasing complexity. Whenever possible, training exercises should be kept to a minimum, and trainees encouraged to perform a wide variety of tasks in different contexts and settings. Examination of the skill requirements which are common to each section, as indicated by the Overall Matrix, shows how trainees may be transferred within the Workshop to allow additional skills to be practised.

The Workshop staff generally found little difficulty in understanding the objectives of using the Checklist to identify the basic skills needed to make a product or carry out an activity. It had to be stressed, however, that basic skill information would not remove the need to allocate tasks to trainees or to ensure that they achieve a proper understanding of the skill by providing them with related knowledge. Tasks are the vehicle through which basic skills are developed. An awareness of the basic skills being used in a sequence of tasks enables both supervisors and trainers to plot the progress in the trainee's mastery of skills.

(iv) Leaving credentials

An important feature of the availability of detailed information about the skills acquired is the opportunity that can now be offered to provide trainees with some form of leaving certificate, if it is felt that it would be in their best interests. Such information would certainly be of assistance and guidance to the Careers Service and prospective employers.

It is likely that a leaving credential could be prepared by the personnel counsellor and would indicate the achievements with an accompanying explanation of how, and in what context, the skills were developed.

6. What happened as a result of the study?

As a result of the study, the manager arranged a meeting with all the Workshop staff to discuss how far the study has gone towards answering the original questions (see page 000). As a consequence, new objectives were developed and a programme was established to discover how they could best be achieved.

It was agreed that basic skill development provided a proper focus for the Workshop activities.

(i) The new objectives

(a) Existing and new products or activities would be exploited to maximize the development of skills. (The slogan was coined: 'Everything we do can have a training content!')

(b) Trainees should sample as many of a section's basic skills as possible

(c) Trainees should be hepled to gain full advantage of a section and to take an active and conscious part in their own development.

(ii) How to meet the objectives — the new learning management model

In considering how to meet such objectives, a new learning management model was developed which showed it was helpful to look at the problems in the form of three fundamental questions:

QUESTION 1 How do we know what basic skills trainees have opportunities to learn?

ANSWER (i) Analyse each product or activity of each section using the Basic Skills Checklist to:

(a) Produce an Overall Basic Skills Matrix, to show profiles of current products and activities

(b) If necessary change methods to exploit existing facilities and equipment and alter Matrix accordingly.

QUESTION 2 What are the trainee's strengths and needs when he/she arrives?

ANSWER (i) Identify what skills are needed on entry to each section (P) by reference to the Overall Basic Skills Matrix

(ii) Produce a profile of these skills ('Can-do' profile)

(iii) During the induction phase, arrange to observe, test or ask trainees what they can do and record it on the profile

(iv) Examine the profile for strengths and needs and use this information to make the section placement decision.

QUESTION 3 How do we monitor learning and how can we let trainees and others concerned know what each trainee has learned?

ANSWER (i) Produce a section Basic Skills Profile ('Has-done' profile), showing what can be learnt

(ii) Give copies of the profile to each person concerned with the trainee's skill development, ie the trainee, supervisor and tutor

(iii) The supervisor and tutor should then allocate work to the trainee in a sequence which aids skill development, ie start with simple jobs related to their existing strengths and build upon them

(iv) The supervisor and tutor should record achievement and monitor progress by signing and dating the profile to record skill acquisition and periodically study the profiles to observe achievement

(v) The supervisor and tutor should discuss progress with the trainee

(vi) Provide trainees with a leaving profile to show employers and others interested in using or developing the trainee's talents.

7. Conclusion

The model of learning management and techniques is now being widely applied and has been found useful in a number of ways.

1. The Checklist:
   (a) provides a common language for communication between learning manager, learners and staff
   (b) can provide a valuable frame of reference for supervisors or teachers entering the area of basic skill training and formulating programmes, which makes them aware of skills which might be developed, and
   (c) enables training staff to confirm the scope of the basic skills that they are able to provide.
2. The Matrix:
   (a) enables the learning manager to consider the effect of different styles of management on trainee development
   (b) allows staff to see how colleagues are contributing to trainee skill development and to consider how their efforts might team together
   (c) indicates areas of skill commonality, where skill transfer might be fostered, and
   (d) provides the basis for 'can-do' and 'has-done' profiles to be produced.
3. The 'Can-do' profile:
   (a) indicates the skills which should be checked out before learning commences
   (b) provides a device for letting the learner and learning manager know what the learner can do
   (c) provides a means for highlighting where learning problems might occur and where remedial help is needed, and

(d) provides information to the learner counsellor or guide in the selection and sequencing of learning assignments.

4. The 'Has-done' profile:

(a) provides a device for showing progress, learning problems and achievements

(b) enables the learner and learning manager to know what basic skills can be and have been learned

(c) provides a means for enabling the learner to take an active interest in his/her own learning, and

(d) enables those responsible for guidance, placement or progression to future learning experience to know what can be built upon.

Although the methods referred to in this paper are at an early stage of development, it is felt that BSA provides a useful tool for the learning manager, which may prove of use in a wide variety of basic skills development programmes for young people. In particular it provides a means for tailoring learning content to the needs of the individual and of providing information for monitoring and exploiting learning opportunities provided.

References

Freshwater, M R (1980a) Making the most of training workshop opportunities using a basic skills checklist, *Vols I and II DTP Report No 22. Manpower Services Commission, Training Services Division, Directorate of Training,* London

Freshwater, M R (1980b) Basic skills checklist and matrix, *DTP Report No 21. Manpower Services Commission, Training Services Division, Directorate of Training,* London

Manpower Services Commission, Special Programmes Division (1980) *Review of the Second Year Special Programmes,* London

Educational Innovation and Technology Transfer: An Ecological Viewpoint

Alexander Romiszowski

The rise and fall of educational innovation

Why is it that educational innovations seldom seem to last? History teaches us that most events and social trends seem to be cyclic in nature. Indeed historians are fascinated by this cyclic nature of things and tend to devote particular study to the reasons behind the 'rise and fall of the Roman Empire' or the 'rise and fall of the Third Reich'. This tendency is so inbred that a friend of mine in university days, who was preparing a doctoral thesis on Elizabethan fashion, instinctively sub-titled it 'the rise and fall of the codpiece' — an idea subsequently vetoed by her supervisor. However, historians have not really established a general theory to account for the phenomenon of periodic expansion and reduction of interest and support for a given educational approach, and still less have they helped us to predict such changes or to avoid them.

Fashion is one explanation often offered to explain the short life of educational innovations. As Oliveira (1980) puts it when discussing the history of educational technology in Brazil, 'if you see a band wagon, jump on it'. Whereas this may be part of the truth, it hardly helps us to predict and control the process. Fashion is largely unpredictable and depends on cyclic periodicity for its very existence. If we were to adopt the 'science' of advertising and the creation of fashion, we would probably decrease the life of educational innovations and increase the periodicity of the cycle of change. The physical sciences help us little. The laws of nature have an inevitability which tends to strengthen the view that innovations never last ('what goes up, must come down'; 'the swing of the pendulum'). Some writers have turned to mythology to explain the phenomenon. Francis Moakley (1979) when describing the history of educational television at the San Francisco State University, draws the analogy between the rise, fall and rebirth of the ETV service and the mythological Phoenix rising from the ashes. John Tiffin (1980), when discussing the history of educational television in Latin America in general, extends the analogy, suggesting that these three stages of rapid expansion, followed by sharp decline and finally a slow and painful rebirth are characteristic, perhaps even necessary, stages in the development of ETV systems.

The phenomenon is not restricted to ETV, as was noted by this author (Romiszowski, 1972) when studying the pattern of growth of programmed instruction in the United Kingdom. A number of factors can be identified to account for this Phoenix-like behaviour, for example the dissipation of the original enthusiasm, the disappointment of initial (perhaps over-optimistic) hopes and the underestimation of necessary operating costs and other resources. Some of these factors can be controlled in the planning and execution of the project and their effects diminished if suitable attention is given to the internal structure of the innovation project. We can therefore call these internal factors, as they are within the control (at least theoretically) of the project managers and designers. I have developed elsewhere (Romiszowski, 1981a) a model for analysing and classifying these internal factors, as an aid to their control during project planning and execution.

There exist in addition, however, other external factors that explain why projects fail but which are not under the control of the project designers and managers. These are the factors which exist in the project's environment and come into play once the project is implemented and reaches certain critical stages in its growth. The project designer cannot usually control or eliminate these factors; he can, however, take them into account and design his project to be compatible, in much the way that a surgeon performing an organ transplant must select the characteristics of the organ to be compatible with the blood group and other critical factors already present in the body of the recipient. In the case of incomplete compatibility, there is a high probability of rejection of the new organ. However, this rejection does not occur immediately. It takes time for the incompatibility to be recognized and to grow to such proportions that the host system can no longer tolerate the presence of the intruding sub-system.

Another medical analogy may help to explain this. One can think of the growth of an innovation in terms of an 'epidemic' model. The 'germs' of a new idea are implanted in an existing system and develop into a practical innovation. This grows, often quite fast, encountering favourable conditions for growth in the absence (for the moment) of any resistance. However, the irritation caused by the incompatibility of the innovation with certain factors in the environment, leads to the formation of antibodies or cells of resistance. These require time to develop and grow to strength, but eventually they win the day and the innovation goes into a rapid decline. Just as in the case of antibodies, there remains a residual resistance, which makes it unlikely for that particular innovation to grow to strength again for some length of time, unless it is modified to eliminate the causes of incompatibility. This modification is usually a process of evolution. Hence the 'slow and painful' Phoenix-like rebirth. Sometimes it is possible to fool the antibodies, by presenting essentially the same innovation under a new guise, for example by changing the name. However, once the deception is discovered, the reaction is swift.

Such disguised innovations generally have an even shorter life than their predecessors. A good example is the Keller Plan and other disguised versions of programmed instruction. The only long-term solution is to

eliminate the causes of incompatibility. As the project designer cannot
control the environmental factors, he can only try to modify the
innovation itself. In some cases he may succeed in achieving compatibility,
but in others he may fail and the innovation is doomed to follow the cycle
of 'rise and fall'. One may influence the period of the cycle, by the
application of 'drugs' such as motivators (money), inhibitors (laws) or
anaesthetics (distractions), but eventually the antibodies will develop the
requisite strength to vanquish the intruder.

Compatibility analysis

In the previous (1980/81) Yearbook, I discussed, in two separate papers,
the topics of 'front-end analysis' and 'transfer of technology'. Both of
these topics are important as starting points for the present discussion of
how one can analyse and seek to improve the level of compatibility
between an educational innovation and the environment in which it is
to be implanted. In the paper on the transfer of educational technology,
I argued that four types of transfer may occur between two social contexts:
transfer of information, of products and services, of techniques or
procedures and of technology. In loose language the term 'transfer of
technology' is used for any combination of these four, but strictly
speaking, the 'true' transfer of *technology* occurs when one society assists
another to solve its own problems by supplying models for the problem-
solving process. One is, in a sense, transferring 'how to think about
problems' rather than ready-made solutions. The paper on front-end
analysis was an illustration of one aspect of how to 'think' about
problems — specifically, how to analyse deficiencies in human performance
and decide whether instruction, or a series of other alternative solutions, is
capable of eliminating the deficiency. The paper presented a series of
'conceptual schemata' — diagrams specifically designed to transfer a way
of thinking about a class of problems. The last of these schemata is
reproduced here, as it summarizes the factors one should take into account
when assessing the 'worth' and the 'practicality' of a given solution or
project. In essence, the task of the project designer is to select or invent
solutions that are compatible with the factors listed. However, at this level
of detail, one has already presupposed that there is a problem to solve.
In a way, one has also decided that the problem appears to be soluble and
that it is therefore worthwhile to seek out the most 'worthy and practical'
solution.

However, not all apparent problems are really quite what they seem. And
not all problems are capable of solution. More precisely, a situation
perceived by one person as a problem may not be considered to be a
problem by another person or by some other system in the environment
that thrives on the supposed problem. In such a case, any attempt to solve
the problem will be seen as a threat. The proposed solution will be
considered a new problem, in its own right. The antibodies will start to
build up.

Figure 1 *A schema for the analysis of the worth and practicality*
of instructional solutions to performance problems

Thus the analyst should ask four questions early on in the project design
process:

1. What is the problem that I am trying to solve? Who perceives it
   as a problem? Do others think differently?
2. Is the problem really soluble? Will an attempt to solve this problem
   create new, perhaps greater problems? Is the solution of this
   problem compatible with the goals of the system as a whole?
3. Is it worth solving this problem? Is it sufficiently important? Who
   will pay? Who will benefit?
4. What are the practical constraints that limit the choice of solutions?

These four questions are answered by means of the performance of a
careful systems analysis, not only of the system which has the problem
but also of related systems and of the overall environment in which these
systems exist. The last two questions may be called the 'worth and
practicality analysis' and the first two are the 'compatibility analysis'.
This 'compatibility analysis' is a form of 'pre-front-end analysis'. It really
is the first stage of project planning. It is, however, often overlooked, and
this is possibly the major reason for the 'rise and fall' phenomenon
mentioned previously. It is of course of particular importance in 'transfer
of technology' projects, in which very often, project design teams are

working in an environment that is unfamiliar to them. They may not perceive the incompatibilities that they are introducing until it is too late, whereas local personnel, familiar with the local environment, may instinctively sense the folly being designed into the project.

However, it is a good idea to supplement instinct with a formal system of analysis, designed to focus attention on potential sources of incompatibility.

Some case studies

The case studies that follow illustrate that it is quite a common occurrence to launch innovative projects which aim to solve problems that are not really soluble or are not really problems. I have chosen two cases, from a larger number published earlier (Romiszowski, 1981b), which are adapted from real life cases, one from the UK and one from the developing countries. However, the real context and the data presented have been slightly modified in order to illustrate the points I wish to make.

Case study 1: the 'teaching effectiveness problem'

Each year, reams of paper are devoted to the 'problems' of teaching and learning. Yet the problems remain and appear undiminished. Are we attacking the problems correctly? Are the problems soluble? Do they indeed exist? Do the 'owners' of the educational system (ie society at large) really see the problem as some of us (teaching professionals) see it? To us, poor system performance, as exemplified by poor examination pass results, is a source of dissatisfaction, but what about the supra-system (society)? Certainly, whatever it 'says', a society does not behave as if the performance of the educational system were a source of dissatisfaction. It does not spend a very large proportion of the resources devoted to education in attempts to improve the system. The size of the educational industry is quite staggering. Austwick (1972) described it as follows:

> I would ask you to imagine a major national industry, with an annual expenditure of about 2500 million pounds, a workforce of about 400,000 and a further 100,000 trainees. The manufacturing time for each product varies between 10 and 20 years and a further 10 or more years are required for evaluation afterwards. The number of items going through the system at any one time is of the order of eight million. The industry itself is very old but has been expanding rapidly during the past 100 years and seems likely to go on doing so. If you ask for a specification of any of the products of the industry you will be told that this is not available, being still under discussion! The industry has no central board of directors, but during the past 25 years has had 15 successive general managers — an average of about 20 months each!
>
> The 'industry' which satisfies these conditions is of course the educational system of England and Wales.

Depending on their technological complexity most manufacturing industries spend between 2 per cent and 15 per cent of their total turnover on research and development. The medical industry (drugs, pharmaceuticals) is one of the biggest spenders in this field. In many

respects the medical and educational industries are very similar, and with
the food industries, they have the greatest influence on the well-being of
man. They are also very similar in their direct action upon man as an
individual: diagnosis of individual needs, presentation of individual
treatments, construction and control of appropriate environments, etc.
Yet while medicine invests heavily in research and development, education
hardly does at all. It would seem that education does not wish to improve,
that the problems of educational efficiency to which lip service is paid by
successive ministers of education are merely pseudo-problems. As an
example of the reasons behind this, let us investigate one case: high drop-
out rates from a course caused by difficulties in learning, attending
regularly and so on. Typical examples of British courses with high
drop-out rates are the Ordinary and Higher National Certificate courses.
These are for people who are in full-time employment in industry, so are
run in the evenings or on a sandwich basis. No doubt this aspect
contributes to the average annual drop-out rate of between 25 per cent
and 30 per cent of students. But overloaded curricula, poor learning
conditions, poor equipment, scarce learning aids and poor teaching also
play their part. These courses are designed to run over five years, three
years up to ONC or a further two years to obtain the HNC. As a result of
the drop-out rates and examination failures, only about 8 per cent of
those who start the course obtain a Higher National Certificate within the
five years. This number swells a little later on, owing to second attempts.
The process seems terribly wasteful. Why is nothing done to improve the
situation? Let us suppose that we could halve the annual drop-out rate
from 30 per cent to 15 per cent, what then? Twice as many students
would be studying for HNC in the fourth and fifth year, requiring twice
as many classrooms, laboratories and workshops, teachers etc. Nearly
three times as many would graduate. Can industry use that many
graduates?

Thus there are constraints both within the system (available resources)
and in the super-system (in this case industry) which militate against
anything being done to improve the situation.

Case study 2: the 'adult literacy problem'

Many countries are very concerned about the levels of illiteracy of their
adult population. Either because schooling opportunities did not exist, or
because existing facilities were inefficient, a proportion of the population
(in some countries quite considerable) reaches adulthood without
acquiring the basic skills of reading and writing. This is bemoaned from
two standpoints:

1. That the lack of these skills makes the person almost unemployable
   in a developing and industrializing nation. The concept of functional
   literacy stems from this: each citizen should at least reach that level
   of literacy which will enable him to hold down a job and fulfil his
   obligations to society (eg write a cheque, pay his taxes, etc). We

Year	Drop-out rate	
	30%	15%
1.	100	100
less drop-outs	−30	−15
2.	70	85
less drop-outs	−21	−13
3.	49	72
less drop-outs	−15	−11
4.	34	61
less drop-outs	−10	−9
5.	24	52
less drop-outs	−7	−8
Number sitting HNC examination	17	44
Number passing at first sitting (at 50 per cent norm-referenced passing grade)	8	22
Maximum number in HNC course: 4th and 5th years combined	58	113

Figure 2 *Number of trainees in ONC/HNC courses; over a hypothetical 5-year period at annual drop-out rates of 30 per cent and 15 per cent*

might label this the human resources standpoint, which views the population as an important resource which society should use efficiently in order to reach its objectives.

2. That the lack of literacy skills closes many doors of self-improvement for the person. In a society as large and complex as most modern nations, the village-level techniques of education and training through personal example and word-of-mouth are ineffective. Not only is there not enough time to learn all that is required for modern living in this way, but there are also many things which can only be effectively learned through reading and writing. We might call this the humanist standpoint, which views the individual as the important system, and is concerned with improving his capabilities of interaction with his environment.

Whichever of the two standpoints one favours, there seem to be strong reasons for doing something about the adult literacy problem.

One country which has put a lot of effort into solving the problem is Brazil. For some years now, an organization called MOBRAL (Brazilian Movement for Literacy) has been running schemes of adult literacy training throughout the country. The stated aims of MOBRAL are to eliminate adult illiteracy by the turn of the century. The techniques MOBRAL uses involve the use of many volunteer teachers, the media, other local and national resources, and are reported to be very successful. Indeed the MOBRAL model has been copied and adapted by several other Latin American and African nations. MOBRAL has become a Brazilian export.

Can it achieve its objective, however? A little bit of systems analysis casts strong doubts on the possibility of MOBRAL *on its own* ever eliminating illiteracy. What do we mean by eliminating in this context anyway? Surely we do not mean that there will be not one illiterate person in the country. Rather, we must have an idea of the percentage of the population which we will tolerate as illiterates. For example, the problem could be stated as:

What is: X per cent of adults over 15 years are illiterate.
What should be: no more than Y per cent of the group should be illiterate.

One really also needs to define illiterate in quantifiable and measurable terms, but we will come back to this point later.

Let us build up a hypothetical systems diagram, based on simplified figures (but figures not far from the Brazilian reality). We shall imagine a 'steady state' before the implementation of adult literacy schemes, which was giving a level of 50 per cent adult literacy. This was arrived at as shown in Figure 3. For every 100 children reaching school age, 90 enter some form of schooling. The other 10 do not (mainly because of no local facilities) and very few of these (a negligible proportion) manage to become literate through their own efforts by the time they reach the school leaving age of 15. Of the 90 who enter schooling, only 50 are literate by the age of 15. This is largely due to heavy drop-out and the process of repeating a grade if standards are not reached (half the nation's schoolchildren are in the first grade). This figure represents a 50/90 or 55.5 per cent efficiency level for the school system.

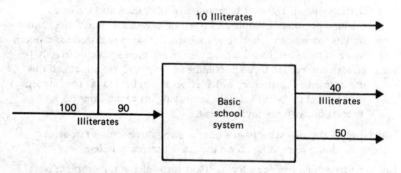

Figure 3 *Steady-state before implementation of adult literacy programme*

Let us now state our problem as:

What is: 50 per cent of adults (15+) are illiterate.
What should be: 10 per cent or less of adults (15+) illiterate.

In order to solve the problem, we construct an adult literacy programme. We implant this system in our hypothetical society and link it to existing systems as shown in Figure 4. This shows a new hypothetical steady state when the problem is 'solved' as we have 90 literates being outputted for every 100 new children entering the system. Notice that we have assumed no change in the efficiency of the school system. What does this imply for the efficiency of the adult literacy programme?

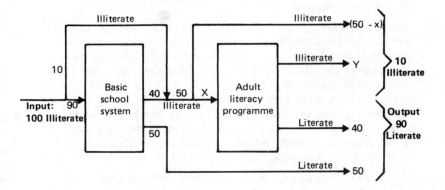

Figure 4 *Steady-state (hypothetical) after the adult literacy programme has been implemented and has reached its objective of maintaining a 10 per cent or less output of illiterates (ie 10 per cent of all children born will remain illiterate)*

Given 50 illiterates aged 15 or over, it must produce 40 literates. This may be achieved in several ways.

1. The programme manages to 'catch' all 50 (ie x = 50). Then in order to output 40 literates, the programme must work at 80 per cent efficiency.
2. It may catch only 40 (any less and it could not reach its target output). This implies an 80 per cent success rate in attracting adults into the programme. But it also implies an impossible 100 per cent efficiency for the programme.
3. Any intermediate stage between 1 and 2. For example, if the adult programme was as successful as the school system in capturing the illiterates (90 per cent), then it would have to operate at a 40/45 or 89 per cent efficiency.

None of these three situations are in the realms of probability. It is unlikely that the percentage coverage of any adult education system could even equal that of the normal school system, given that the former is voluntary and the latter is compulsory, and that *all* those who nevertheless managed to evade the compulsory system are in the clientele.

It is also unlikely that an adult programme could be over one and a half times more efficient than the school system (80 per cent to 90 per cent as compared to 55 per cent) given that adults as a rule have more learning difficulties, and the 'natural' good learners have in the main succeeded in the schools, and the ones we are now dealing with are the poorer learners who have already experienced failure (unless of course there were to be a breakthrough in instructional methods).

Finally, one should note that the throughput capacity of the adult programme in our example is about half that of the school system. This will represent quite a high investment.

The systems analyst/project planner may well ask at this stage such questions as: 'Should we not do something, about the efficiency and coverage of the school system, at the same time as (or even before) we implement an adult literacy programme?' 'If there are techniques which can give 80 per cent or more efficiency in the teaching of reading and writing, would it not be more economical to spend our resources on implementing these at the school level?' He may even be led further into systems analysis, to consider whether he ought to be designing adult literacy programmes at all. He might, for instance, get more interested in the efficiency of the school system.

Similar case studies abound. In all cases, there exists some source of incompatibility between the system that we seek to improve and some factors in the system's environment. In the first case, the environment has neither the resources or the 'market' available to sustain a really significant improvement in teaching system productivity. In the second case, the environment contains two related systems that appear to be working in opposing directions. The normal school system appears to be an efficient 'producer of illiteracy'. The adult education system is unable to cope with this production.

There exist many other possible sources of incompatibility. For example, there may be competition between rival systems for the same type of scarce resources, as in the case of several innovation projects competing for the same sources of finance. There may also be competition for the 'market' available for our system's products, as in the case of several educational institutions producing large numbers of specialist professionals. for whom few jobs exist — the case of doctors in India, lawyers in Brazil or sociologists in the UK. Such limits on the resources available and on the extent of the market, limit the total growth potential and the existence of competing systems in this context generally means that some of them will go to the wall.

An interesting case in point is the situation of educational technology in eastern Europe. As long as educational technology was seen to be concerned with the use of gadgets and audiovisual media in education, it was allowed to grow alongside the existing disciplines of education, though much in the role of a junior, non-academic, partner. Once it was perceived that educational technologists see themselves as problem-solvers in any sphere related to education, capable of applying theoretical models to the practical purposes of curriculum design, improving teaching methods, or evaluating the teaching-learning process, conflict developed between them and the established professors of didactics. The environment had been threatened. The antibodies of resistance were activated and as a result educational technology is having a rough time. Whether it will survive as a respectable academic discipline is in doubt. The 'rise and fall' phenomenon is all too evident. We must wait to see whether the painful Phoenix-like rebirth will occur.

Yet another very common source of incompatibility is the existence of a conflict of interests, or objectives, between the system that we are investigating and its environment. In many countries of the third world, for example, there exists a real conflict between the overall objectives of the education system, as officially stated, and the objectives of the ruling classes. The last thing that many governments want is an education system for the masses that is really effective. As the provision of no education is not feasible, both politically and economically, it is important to ensure that what is provided is effective only in those areas that interest the dominant class — vocational training, for example. Any attempt at improving other aspects of education, such as the ability of the masses to think for themselves, is most unwelcome, however. A practical example of this phenomenon in action was the banishment of Paulo Freire and other progressive educators by the Brazilian military junta in 1964. This process has now happily been reversed and the slow rebirth of popular education has begun. It remains to be seen whether the environment has really changed sufficiently to accept the new attempts at improvement of mass education, or whether a critical point will be reached, when incompatibility of interests will reactivate the antibodies of resistance.

A schema for compatibility analysis

In order to summarize the arguments presented here, Figure 5 presents a schema of the principal sources of incompatibility illustrated by the cases and examples discussed above. In the case of the transfer of technology (particularly educational technology) there is a current tendency to criticize the wholesale transfer of projects from one country to another. Such transfers have seldom worked. The culprit is usually identified as the agent of the 'donor' system — the foreign consultant who fails to appreciate the cultural differences that render the imported processes, techniques or organizational structures inappropriate for operation in the recipient system. However, these sources of problems *are* within the control of the project designers. The blame should at least be shared between the donors and the recipients. In very few cases is the 'colonialist' influence of the donor so strong that the recipient has no say in whether a particular imported solution should be adopted or not.

However, the issue here is not to apportion the blame for unsuccessful technology transfer projects, but rather to examine the causes of failure. My argument here is that too much emphasis is placed on the internal factors of project structure and its ability to operate in the new environment, and too little attention is paid to the interrelations, and possible conflicts, that may exist between the project as a whole and its environment. These external factors are generally outside the sphere of

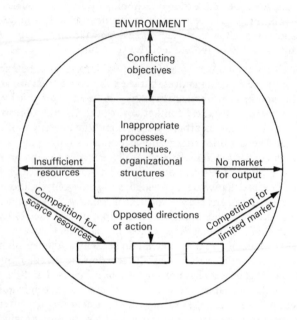

Figure 5 *A schema of the sources of incompatibility between a system and its environment*

control of the project designers and are often subtly hidden or disguised. An overall systems analysis, centring on the *analysis of compatibility,* might ensure that projects with no real chance of survival in the real environment will not even be launched. It is my contention here that the cyclic 'rise and fall' phenomenon, so common in the area of educational innovation projects (whether a cross-cultural transfer is involved or not), can be largely explained by the ecological concept of compatibility with the environment. This aspect of project planning would seem to merit more formal attention.

References

Austwick, K (1972) The message, the medium and post-literate man, in Austwick, K and Harris, N D C (eds) *Aspects of Educational Technology VI,* Pitman, London

Moakley, F X (1979) The television Phoenix at San Francisco State University, in Page, G T and Whitlock, Q (eds) *Educational Technology Twenty Years On — Aspects of Educational Technology XIII,* Kogan Page, London

Oliveira, J B A (1980) The status of educational technology in Brazil, *Programmed Learning and Educational Technology,* 17 (4), 210-17

Romiszowski, A J (1972) Changes in the pattern of programmed materials available commercially in Britain, in Austwick, K and Harris, N D C (eds) *Aspects of Educational Technology VI,* Pitman, London

Romiszowski, A J (1981a) Troubleshooting in educational technology or, why projects fail, *Programmed Learning and Educational Technology,* 18 (3), 168-89

Romiszowski, A J (1981b) *Designing Instructional Systems: Decision Making in Course Planning and Curriculum Design*, Kogan Page, London
Tiffin, J (1980) Educational television: a Phoenix in Latin America? *Programmed Learning and Educational Technology*, 17 (4), 257-61

An Appreciation of the Life and Work of Piaget

Professor K Lovell, *The School of Education, University of Leeds*

Piaget was one of the great scholars of the twentieth century. Born in 1896 at Neuchâtel (Switzerland), he was in boyhood and early adolescence a productive biologist. In later adolescence there followed a period of religious, philosophical and political searching. It was this early interest in biology and philosophy that shaped his life's work, for whether his work is thought of as biology, philosophy or psychology, it was all directed to building a theory of knowledge, of how the individual comes to know his world. For Piaget it was fundamental to know how the individual passes from a lesser degree of knowledge to a greater one. It was this study of the progressive adjustment of knowledge that Piaget termed genetic epistemology, and to pursue this he turned to, as one source, a study of children's intellectual development.

His genius lay in asking good questions and in thoughtfully analysing his observations and interview data, and for 60 years he published, either alone or with his colleagues, a stream of books and articles on his findings. But a careful reading of his works reveals that on many issues his views changed; indeed he wrote that he himself was his own chief revisionist. He did not wish to leave behind a school of thought, but a set of ideas which could be accepted or rejected in whole or in part, and developed. The one proposition that was constant for him was that knowledge is constructed out of the interaction between the person and the world. The cognitive structures involved in knowing are given neither in the object nor in the person but in the interaction between them. He employed at this point a biological process model using a self-regulating mechanism which allowed the person's cognitive resources and his experience to be brought into balance.

For those in education, Piaget's greatest contribution is likely to be in the field of developmental psychology, for in this area he was a giant. He has left us a great corpus of facts about children's conceptual development. Not all the early Genevan claims have stood the test of research by others; in particular his notion of 'stages' — so well known to educators — has been a focus of much controversy. Again his theory of intellectual growth has been criticized for taking too little account of societal, phenomenological and emotional aspects of mind. Yet in spite of the inaccuracies and weaknesses in his work, his contribution to psychology has been enormous, for he largely reshaped our thinking about the development of human intelligence. While he stressed the importance of children's mental activity in the construction of knowledge, he thought educational technology valuable in some situations. (Piaget in *The Essential Piaget*, eds H E Gruber and J J Voneche, 1977, p 718.

Piaget's work has direct relevance for the classroom in three ways. First, the methodology enables us to explore children's thoughts and not determine merely if they are right or wrong. Second, a mine of information is given about the notions and prototypes pupils employ and discard in the construction of significant ideas. Teachers ignore at their peril these misconceptions/alternative frameworks held by pupils and older students to explain things and events. Third, his theory suggests that educators should provide increased opportunities for reflective activity.

When he died on 17 September 1980 there passed from us a scholar who could excite and motivate colleagues and students, elaborate theory, and bring together trends in a number of academic disciplines.

Study Skills as a Province of Educational Technology

Anne Howe, *Middlesex Polytechnic*

'Study skills' is the area of work which is directed to efforts to improve students' approaches to academic work and their study habits and methods. A large and increasing amount of work has been done in this field over the past few years, mostly within institutions of higher and further education, including a large number of studies at academic level, and the provision of study skills courses and counselling facilities.

There is no intrinsic reason why this work is concentrated at post-compulsory levels of education, except that these seem to offer the most supportive environment for educational innovations generally; indeed there is hardly a course leader but will, faced with the need to support a study skills course, bewail the fact that his students did not acquire these skills in the sixth form, the fifth form, the first year of secondary education, or even the primary school. While acknowledging, then, that some initiatives do exist at school level, this article deals with study skills as developed in post-compulsory education, where it has, for an educational innovation, been accepted remarkably widely and smoothly. The particular background of this article is the Middlesex Polytechnic's Learning Systems Group's experience with developing and teaching study skills courses for new students, an effort in which all the members of the Group have participated and in which we have freely borrowed each other's ideas as well as drawing on those of outsiders. My own background being in educational technology, I have been concerned to relate study skills work to the rest of the field and also to see what educational technology precepts could be directly applied within the course. First, then, to place study skills in the field of educational technology.

The traditional approach of educational technology

Educational technologists can be and are concerned with this sort of work in several sorts of ways. At a purely practical level, if students seem to need this kind of help, it may be logical and convenient for the work to be taken on by a generalist group like the 'Ed Tech Unit', 'The Educational Development Group', 'Learning Systems' or whatever name the institution's educational technologists trade under. Again, the design and development of a course in study skills can be approached like those of any other course, using educational technology techniques. But, of course, there is a special sense in which study skills can be regarded as a branch of educational technology itself. After all, if educational technology is the 'development, application and evaluation of systems, techniques and aids to improve the process of human learning', study skills falls within its scope; in this light it seems such a natural concern of educational technology that one is only surprised to realize that it has not always been a central activity.

That it is relatively new within the spectrum of educational technology will be recognized by those readers who recall the systems approach as it was introduced in the late 1960s. They will remember that, somewhere at the top of that magic algorithm, there was a box containing an essential part of the spell — the formula 'Analysis of Target Population'. Proper development of the system, it was acknowledged, involved studying the background, attitudes and motivation, and present state of knowledge of the prospective students; but these students were, implicitly and sometimes explicitly, strictly to be regarded as 'given' — the educational technologist was stuck with them and might indeed regard his art as the selection and use of techniques which, given enough resources, and a presumably greatly extended human lifespan, would be capable of teaching anything to anybody — the 90/90 criterion.

A coarse-minded person might find it hard to perceive any real difference between the student in this situation and a rat up for conditioning in a behaviourist's laboratory. In accordance with this general approach, primitive educational technology was almost exclusively directed to improving *teaching* in one way or another, and teachers rather than learners were and are the practitioners of educational technology methods. One of the purposes of this article will be to explore whether there is any reasonable way in which the techniques and methods of educational technology can be put at the disposal of learners to help them directly *as* learners.

That taking on study skills represents a sort of reversal within educational technology will be realized if you open almost any book on the subject; you will find that it describes ways of setting up, managing, evaluating or otherwise controlling a situation in which someone other than the writer is doing the learning. The process of learning is assumed to be a function of the learning situation rather than an activity controlled by the learner. In this sense educational technology may have claimed to generate 'learner-centred' courses, but its focus was unwaveringly on the methodology and techniques of teaching and presenting learnable materials and lessons. Work on study skills has an exactly opposite emphasis. Here the 'givens' are the subject matter and its texts and teachers, and the focus is on improving approaches, methodology and techniques of learning.

Primitive educational technology was very much a product of its time; 'learning by objectives' matches in spirit 'management by objectives', and both ideas were typical of the contemporary worship of efficiency and submission to technology; one can see the subsequent assertion of humanistic values as in its way a backlash. At its beginning, educational technology claimed to be the means of offering ways in which the young could acquire knowledge and skills demonstrably more efficiently than by the old methods. To put these new methods into effect would demand radical changes in the system and considerable resources. The expectation that the offer would be taken up in the education system rested both on the faith that efficiency in this function was an important objective of the system, and, to a large extent, an obliviousness to its other functions. Unless we are prepared to accept the numbers of television sets available to schools or some equally crass measure as a criterion, it has to be accepted that the impact of educational technology in the education system at large has been disappointing.

This partial failure is no doubt to some extent attributable to the factors mentioned above, but it is also at least partly because in spite of exaggerated early claims, primitive educational technology simply cannot deliver in certain areas of learning. Macdonald-Ross resoundingly denounced its failure to cope with higher learning objectives in the context of the development of Open University courses in 1972. Just as important, it did not even claim to do much for 'personal development' in the sense that humanistic thinkers use that term. Even in training, which really does value efficiency and where educational technology had been relatively successful, educational technologists found themselves increasingly faced with problems of training people in interpersonal skills at different levels, where the systems approach and the behavioural objective proved quite inadequate to meet the requirements. Increasingly, therefore, they turned to the humanistic based techniques emanating from the 'growth movement' for solutions to these problems, whose perceived importance was growing both in education and in industry.

The relevance of humanistic techniques

One can view these developments either as a departure from educational technology or as an extension of the field. I think it is more reasonable and more productive to take the latter view. This involves recognizing that the 'knowledge content' of educational technology is *all* the techniques and skills which educational technologists use to solve problems arising in their professional lives. Educational technology, finding that it needed management skills to establish innovations, had no difficulty in taking these on as part of the canon, and they appear on the syllabus of every 'Dip Ed Tech' in the UK. A similar *de facto* recognition of the relevance of 'human relations' techniques is taking longer, even though many educational technologists made extensive use of them, and they offer approaches traditional educational technology cannot provide to some of the problems of the profession.

This article is not really about the humanistic techniques except in the context of study skills, where they form the basis of many courses and approaches, but a short description of their general nature may help to explain why they are relevant in that context and also why they do not easily fit in with what many people think educational technology means. Such a summary is rather difficult to attempt, by reason of the fact that the techniques are experiential and need, as it were, to be experienced to be believed. Roughly one may say that the general aim is to make people conscious of their own and others' behaviour and interactions and more aware of the feelings from which this behaviour springs. The assumption is that such awareness will in itself enable individuals to direct their feelings into changed behaviours which will make their lives easier and happier, in particular enabling them to relate more effectively with others in their personal and working lives. The techniques involved were devised and used first in therapeutic rather than academic or training circumstances, and the transfer has not been universally happy; especially as sessions using them need to be conducted with a skill and insight which are not automatically part of the repertoire of the ordinary academic — one reason, incidentally, why, if educational technologists are going to use these techniques, they should be studied and trained for. Such techniques are aimed at helping individuals to 'become', and their practitioners usually claim emphatically that their courses etc are strictly 'non-directive' — a claim that will be briefly examined later. Traditional educational technology, with its central preoccupation with defined objectives, aims at helping individuals to 'be able to' and is usually extremely directive.

We have found that emphatically non-directive courses do not provide a universally satisfactory answer to the problems actually complained of by students, and as our courses have developed we have devised a range of exercises and approaches, some of them drawn straight from the educational technology repertoire, to meet the commonest types of questions raised by students, as well as the kinds of needs their teachers sometimes perceive more clearly than they may do.

Students' attitudes to learning

An attempt at a formal systematic analysis of these problems would be much too long for a short article and could hardly hope to succeed, since there are as many different ways of perceiving these problems as there are analysts, let alone students. It is possible to discern three main strands, however, though quite a different matter to separate them out in the case of any one student. In the first place there may be what can be called an inadequate perception of the nature and purpose of higher education. This may take the form of a sort of basic mystification — the student keeps up with the work but is not really in tune with the nature of his discipline and its demands. Or it may be perceived as a limited and rigid approach to study, where the rote absorption of knowledge becomes the be-all and end-all; these sorts of problems can be crudely defined as inadequacies of *attitude.* Secondly, we can identify lack of actual

knowledge, about study rather than about the subject of study. There is
an obvious overlap here; sometimes students are insecure and rigid in
their attitudes because they are uncertain about a whole range of different
norms — what standards they are expected to meet, how long they should
work each week, what they 'should' be able to achieve in terms of memory
or concentration, and so forth. But it is most unjust to interpret this
search for norms simply as the product of insecurity or of an unseemly
dependence on authority. New students in particular are in a situation
analogous to that of an older person taking on a new job. To ask what is
expected of him is perfectly reasonable; not to do so might merely be a
sign of folly or over-confidence. There is thus good reason to try to
provide solid information which will help students decide how to study
in the context of how others do so successfully. Thirdly, one can draw up
a list of essential basic *skills* — to read effectively, complete written work,
take part in seminars, together with a host of minor skills, like using the
library and making correct lists of references; again, these 'skills' cannot
really be isolated from other problems and for each student there are
different areas of difficulty which involve all three aspects of the
problem. (It may be suggested here that a fourth identifiable category
should be included, those students who lack prerequisite skills, usually
in English or mathematics. While these lacks do indeed compound study
problems, the study skills group is not really the place to deal with the
necessary specialized remedial teaching and they are consequently not
considered here.)

Study skills has been claimed as an educational innovation, and the quite
new level of academic interest as well as the extensive provision of courses
and other help would justify this claim. But the idea of helping people to
learn more efficiently is nothing new, and is represented by an extensive
literature on the subject.

This literature goes back a very long way, and some of it is full of sensible
advice, whose only major demerit is that so many students find it
impossibly hard to follow. No set of detailed procedures for note-taking,
reading and written work suits everyone — these are highly individual
processes — and these 'hints and tips' can be positively demoralizing to
those who can't follow them but may nevertheless be left feeling that they
represent a single 'proper' mode of approaching the tasks concerned. The
realization of this difficulty accounts for some of the emphasis on 'non-
prescriptiveness' of modern study skills courses, and the fact that they
are often so heavily based on experiential techniques.

Such courses are designed to change attitudes to study, and are really quite
prescriptive in practice, for they aim to encourage openness, awareness
and independence, though they do not prescribe the precise behaviour by
which the student will manifest these qualities.

It is certainly true that the simple act of considering study as an activity
and comparing one's attitude and approach to it with those of others in a
reasonably open discussion may produce possible radical insights and

usually a better general understanding about the nature of study and the academic requirements of undergraduate work. This kind of approach does, then, need to be built into study skills courses, but it does not answer all the problems raised, and, like any other approach to study skills, it is not equally successful with all students.

In the first place, academics who resist the pressure to change from the conventional lecture to other, more open, forms of teaching are often solidly backed in this attitude by their students. Experience suggests that students perceive study difficulties mostly in the context of solitary work — reading and writing; the long slog to get command of the basics of their subject, and the sporadic slog to turn out written work to a standard they are never quite sure of. This is not to deny that the classroom situation produces some perceived areas of difficulty, but the average group of students does not complain very much about modes of class teaching — some would say, not enough. Many students like to feel that they are getting, in the form of lectures, safe and usable information straight from the horse's mouth; the concept of education as the process of passing information from the teacher through the student and on to an exam paper is not unique to teachers.

This has implications both for the objectives and the content of study skills courses; we must aim to make students aware that there are other ways of regarding the nature and objectives of higher education. However, we must also recognize, in the first place, that many current assessment procedures suggest that it is not wholly unreasonable for students to see their education in this limited way; many students, while they may appreciate that they could get more out of their course than the degree, prefer to do without the 'more' to ensure the degree. In the second place, it has to be recognized that the individual will only change his mind about the ways he could approach his work when he is ready to — you cannot really 'force them to be free'. If he has come to learn techniques for better implementing whatever he perceives to be the academic process, he will not necessarily stay to revise his perception of that process if he thinks he is not getting what he came for. It is reasonable, anyway, to hope that everyone who comes on such a course will gain something from it, even if the benefit he receives is not the one we might most wish for him. Thirdly, most groups of students on such courses contain a number of individuals who *do* want to learn how to carry out certain study tasks, either because the tasks may be wholly new to them, or because they have no confidence in the techniques they have learnt elsewhere, or because they are open-mindedly seeking any help that may be useful to them. A course which aims to provide what these students want does not have to be rigorously prescriptive. On the contrary, it needs to admit that no single set of techniques is infallible, and that the best one can do is to offer ways of approaching different tasks that may help individuals develop ways of working to suit them. It is in this sort of area that traditional educational technology has quite a lot to offer by way of 'study skills content', because much of it has been developed to meet the need to define and re-present material, and therefore can be applied to defining and re-presenting material in wider contexts, such as essay writing. It has also drawn on learning theory to provide information about the way people learn and some practical and well-supported principles for making material learnable; some of these can be applied by students for themselves quite as readily as by teachers for students.

Applying the concepts of educational technology to study skills

Objectives

The concentration on aims and objectives is perhaps educational technology's main strength, though it is not the exclusive property of educational technology and does not have to refer only to tightly specified behavioural objectives. In this looser sense, it can be put at the disposal of students to help them think about study at a number of different levels, of which I shall here mention only two.

I alluded above to the common problem that students are often frightened by their work because they are not sure what sort of standards they are supposed to be aiming at. One may see this in a general way when they try to identify the overall purpose of their course and what they hope to gain from it, and in a more specific way when they approach the problems of written work. The concept of objectives can put a framework on this problem at both levels: by trying to identify the sorts of skills the course work demands, they can develop some insight into the problem of expected standards. This can be done using objectives in quite a formal way; for example: a particular group of students was identifying their 'study problem', as lying in the general area of learning and remembering material, but they were also very unclear about what was really expected of them: it proved possible to use a set of essay titles to draw out a list of the kinds of skills they were actually expected to develop — the titles included items such as 'examine this statement', 'analyse', 'discuss', 'compare', 'account for', etc. It was possible to use Bloom's taxonomy both to show the students the relationship between the low level skills they were worried about and the objectives implied by the kinds of written tasks they were expected to do, and also to help them increase their understanding of the nature of these tasks, and to develop their techniques for tackling written work.

At quite another level, some students find their work daunting because there is no apparent end to it. Especially in humanities and social science subjects it is never really possible to feel one 'knows it'; there are always more angles to consider and more authors to read. The idea of using objectives to define and limit the content of study can be helpful here: most students will readily agree that the reading they do for an essay is reading with a specific objective in mind; it suits some students well to use the titles of essays they do not have to write as a sort of self-imposed objective for their general reading. Tony Buzan recommends the posing of specific questions, to answer which becomes the objective of the reading, and some students find this helpful (though for others it is difficult to think of questions about unfamiliar subject matter). Objectives for reading can also be interpreted at a much simpler level, just to cover a certain amount and produce usable notes, within a certain amount of time. The simple process of setting oneself to achieve an observable end result of some sort — what in other contexts might be called a measurable objective — can relieve some of the difficulties of reading; though, as ever, it does need to be repeated that these approaches do not work for all students, they are worth prescribing because some will find them useful.

Learning as an active process

Turning now to the concepts about the process of learning that educational technology uses, it will be useful to leave ideas about feedback and evaluation to be discussed later.

First, one of the underlying assumptions of educational technology is that learning is an *active* process. Traditional educational technology seeks to provide for the teacher to control this activity in more or less detail — most in the case of linear programmes, much less in the case of, for example, the Open University texts. But at some level the student is responding to the material. His responses need not be particularly creative; they may just be designed to ensure that he has understood a simple statement correctly. A student who is seeking to 'absorb' material is often not active even in this sense; he may just be waiting for it to sink in. Students may assume that the process of taking notes is 'activity' in the desired sense, and so it may be; but one needs to distinguish between a simple copying process, and notes which are the result of some positive interaction with the material. The possible nature of such interactions can be described in various ways; the educational technology principles of building into the learning process repetition and practice can be used as a focus for some of them.

Repetition and practice are not highly regarded in modern study skills courses, because of the obvious implication that students ought to learn by rote. It is difficult to see, however, how people can remember and apply detailed knowledge without using these aids in some way. Students will certainly try to do so. It is reasonable to assume that they will need to 'repeat', to look more than once at, their texts; the unproductive approach for most is to do this by rereading every successive sentence two or three times in the effort to grind it into memory. The idea of two or more reads with different objectives can be helpful (particularly for students who do not consider skimming to be faintly disreputable). Similarly, at first sight the idea of 'practice' seems difficult to apply if one does not wish to encourage rote learning. But 'practising' an idea can usefully be interpreted as thinking about it and its implications — in this

sense one need not learn the works of Hume, for example, off by heart, to
get plenty of 'practice' of his ideas. Again, the act of notetaking can be
used creatively as 'practice' of the material rather than as mere copying.

Pacing

Another relevant educational technology principle is that of 'pacing'. It is
not quite clear what the nature of this particular principle may be, since
though it was at first the aim of educational technologists to provide for
students to learn at their own pace and great advantages were seen in
doing so, it was subsequently established that many learners either romp
or dawdle through the material and actually benefit from being set an
allocated time for a particular task. 'Pacing' is a matter of great concern to
many students; they are anxious to know how long they 'should' be
spending on particular types of task and on their work overall. The general
acceptance within educational technology about the variable pace of
individual learners can relax a rather uncomfortable and unproductive hunt
for a norm to live up to. The difficulty educational technology has had
with this question of pacing is also quite reassuring; in the first place it
clarifies the point that students cannot learn at any pace but their own,
and in the second place it suggests that they may be capable of a greater
flexibility than they expect in choosing what their own pace is, a point
that can be reinforced by paced reading exercises.

Memory

Similarly educational technology draws on certain facts about the nature
of memory and concentration spans which can be helpful background
knowledge for students seeking reassurance about what is 'normal'. One
sometimes finds a student who says he 'can't concentrate', and who turns
out to expect that he will be able to read a difficult text for three hours
without a break and remember everything he has read. Again, it is often
helpful to examine what it is reasonable for students to expect of their
powers of memory, and to explore with them the ways in which their
memory actually works.

Reinforcement and feedback

The approaches suggested have been used in response to particular needs
and readers familiar with the common ground of educational technology
will perceive many other ways in which its ideas and approaches might be
used by students for themselves. But it will also be obvious that there are
several ideas basic to educational technology which are not so easy to
turn around in the sort of ways described. The most important of these
are the concepts of reinforcement and feedback. For obvious reasons it is
difficult for the solitary learner to get feedback, but since it is so centrally
important in the process of learning, the difficulty is one which ought to

be met by a really satisfactory study skills course. Though some approaches to the problem can be described, there are many students to whom these do not seem very helpful.

Much of students' mystification about standards arises from the fact that they do not get enough feedback and that they are sometimes deaf to the feedback they do get. In this sense, ways of sharpening students' perceptions of 'cues' are ways of showing them how to look for feedback (or, often, feedforward). This helps, but it does not provide for situations in which there is hardly any feedback to be perceived.

Failure to provide enough feedback could be partially accounted for by the often exaggerated importance attached to marks, rather than to comments, on written work, by staff and students alike. Perhaps, incidentally, this is a particular disadvantage of continuously assessed courses, where written work can easily be seen as a product, rather than part of the process of, learning. Most students readily appreciate the principle that feedback is essential to learning and will admit what they have probably often heard before, that it is good practice to study available comments on their written work; and sometimes one can help individuals use these comments more effectively.

But these comments most often relate to matters like essay structure, clarity of presentation, use of particular concepts, and so forth. It may only be by implication that the student can interpret from them his tutor's thoughts on general matters like the level at which he is approaching the subject.

Since cues and written comments from staff are often few and nearly always far between, it is also necessary to cast about for other sources of feedback within the learning environment. Peers are an obvious possibility, but most groups I have worked with have not taken particularly kindly to the idea that they could work with a 'study buddy' or something similar as a regular thing, though they may be able to do so quite happily within the 'study skills' environment. The common situation is that feedback from peers is sparse and random as well as variable in quality, and one is left looking for ways in which the individual student might give himself feedback about his own learning processes.

If such feedback existed, what would it be? Knowledge of results, of course; but this familiar phrase disguises the fact that the student needs not only to know what his results are, but also to be able to evaluate them. By setting himself 'objectives' the student can indeed provide himself with results, but criteria for evaluating them are a different matter. Most individuals seem to be reasonably confident that they can evaluate the quantity of what they have learnt — they know whether a certain piece of material is or is not familiar to them in the sense that they can or cannot recall and repeat the information it contains. But can they? By definition, people don't know what they don't know, and if the learner misses or misunderstands the significance of a point, he can still be quite happy that he has 'learnt' the material. The taking of notes 'unseen' and other devices may help here, but the notes need to be checked carefully against the text and even then the student will not necessarily notice that he has mistaken a major for a minor point, or misunderstood a concept.

The matter of 'quality of learning' is even more difficult for the learner to assess. The perception that there are other objectives to 'learning' than recall and repetition is only a beginning. This is the sort of area in which comments on written work ought to be more helpful than they usually are, but as even helpful comments are frequently addressed to other problems, the student is quite often, for all practical purposes, out on his own. With hindsight, he may perceive how much his approaches have changed over a period, but ways in which he can monitor the process of change are difficult to devise, especially since one can neither prescribe nor predict the nature, rate and destination of an individual's intellectual development.

This perhaps brings us round full circle; basic educational technology offers the perception of the solitary learner's need for feedback but no very convincing way of providing it, at the appropriate level, except through the structure of the learning situation. For the individual student, experiential techniques seem to be the best source of possible feedback about his own development and for the study skills teacher the most obvious point of departure for work in this area. Unfortunately, the value of these approaches has perhaps led such teachers to overlook the possible contributions from other older aspects of educational technology, and it does seem clear that these can be considerable and are capable of development.

References

Buzan, T (1972) *Advanced Learning and Reading* (a set of videotapes produced at the University of Sussex).
Macdonald-Ross, M (1972) Behavioural objectives and the structure of knowledge, in Austwick, K and Harris, N D C (eds) (1972) *Aspects of Educational Technology VI*, Pitman Publishing, London

Section 2: Projects and Developments

The Microelectronics Education Programme

Richard Fothergill, *Director, Microelectronics Education Programme, Cheviot House, Coach Lane Campus, Newcastle upon Tyne NE7 7XA*

Recognizing the major changes facing industry and society as a result of the microelectronic revolution, the government has initiated a development programme with a limited duration, currently planned to terminate in 1984. It was announced in March 1980 with my appointment as director beginning at the end of the year. The full central team of the Microelectronics Education Programme (MEP) started implementing the strategy from April 1981. The paper expressing this strategy was approved by the Departments of Education for England, Northern Ireland and Wales earlier as the basis for the Programme's activity, and has been widely distributed since then.

In this report of the Programme so far, I will try to expand the plans expressed in that paper and reveal some of the thinking behind current activities. It will be appreciated that the Programme is not generously resourced and that to deal with all that is intended requires support and positive help from other sources. In particular, there is a need for contributions from local education authorities to assist with INSET work. The Programme cannot afford to pay for teachers to attend courses, and of these it can only afford a limited number. It is quite clear already that support of that kind has and will be forthcoming to a large extent, and we are most grateful for the positive approach that we are meeting from the authorities.

The aims of the Programme are to provide teachers with guidance on helping children learn about microelectronics and its effects, and to help them to use the technology to motivate and encourage children to learn more effectively throughout the curriculum. As will be clear from the above the target audiences for the results of the Programme's activities are children from five to 18 at school and their teachers. Those in other parts of the education system like further education will reap benefit from the Programme where they can make use of the materials produced, or where they are involved in other work like INSET. Another Programme may be initiated to cover the tertiary sector in the future.

While the subject area of the Programme is wide, ranging from work on the technology in one part of the curriculum to office studies in another, it is also important to emphasize the need to cover the full spectrum of ability levels of children, and to cater also for those in special education. Much of the work that has been apparent at the beginning of our survey of current activities has shown a preponderance in the direction of the high ability child and this is likely to increase further the distance between them and their contemporaries, so the Programme will make a special effort to ensure that there is a relevant library of materials and guidance prepared for those of average and lower ability.

In order to provide a framework for the Programme, it was decided to divide the activities into three areas, teacher training, curriculum development and supporting resources. Work would be undertaken in each of these in all parts of the subject area that was being covered. At the same time it was felt essential to bring the LEAs, the principal providers of education, as close to the work of the Programme as possible without detracting from the national coherence that was being established. To this end, it was agreed that a considerable part of the Programme's activities would be determined through joint applications from LEAs. They were therefore invited to form regional groups, so that no more than 14 were established. In each, there would be an Information Centre, INSET courses and curriculum development activities.

Additionally, it was planned to have a number of national projects which would work independently of this structure, although all would keep every region fully informed about their activities.

Information Centres

This, then, is the essence of the strategy of the Programme and it is to implement this that the work of the staff has been directed during the first year. The education authorities agreed to form regions, and all have now appointed staff to run their Information Centres. In many cases, the Centre director has also been appointed as a regional co-ordinator of the other elements of the Programme, responsible to a steering committee that has membership from all the authorities and some of the institutions of higher education. The Centres themselves are in various types of site, a university, several polytechnics, schools and teachers centres, and a full list of these is to be found elsewhere in this publication.

While to some extent these are the regional outposts of the Programme staff, keeping the central team informed about activities in the region and passing on information about other work from the Programme to the local teachers, we wish them to have a positive and responsive role in reflecting and influencing attitudes within their own regions. By asking the local education authorities to join together in making the appointment and overseeing the setting up of the organization, the Programme is trying to effect a partnership between itself and local activities, and the Centres are the places where an appropriate dialogue is maintained. The library of software and other materials which the Centres will have will be based largely on nationally available and produced items, but will also incorporate those prepared locally and having perhaps only a regional value. Similarly advice and recommendations given to teachers calling on the Centre will be combinations of national guidance and the particular inclinations of the LEAs that form the region. Thus the leaders of these Centres will need to observe closely the wishes of LEA advisers and link these with the suggestions from national policy.

INSET

It is co-operation between the national Programme and regional needs that is at the foundation of MEP philosophy. In the policy for INSET, the work is similarly directed. The Programme has identified four domains for teacher training, the technology, the computer as a device, computer-based learning and communications technology, the last a combination of office studies and information retrieval. There are considerable overlaps between these, but this is one division of the territory of the Programme that proves satisfactory in creating manageable units.

After lengthy consultation with many teachers, course objectives and lists of useful materials for a range of planned modules have been prepared, and regions have agreed to a number of courses for teachers. Again, co-operation is built into the agreement, for about two-thirds of the objectives on courses they run will be determined from the national list, and the remaining one-third selected by the advisers and teachers in the region to bias the courses towards their own inclinations. In order to represent the viewpoint of the Programme, and to give advice to those teaching the courses in the regions, MEP has appointed five national co-ordinators, two for the domain of communications technology and one each for the others. Their remit is directed towards INSET initially, but they will be involved in helping to determine which materials should be prepared for various courses and, with advice from groups of teachers from various parts of the educational system, offering patterns of courses for the school curriculum and advising on structures for pre-service training.

The national co-ordinators are the experts on their domains, the lynchpins around which the teacher training strategy revolves. Further teacher training opportunities will be provided by various distance learning strategies, in particular a course being developed by the Open University, but also links to the BBC programmes for continuing education and packages associated with the equipment programme for schools arranged through the Department of Industry. In order to cross-match these various arms of the teacher training activities, it is essential that the national co-ordinators are associated with them also.

Curriculum development

Reference has already been made to courses in schools, and MEP will be producing some thoughts about this later in its operation. However, work on this and on discussions with examination boards will occur simultaneously with the preparation of a wide range of teaching materials. It is noteworthy that these will not wait for course analysis, the traditional method of curriculum development, for it is essential that the rate of change which is the result of the technology is taken into account in determining the order of approaching development. Lengthy analysis delays progress too long, and there must be respect for the professional judgements of practising teachers in determining where work should be focused. This is not the place to elaborate this point, but it is an important guiding principle of the Programme.

While there are some centres for curriculum development, like Chelsea and Fiveways Software, working on a national basis, the majority of the work will be undertaken within the regions by local groups. The selection of what they do will be guided by national needs and the product of their work will be circulated throughout the country. To assist MEP, a special group of people from the Schools Council have been appointed to help in monitoring the choice of projects and ensuring that appropriate progress is maintained.

In addition, MEP will be commissioning a variety of single short term projects to add to the library of materials for teachers to use. Together, all these activities should provide a solid foundation of resources that will assist teachers in meeting the aims of the Programme.

In this short report, there is no space to outline the work being done in special education, nor to examine the planning of publication and promotion. As a development programme, MEP is attempting to break some new ground and introduce particular philosophies into the education scene. Whether these succeed or not remains to be seen, but they all result from a particular interpretation of the effects of the microelectronic revolution on society, and so MEP is at least trying to practise what it preaches.

Regional information

Southern counties

Membership
Berkshire, East Sussex, Hampshire, Isle of Wight, Kent, Surrey, West Sussex

RIC address
Robert May Middle School, Crawley

RIC staff
Director: Mr P Neate (in post 1.1.82)

West & North Yorkshire

Membership
Bradford, Calderdale, Kirklees, Leeds, North Yorkshire, Wakefield

RIC address
Queenswood House, Leeds Polytechnic, Becketts Park Site, Leeds
LS6 3QS. Tel: 0532 783437/8

RIC staff
Co-ordinator: Ray Leigh
Technician: Diane Warburton

The North

Membership
Cleveland, Cumbria, Durham, Gateshead, Newcastle upon Tyne, North
Tyneside, Northumberland, South Tyneside, Sunderland

RIC address
Resources Centre, Newcastle Polytechnic, Coach Lane Campus,
Newcastle upon Tyne NE7 7XA. Tel: 0632 665057

RIC staff
Director: Roger Edwardson (in post 1.1.82)
Admin Assistant: Mrs Tina Carr

South Yorkshire and Humberside

Membership
Barnsley, Doncaster, Humberside, North Derbyshire, Rotherham, Sheffield

RIC address
Beechfield School, Chequer Road, Doncaster DN1 2AF. Tel: 0302 4041
Ext 53

RIC staff
Director: Mr Peter Avis (in post 1.1.82)
Acting Part-time Director: Mr Denys Gaskell
Secretary: Ann Swainston

South West

Membership
Avon, Cornwall, Devon, Dorset, Gloucestershire, Somerset, Wiltshire

RIC address
Bristol Polytechnic, Coldharbour Lane, Frenchay, Bristol BS16 1QY.
Tel: 0272 656261

Sub-centre
College of St Mark and St John, Derriford Road, Plymouth.
Tel: 0752 777188

RIC staff
Director: Mr Richard Margetts (at Bristol Polytechnic)

East Midlands

Membership
Derbyshire, Leicestershire, Lincolnshire, Northamptonshire, Nottinghamshire

RIC address
Leicester Polytechnic

RIC staff
Director: Dr Max Bramer (in post 1.1.82)

Eastern

Membership
Barking, Essex, Havering, Newham, Norfolk, Redbridge, Suffolk, Waltham Forest

RIC address
Chelmer Institute of Higher Education, Victoria Road South, Chelmsford, Essex. Tel: 0245 354491

RIC staff
Director: David Want (in post 1.1.82)

Chiltern

Membership
Barnet, Bedfordshire, Brent, Buckinghamshire, Cambridge, Enfield, Haringey, Harrow, Hertfordshire, Hillingdon, Oxfordshire

RIC address
Advisory Unit for Computer Based Education, Endymion Road, Hatfield, Herts AL10 8AU. Tel: 070-72 66121/74518

RIC staff
Director: Dr Bill Tagg

Merseyside with Cheshire

Membership
Cheshire, Knowsley, Liverpool, St Helens, Sefton, Wirral

RIC address
Rodney House, 70 Mount Pleasant, Liverpool L3 5UX. Tel: 051-207 3581

RIC staff
Information Officer: Mrs Shirley Evans

Greater Manchester and Lancashire

Membership
Bolton, Bury, Lancashire, Manchester, Oldham, Rochdale, Salford, Stockport, Tameside, Trafford, Wigan

RIC address
Manchester Polytechnic, Didsbury School of Education, 799 Wilmslow Road, Manchester M20 8RR. Tel: 061-445 7871

RIC staff
Director: Robert Chantry-Price

Capital

Membership
Bexley, Bromley, Croydon, Ealing, Hounslow, ILEA, Kingston, Merton, Richmond, Sutton

RIC address
Kennington Computer Centre, Bethwin Road, London SE5 0PQ.
Tel: 01-735 4283

RIC staff
Director: Michael Doran
Information Officer: Sandra Crapper

Northern Ireland

RIC address
Microelectronics Education Information Centre, South Building, Suite B140, New University of Ulster, Coleraine, Northern Ireland. Tel: 0265 4141 Ext 341

RIC staff
Director: Harry McMahon
Information Officer: Marilyn Lento
Secretary: Elizabeth Blair
Education Secretary/Back-up WP Operator: Pearl Watton
Programmer: Colin Nelson
Regional Officer: Garry Dearden

Wales

RIC address
Welsh Joint Education Committee, 4th Floor, Arlbee House, Greyfriars Road, Cardiff CF1 3AE. Tel: 0222 25511

RIC staff
Co-ordinator: Lionel Taylor, Microprocessor Development Centre, Coach House, Kelsterton Road, Flint, Clwyd. Tel: 0244 816236
Information Officer: Mrs M Hopkin (at Arlbee House. Tel: 0222 25511)

West Midlands

Membership
Birmingham, Coventry, Dudley, Hereford and Worcester, Sandwell, Shropshire, Solihull, Staffordshire, Walsall, Warwickshire, Wolverhampton

RIC address
Four Dwellings School, Dwellings Lane, Quinton, Birmingham B32 1RJ. Tel: 021-421 6361

RIC staff
Director: Ian Glen
Information Officer: Chris Pedley
Admin Assistant: Janet Williamson
Technician: Mike Moore

The Association for Educational and Training Technology Register of Consultants

A J Trott and R E Williams

Some years ago it was suggested that our organization should compile a list of members interested in consultancy work overseas. For a while this initiative faltered; there were problems inherent in an innovation such as this. Questions concerning the availability of consultants, the financing of the operation, the suitability of those volunteering for particular posts, and the briefing and preparation of members who had not done this kind of work before, all needed to be discussed in detail.

After a first attempt, when some 'brave souls' completed questionnaires and were duly placed upon the register, it became apparent that if the initiative was to prosper, more members must be enrolled and a permanent secretariat with overseas experience was needed. The Association entered into discussions with the Guildford Educational Services, a member of AETT, about this, and after a number of meetings upon outline specifications the functions, purposes and administration details were worked out.

The AETT Council was still unsure of the number of members likely to use the register. It decided that an attempt should be made to enrol more members at the Aberdeen 1981 Educational Technology International Conference, and that if a poor response was received on this occasion, the idea would be dropped and no further action would be taken. A few months after the conference, 40 members had indicated their interest, and there are now over 50 names on the register. The need for such a register was thus established.

The purpose of the register is to provide an up-to-date list of educational and training consultants based in the United Kingdom, who are qualified, possibly experienced and certainly prepared to undertake educational technology projects throughout the world. Many members of AETT have had considerable overseas experience and have undertaken consultancy work in Australia, Canada, Egypt, India, Indonesia, Iraq, Jordan, Kenya, Malaysia, Mauritius, Morocco, Nigeria, Pakistan, South America and Thailand.

Consultancy subjects were grouped under 12 headings which illustrate the wide range of member interests:

1. the design of and training in learning systems, including distance and open learning, learning by appointment and other systems;
2. computer-based learning techniques, including the associated

hardware and software;
3. curriculum development;
4. educational management;
5. the production and use of learning materials;
6. the training of lecturers and trainers, teachers and other personnel concerned with education;
7. the identification, use and measurement of teaching skills;
8. evaluation and assessment;
9. vocational preparation and the training of careers staff;
10. role playing, simulation and gaming;
11. the evaluation and use of educational equipment and audiovisual aids, including television;
12. advice on the suitability and purchase of microprocessor teaching equipment.

In addition, individuals were found to have highly specific experience in areas which could not be included in the 12 composite headings above — such as the training of technical demonstrators, the education and training of nurses, course design for agricultural trainers and interpersonal communication skills training.

Members who wished to become consultants completed curriculum vitae forms, and the details were entered on to a master matrix.

It was thought that the register might perform all or some of the following functions:

1. the establishment of project aims, objectives and specifications
2. the negotiation of terms of service
3. pre-departure administration
4. briefing
5. back-up facilities whilst overseas including replacement in the event of premature return
6. debriefing upon return
7. guidance in the construction and writing of the final report, and in arranging for its reproduction.

Members of AETT Council and GES concerned with this project have had discussions with possible employing agencies. Approaches have been made to various departments of the British Council, ILO (Geneva), the Commonwealth Secretariat, the LOME Convention, several divisions of Unesco, and the Overseas Development Administration. In addition, selected Embassies and Ministry officials of other countries have been contacted.

For employing agencies, the advantages of using the AETT Register of Consultants are that quality is ensured, that back-up facilities are guaranteed, that many different combinations of educational technology expertise are available, and that large and continuing projects can be staffed easily.

Now the consultancy register has been firmly established, members of AETT who would like to work abroad for short periods, or prospective employing agencies who need educational or training technologists should contact either AETT or Guildford Educational Services.

Some Reservations on the Educational Potential of PRESTEL

C W Osborne, *Learning Systems Group, Middlesex Polytechnic*
with a comment by **J Tillotson**

In an earlier (1978/79) edition of the *Yearbook*, S Fedida and B Dew wrote on 'Viewdata in Education', since when great interest has been developing in the potential role of viewdata systems such as PRESTEL for teaching/learning; the CET has set up its 'PRESTEL Umbrella' project to explore this very issue. In this article I wish simply to express some reservations, a word of caution, on this new medium, with particular emphasis on the potential limitations of PRESTEL as the particular and best known example of videotex in the UK (I am not concerned here with CEEFAX and ORACLE which are teletext systems); my colleague John Tillotson will then make some brief comments on alternative possibilities in viewdata.

Very briefly, PRESTEL is a national videotex system whereby a central database on a British Telecom computer is disseminated via the public telephone network to all PRESTEL subscribers. Information is supplied by 'information providers' (IPs) who pay British Telecom both to register and for each frame (currently £5000 pa and £5 pa respectively), so there is a strong commercial motive; British Telecom takes no active part in presenting the information, other than checking the legal observations — information display is left to the IPs. The strengths of the system are that the database can be vast, and yet almost instantaneously available wherever there is a suitable telephone point; and the system is interactive — the user can 'find his own route' through the database and communicate with IPs. It is these features that have attracted educational interest.

The point to make immediately is that PRESTEL markets (and sells) information, mostly put there for commercial or public awareness functions, not for educational goals as such. This is not to deny the potential value of such information for educational purposes, but it clearly shows that the teacher will play a vital role in ensuring the use of this material; at present, however, there is little, if any, material on PRESTEL with a planned learning element. I will now look at reasons why PRESTEL, and these two 'products' of the system, may fail to live up to educational hopes.

First, there is the question of equipment and costs. Education is not the wealthiest of sectors and demands value for money: traditional sources of information (eg books) offer repeated use for the initial outlay, whereas PRESTEL requires an initial capital outlay for equipment (in real terms,

---

* This article is a condensed form of one written for the Middlesex Polytechnic *Learning Resources;* I welcome comments or queries from interested readers.

not a great deal of money) followed by payment of running costs. Whether or not these running costs are significant (there has been much dispute on this and on the *real* cost of running a reference library), they tend at the outset to be an open commitment (which can be intimidating) and they are confusing — the user stands to pay computer access time, *plus* frame charges (anything from 'free' to 50p per frame), *plus* telephone time. Also, it is unfortunate, to say the least, that the 'off-peak' rates for two of these charges apply only at times when educational users are least likely to be able to use the system. One predictable response to cost, therefore, might be closely to monitor and control usage — which may defeat much of PRESTEL's educational potential.

Further, the equipment can be unreliable. Too many users have reported difficulties in gaining access to the computer when they wished to, usually for no apparent reason. There can be 'noise' on the telephone line, resulting in a distorted or corrupted display. Neither of these features is desirable to the teacher.

Some of these difficulties can be overcome by one interesting potential of the system, namely the possibility of recording frames from PRESTEL as audio signals on a normal cassette tape recorder (or indeed in a hard-copy print-out form), to be re-used later as required. Indeed, on a stereo cassette recorder, it is possible to have a 'voice-over' effect wherein the teacher can comment, or give instructions, on the information displayed; or the tape can be looped to give a cyclic display. However, it would be my contention that, although such devices do indeed solve some problems, they do so only by 'translating' them into other forms. The teacher now has to pre-select his chosen frames and thereby 'programme' his PRESTEL material (conceivably almost to a level where he could transfer it to a hard-copy handout format); all routing options indicated on frames are invalidated; pupils are denied the freedom, initiative and experience of operating a real viewdata system with access to a real computer database; the interactive or response facility is lost; and even the novelty or 'gimmick' of the medium (which may well be a valuable feature of its usage in some educational situations) is seriously diminished. In short, economies are bought by potential educational loss of effectiveness and impact.

Looking now at the PRESTEL system itself, there is evidence that many users do not find it a friendly, welcoming or easy-to-operate system. The implications of this are that a teacher would need to keep a close watch over students or pupils using PRESTEL, certainly during the initial encounters. In situations where it was intended to allow users individual access to the database, this could prove very expensive in staff time, whether this be in terms of teacher or librarian.

Part of this difficulty is related to the routing scheme operating on PRESTEL. For, rightly, the opportunity to route oneself through the database, assuming either possession of a hard-copy index or of good instructions offered by IPs, is seen to be a great strength of PRESTEL, and undoubtedly offers great flexibility. But it is perhaps less frequently realized that this routing is often strictly *uni-directional* — not necessarily surprising, but equally not without disadvantages. How does this come about in what seems to be a well-ordered system? First, it must be remembered that virtually all information on PRESTEL is put there by a multitude of IPs (usually for a commercial motive); so, to use this information, it is almost inevitable that the educational user will want to move from one IP's data to that of another IP, possibly a commercial rival; and there is little incentive for an IP to route a user out of *his* data into that of someone else. There are exceptions: the CET, for example, is very good in routing users out into commercial IPs' frames, but once there, whether by routing through CET or through PRESTEL's own index, one's further routing possibilities are determined solely by the IP providing the frame on-screen. And, since he has no way of knowing each user's starting point, he cannot provide a route back even if he so wishes. (There is the * facility which allows the user to return to any of the last three frames accessed, but this is at best only a partial solution.) So, *unless the user has noted previous key frame numbers* to reprogramme directly, he has no recourse but to return either to his initial starting point or to study his hard-copy index to determine a new one. Quite apart from frustration, all of this takes time — and on PRESTEL time costs money.

A more serious limitation of the system in my opinion, however, concerns the nature of the medium itself when compared to traditional educational materials, notably the book. It is noticeable, for example, that some IPs seem to feel it is adequate simply to transfer printed data on to the viewdata screen and thereby to offer a PRESTEL service. The folly of this assumption soon becomes apparent, and it is clear that, for information to be well-presented and *received*, it almost inevitably has to be designed for, or restructured and re-edited into, a 'viewdata presentation style'. As a simple example, it is noticeable that visually impressive and easy-to-assimilate text on PRESTEL bears a much closer resemblance to the tabloid newspaper style (where virtually every sentence is a paragraph) than to that of *The Times*.

However, the key limitation of PRESTEL is that it is, by necessity, an 'opaque' medium. It has undoubted strengths but *the only usable text at any time is that which is currently displayed on-screen*. It is this opacity which, in my opinion, confirms PRESTEL as no real threat to the traditional, hard-copy, book medium for a number of reasons:

(a) a frame cannot accommodate more than 20 lines of 40 characters to compile its text, and in fact is likely to hold less than this, once allowances have been made for spacing and effective layout. On purely practical grounds, therefore, several frames would be needed to convey the equivalent of one book page of text (even assuming that it were not necessary to modify the text layout and style to be in keeping with the altered medium). The result of this 'translation' could well be a dilution of the force of an argument or of the coherence of a developing statement.

(b) an important feature of book use is the option of scanning the complete book in very short time, whether to assess its relevance to one's need, to determine its nature or proposition, to view its conclusions, or just to gauge its readability. This option is not available on PRESTEL where future frames are an entirely unknown quantity (and, in some instances, potentially an unknown cost). It is not inconceivable that after a lengthy session on PRESTEL the user will find that he was on a wild goose chase all the time.

(c) a very similar criticism relates to the revision potential of the book, and to the ease of verification of earlier text and its statements. Not only does the PRESTEL user have to note the precise identification of each frame he consults (page number *and* letter), but also he would be advised to make adequate notes of its contents to enable its subsequent identification should he need to return to it; for he *cannot* assume he will simply be able to backtrack along his route. Additionally, individual frames are much less likely than book pages to have their own 'pattern' which, for me at least, is an important means whereby I can fairly readily locate an earlier-read passage within a text. Similar benefits obtain when revision data may occur in a range of different books, identifiable in the memory in terms of size, colour, typescript, thickness, etc. This may seem a trivial point; but as one who has had frequent need to 'chase up' information, I consider that such seeming irrelevancies are an important determinant of success or failure in quickly relocating sought information.

(d) the limited information display on a frame also has disadvantages when *comparison* is a desirable feature, whether this comparison be in the form of textual argument, conflicting views from two separate sources, a 'for and against' table layout, or, perhaps most important of all, the use of a diagram or graph to reinforce and illustrate a textual point. Not only is PRESTEL sorely limited in its ability to portray diagrams (it cannot portray a thin line, let alone diagonals or curves), but these are very demanding of frame space and render it most unlikely that the frame would also accommodate any significant text.

(e) finally, as an indirect consequence perhaps of (c), some users at Middlesex Polytechnic have commented that they developed eyestrain or headaches when using PRESTEL. This they put down to poor legibility on some frames or sets, but also to the need to keep switching their eyes from the (flickering) set to the paper on which they were noting information. In this context, it is interesting that Philips conducted market research into *teletext* and are reported to have found that 25 per cent of users had difficulty reading the text; which as the 'typical' user was 25-44 years old can hardly be ascribed solely to poor eyesight. Since teletext presentation is usually of a higher standard than that of viewdata (including PRESTEL), this is particularly significant.

PRESTEL does have some advantages over books which should not be overlooked: it has a 'novelty' value which may be very important to initiate some student interest in learning; it carries certain connotations very different from those associated with books; it can offer colour; and it can offer a form of motion with its ability to flash. But it also has to come to terms with some problems already well-known in publishing — notably *copyright*. Some IPs already state on their lead frames that their material is copyright protected; with others this may be assumed to be the case. At present, when users are only able to copy single frames on to audio tape, copyright is perhaps not a major issue (although the IP who loses several frame charges thereby as well as having his material plagiarized might think differently); but it certainly becomes one when a user has the potential for recording whole sections of a database with no trace, and with the IP having no control over subsequent usage of such material. An example may illustrate the commercial aspect of this point.

One educational use of PRESTEL that has been strongly advocated is that of distributing computer programmes or packages between computers or on to micros. It has been calculated that a simple computer programme could be accommodated on some ten PRESTEL frames. Given that the current maximum frame charge is 50 pence, this represents £5 per programme maximum fee that the IP might receive for each access. So a small producer of packages (five programmes, say) which he wishes to market through an IP (which we'll assume to be CET because of its very low fee of £16 per rented frame) would need to buy some 55 frames (allowing for introductory and routing frames) at an annual cost of £880, or £176 per programme. It follows that, simply to recoup his marketing costs, he needs a minimum of 36 accesses per programme in any and every year. This might not appear unrealistic, but there is a serious risk nevertheless that 'pirated' copies-of-copies (as now well known in the video film market) could seriously undermine the chances of commercial success (a risk exacerbated by the prospect of a cautious potential user's 'just borrowing someone else's copy to evaluate it under trial'). And remember that we are talking here of a very simple, and thereby relatively low cost, programme, with no *consideration* of such matters as the producer's *development* costs; as programmes get larger and thereby more expensive the copyright problem becomes even larger.

Turning now to the database itself, one of its vaunted strengths is its immediacy — its information can be updated by the minute — and its vastness. Unfortunately, neither of these two advantages need be of great value to education in themselves. As already suggested, PRESTEL and its information are strongly commercial; not surprisingly, therefore, the database is deficient in those areas where information is not a commercially marketable commodity. So it is that CET feedback from FE and HE users records the shallowness and inadequacy of information uncovered, which, furthermore, was arranged and presented by non-educational criteria (the view was expressed that a hard-copy 'Educational Index' was not so much desirable as 'imperative' — CET is now tackling this need). Nor is 'immediacy' an unmitigated strength — sometimes educational users may find 'yesterday's papers' of equal or greater value than today's, or of interest for purposes of comparison; PRESTEL does not save such 'outdated' information. In short, it is possible to argue that the advantages of the present PRESTEL database over traditional sources of information are few (it is best seen as a complement rather than competition), and that its main educational benefit may reside simply in the *process* and experience involved in a student using the system rather than in the 'product' he obtains (which is the very claim made by school-level users in the CET's field trials).

By now the reader could be forgiven for thinking that I have little regard for the educational potential of PRESTEL. This might be true if the system were at the limits of its capability and capacity; but fortunately this is far from the truth, and the Gateway scheme, for example, may offer new prospects (even if at present the projected 'membership' costs look likely to prevent any educational institution becoming an IP in its own right). It must be said, I have been deliberately playing 'devil's advocate' and taking a pessimistic view: the fact is that PRESTEL is very much in its infancy — and who, in the 1930s, would have predicted the success of TV as a medium? Education already ranks amongst the top five users of PRESTEL and, although much of the database is unsuitable to educational use, it may be hoped that organized educational representation, perhaps through a central co-ordinating body, will lead to an improvement, and indeed to the presentation of specifically educational material. For this is PRESTEL's real problem: unlike television in its early years, PRESTEL is *not* being launched and paid for as a public service, and what it currently lacks, and needs, is either an educational philanthropist who will provide information with no significant consideration of revenue return, or for an educational consortium to be created big enough to organize itself to take full advantage (maybe even at a commercial break-even level) of the future possibilities of PRESTEL and Gateway. Perhaps then PRESTEL can be a medium not only of computer package exchanges and, of course, of information, but also of educational 'starter kits' and maybe even learning packages such as study skills.

There are other, minor, criticisms of PRESTEL that I could record, much as there are strengths I have deliberately not developed. But my concern in writing this article has been partly to review the current situation, and also to issue a cautionary note against a too rapid and *uncritical* acceptance of PRESTEL — to be shortly followed by an equal but conclusive rejection. The history of education, and particularly educational technology, is littered with innovations that failed — not necessarily because they had nothing to commend them but because, in a sense, they grew too fast and outgrew their true strength. PRESTEL has some obvious advantages and attractions, as well as obvious penalties; equally, however, it has some less obvious attributes that, in the long run, may be more significant than their perceived counterparts. In any final assessment, *all* such factors should be weighed. There is a real risk that PRESTEL in its present form could be 'written off' by education, perhaps justifiably in times of economy; but equally, it has real potential, if rightly developed, to be a valuable addition to the educational armoury. Even if PRESTEL has limitations as one example of videotex, these need not be shared by all systems, as the following account of development work at Middlesex Polytechnic may show.

Bibliography

Council for Educational Technology (1981) *PRESTEL and Education — A Report of a One-year Study,* CET, London

Fedida, S *et al* (1978) Viewdata in education, in *International Yearbook of Educational and Training Technology 1978/79 (AETT),* pp 78-86, Kogan Page, London

Nicholson, R and Consterdine, G (1980) *The PRESTEL Business,* Northwood Books, London

Philips Industries (1981) Teletext survey, reported in *In View,* Oct 1981, Mills and Allen Communications Ltd

Other information sources

Council for Educational Technology (1981) *Educational Trial of PRESTEL:* Schools Feedback Conference, 10 March 1981; FE/HE Feedback Conference, 17 March 1981

LASER/British Library (1981) *LASER, PRESTEL and Libraries,* One-day Conference, 9 March 1981

New directions in videotex

J Tillotson, *Lecturer in Engineering/Computing, Middlesex Polytechnic*

Working with a small grant from the World Health Organization and in collaboration with Dr Ben Essex, who is a leading WHO consultant, a small group at the Polytechnic began, early in 1979, to look at the possibility of producing truly effective computer hardware for use in the often harsh conditions of developing countries.

The first part of the investigation has been substantially completed and has produced a design for an information retrieval system which is to some extent inspired by PRESTEL. A demonstration unit has been produced and demonstrated at WHO headquarters in Geneva.

The machine permits the display and manipulation of text (flowcharts) on a domestic television. The user's text comes from a floppy disc where it is held in a specially packed form to maximize economy.

The overall scheme anticipates that the flowcharts will have been designed originally for a booklet and are to be transcribed on to the microcomputer. When flowcharts are prepared to be printed in a booklet each page holds information which is a natural entity. Putting this information into PRESTEL, for example, would force one to break up this natural entity into separate pages. With the new system, the integrity of the page is maintained and when the user requests a page from the disc (eg, 'Page 2390') the whole page is loaded into the memory of the system's controller. Because the text is in packed form a great deal of material can be held in a small control memory area. Of course, only the first screenful of the page's text is displayed initially but the system allows, for example: scrolling, branching, split screen display (three levels of display), return to top of page, return to the previous page called (up to six page recall — not screens!), as well as effective trapping of keying errors.

Also, the response is virtually instantaneous. It takes only two seconds or so to pull down a page from the disc which holds 4000 characters. These 4000 characters may contain 20 or more screen presentations. The rules for using the machine are very simple; the keypad is very small, and the system has been designed for minimum hardware. There is a system teaching package which teaches the user how to use the machine itself.

The applications to education are self-evident: the system can provide teaching packages which do not require dynamic re-routing. It would not be difficult to produce a version where the floppy disc is shared by six to eight users, each having a controller and domestic television. The system does not offer colour, but who can afford colour sets in the classroom?

Again, it would not be difficult to dispense with the floppy disc and design the controller so that it acts as a terminal to a mini- or mainframe-computer, from which it gets its text. Here we are, back at a version of PRESTEL, but smaller.

The project is, of course, the victim of cuts and seems unlikely to come to fruition. Such is the state of British support for high technology!

A Look at Educational Technology in the US and Canada during the 80s

Carl H Hendershot, EdD, *CONSULTANT — Programmed Instruction Education and Training Systems and COMPILER — Hendershot Bibliography of Programmed Learning and Individually Based Instruction*

Instructional technology in the 1980s is oriented to improving the learning skills and effective performance of the individual whom we tend to refer to as the learner. Emphasis is upon this learner's involvement, interaction with the instructional material, retention and future application.

Techniques attributed to a number of approaches combine to form the technology base available to today's instructional developer. These procedures include criterion referenced instruction, programmed instruction, front end analysis, competency-based instruction and instructional systems. All are concerned with the performance of the learner after the successful completion of the instruction and place a considerable part of the responsibility for the learner's successful achievement upon the instruction.

All is not new: the Socratic approach requires learner participation and prompt feedback regarding responses. The aforementioned technology and other similar approaches have been developing and undergoing testing and refinement during the past quarter of a century. Time proven techniques have been incorporated with the results of research and practical applications in schools, colleges, business, industry and in the military.

Emerging technology is now facilitating the application of techniques which were introduced earlier. For example, Tom Gilbert's approach to programmed learning wherein the learner received corrective instruction when other than the best multiple-choice question was selected can now be conveniently presented via a video disc with mini-computer controls. Video discs have an enormous storage capacity, are computer controllable and permit random access to information. One disc the size of a phonograph record will store over 100,000 separate colour pictures as well as sound and machine programming instruction. One video disc can replace many volumes of printed material. A video disc player with discs can provide on the site random access trouble shooting instruction for sophisticated industrial equipment. At the present time, video disc recording is expensive and mass duplication techniques are still being developed.

The videotape and videotape player serve well in presenting less voluminous instruction. When a computer is coupled with this player, interactive branching instruction can adjust the instruction to learner needs.

Another developing approach is broadcast teletext instruction wherein pages of information are broadcast for television reception. With the use of a decoding device, pages of instruction can be selected, multiple-choice questions posed and suitable answers revealed to the learner.

Videotext presentation of instruction is in experimental use in at least seven Canadian universities. These employ the Canadian developed Telidon system which has good presentation of graphics. In the US this technique is being used for communicating business or news information.

Inflation is pushing the cost of people time beyond that of relatively sophisticated instructional equipment and well developed instructional units for use therewith. Also, today's learners are accustomed to using television as a source of news, information and videotaped instruction. They use hand calculators at an early age in the solution of increasingly complex problems. With the use of computers touching the lives of all, from grocery store pricing to one's personal bank account, the use of computers to support and facilitate instruction is a natural development. Mini-computers are now affordable. They can be used in combination with audiovisual equipment to control the presentation of corrective information a learner needs as shown by his selection of an incorrect answer.

Computer controlled systems including readily available videotape players, film slide, filmstrip and motion picture projectors as well as audiocassette players are currently in use to provide learner-paced self instruction involving audio, visual and printed materials.

Small hand portable projection devices which have synchronized audiovisual projection and learner start-stop capacity are in wide use. These nearly trouble free units have proved that learner paced audiovisual instruction is effective and cost efficient. The use of these units both in the portable and learning centre carrel form will continue to be popular because of their low cost, dependability and because the preparation or revision of the instruction is financially practical.

Videotaped instruction is nearly as common in our academic and industrial classrooms as is the motion picture. Likewise, broadcast television continues to enhance home study by providing an audiovisual lecture type of contact with the instructor. Commercial television stations are providing interactive discussion programmes where home viewers are in voice contact with the persons presenting a discussion at the television studio.

When compared with computers the microfiche seems unimposing. However, the use of microfiche is reducing the cost of reproducing, storing and mailing periodicals and other printed materials. Because of its use, our libraries and other resource centres are able to maintain and supply us with a far greater base of technical and other resource materials than would be feasible otherwise.

Educational technology means different things to different people. What some have tried and considered to be commonplace or discarded, others are just placing in exciting applications. With the use of selected aspects of currently available educational technology, we can better meet the needs of both each instructional situation and its particular learners.

Characteristic of the current application of instructional technology is the analysis performed as a beginning step in the development of the instruction. What has to be learned and how the achievement of this learning can be evaluated is determined. The characteristics and range of needs of the learning population are considered. After this, the best techniques within the practical limitations of cost, learning facilities, instructors' availability and concerns, etc, are considered. Learner involvement during instruction so that both retention of information and the likelihood of on-the-job application is enhanced is representative of other aspects which are included.

Learner-oriented instruction developed under the instructional technology concept is tried on learners typical of the expected learner population and rewritten and retested until it accomplishes the prestated goals and objectives. Current thinking considers the learner, the content expert and the instructional developer as members of a team who share responsibility for the successful communication of needed facts, skills and attitudes.

All levels of learners are expecting more relevant, efficient and effective instruction. By selecting and applying the aspects of instructional technology which best fit each situation, we can meet this challenge with success.

Section 3: Resources in Educational Technology

A Selected Bibliography of Educational Technology

Compiled by **Rodney Battey, MA, MA(Ed),** *Senior Lecturer in Materials Technology/Learning Resources at Middlesex Polytechnic*

Editor's note: it is unnecessary, and undesirable, for the *Bibliography of Educational Technology* to be simply cumulative from one edition of the Yearbook to the next; rather, it seeks to give an overview of recent thinking and developments in the field of educational technology whereby interested parties can survey the subject(s) and trace earlier material needed. Accordingly, the bulk of the *Bibliography* comprises post-1970 publications; where older, seminal texts are of continuing importance, they too are included.

Selected books have been listed under the following group headings:

1. General/overview
2. Reference books/Bibliographies
3. Theories of learning/teaching
4. Systems approach, cybernetics and the management of learning
5. Task analysis, stating objectives and curriculum design
6. Instructional methods – characteristics, selection, use
7. Instructional media – characteristics, selection, production
8. Study skills
9. Principles and applications of programmed learning
10. Validation, evaluation, assessment
11. Organization – resource centres, media libraries
12. Applications in general education
13. Applications in higher and further education
14. Applications in industry and commerce
15. Computers in education
16. Films and audiovisual packages concerned with educational technology

Journals relevant to educational technology are appended in a separate section.

1. General/Overview

Adams, J (ed) (1977) *Education Technology in the Community: Papers for Discussion.* Scottish Community Education Centre, Edinburgh.

Akeroyd, J (ed) (1972) *Proceedings of the Canadian Symposium on Instructional Technology.* National Research Council of Canada, Ottawa.

Armsey, J W and Dahl, D C (1973) *Enquiry into the Uses of Instructional Technology.* Ford Foundation, New York.

(*Note:* See also the 10 volumes of *Aspects of Educational Technology* listed in Section 9 of this bibliography.)

Briault, E W H (1969) *Learning and Teaching Tomorrow.* CET Occasional Paper No 2, Councils and Education Press, London.

Centre for Education Research and Innovation (CERI) (1971) *Educational Technology: the Design and Implementation of Learning Systems.* OECD, Paris.

Clarke, J and Leedham, J (1976) *Individualised Learning: Aspects of Educational Technology Vol X.* Kogan Page, London.

Coffey, J (1977) *Educational Technology Courses for Teachers in Training.* Council for Educational Technology, London.

Council for Educational Technology (1979) *The Contribution of Educational Technology & Higher Education in the 1990's.* CET, London.

Councils and Education Press *Copyright and Education.* Councils and Education Press, London.

Crabb, G (1976) *Copyright Clearance – A Practical Guide.* CET Guideline No 2, Council for Educational Technology, London.

Davies, I K and Hartley, J (eds) (1972) *Contributions to an Educational Technology.* Butterworth, London.

Department of Education and Science (1972) *Central Arrangements for Promoting Educational Technology in the United Kingdom.* HMSO, London.

Dockrell, W B and Hamilton, D (eds) (1980) *Rethinking Educational Research.* Hodder and Stoughton, London.

Duane, J E (ed) (1975) *Individualized Instruction – Programs and Materials: Selected Readings and Bibliography.* Educational Technology Publications, Englewood Cliffs, New Jersey.

Duzs, J (1974) *The Audio-Visual Services in Socialist Countries.* International Council for Educational Media, Holland, NIAM, 2nd ed.

Educational Technology Research Reports Series. Educational Technology Publications, Englewood Cliffs, New Jersey.

Educational Technology Reviews Series (1975). Educational Technology Publications, Englewood Cliffs, New Jersey.

Gillett, M (1973) Educational Technology: Towards Demystification. Prentice-Hall, Scarborough, Ontario.

Glaser, R (ed) (1965) *Teaching Machines and Programmed Learning II: Data and Directions.* National Education Association, Washington.

Haney, J B and Allmer, E J (1975) *Educational Communications and Technology: An Introduction for Teachers.* Wm C Brown Co, Dubuque, Iowa.

Hartley, J and Davies, I K (eds) (1978) *Contributions to an Educational Technology.* Kogan Page, London.

Hills, P and Gilbert, J (1977) *Aspects of Educational Technology XI.* Kogan Page, London.

Hyer, A L (1974) *The Audio-Visual Services in Canada and the United States.* International Council for Educational Media, Holland, NIAM, 2nd ed.

Jongbloed, H J L (1973) *The Audio-Visual Services in 15 African Countries.* International Council for Educational Media, Holland, NIAM.

Knirk, F G and Childs, J W (ed) (1968) *Instructional Technology: A Book of Readings.* Holt, Rinehart & Winston, New York.

Latchem C R (1977) *Feasibility Study on the Organization of Educational Technology in Northern Ireland.* Council for Educational Technology, London.

Leedham, J (1973) *Educational Technology: A First Book.* Pitman, London.

Lipsitz, L (ed) (1975) *Technology and Education.* Educational Technology Publications, Englewood Cliffs, New Jersey.

Marchant, G (1976) *A Review of Audio-Visual Services in Advanced and Developing Countries*. ICEM/Unesco, Paris/Washington.

Richmond, W K (1967) *The Education Industry*. Methuen, London.

Richmond, W K (1967) *The Teaching Revolution*. Methuen, London.

Richmond, W K (ed) (1970) *The Concept of Educational Technology*. Weidenfeld & Nicholson, London.

Rowntree, D (1974) *Educational Technology in Curriculum Development*. Harper & Row, New York.

Saettler, P (1968) *A History of Instructional Technology*. McGraw-Hill, New York.

Schmid, F (1974) *The Audio-Visual Service in Western European Countries: Comparative Study on the Administration of Audio-visual Services in Advanced and Developing Countries; A Report under Contract with Unesco*. International Council for Educational Media, Holland, NIAM, 3rd ed.

Taylor, C (ed) (1970) *The Teacher as Manager – A Symposium, National Council for Educational Technology*. Councils and Education Press, London.

UCODI, Centre Imago (1975) *Documentation on Instructional Multimedia Systems*. UCODI, Henerlee, Belgium.

Unesco/CEREP (1976) *Multinational Exchange Mechanisms of Educational Audio-Visual Materials*. Unesco (on request).

Wittich and Schuller, C F (1979) *Instructional Technology: Bits, Nature and Use*. Harper & Row, New York and London.

2. Reference books/bibliographies

Audio-Visual Marketplace: A Multimedia Guide (1974). R R Bowker Co, New York.

BACIE *Bibliography*. British Association for Commercial and Industrial Education, London. Vol 1, 1960-62; Vol II, 1963-67.

Barhydt, G C and Schmidt, C T (1968) *Information Retrieval Thesaurus of Education Terms*. Press of Case Western Reserve University, Cleveland.

Bielawski, J G (1973) *A Guide to Educational Technology – Early Childhood Education*. Technomic Publishing Co, USA.

Boorer, Dr and Murgatroyd, S J (1973) *Personality and Learning – A Select Annotated Bibliography*. MTM Publishing House, Wales.

British Council (1973) *Educational Technology – A Select and Annotated List*. British Council, London.

British Council (1977) *Catalogue of Radio and Television Training Materials from the United Kingdom*. British Council, London.

Brown, J W (ed) (anually) *Educational Media Yearbook*. R R Bowker Co, New York.

Brown, L C (1975) *Core Media Collection for Secondary Schools*. R R Bowker Co, New York.

Cannon, R A (ed) *Yearbook of the Australian Society of Educational Technology*. From ACVE, University of Adelaide.

Carr, M (1976) *Economically Appropriate Technologies for Developing Countries: An Annotated Bibliography*.

CELPIS (1973) *A First List of Audio-visual and Other Materials made by Colleges and Departments of Education*. Council for Educational Technology, London.

Centre for Advanced TV Studies (1974) *UK Video Index*. Centre for Advanced TV Studies.

Centre for World Development Education (1975) *Technology for Development.*

Clarke, J L (ed) (1981) *Educational Development: A Select Bibliography.* Kogan Page, London.

Council for Cultural Co-operation, Programmed Learning (1970) *1. Survey of Projects. 2. Institutions and Their Activities.* Survey of European Research, Council of Europe, Strasbourg.

Council of Europe (1970) *Catalogue of Audio-visual Documents for the training of Teachers.* Council of Europe, Strasbourg.

Department of Employment and Productivity (updated regularly) *Training Research Register.* HMSO, London.

Department of Employment and Productivity *Training Research Abstracts.* Department of Employment and Productivity, Training Division, 168 Regent Street, London W1.

Doak, W A *et al* (eds) (1975) *International Index to Multi-media Information.* Audio-Visual Associates, USA.

Eraut, M and McColvin Stagg, (1975) *Annotated Select Bibliography of Educational Technology.* Council for Educational Technology, London.

Fairfax, O (ed) (1974) *Directory of Information Sources and Advisory Services in Educational Technology.* Council for Educational Technology, London.

Falus, I and McAleese, W R (Jan 1975) A bibliography of microteaching, *PLET Journal,* Vol 12, No 1.

Files, P (1975) *A Guide to Educational Resources, 1975-76. A Catalogue of Catalogues.* ERIC Clearinghouse on Informational Resources.

Gage, N L (ed) (1963) *Handbook of Research on Teaching.* Rand McNally, Chicago.

Gardner, M (1978) *Sources of Resource Materials,* National Youth Bureau, UK.

Hartley, J *et al* (1974) A selected bibliography of typographical research relevant to the production of instructional materials, *AV Communication Review,* 22, 174-90.

HELPIS (Mar 1971, May 1972, Sept 1973) *Catalogue of Materials Available for Exchange.* CET, Councils and Education Press, London, updated occasionally.

Hendershot, C H (1976) *Programmed Learning and Individually Paced Instruction Bibliography.* Hendershot Programmed Learning, 4114 Ridgewood Drive, Bay City, MI 48706.

Horder, A (1975) The application of microforms in education: a survey of the literature, *British Journal of Educational Technology,* 6, 38-54.

Index to Instructional Media Catalogs (an index to catalogs containing all types of materials used in educational programs). R R Bowker Co, New York.

Lester, L J (ed) (1975) *A Directory of Sources of Assistance on Educational Technology for Development.* Information Center on Instructional Technology, USA.

Limbacher, J L (1972) *A Reference Guide to Audiovisual Information.* R R Bowker Co, New York.

McAleese, R (1978) *Encyclopaedia of Educational Media Communication and Technology.* Macmillan, London.

McDaniel, R (ed) (1976) *Resources for Learning.* R R Bowker Co, New York.

National AV Association (1977/78) *The Audio-Visual Equipment Directory.* National AV Association, USA.

Nicholson, J (ed) (1975) *Australian Audio-Visual Reference Book 1975.* Thorpe.

The contents include information on film acquisition, material available from departments of education and detailed lists of software and hardware.

Page, G T and Thomas, J B (eds) (1977) *International Dictionary of Education.* Kogan Page, London.

Raddon, R (ed) (1980) *An Annotated Bibliography on Educational Resource Organization and Related Topics.* Council for Educational Technology, London.

Rawnsley, D E (1975) *A Comparison of Guides to Non-Print Media.* ERIC (ED 104375).

Razik, T A and Ramroth, D M (1974) *Bibliography of Research in Instructional Media.* Educational Technology Publications, Englewood Cliffs, New Jersey.

Richards C (ed) (1978) *Curriculum Studies: An Annotated Bibliography.* Nafferton Books, Driffield, UK.

Richmond, W K (1972) *The Literature of Education, a Critical Bibliography, 1945-70.* Methuen, London.

Stagg, S and Grant, M (1975) *The Second Select Bibliography of Educational Technology.* Council for Educational Technology, London.

Tansey, P J and Unwin, D (1969) *Simulation and Gaming in Education, Training and Business – A Bibliography.* New University of Ulster.

Thorpe, F (ed) (1977) *Directory of British Film and Television Libraries.* British Universities Film Council, London.

Unesco (1973) *International Directory of Programmed Instruction.* Unesco, Paris.

Unwin D and McAleese R (eds) (1978) *The Encyclopaedia of Educational Media Communications and Technology.* Macmillan, London.

Wall, C E (1976) *Media Review Digest 1975-76: Guide to Reviews of Non-Book Media.* Pierian Press, Michigan.

Whiston, T (ed) (1980) *An Annotated Bibliography on the Relationship Between Technological Change and Educational Development.* Unesco, Paris.

3. Theories of learning/teaching

Atwood, B C (1975) *Building Independent Learning Skills.* Professional Education Publications.

Ausubel, D P (1968) *Educational Psychology – A Cognitive Review.* Holt, Rinehart & Winston, New York.

Barnes, D and Todd, F (1977) *Communication and Learning in Small Groups.* Routledge & Kegan Paul, London.

Beard, R M (1970) *An Outline of Piaget's Developmental Psychology for Students and Teachers.* Routledge & Kegan Paul, London.

Bigge, M L (1971) *Learning Theories for Teachers.* Harper & Row, New York, 2nd ed.

Block, J H (ed) (1971) *Mastery Learning – Theory and Practice.* Holt, Rinehart & Winston, New York.

Borger, R and Seaborne, A E (1966) *The Psychology of Learning.* Penguin, London.

Bruner, J S (1960) *The Process of Education.* Random House, New York.

Bruner, J S (1966) *Towards a Theory of Instruction.* Norton, New York.

Cherry, C (1957) *On Human Communication.* Wiley, New York.

Clark, R E and Snow, R E (1976) *Alternative Designs for Instructional Technology Research.* ERIC Clearinghouse on Information Resources.

Collins, K T *et al* (1973) *Keywords in Education.* Longman, London.

Croll and Husband (1975) *Communication and Community: A Study of the Swindon Cable TV Experiment.* Centre for Mass Communication Research, Leicester University.

Dieuzeide, H (1971) *Educational Technology: Sophisticated, Adapted and Rational Technology.* Unesco Publications, Paris.

Farnham-Diggory, S (1979) *Learning Disabilities.* Fontana, London.

Faure, E (1972) *Learning to Be.* Unesco, Paris.

Flaherty, C, Hamilton, L W, Gandelman, R and Spear, N E (1977) *Learning and Memory.* Rand McNally, Chicago.

Flavell, J H (1963) *The Developmental Psychology of Jean Piaget.* Van Nostrand, London.

Gage, N L and Berliner, D C (1979) *Educational Psychology.* Rand McNally, Chicago, 2nd ed.

Gagné, R M (1977) *The Conditions of Learning.* Holt, Rinehart & Winston, New York, 3rd ed.

Gagné, R M and Briggs, L J (1974) *Principles of Instructional Design.* Holt, Rinehart & Winston, Montreal.

Gardner, D (1974) *Developments in Communication – Their Implications for Education.* CET Seminar Report No 1, Council for Educational Technology, London.

George, F (1970) *Models of Thinking.* Allen & Unwin, London.

Gilbert, T F (1969) *Mathetics – An Explicit Theory for the Design of Teaching Programmes. Reprinted in Supplement 1 of Review of Educational Cybernetics and Applied Linguistics.* Longman, London.

Glaser, R (1978) *Advances in Instructional Psychology,* Vol 1 (Dec). Wiley, Sussex.

Glaser, R (1976) Components of a psychology of instruction: toward a science of design, *Review of Educational Research,* 46, 1.

Grandstaff, M (1975) *Alternatives in Education: A Summary View of Research and Analysis on the Concept of Non-Journal Education.* Michigan State University, East Lanzing.

Harmon, G (1973) *Human Memory and Knowledge – A Systems Approach.* Greenwood Press, London.

Johnston, J M (ed) (1975) *Behavior Research and Technology in Higher Education.* Charles C Thomas, London.

Logan (1978) *Systematic Analyses of Learning and Motivation.* Wiley, Sussex.

Massaro, D W (1975) *Experimental Psychology and Information Processing.* Rand McNally, Chicago.

Neisser, U (1976) *Cognition and Reality.* Freeman, Reading.

Peterson, L R (1978) *Learning.* Scott, Foresman & Co, Glenview, Illinois.

Phillips, J L (1975) *The Origins of Intellect: Piaget's Theory.* Freeman, Reading.

Piaget, J (1970) *Science of Education and the Psychology of the Child.* Orion, New York.

Platt, J M (1975) *Visual Literacy: What Research Says to the Teacher.* National Educational Association, USA.

Popper, K R (1972) *Objective Knowledge.* Oxford University Press, London.

Powell, L S (1973) *Communication and Learning.* Pitman, London.

Rachlin, H (1976) *Behaviour and Learning*. Freeman, Reading.

Richmond, W K (ed) (1975) *Lifelong Learning in an Age of Technology*. Methuen, London.

Royer (1977) *Psychology of Learning*. Wiley, Sussex.

Sahakian, W S (1976) *Introduction to the Psychology of Learning*. Rand McNally, Chicago.

Sahakian, W S (ed) (1976) *Learning Systems: Models and Theories*. Rand McNally, Chicago.

Schramm (ed) (1963) *The Science of Human Communication*. Basic Books, New York.

Shulman, L S and Keisler, E R (eds) (1967) *Learning by Discovery: A Critical Appraisal*. Rand McNally, Chicago.

Sills, P A (1973) *The Behavioural Sciences: Techniques of Application*. Institute of Personnel Management, London.

Skinner, B F (1968) *The Technology of Teaching*. Appleton-Century-Crofts, New York.

Stones, E (ed) (1970) *Readings in Educational Psychology: Learning and Teaching*. Methuen, London.

Toye, M H (1973) *Psychological Theories of Learning: Their Application to Education and Training*. ITRU Research Paper TR5

Vernon, P E (1979) *Intelligence: Heredity and Environment*. Freeman, Reading.

Wong and Raulerson, J D (1975) *A Guide to Systematic Instructional Design*. Educational Technology Publications, Englewood Cliffs, New Jersey.

Yates, A (ed) (1970) *The Role of Research in Educational Change*. Unesco Institute for Education, Hamburg.

4. Systems approach, cybernetics and the management of learning

Armitage, P *et al* (1969) *Decision Models for Educational Planning*. Allen Lane, Penguin Press, London.

Ashby, W R (1964) *An Introduction to Cybernetics*. Methuen, London.

Birley, D (1972) *Planning and Education*. Routledge & Kegan Paul, London.

British Broadcasting Corporation (1972) *Games and Simulations*. BBC Publications, London.

Bung, K (1975) *A Theoretic Model for Programmed Language Instruction*. Longman Research Publications Services, London.

Champagne, D W and Goldman, R M (1975) *Handbook for Managing Individualised Learning in the Classroom*. Educational Technology Publications, Englewood Cliffs, New Jersey.

Chapanis, A (1965) *Man-Machine Engineering*. Tavistock Publications, London.

Clarke, J L (1981) *Educational Development: A Select Bibliography*. Kogan Page, London.

Coombs, P H (1970) *What Is Educational Planning?* International Institute for Educational Planning, Unesco, Paris.

Davies, I K (1971) *The Management of Learning*. McGraw-Hill, New York.

Davies, K (ed) (1973) *The Organization of Training*. McGraw-Hill, New York.

Gagné, R M (ed) *Psychological Principles in System Development*. Holt, Rinehart & Winston, New York.

Hartley, H J (1968) *Educational Planning – Budgeting, A Systems Approach.* Prentice-Hall, Englewood Cliffs, New Jersey.

Havelock, R G (1973) *The Change Agent's Guide to Innovation in Education.* Educational Technology Publications, Englewood Cliffs, New Jersey.

Hilton, V B (1975) *Language Teaching: A Systems Approach.* Methuen, London.

Hoyle, E and Megarry, J (eds) (1980) *World Yearbook of Education 1980: Professional Development of Teachers.* Kogan Page, London.

ITRU (1973) *Cramp: A Guide to Training Decisions.* ITRU, 32 Trumpington Street, Cambridge.

Kogan, M (ed) (1971) *The Politics of Education.* Penguin, London.

Kurpius, D J, Baker, R D and Thomas, I D (1977) *Supervision of Applied Training: A Comparative Review.* Greenwood Press, London.

Landa, L (1974) *Algorithmization in Learning and Instruction.* Educational Technology Publications, Englewood Cliffs, New Jersey.

Landa, L (1976) *Instructional Regulations and Control: Cybernetics, Algorithmization and Heuristics in Education.* Educational Technology Publications, Englewood Cliffs, New Jersey.

Laszlo, E (ed) (1972) *The Relevance of General Systems Theory.* George Brazilier, New York.

McCorduck, P (1979) *Machines Who Think.* Freeman, Reading.

Pask, G and Lewis, B (1972) *Teaching Strategies: A Systems Approach.* Open University Press, Milton Keynes.

RAF School of Education *A Systems Approach to Training.* RAF School of Education, Upwood, Huntingdon, UK.

Raphael, B (1976) *The Thinking Computer.* Freeman, Reading.

Romiszowski, A J (ed) (1970) *The Systems Approach to Education and Training, Conference Proceedings.* Kogan Page, London.

Romiszowski, A J (1980) *Designing Instructional Systems.* Kogan Page, London.

Saturen, S C *et al* (1972) *Handbook of Organisational Development in Schools.* Mayfield, USA.

Schank, R C and Colby, K M (1973) *Computer Models of Thought and Language.* Freeman, Reading.

Schmidbauer, M (1971) *New Educational Technology and its Implications for the Efficiency of Education Systems.* Unesco Publications, Paris.

Smith, R G (1966) *The Design of Instructional Systems.* Human Resources Research Office, Washington DC.

Stewart, D (1975) *A Behavioural Learning Systems Approach to Instruction: Analysis and Synthesis.* USA State Services.

Stoller, N (1978) *Supervision and the Improvement of Instruction.* Educational Technology Publications, Englewood Cliffs, New Jersey.

Sutherland, John W (1973) *A General Systems Philosophy for the Social and Behavioural Sciences.* George Braziller, New York.

Taylor, G (ed) (1970) *The Teacher as Manager – A Symposium.* Councils and Education Press, London.

Temkin, *et al* (1975) *Handbook of Comprehensive Planning in Schools.* Educational Technology Publications, Englewood Cliffs, New Jersey.

Thomas, C A (ed) *Pre-Structured Instruction.* RAF School of Education, Upwood, Huntingdon.

Vaughan, B W (1978) *Planning in Education (Application of Network Analysis to Curriculum Planning and School Organisation).* Cambridge Universty Press.

Von Bertalanffy, L (1968) *General Systems Theory.* George Braziller, New York.

Washburn, D and Smith, D (1974) *Coping with Increasing Complexity.* Gordon and Breach, London.

Wiener, N (1948) *Cybernetics.* MIT, Cambridge, Mass.

5. Task analysis, stating objectives and curriculum design

Beard, R M *et al* (1974) *Objectives in Higher Education.* Society for Research into Higher Education, Guildford, UK.

Bloom, B S *et al* (1956) *Taxonomy of Educational Objectives, Handbook 1 – Cognitive Domain.* Longman, London.

Boston, R E (1972) *How to Write and Use Performance Objectives to Individualise Instruction.* Educational Technology Publications, Englewood Cliffs, New Jersey.

Brigg, L J *et al* (1977) *Instructional Design: Principles and Applications.* Educational Technology Publications, Englewood Cliffs, New Jersey.

Burns, R W, Brooks, G D *et al* (1970) *Curriculum Design in a Changing Society.* Educational Technology Publications, Englewood Cliffs, New Jersey.

Burns, R W, Klingstredt, J L *et al* (1973) *Competency-Based Education (an Introduction).* Educational Technology Publications, Englewood Cliffs, New Jersey.

Butler, F C (1972) *Instructional Systems Development for Vocational & Technical Training.* Educational Technology Publications, Englewood Cliffs, New Jersey.

Cummings, L L, and Schwab, D P (1973) *Performance in Organisations.* Scott, Foresman & Co, Glenview, Illinois.

Dick, W and Carey, L (1978) *The Systematic Design of Instruction.* Scott, Foresman & Co, Glenview, Illinois.

Drumheller, S J (1971) *Handbook of Curriculum Design for Individualised Instruction.* Educational Technology Publications, Englewood Cliffs, New Jersey.

Gagné, R M (1977) *The Conditions of Learning.* Holt, Rinehart & Winston, London, 3rd ed.

Gillespie, J (1980) *Media Resources in Curriculum Development.* Scottish Council for Educatonal Technology, Glasgow.

Golby, M, Greenwald, J and West, R (1975) *Curriculum Design.* Croom Helm, London.

Harris, A, Lawn, M and Prescott, W (1975) *Curriculum Innovation.* Croom Helm, London.

Harrow, A (1970) *A Taxonomy of the Psychomotor Domain.* David Mackay, New York.

ILO (1973) *Introduction of a Vocational Training System using Modules of Employable Skill.* International Labour Office, Geneva.

Jenkins, D and Shipman, M D (1976) *Curriculum: An Introduction.* Open Books, London.

Kapfer, M B (ed) (1971) *Behavioural Objectives in Curriculum Design.* Educational Technology Publications, Englewood Cliffs, New Jersey.

Kapfer, M B *et al* (1978) *Behavioural Objectives: The Position of the Pendulum.* Educational Technology Publications, Englewood Cliffs, New Jersey.

Kaufman, R and English, F W (1979) *Needs Assessment: Concept and Application.* Educational Technology Publications, Englewood Cliffs, New Jersey.

Kelly A V (ed) (1980) *Curriculum Context.* Harper & Row, New York.

Kibler, R J *et al* (1974) *Objectives for Instruction and Evaluation.* Allyn & Bacon, Boston.

Krathwohl, D R *et al* (1964) *Taxonomy of Educational Objectives, Handbook 2 – Affective Domain.* Longman, London.

Langdon, D (ed) (1978) *Instructional Design Library.* Educational Technology Publications, USA. A series of 20 booklets on various specific instructional design techniques. Those planned for current publication include: Adjunct Study Guide; Algorithms; Audio-tutorial; Audiovisual Modules; Audio/Workbook; Backward Chaining; Construct Lesson Plan; Guided Design; Group Programs; Inquiry Plan; Project Plan; Individually Responsive Instruction; Simulation Games; PSI; PI; Session Plan; Student Contracts; Teaching Learning Unit; Token Economy; Tutoraids. Each booklet written by experienced practitioners of the technique described.

Mager, R F (1973) *Measuring Instructional Intent.* Fearon, Palo Alto, Cal.

Mager, R F (1975) *Preparing Instructional Objectives.* Fearon, Palo Alto, Cal. 2nd ed.

Mager, R F and Beach, K M (1967) *Developing Vocational Instruction.* Fearon, Palo Alto, Cal.

Mager, R F and Pipe, P (1970) Analyzing Performance Problems, or You Really Oughta Wanna. Fearon, Palo Alto, Cal.

McAsham, H M (1979) *Competency-Based Education and Behavioural Objectives.* Educational Technology Publications, Englewood Cliffs, New Jersey.

Open University *Curriculum: Context, Design and Development: A Series of 17 Units.* Open University Press, Milton Keynes, UK.

Orlosky, D E and Smith, B (1978) *Curriculum Development Issues and Insights.* Rand McNally, Chicago.

Popham, W J and Baker, E L (1970) *Establishing Instructional Goals. A Programmed Text.* Prentice-Hall, Englewood Cliffs, New Jersey.

Pratt, D (1980) *Curriculum: Design and Development.* Harcourt Brace. Jovanovich, New York.

Rackham, N and Morgan, T (1977) *Behaviour Analysis in Training.* McGraw-Hill, London.

Richards, C (1978) *Power and the Curriculum.* Nafferton Books, Driffield, UK.

Rowntree, D (1974) *Educational Technology in Curriculum Development.* Harper & Row, New York.

Rowntree, D (1981) *Developing Courses for Students.* McGraw-Hill, London and New York.

Tanner, D and Tanner, L (1980) *Curriculum Development: Theory and Practice.* Collier Macmillan, London and New York.

Segall *et al* (1976) *Systematic Course Design for the Health Fields.* Information Resources Inc, Box 417, Lexington, Mass.

Seymour, W D (1966) *Skills Analysis Training.* Pitman, London.

Simpson, E (1967) *The Classification of Educational Objectives in the Psychomotor Domain.* University of Illinois. (Report No BR-5-0090/ERD-251-65)

UTMU (1976) *UTMU Studies in Course Design.* University of London Teaching Methods Unit.

Vargas, J S (1972) *Writing Worthwhile Behavioural Objectives.* Harper & Row, New York.

Welford, A T (1976) *Skilled Performance*. Scott, Foresman & Co, Glenview, Illinois.

6. Instructional methods – characteristics, selection, use

Abercrombie, M L J and Terry, D M (1974) *Aims and Techniques of Group Teaching*. Society for Research into Higher Education, Guildford, UK.

Ackerman, J and Lipsitz, L (eds) *Instructional Television Status and Directions*. Educational Technology Publications, Englewood Cliffs, New Jersey.

Allen, D W and Ryan, K A (1969) *Microteaching*. Addison-Wesley, Reading, Mass.

Armstrong, R H R and Taylor, J L (eds) (1970) *Instructional Simulation Systems in Higher Education*. Cambridge Institute of Education.

Armstrong, R H R and Taylor, J L (eds) (1971) *Feedback on Instructional Simulation Systems*. Cambridge Institute of Education.

Avedon and Sutton Smith, B (1971) *The Study of Games*. Wiley, London.

Belbin, R M (1970) *The Discovery Method in Training*. HMSO, London.

Bell, N T and Abedor, A J (1977) *Developing Audio-Visual Instructional Modules for Vocation and Technical Training*. Educational Technology Publications, Englewood Cliffs, New Jersey.

Bligh, S and Schild, E O (eds) (1968) *Simulation Games in Learning*. Sage Publications, Beverly Hills, Cal.

Briggs, L J *et al* (1967) *Instructional Media – A Procedure for the Design of Multi-media Instruction*. American Institute for Research, Pittsburgh, Pa.

Briggs, L J (1970) *Handbook of Procedures for the Design of Instruction*. AIR Monograph No 4, American Institute for Research, Pittsburgh, Pa.

British Broadcasting Corporation (1972) *Games and Simulations*. BBC Publications, London.

Broudy, H S and Palmer, J R (1965) *Exemplars of Teaching Method*. Rand McNally, Chicago.

Brown, G (1975) *Microteaching – A Programme of Teaching Skills*. Methuen, London.

Bung, K (1975) *A Theoretic Model for Programmed Language Instruction*. Longman Research Publications Services, London.

Burns, R W and Kingstedt, J L (1973) *Competency Based Education: An Introduction*. Educational Technology Publications, Englewood Cliffs, New Jersey.

Champagne, D W and Goldman, R M (1975) *Handbook for Managing Individualized Learning in the Classroom*. Educational Technology Publications, Englewood Cliffs, New Jersey.

Coffey, J (1978) *Development on an Open Learning System for Further Education*. Council for Educational Technology, London.

Council for Educational Technology (1980) *How to Write a Distance Learning Course: A Self Study Pack for Authors*. A set of 11 units, CET, London.

Costin, F (1972) Lecturing versus other methods of teaching: a review of research, *British Journal of Educational Technology*, 3, 4-31.

Davies, W J K (1980) *Alternatives to Classroom Teaching in Schools and Colleges*. Council for Educational Technology, London.

Davies, W K J (1978) *Implementing Individualized Learning in Schools and Colleges*. Council for Educational Technology, London.

Duane, J E *et al* (1973) *Individualised Instruction – Programs and Materials*. Educational Technology Publications, Englewood Cliffs, New Jersey.

Duchastel, P C and Merrill, P F (1973) The effects of behavioural objectives on learning: a review of empirical studies, *Review of Educational Research,* 43, 53-69.

Dukes, R L and Seidner, C J (eds) (1978) *Learning with Simulations and Games.* Sage Publications, London.

Ellington, H I, Addinall, E and Percival, F (1981) *Games and Simulations in Science Education.* Kogan Page, London.

Falus, I (1975) *The Use of Microteaching and Allied Techniques for the Training of Educational Personnel in Sweden, the Federal Republic of Germany and the United Kingdom.* Unesco (on request).

Freeman, J (1969) *Team Teaching in Britain.* Ward Lock Educational, London.

Gibbs, G I and Howe, A (eds) (1974) *Academic Gaming and Simulation in Education.* Kogan Page, London.

Gordon, G N and Falk, I A (1972) *Videocassette Technology in American Education.* Educational Technology Publications. Englewood Cliffs, New Jersey.

Greenblatt, C S and Duke, R D (1975) *Gaming: Rationale, Design and Applications.* Wiley, New York.

Greenblatt, C S and Duke, R D (1975) *Gaming Simulation: Rationale, Design and Applications.* Walstead Press, New York.

Gropper, G L (1974) *Instructional Strategies.* Educational Technology Publications, Englewood Cliffs, New Jersey.

Heidt, E U (1978) *Instructional Media and the Individual Learner.* Kogan Page, London.

Holding, D H (1965) *Principles of Training.* Pergamon, Oxford.

Holmberg, B (1977) *Distance Education: A Survey and Bibliography.* Kogan Page, London.

Holmberg, B (1981) *Status and Trends of Distance Education.* Kogan Page, London.

Horn, R E (1976) *How to Write Information Mapping.* Information Resources Inc, Box 417, Lexington, Mass.

Howe, J A M and Ross, P M (1981) *Microcomputers in Secondary Education.* Kogan Page, London.

Introduction to Individualized Instruction (10 modules). Educational Technology Publications, Englewood Cliffs, New Jersey.

Johnson, D W and Johnson, R T (1975) *Learning Together and Alone: Cooperation, Competition and Individualization.* Prentice-Hall, Englewood Cliffs, New Jersey.

Jones, R (1980) *Microcomputers: Their Uses in Primary Schools.* Council for Educational Technology, London.

Kaye, T and Rumble, G (eds) (1980) *Distance Teaching for Higher Education.* Croom Helm, London.

Klein, J (1974) *Working with Groups.* Routledge & Kegan Paul, London.

Knirk, F G (1979) *Designing Productive Learning Environments.* Educational Technology Publications, Englewood Cliffs, New Jersey.

Kohl, H R (1974) *Writing Maths and Games.* Methuen, London.

Landa, L (1974) *Algorithmization in Learning and Instruction.* Educational Technology Publications, Englewood Cliffs, New Jersey.

Landa, L (1976) *Instructional Regulation and Control: Cybernetics, Algorithmization and Heuristics in Education.* Educational Technology Publications, Englewood Cliffs, New Jersey.

Langdon, D G (1973) *Interactive Instructional Designs for Individualized Learning.* Educational Technology Publications, Englewood Cliffs, New Jersey.

Langdon, D (ed) (1978) *Instruction Design Library – Series II* (20 titles). Educational Technology Publications, Englewood Cliffs, New Jersey. *The Core Package,* Mentzer, R C; *Direct Instruction,* Engelman, S; *Experiential Learning Packages,* Thiagarajan, S; *Instructional Frame Games,* Stolovitch, H and Thiagarajan, S; *Job Aids,* Lineberry, C and Bullock, D; *Learner Controlled Instruction,* Wydra, F T; *The Lecture Method of Instruction,* Broadwell, M; *Peer Tutorial Instruction,* Endsley, W; *The Pigors Incident Process of Case Study,* Pigors, P and F; *PLATO,* Fratini, R, Gesquiere, J and Rahmlow, H; *Protocol Packages,* Thiagarajan, S; *Role Playing,* Wohlking, W and Gill, P; *Rolemaps,* Dormant, D; *Structured Tutoring,* Von Harrison, G; *Student Planned Acquisition of Required Knowledge* (SPARK), Norton, M, Bozeman, W and Nadler, G; *Suggestive-Accelerative Learning and Teaching,* Caskey, O; *Teams-Games-Tournament: The Team Learning Process, Teletechniques: An Instructional Model for Interactive Teleconferencing,* Parker, L and Monson, M; *The Three-Stage Model of Course Design,* Feldhausen, J; *TICCIT,* Merill, M D, Schneider, E and Fletcher, K. (The final ten volumes of this 50-volume series are to be published in 1981-82.)

Levine, D M (1976) *Performance Contracting in Education – An Appraisal.* AERA/ETP, Chicago.

Lewis, B N *et al* (1967) *Flow Charts, Logical Trees and Algorithms for Rules and Regulations.* HMSO, London.

Lickley, A (1977) *Towards Individualised Learning for Teacher Education: Dundee College of Education Case Study.* Council for Educational Technology, London.

Lozanov, G (1977) *Suggestology.* Gordon & Breach, London.

MacKenzie M L (ed) (1978) *Deciding to Individualize Learning: A Study of the Process.* Council for Educational Technology, London.

Mager, R F (1969) *Developing Attitudes Towards Instruction.* Fearon, Palo Alto, Cal.

Mager, R F and Beach, K M (1967) *Developing Vocational Instruction.* Fearon, Palo Alto, Cal.

McAleese, R (1978) *Perspectives on Academic Gaming and Simulation 3.* Kogan Page, London.

Megarry, J (1977) *Aspects of Simulation and Gaming.* Kogan Page, London.

Megarry, J (1978) *Perspectives on Academic Gaming & Simulation 1 & 2.* Kogan Page, London.

Musgrave, G R (1975) *Individualised Instruction: Teaching Strategies Focussing on the Learner.* Allyn & Bacon, Boston.

Nicholson, M (1967) *The Structuring of Games and Simulations: Hypothesis, Formation and Testing.* Political Studies Association, Urbana, Illinois.

Noble, P (1980) *Resource Based Learning in Post Compulsory Education.* Kogan Page, London.

Pearson, C and Marfuggi, J (1976) *Creating and Using Learning Games.* Professional Educational Publications, Urbana, Illinois.

Percy K, and Ramsden, P (1980) *Independent Study: Two Examples from English Higher Education (Monograph 40).* Society for Research in Higher Education, Guildford, UK.

Perlberg, A (1975) *Recent Approaches on Micro-Teaching and Allied Techniques Which can be Implemented Easily in Developing Countries.* Unesco (on request), Paris/Washington.

Petrequin, G (1968) *Individualizing Learning through Modular-Flexible Programming*. McGraw-Hill, London.

Pfeiffer, J W and Jones, J E (1970) *A Handbook of Structured Experiences for Human Relations Training*. University Association Press, Iowa.

Powell, L S (1969) *Communication and Learning*. Pitman, London.

Ruskin, R F (ed) (1976) *An Evaluative Review of the Personalized System of Instruction*. Center for Personalized Instruction, Georgetown University, Washington DC.

Sharan, S and Sharan, T (1976) *Small Group Teaching*. Educational Technology Publications, Englewood Cliffs, New Jersey.

Sledge, D (ed) (1979) *Microcomputers in Education*. Council for Educational Technology, London.

Spencer, D C (1980) *Thinking about Open Learning Systems*. Council for Educational Technology, London.

Talmadge, H (ed) (1975) *Systems of Individualized Instruction*. McCatchan, Berkeley, Cal.

Tansey, PJ (1971) *Educational Aspects of Simulation*. McGraw-Hill, New York.

Tansey, PJ and Unwin D (1969) *Simulation and Gaming in Education*. Methuen, London.

Taylor, J L and Walford, R (1972) *Simulation in the Classroom*. Penguin, Harmondsworth.

Tillman, M, Bersolf, D and Dolly, J (1976) *Learning to Teach*. D C Heath & Co, Massachusetts.

Travers, R M (ed) (1973) *Second Handbook of Research on Teaching*. Rand McNally, Chicago.

Trott, A J (1977) *Selected Microteaching Papers*. Kogan Page, London.

Wheatley, D M and Unwin, A W (1972) *The Algorithm Writer's Guide*. Longman, London.

Whitaker, G (1965) *T-Group Training – Group Dynamics in Management Education*. Blackwell, Oxford.

Willings, D R (1968) *How to Use Case Study Training for Decision-Making*. Business Publications, London.

Wittrock, M (ed) (1972) *Changing Education: Alternatives from Educational Research*. AERA/Prentice-Hall, Chicago.

Yorke, D M (1981) *Patterns of Teaching*. Council for Educational Technology, London.

Zachert, M J K (1975) *Simulation Teaching of Library Administration*. R R Bowker Co, New York.

7. Instructional media – characteristics, selection, production

BACIE (updated regularly) *Training Aids Index*. British Association for Commercial and Industrial Education, London.

BACIE (1970) *Case Studies*.

BACIE (1971) *Books for Training Officers*.

BACIE (1977) *Case Studies for Practical Training*.

Barwick, J and Kranz, S (1973) *The Compleat Videocassette User's Guide*. Knowledge Industry Publications, 2 Corporate Park Drive, White Plains, NY 10604.

Beal, J D (1968) *How to Make Films at School.* Focal Press, London.

Beaumont-Craggs, R (1975) *Slide-Tape and Dual Projection.* Focal Press, London.

Bennett, W A (1968) *Aspects of Language and Language Teaching.* Cambridge University Press, Cambridge.

Bermingham, A *et al* (1976) *The Small TV Studio.* Focal Press, London.

Blake, R H and Haroldson, E O (1975) *A Taxonomy of Concepts in Communication.* Focal Press, London.

Borwick, John (ed) (1976) *Sound Recording Practice.* Oxford University Press, London.

Boucher, B G, Gottlieb, M J and Morganlander, M L (1973) *Handbook and Catalogue for Instructional Media Selection.* Educational Technology Publications, Englewood Cliffs, New Jersey.

Bretz, R (1971) *A Taxonomy of Communication Media.* Educational Technology Publications, Englewood Cliffs, New Jersey.

Brown, J W *et al* (1973) *A V Instruction: Media and Methods.* McGraw-Hill, New York.

Brown, J W *et al* (1973) *A V Instructional Technology: Media and Methods.* McGraw-Hill, New York, 4th ed.

Bullard, J R and Mether, C E (1974) *Audiovisual Fundamentals: Basic Equipment Operation and Simple Materials Production.* Wm C Brown Co, Dubuque, Iowa.

Campeau, P L (1974) Selective review of the results of research on the use of audio-visual media to teach adults, *A V Communication Review,* 22, 5-40.

Carpenter, C R (1971) Instructional film research – a brief review, *British Journal of Educational Technology,* 3, 229-46.

Cavert, C E (1974) *An Approach to the Design of Mediated Instruction.* Association for Educational Communications and Technology, 1201 16 St NW, Washington DC 22036.

Cavert, C E (1974) *Procedural Guidelines for the Design of Mediated Instruction.* Association for Educational Communications and Technology, Washington DC.

Coombes, P and Tiffin, J (1977) *Television Production for Education.* Focal Press, London.

Coppen, H E (1969) *Aids to Teaching and Learning.* Pergamon, Oxford.

Council for Educational Technology: USPEC 1. *8mm Cassette Systems;* USPEC 2. *Synchronised Tape/Visual Systems (using Compact Cassettes);* USPEC 3. *Overhead Projectors;* USPEC 4. *Cassette Audio Tape Recorders and Playback Units (monophonic);* USPEC 6. *Combined Filmstrip/Slide Projectors;* USPEC 11. *Pens and Inks for OHPs;* USPEC 14. *Microform Readers;* USPEC 16. *Synchronised Tape/Visual Operating Practice;* USEC 17. *Headphones;* USPEC 20. *Transparancy Frames for OHPs; USPEC 22. Slide and Filmstrip Viewers for Individual Use;* USPEC 23. *Magazine Slide Projectors for 50 mm x 50 mm slides;* USPEC 25. *A Guide to the Selection of Electronic Calculators;* USPEC 26. *Focus on Safety;* USPEC 32. *A Guide to the Selection of Microcomputers.*

CET/BMA (1973) *Film in Medical Education.* Council for Educational Technology, London.

Cowlan, B *et al* (1973) *Broadcast Satellite for Educational Development: The Experiments in Brazil, India and the United States.* Academy for Educational Development.

Crabbe, G (1976) *Copyright Clearance – A Practical Guide.* Council for Educational Technology, London.

Crocker, A H (1978) *The Testing, Evaluation and Selecting of Audio-visual Equipment*. ICEM, The Hague, Holland.

Dakin, J (1973) *Language Laboratory and Language Learning*. Longman, London.

Department of Education and Science (1968) *Language Laboratories*. HMSO, London.

Edera, B (1978) *Full-Length Animated Feature Films*. Focal Press, London.

Emery, F and Abrahams, B (1975) *Video Access Centres, a Feedback Evaluation*. Centre for Continuing Education, Australian National University, PO Box 4, Australia 2600.

Filep, R T *et al* (1975) *Communication Satellites and Social Services: Focus on Users and Evaluations – An Annotated Bibliography*. University of Southern California, Learning Systems Centre.

Flood Page, C and Kitching, J (1976) *Technical Aids to Teaching*. Society for Research into Higher Education, Guildford, UK.

Fulton, W R (ed) revised by King, K I (1969) *Evaluative Checklist: An Instrument of Self-Evaluating an Education Media Program in School Systems*. Association for Educational Communications and Technology, Washington DC.

Gaddy, D (1974) *A Microform Handbook*. National Microfilm Association.

Gee, B (1979) *The 16mm Film in School Science and Technology*. College of St Mark and St John, Plymouth, Devon.

Gibson, T (1970) *The Use of ETV – A Handbook for Students and Teachers*. Hutchinson, London.

Gibson, T (1972) *The Closed Circuit Television, Single-Handed*. Pitman, London.

Gordon, G N and Falk, I A (1972) *Videocassette Technology in American Education*. Educational Technology Publications, Englewood Cliffs, New Jersey.

Gordon, G N (1975) *Communication & Media: Constructing a Cross Discipline*. Focal Press, London.

Gorman, D A (1976) *An Instructional Materials Selection/Decision/Prescription Model*. Kendall/Hunt, Dubuque, Iowa.

Green, Oliver & Boyd (1975) *The Language Laboratory in School*. Methuen, London.

Gropper, G L (1975) *Diagnosis and Revision in the Development of Instructional Materials*. Educational Technology Publications, Englewood Cliffs, New Jersey.

Gropper, G L *et al* (1971) *Criteria for Selection and Use of Visuals in Instruction*. Educational Technology Publications, Englewood Cliffs, New Jersey.

Halas, J (ed) (1975) *Visual Scripting*. Focal Press, London.

Halas, J and Manvell, R (1976) *The Technique of Film Animation*. Focal Press, London.

Hancock, A (ed) (1976) *Producing for Educational Mass Media*. Unesco Press/Longman, London.

Haney, J and Ullmer, E J (eds) (1970) *Educational Media and the Teacher*. Wm C Brown Co, Dubuque, Iowa.

Harris, D (1979) *Preparing Educational Materials*. Croom Helm, London.

Hartley, J (1978) *Designing Instructional Text*. Kogan Page, London.

Hartley, J and Burnhill, P (March 1975) A brief anotated bibliography of typography, *PLET Journal*, Vol 12, No 2.

Hartley, J and Burnhill, P (1975) *Textbook Design: A Practical Guide*. Unesco (on request).

Heidt, E U (1975) In search of a media taxonomy: problem of theory and practice, *British Journal of Educational Technology,* 6, 1.

Heidt, E U (1978) *Instructional Media and the Individual Learner.* Kogan Page, London.

Hollwell, M L (ed) (1975) *Cable Handbook, 1975-76: A Guide to Cable and New Communications Technologies.* Communications Press.

Hood, S (1976) *Radio and Television.* David and Charles, Newton Abbot, UK.

Hopkins, J *et al* (1975) *Socio-Cultural Applications of Television Technology in the UK.* Document CCC/DC(75)24, Council of Europe, Strasbourg.

Hornsey, A W (1975) *Handbook for Modern Language Teachers.* Methuen, London.

Jones, J G (1972) *Teaching with Tape.* Focal Press, London.

Judd, R *Teaching by Projection.* Focal Press, London.

Kapfer, P G and Ovard, G F (1971) *Preparing and Using Individualized Learning Packages for Upgraded Continuous Progress Education.* Educational Technology Publications, Englewood Cliffs, New Jersey.

Kirk, D (1975) *Audio and Video Recording.* Faber, London.

Klasek, C B (1972) *Instructional Media in the Modern School.* Professional Educators Publications Inc, Box 80728 Lincoln, NE 68501.

Klinge, P L (ed) (1975) *American Education in the Electric Age: New Perspectives on Media and Learning.* Educational Technology Publications, Englewood Cliffs, New Jersey.

Lamb, B (1971) *Filmstrip and Slide Projectors in Teaching and Training.* NCAVAE, London.

Leedham, J (ed) (1974) *The Imaginative Uses of CCTV in the Training of Staff and Managers.* Unesco.

Leedham, J and Romiszowski, A J (eds) (1973) *Videocassettes in Education and Training. Conference Proceedings.* APLET Occasional Publication. Kogan Page, London.

Leggatt, R (1970) *'Showing-off' or Display Techniques for the Teacher.* NCAVAE, London.

Lloyd, J M (1975) *The All-in-One-Tape Recorder Book.* Focal Press, London.

Maclean, R (1968) *Television in Education.* Methuen, London.

McLuhan, M (1964) *Understanding Media.* Routledge & Kegan Paul, London.

Melton, H (ed) (1976) *A Guide to Independent Film & Video.* Anthology Film Archives, New York.

Mertens, J (1979) *Systems for the Selection and Control of the Quality of Software and Hardware by Educational Authorities,* ICEM, The Hague, Holland.

Middleton, J (1979) *Cooperative School Television and Educational Change.* Agency for Instructional TV, Bloomington, Indiana.

Millerson, G (1974) *TV Camera Operation.* Focal Press, London.

Millerson, G (1976) *Effective TV Production.* Focal Press, London.

Milton, R (1969) *Radio Programming – A Basic Training Manual.* Bles, London.

Minter, L F (1970) *How to Title.* Focal Press, London.

Monaco, J (1977) *How to Read a Film.* Oxford University Press, London.

Neale, D M (revised by Hole, R A) (1969) *How To Do Sound Films.* Focal Press, London.

Newsome, J (1966) *Still Photography in Education*. NCAVAE/EFVA, London.

Nisbett, A (1970) *The Technique of the Sound Studio*. Focal Press, London.

Nisbett, A (1976) *The Use of Microphones*. Focal Press, London.

Norberg Brown, J and Srygley, S (1972) *Administering Educational Media*. McGraw-Hill, New York.

Nystrom, A (1975) *Manual for Selection, Production and Evaluation of Textbooks*. University of Stockholm, Institute for the Study of International Problems in Education.

Oates, S C (1975) *Audiovisual Equipment Self-Instruction Manual*. Wm C Brown Co, Dubuque, Iowa.

Ofeish, G D and Rompf, E C (1975) *The Rise and Decline of an Electronic Instructional Medium: Dial Access*. Ofeish Associates, Washington.

Olson, D E (ed) (1974) *Media and Symbols: The Forms of Expression, Communication and Education*. Chicago University Press.

Perisic, Z (1976) *The Animation Stand*. Focal Press, London.

Phelan, A (1966) *The Law and Your Tape Recorder*. Print and Press Services Ltd, London.

Pit Corder, S (1966) *The Visual Element in Language Teaching*. Longman, London.

Poclyn, K A (1975) *An Educator's Guide to Communication Satellite Technology*. University of Wisconsin.

Powell, G H and Powell, L S (1967) *A Guide to the 8mm Loop Film*. British Association for Commercial and Industrial Education, London.

Powell, L S (1974) *A Guide to the Overhead Projector*. British Association for Commercial and Industrial Education, London 2nd ed.

Powell, L S (1978) *A Guide to the Use of Visual Aids*. British Association for Commercial and Industrial Education, London, 3rd ed.

Rigg, R P (1969) *Audio-Visual Aids and Techniques in Managerial and Supervisory Training*. Hamish Hamilton, London.

Robertson, A (1979) *The Video Yearbook*. Dolphin Press/Blandford Press, Poole, Dorset.

Robinson, J F (1975) *Videotape Recording*. Focal Press, London.

Robinson, J F and Beards, P H (1976) *Using Videotape*. Focal Press, London.

Romiszowski, A J (1974) *The Selection and Use of Instructional Media: A Systems Approach*. Kogan Page, London.

Rowatt, R W (1980) *A Guide to the Production of Tape Slide Programmes*. Scottish Council for Educational Technology, Glasgow.

Rowatt, R W (ed) (1980) *A Guide to the Use of the Overhead Projector*. Scottish Council for Educational Technology, Glasgow.

Rowatt, R W (1980) *A Guide to the Use of Portable Video Equipment*. Scottish Council for Educational Technology, Glasgow.

SAGSET (1980) *Resource Lists of Games and Simulations in Mathematics, Chemistry, Business and Management Training, and Economics*. Society for Academic Gaming and Simulation in Education and Training, Loughborough, UK.

Schillaci, A and Culkin, J (eds) (1970) *Films Deliver: Teaching Creatively with Film*. Citation Press, New York.

Schramm, W (ed) (1973) *Quality in Instructional Television*. The University Press of Hawaii, Honolulu.

Scottish Film Council (1976) *Video in Scotland: A Survey of Video Facilities in Scotland*. Scottish Council for Educational Technology, Glasgow.

Shaffer, D E. Publications available from 437 Jennings Ave, Salem, Ohio 44460, USA.

Shaffer, D E (1972) *The Filmstrip Collection: Complete Instructions on How to Proceed and Organise*.

Shaffer, D E (1972) *The Library Picture File: A Complete System of How to Process and Organise*.

Shaffer, D E (1973) *The Audio Tape Collection: A Library Manual on Sources, Processing and Organisation*.

Shaffer, D E (1973) *A Basic Audio Tape Collection: Lecture Programmes for the Academic Library*.

Sherrington, R (1973) *Television and Language Skills*. Oxford University Press, Oxford.

Stack, E M (1971) *The Language Laboratory and Modern Language Teaching*. Oxford University Press, Oxford.

Taylor, L C (1971) *Resources for Learning*. Penguin, Harmondsworth.

Theroux, J (1978) *Techniques for Improving Educational Radio Programmes*. Unesco, Paris.

Turner, J D (1965) *Introduction to the Language Laboratory*. University of London.

Turner, J D (1969) *Using the Language Laboratory*. University of London.

Unwin, D (ed) (1969) *Media and Methods – Instructional Technology in Higher Education*. McGraw-Hill, London.

Vernon, P J (1973) *The Audiovisual Approach to Modern Language Teaching*. NCAVAE, London.

Weisburger, R A (ed) (1968) *Instructional Process and Media Innovation*. Rand McNally, Chicago.

Weston, J (1968) *The Tape Recorder in the Classroom*. NCAVAE/EFVA, London.

Williams, B and Fothergill, R (1977) *Microforms in Education*. Council for Educational Technology, London.

Wilson, A J (1973) *ETV Guidelines: Writing, Directing and Presenting*. Hutchinson, London.

Wright, A (1966) *Visual Materials for the Language Teacher*. Longman, London.

Wyman, R A (1976) *Mediaware: Selection, Operation and Maintenance*. Wm C Brown Co, Dubuque, Iowa.

Young, J B (1970) *Reprographic Principles Made Easy*. NCAVAE/EFVA, London.

8. Study skills

Abercrombie, M L J (1969) *The Anatomy of Judgement*. Penguin, London.

Anderson *et al* (1969) *Study Methods*. McGraw-Hill, New York.

Baker, E I (1975) *A Guide to Study*. BACIE, London.

Barzun, J and Graffe, H F (1977) *The Modern Researcher*. Harcourt Brace Jovanovich, New York.

Berry, R (1966) *How to Write a Research Paper*. Pergamon, Oxford.

Beveridge, W M (1965) *The Art of Study*. Oxford University Press, London.

Bjernum, V (1971) *Study Technique: Hints for Students*. Harrap, London.

Burnett, J (1979) *Successful Study*. Teach Yourself Books/Hodder and Stoughton, London.

Burton, W H et al (1960) *Education for Effective Thinking*. Appleton-Century-Crofts, New York.

Buzan, T (1974) *Use Your Head*. BBC Enterprises, London.

Buzan, T (1981) *Make the Most of Your Mind*. Pan Books, London (originally Colt Books, 1977).

Cary, G V (1976) *Mind the Stop: A Brief Guide to Punctuation*. Penguin, London.

Castle, E B (1965) *How to Study*. Oxford University Press, London.

Chaplen, F (1970) *Paragraph Writing*. Oxford University Press, London.

Compton, H (1973) *How to Study*. Institute of Supervisory Management, Lichfield, UK.

Cooper, B M (1974) *Writing Technical Reports*. Penguin, London.

Corfield, T (1967) *How to be a Student*. Workers Educational Association, London.

Courteney, J W (1970) *Study for Success*. Intertext, London.

Dadourian, H M (1957) *How to Study: How to Solve*. Addison-Wesley, London.

Davis, N (1967) *Vocabulary Improvement*. McGraw-Hill, New York.

De Bono, E (1967) *The Use of Lateral Thinking*. Jonathan Cape, London.

De Bono, E (1972) *The Five Day Course in Thinking*. Penguin, Harmondsworth.

De Leeuw, M and E (1966) *Read Better: Read Faster*. Penguin, London.

Diack, H (1967) *101 Aids to Exam Success*. Dickens.

Diack, H (1967) *Study – The Easy Way*. Corgi, London.

Gordon, W J J (1961) *Synetics: The Development of Creative Capacity*. Harper & Row, New York.

Gowers, E (1954) *The Complete Plain Words*. HMSO, London.

Guinery, M (1967) *How to Study*. Allen & Unwin, London.

Hills, P J (1973) *Study to Succeed*. Pan, London.

Hills, P J (1976) *The Self-Teaching Process in HE*. Croom Helm, London.

Hills, P J (1979) *Teaching and Learning as a Communication Process*. Croom Helm, London.

Hills, P J and Barlow, H (1980) *Effective Study Skills*. Pan Books/ Heinemann Educational, London.

James, D E (1967) *A Student's Guide to Efficient Study*. Pergamon, Oxford.

Laing, A (1963) *The Art of Study*. University of Leeds.

Leedy, P D (1963) *Improve Your Reading*. McGraw-Hill, New York.

Leedy, P D (1963) *Read with Speed and Precision*. McGraw-Hill, New York.

Lorayne, H (1962) *How to Develop a Superpower Memory*. Thomas, Wellingborough.

Mace, C A (1963) *The Psychology of Study*. Penguin, Harmondsworth.

Maddox, H (1963) *How to Study*. Pan, London.

Mager, R F (1968) *Developing Attitude Towards Learning*. Fearon, Palo Alto, Cal.

Main, A (1980) *Encouraging Effective Learning*. Scottish Academic Press, Edinburgh.

Mares, C (1964) *Efficient Reading*. EUP, Edinburgh.

Mayer, R E (1977) *Thinking and Problem Solving*. Scott, Foresman & Co, Glenview, Illinois.

Mitchell, J (1974) *How to Write Reports*. Fontana/Collins, London.

National Extension College (1979/80) Titles in the Study Skills series, Cambridge, UK. Freeman, R *How to Study Effectively;* Lewis, R *How to Write Essays;* Rouse, S *Writing Essays in Social Science;* Moor, C *Answer the Question;* Inglis, J and Lewis, R *Clear Thinking;* Sullivan, A *Reading and Understanding;* Lewis, R and Pugmire, M *How to Use Your Dictionary*.

Open University (1973) *How to Study*. Open University Press, Milton Keynes, UK.

Open University (1979) *Preparing to Study*. Open University Press, Milton Keynes, UK.

Parsons, C J (1973) *Library Use in Further Education*. Edward Arnold, London.

Parsons, C (1977) *How to Study Effectively*. Arrow, London.

Partridge, E (1973) *Usage and Abusage*. Penguin, Harmondsworth.

Polya, G (1957) *How To Solve It*. Doubleday, New York.

Rowntree (1970) *Learn How to Study*. Macdonald, London.

Spache, G D and Berg, P C (1966) *The Art of Efficient Reading*. Collier Macmillan, New York.

Styler, W E (1963) *How to Study*. Workers Educational Association, London.

Turubian, K L (1969) *A Student's Guide for Writing College Papers*. Chicago University Press.

Turubian, K L (1973) *Manual for Writers*. Chicago University Press, 4th ed.

Wainwright, G R (1972) *Rapid Reading – Made Simple*. W H Allen, London.

Wertheimer, M (1961) *Productive Thinking*. Tavistock, London.

Wickelgren, W A (1974) *How to Solve Problems*. Freeman, Reading.

Woodley, C H (1959) *How to Study*. Angus & Robertson, Sydney.

9. Principles and applications of programmed learning

Austwick, K and Harris, N D C (1972) *Aspects of Educational Technology VI*. Proceedings of 1972 APLET Conference, Pitman, London.

Budgett, R and Leedham, J (eds) (1973) *Aspects of Educational Technology VII*. Proceedings of 1973 APLET Conference, Pitman, London.

Callendar, P (1969) *Programmed Learning: Its Development and Structure*. Longman, London.

Davies, I K and Hartley, J (eds) (1972) *Contributions to an Educational Technology*. Butterworth, London.

Dodd, B (1967) *Programmed Instruction for Industrial Training*. Heinemann, London.

Dorsett, L G (1971) *Audio-Visual Teaching Machines*. Educational Technology Publications, Englewood Cliffs, New Jersey.

Dunn, W R and Holroyd, C (eds) (1968) *Aspects of Educational Technology II* Proceedings of 1968 APLET Conference, Methuen, London.

Evans, L and Leedham, J (eds) (1975) *Aspects of Educational Technology IX*. Proceedings of 1975 APLET Conference, Kogan Page, London.

Glaser, R (ed) (1965) *Teaching Machines and Programmed Learning 2 – Data and Decisions*. National Education Association, Washington.

Hartley, J (ed) (1972) *Strategies for Programmed Instruction: An Educational Technology.* Butterworth, London.

Hartley, J (1974) Programmed Instruction 1954-1974: a review, *PLET Journal, 11, 278-91.*

Horn, R E (1976) *How to Write Information Mapping.* Information Resources, Box 417, Lexington, Mass.

Johnson, R B and Johnson, S R (1973) *Assuring Learning with Self-Instructional Packages (or – Up the Up Staircase).* Addison-Wesley, Reading, Mass.

Kay, H *et al* (1969) *Teaching Machines and Programmed Learning.* Penguin, Harmondsworth. Out of print but available in many libraries.

Leedham, J F and Bajpai, A (eds) (1970) *Aspects of Educational Technology IV.* Proceedings of 1970 APLET Conference, Pitman, London.

Leith, G O M (1969) *Second Thoughts on Programmed Learning.* CET Occasional Paper No 1, Council for Educational Technology, London.

Lenn, P D (1974) *Five Ways to Help Your Students: A Workshop on Instructional Techniques.* American Analysis Corporation, 2169 Union Street, San Francisco, Ca 94123.

Mann, A P and Brunstrom, C K (eds) (1969) *Aspects of Educational Technology III.* Proceedings of 1969 APLET Conference, Pitman, London.

National Centre for Programmed Learning (1969) *Programmed Learning – A Symposium,* NCAVAE, London.

National Society for the Study of Education (1967) *Programmed Instruction – 66th Yearbok of NSSE.* Chicago University Press, Chicago.

NCAVAE *A Series of Case Histories of the Use of Programmed Learning.* Occasional Paper No 16, NCAVAE, London.

Ofeish, G D and Meirhenry, W C (1964) *Trends in Programmed Instruction.* Department of Audio-Visual Instruction, National Education Association, USA.

Packham, D *et al* (eds) (1971) *Aspects of Educational Technology V.* Proceedings of 1971 APLET Conference, Pitman, London.

Pipe, P (1966) *Practical Programming.* Holt, Rinehart & Winston, New York.

Popham, W J and Baker, E L (1970) *Planning an Instructional Sequence.* Prentice-Hall, Englewood Cliffs, New Jersey.

Rowntree, D (1966) *Basically Branching.* Macdonald, London.

Thomas, C A et al (1963) *Programmed Learning in Perspective.* Lamson Technical Products, London.

Tobin, M J (ed) *Problems and Methods in Programmed Learning.* Proceedings of the 1967 APLET Conference. Part 1 – 122 pp, Part 2 – 109pp, Part 3 – 104pp, Part 4 – 123pp, Part 5 – 61pp. School of Education, University of Birmingham.

Unwin, D and Leedham, J (eds) (1966) *Aspects of Educational Technology I.* Proceedings of 1966 APLET Conference, Methuen, London.

Programme Writing

Brethower, *et al* (1964) *Programmed Learning: A Practicum.* Ann Arbor Publishers, Michigan.

Espich, J E and Williams, W (1967) *Developing Programmed Instructional Materials.* Pitman, London.

Lewis, B N and Woolfenden, P J (1969) *Algorithms and Logical Trees. A Self Instructional Course.* Algorithms Press, Cambridge.

Markle, S (1969) *Good Frames and Bad — A Grammar of Frame Writing.* Wiley, New York, 2nd ed.

10. Validation, evaluation, assessment

Bates, A and Robinson, J (eds) (1977) *Evaluating Educational Television and Radio.* Open University Press, Milton Keynes, UK.

Bellack, A and Kliebard, H (eds) (1976) *Evaluation and Curriculum Development.* AERA/Wiley, New York.

Billings, D (ed) (1979) *Indicators of Performance.* Society for Research in Higher Education, Guildford, UK.

Bloom, B S *et al* (1971) *Handbook on Formative and Summative Evaluation of Student Learning.* McGraw-Hill, New York.

Borich, G D (ed) (1974) *Evaluating Educational Programmes and Products.* Educational Technology Publications, Englewood Cliffs, New Jersey.

Clift, J C and Imrie, B W (1981) *Assessing Students, Appraising Teaching.* Croom Helm, London.

Cooley, W W and Lohnes, P R (1976) *Evaluation Research in Education.* Wiley, Sussex.

Copperud, C (1979) *The Test Design Handbook.* Educational Technology Publications, Englewood Cliffs, New Jersey.

Donovan, K G (1981) *Learning Resources in Colleges.* Council for Educational Technology, London.

de Gruiter, D N M and van der Kamp, L H Th (1977) *Advances in Psychological and Educational Measurement.* Wiley, Sussex.

Flood-Page, C (1974) *Student Evaluation of Teaching: the American Experience.* Society for Research into Higher Education, Guildford, UK.

Gropper, G L (1975) *Diagnosis and Revision in the Development of Instructional Materials.* Educational Technology Publications, Englewood Cliffs, New Jersey.

Grossman, H (1969) *Evaluation Activity of Curriculum Projects.* Rand McNally, Chicago.

Hamilton, D (1976) *Curiculum Evaluation.* Open Books, London.

Harris, D and Bailey, J (1980) *Education Resource Pack.* Council for Educational Technology, London.

Henderson, E S (1978) *Evaluating In-Service Teacher Training.* Croom Helm, London.

Heywood, J (1977) *Assessment in Higher Education.* Wiley, Sussex.

ITRU (1973) *What's In a Style?* ITRU, 32 Trumpington Street, Cambridge.

Jamison, D, Klees, S and Wells, S (1978) *The Costs of Educational Media: Guidelines for Planning and Evaluation.* Sage Publications, London.

Kibler, R H *et al* (1974) *Objectives for Instruction and Evaluation.* Allyn & Bacon, Boston.

Knapper, C K (1980) *Evaluating Instructional Technology.* Croom Helm, London.

Lacey C, and Lawton, D (1980) *Issues in Accountability and Evaluation.* Methuen, London.

Lawson, T E (1974) *Formative Instructional Product Evaluation.* Educational Technology Publications, Englewood Cliffs, New Jersey.

Lewis, D G (1967) *Statistical Methods in Education.* University of London Press.

Mardle, G and Gleeson, D (1980) *Further Education or Training? A Case Study in the Theory and Practice of Day Release Education.* Routledge & Kegan Paul, London.

Martin, A O (1968) *Assessing Training Effectiveness.* Department of Employment and Productivity, London.

McLaughlin, G H (1972) *Educational Television on Demand: An Evaluation of the Ottawa IRTV Experiment.* Ontario Institute for Studies in Education, Toronto.

Miller, C M and Parlett, M (1974) *Up to the Mark.* Society for Research in Higher Education, Guildford, UK.

Nathenson, M B and Henderson, E S (1980) *Using Student Feedback to Improve Learning Materials.* Croom Helm, London.

Partlett, M and Dearden, G (eds) (1981) *Introduction to Illuminative Evaluation: Studies in Higher Education.* Society for Research in Higher Education, Guildford, UK.

Payne, D A (1974) *The Assessment of Learning.* D C Heath & Co, Massachusetts.

Popham, W J *et al* (1971) *Criterion-Referenced Measurement: An Introduction.* Educational Technology Publications, Englewood Cliffs, New Jersey.

Pratt, D (1972) *How to Find and Measure Bias in Textbooks.* Educational Technology Publications, Englewood Cliffs, New Jersey.

Rahmlow, H F and Woodley, K K (1979) *Objectives-Based Testing: A Guide to Effective Test Development.* Educational Technology Publications, Englewood Cliffs, New Jersey.

Roberson, E W *et al* (1971) *Educational Accountability through Education.* Educational Technology Publications, Englewood Cliffs, New Jersey.

Seager, R and Dave, R H (1977) *Curriculum Evaluation for Lifelong Education.* Pergamon Press, Oxford.

Spradley, J (1980) *Participant Observation.* Holt, Rienhart & Winston, New York.

Straughan, R and Wrigley, J (1980) *Values and Evaluation in Education.* Harper & Row, London.

Tittle, C K and Miller, K M (1976) *Assessing Attainment.* IARC, 57 Marylebone High Street, London W1.

Tyler, R (ed) (1969) *Educational Evaluation: New Roles, New Means.* University of Chicago Press, Chicago.

Unesco *International Project on the Evaluation of Educational Achievement, Bulletin No 1.* Unesco Institute for Education, Hamburg.

Verma, G K and Beard, R M (1981) *What is Educational Research?* Gower, Aldershot, UK.

Vernon, P E (1956) *The Measurement of Abilities.* University of London Press.

Wagner, L (1980) *Cost Analysis and Educational Media Decisions.* Polytechnic of Central London, London.

Walberg, H J (ed) (1974) *Evaluating Educational Performance.* McCutchan, Berkeley, Cal.

Warr, P *et al* (1970) *Evaluation of Management Training.* Gower, London.

Wilhelms, F T (ed) (1967) *Evaluation as Feedback and Guide.* ASCD Yearbook, Association for Supervision and Curriculum Development.

Wittrock, M G and Wiley, D E S (1971) *Problems in the Evaluation of Instruction.* Holt, Rinehart & Winston, New York.

11. Organization – resource centres, media libraries

Atherton, B (1980) *Adapting Spaces for Resource Based Learning.* Council for Educational Technology, London.

AECT (1975) *Media Centres: Reading from Audio-Visual Instruction.* Association for Educational Communications and Technology, London.

AECT (1975) *Standards for Cataloging Non-print Materials: An Interpretation and Practical Application.* Association for Educational Communications and Technology, London.

Beswick, N W (1972) *School Resource Centres: Schools Council Working Paper 43.* Evans/Methuen Educational, London.

Beswick, N W (1975) *Organising Resources: Six Case Studies.* Heinemann Educational, London.

Bomar, C P *et al* (eds) (1973) *Guide to the Development of Educational Media Selection Centres.* American Library Association, 50 E Huron Street, Chicago, IL 60611.

Briault, E (1974) *Allocation and Management of Resources in Schools.* Council for Educational Technology, London.

Davies, W J K (1974) *Learning Resources? An Argument for Schools.* Council for Educational Technology, London.

Davis, C H and Rush, J E (1979) *Guide for Information Science.* Greenwood Press.

Edwards, R P A (1973) *Resources in Schools.* Evans, London.

Fothergill, R (1973) *Resource Centres in Colleges of Education: National Council for Educational Technology Working Paper 10.* Council for Educational Technology, London.

Fothergill, R and Butchart I (1978) *Non-book Materials in Libraries – A Practical Guide.* Bingley, London.

Garnett, E (1973) *Area Resources Centre: An Experiment.* Edward Arnold, London.

Gray, H L (1980) *Management in Education.* Nafferton Books, Driffield, UK.

Hicks, W B and Tillin, A M (1976) *Managing Multi-Media Libraries.* R R Bowker Co, New York.

Holder, M and Mitson, R (1974) *Resource Centres.* Methuen, London.

Library Association (1972) *School Library Resource Centres: Recommended Standards for Policy and Provision (1970).* A supplement on non-book materials.

Loertscher, D W (1975) *Budgeting for School Media Centres: An Annotated Bibliography.* ERIC Clearinghouse.

Malcolm, A H (ed) (1973) *A Resource Centre...is a State of Mind.* Scottish Film Association, Glasgow.

Mankovsky, V S (1971) *Acoustics of Studios and Auditoria.* Communications Arts Books, Hastings House Publishers, New York.

Owen, J G (1973) *Management of Curriculum Development.* Cambridge University Press.

Shiffrin, M R (1973) *Information in the School Library: An Introduction to the Organisation of Non-Book Materials.* Bingley, London.

South, P (1974) *Questions to Ask when Designing Primary and Secondary Schools for the Use of Educational Technology.* Council for Educational Technology, London.

South, P (1974) *The Design of Learning Spaces.* Council for Educational Technology, London.

Sullivan, P (1971) *Problems in School Media Management.* R R Bowker Co, London.

Tanner, C K and Williams, E J (1981) *Educational and Decision Making: A View through the Organizational Process.* Lexington Books.

Taylor, L C (1972) *Resources for Learning.* Penguin, Harmondsworth.

Tillin, A M and Quinley, W J (1976) *Standards for Cataloging Nonprint Materials.* Association for Educational Communications and Technology, London, 5th ed.

Tucker, R N (1979) *The Organization and Management of Educational Technology.* Croom Helm, London.

Unesco (1976) *Transformation of School Libraries into Multi-Media Centres.* Unesco (on request).

Walton, J and Rusk, J (eds) (1975) *Resources and Resource Centres.* Ward Lock Educational, London.

Winslade, B A J and Beswick, N W (1971) *Resource Centres: An Annotated Bibliography.* College of Librarianship, Wales.

Working Papers published by the Council for Educational Technology, UK, relevant to the organization and management of media centres and libraries. Obtainable from Councils and Education Press. Please quote the code numbers.
  No 4 *A Challenge for Librarians?* (1970) R Fothergill. ISBN 0 902204-05-X.
  No 6 *Non-book Materials: Their Bibliographic Control* (1971) L Gilbert and
    J W Wright. ISBN 0 900313-21-8.
  No 8 *Copyright and Education* (1974) ISBN 0 900313-33-1.
  No 9 *Training for Educational Media Design* (1973) Wright.
    ISBN 0 902204-11-4.
  No 10 *Resource Centres in Colleges of Education* (1973) R Fothergill.
    ISBN 0 902204-12-2.
  No 11 *Non-Book Materials: Cataloging Rules* (1973) ISBN 0 902204-22-X.
  No 12 *Audio-Visual Materials: Development of a National Cataloging and
    Information Service* The British Library and the Council for Educational
    Technology. ISBN 0 902204-64-5.

12 Applications in general education

Ausubel, D P (1969) *School Learning: An Introduction to Educational Psychology.* Holt, Rinehart & Winston, New York.

Bell, P (1970) *Basic Teaching for Slow Learners.* Muller Educational, London.

Bending, C W (1970) *Communication and the Schools.* Pergamon Press, Oxford.

Bielawski, J (1973) *Guide to Educational Technology: Early Childhood Education.* Techmonic Publishing Co; 265 Post Road West, Westport, CT 06880.

Bishop, L K (1971) *Individualising Educational Systems.* Harper & Row, New York.

Blackwell, F (1975) *Children in the Picture.* Council for Educational Technology, London.

Brown, M and Precious, N (1969) *The Integrated Day in the Primary School.* Ward Lock, London.

Bung, K (1968) *Programmed Learning and the Language Laboratory.* Longman, London.

Cleary, A *et al* (1975) *Educational Technology: Implications for Early and Special Education.* Wiley, Sussex.

Cohen, M D (ed) (1973) *Children are Centres for Understanding Media.* Association for Childhood Educational International, 3615 Wisconsin Ave NW, Washington DC 20016.

Dave, R H (1973) *Lifelong Education and School Curriculum.* Unesco Institute for Education, Hamburg.

Davies, W J K (1975) *Learning Resources? An Argument for Schools.* CET Guideline No 1, Council for Educational Technology, London.

Johnson, O G (1963) *Education for the Slow Learners.* Prentice-Hall, Englewood Cliffs, New Jersey.

Kapfer, P G and Ovard, G F (1971) *Preparing and Using Individualized Learning Packages for Ungraded, Continuous Progress Education.* Educational Technology Publications, Englewood Cliffs, New Jersey.

Leedham, J and Unwin, D (1965) *Programmed Learning in Schools.* Longman, London.

McAnanay, E (1973) *Radio's Role in Development: Five Strategies of Use.* Information Center on Instructional Technology, Academy for Educational Development, NY.

Nichols, C A (1979) *A-Level Tuition and Educational Technology in Schools and Colleges.* Council for Educational Technology, London.

Richardson, E (1973) *The Teacher, the School and the Task of Management.* Heinemann, London.

Robinson, A and Embling, J H (1975) *Primary School Education and Technology.* CET Occasional Paper No 6, Council for Educational Technology, London.

Sealey, L G W and Gibbon, V (1964) *Communication and Learning in the Primary School.* Blackwell, Oxford.

Taylor, G (ed) (1970) *The Teacher as Manager. A Symposium.* Councils and Education Press, London.

Taylor, G (ed) (1970) *The Teacher as Manager. A Symposium.* Councils and Education Press, London.

Turner, P and Atkinson, C R M *An Experiment in Closed Circuit Television at Millfield School.* NCAVAE Visual Education Book Service, London.

Turner, P *Television in the Service of a School.* NCAVAE Visual Education Book Service, London.

Unesco (1974) *New Trends in the Utilization of Educational Technology for Science Education.* Unesco.

Unruh, G G *et al* (1970) *Innovations in Secondary Education.* Holt, Rinehart & Winston, New York.

Warwick, D (1971) *Team Teaching.* University of London Press.

13. Applications in higher and further education

AECT (1971) *Basic Guidelines for Media and Technology in Teacher Education.* Association for Educational Communications and Technology, Washington DC.

Armstrong, R H R and Taylor, J L (1971) *Instructional Simulation Systems in Higher Education.* Cambridge Institute of Education.

Beard, R M (1970) *Teaching and Learning in Higher Education.* Penguin, Harmondsworth.

Bridge, W and Elton, L (1977) *Individual Study in Undergraduate Science.* Heinemann Educational Books, London.

Brown, J W and Thornton, J W (eds) (1963) *New Media in Higher Education.* NEA, Washington.

Browne, J D (1970) *The Development of Educational Technology in Colleges of Education.* Councils and Education Press, London.

Carnegie Foundation (1972) *The Fourth Revolution: Instructional Technology in Higher Education.* McGraw-Hill, New York.

Clarke, J (1978) *Learning Resources for an Institution of Higher Education – A Feasibility Study.* Dundee College of Education.

Cleugh, M F (1962) *Educating Older People.* Tavistock Publications, London.

Diamond, R M *et al* (1975) *Instructional Development for Individualized Learning in Higher Education.* Educational Technology Publications, Englewood Cliffs, New Jersey.

Flood-Page, C J (1971) *Technical Aids to Teaching in Higher Education.* SRHE Monograph 15, Society for Research in Higher Education, Guildford.

Flood-Page, S and Greenaway, H (eds) (1976) *Innovation in Higher Education.* SRHE 7th Annual Conference papers, Society for Research in Higher Education, Guildford.

Goldschmid, B and Goldschmid, M L (1972) Modular instruction in higher education: a review, *Higher Education,* 2, 15-32.

Goldschmid, B and Goldschmid, M L (1973) Individualizing instruction in higher education: a review, *Education,* 3, 102-4.

Group for Research and Innovation in Higher Education. General Reports (1972-75): *The Drift of Change; Supporting Teaching for a Change; Interdisciplinarity; Units and Modules; Towards Independence in Learning; Studies in Laboratory Innovation; Sociology at Keele; A Question of Degree; Course Teams; Case Studies in Interdisciplinarity – (1) Environmental Sciences, (2) Science, Technology and Society, (3) Integrated Social Sciences I, (4) Integrated Social Sciences II, (5) Humanities/ Human Science; Newsletters, 1, 2, 4, 5, 6.* All published by Nuffield Foundation, London.

Harris, N D C (1976) *Educational Technology in European Higher Education.* CET Seminar Report No 2. Council for Educational Technology, London.

Harrison, S A and Stolurow, L M (eds) (1975) *Improving Instructional Productivity in Higher Education.* Educational Technology Publications, Englewood Cliffs, New Jersey.

Johnston, J M (ed) (1975) *Behaviour Research and Technology in Higher Education.* Charles C Thomas, Springfield, Illinois.

Kosma, R B, Belle, L W and Williams, G W (1978) *Instructional Techniques in Higher Education.* Educational Technology Publications, Englewood Cliffs, New Jersey.

Mackenzie, N *et al* (1970) *Teaching and Learning – An Introduction to New Methods and Resources in Higher Education.* Unesco and the International Association of Universities, Paris.

Mackenzie, N *et al* (1975) *Open Learning: Systems and Problems in Post-Secondary Education.* Unesco.

NCET *Support Materials for Courses in Educational Technology* (see details in Section 16 of this Bibliography).

Nieme, J A (ed) (1971) *Mass Media and Adult Education.* Educational Technology Publications, Englewood Cliffs, New Jersey.

Ogborn, J (1977) *Small Group Teaching in Undergraduate Science.* Heinemann Educational, London.

Open University (1972) *The Early Development of the Open University.* Open University, Milton Keynes, UK.

Rice, A K (1970) *The Modern University – A Model Organization.* Tavistock, London.

Rogers, D (1974) *Educational Technology in Curriculum Development.* Harper & Row, New York.

Ruskin, R S and Johnson, K R (1975) *Individualised Instruction in Higher Education. An Annotated Review of the Literature.* Centre for Personalized Instruction, Georgetown University, Washington.

Society for Research in Higher Education (1972) *Innovation in Higher Education.* SRHE, London.

Society for Research in Higher Education (1973) *Motivation: Non-cognitive Aspects of Student Performance.* SRHE, London.

Thornton, J and Brown, J (eds) (1969) *New Media and College Teaching.* Association for Educational Communications and Technology, London.

Unwin, D (ed) (1969) *Media and Methods – Instructional Technology in Higher Education.* McGraw-Hill, London.

14. Applications in industry and commerce

BACIE *Bibliography.* British Association for Commercial and Industrial Education, London, Vol 1 1960-62; Vol II 1963-67.

Balderston, J B and Ritzen, J M *Methodology for Planning Technical Education.* Praeger Publishers, New York.

Barber, J W (ed) (1968) *Industrial Training Handbook.* Iliffe, London.

Bass, B M and Vaughan, J G (1966) *Training in Industry.* Tavistock, London.

Belbin, E (1964) *Training the Adult Worker.* HMSO, London.

Belbin, E and Belbin, R M (1972) *Problems in Adult Retraining.* Heinemann, London.

Brosgall, J (1973) *Some Examples of Innovative Activity in Industrial Training.* Council for Educational Technology, London.

Burby, R J (1968) *Managing with People.* Addison-Wesley, Reading, Mass.

Butler, F C (1972) *Instructional Systems Development for Vocational and Technical Training.* Educational Technology Publications, Englewood Cliffs, New Jersey.

Department of Employment and Productivity (1969) *Training Research Register.* HMSO, London.

Department of Employment and Productivity (1971) *Glossary of Training Terms.* HMSO, London.

Gane, C (1972) *Managing Training Using Instructional Technology and Systems Concepts.* Allen & Unwin, London.

Holding, D H (1965) *Principles of Training.* Pergamon, Oxford.

ILO (1973) *Introduction of a Vocational Training System Using Modules of Employable Skill.* International Labour Office, Geneva.

ITRU (1973) *Versatility at Work: A Study of Self Training and Autonomous Working Groups.* ITRU, 32 Trumpington Street, Cambridge.

Kenney, J and Donnelly, E (1972) *Manpower Training and Development.* Harrap, London.

Leedham, J (1974) *The Imaginative Uses of CCTV in the Training of Staff and Managers.* Unesco.

Lyne, R W (ed) (1967) *Programmed Instruction in Industry. A Reference Series of Case Histories (Vol 1).* Pergamon, Oxford.

Lyne, R W (ed) (1968) *Programmed Instruction in Industry. A Reference Series of Case Histories (Vol II)*. Pergamon, Oxford.

Lyne, R W (ed) (1969) *Training Systems in Industry. A Reference Series of Case Histories*. Pergamon, Oxford.

Mager, R F and Beach, K M (1977) *Developing Vocational Instruction*. Fearon Publishers, Palo Alto, Cal.

Odiorne, G (1970) *Training by Objectives*. Collier Macmillan, London.

Robinson, J and Barnes, N (eds) (1968) *New Media and Methods in Industrial Training*. Business Books, London.

Seymour, W D (1966) *Industrial Skills*. Pitman, London.

Seymour, W D (1968) *Skills Analysis Training*. Pitman, London.

Shirley-Smith, K (1968) *Programmed Learning in Integrated Industrial Training*. Gower Press, London.

Singer, E J (1966) *Industrial Skills*. Pitman, London.

Singer, E J and Ramsden, J (1969) *Practical Approach to Skills Analysis*. McGraw-Hill, New York.

Taylor, E A (1966) *A Manual of Visual Presentation in Education and Training*. Pergamon, Oxford.

Warren, M W (1969) *Training for Results: A Systems Approach to the Development of Human Resources in Industry*. Addison-Wesley, Reading, Mass.

Welford, A T (1968) *Fundamentals of Skill*. Methuen, London.

Wellens, J (1974) *Training of Physical Skills*. Business Books, London.

Wheatcroft, E (1973) *Simulators for Skill*. McGraw-Hill, London.

Wheatley, D M and Unwin, A W (1972) *The Algorithm Writer's Guide*. Longman, London.

Yee, Albert H *et al* (1975) *Perspectives on Management Systems Approaches in Education*. Educational Technology Publications, Englewood Cliffs, New Jersey.

Zoll, A A (1969) *Dynamic Management Education*. Addison-Wesley, London.

15. Computers in education

Annett, J and Duke, J (eds) (1970) *Proceedings of a Seminar on Computer-based Learning Systems*. National Council for Educational Technology, Councils and Education Press, London.

Atkinson, R V and Wilson, H A (1969) *Computer-Assisted Instruction: A Book of Readings*. Academic Press, New York.

Bailey, D E (ed) (1978) *Computer Science in Social and Behavioural Science Education*. Educational Technology Publications, Englewood Cliffs, New Jersey.

Baker, F B (1976) *Computer Managed Instruction Theory and Practice*. Educational Technology Publications, Englewood Cliffs, New Jersey.

Beard, M (1976) *Computer-Assisted Instruction: The Best of ERIC 1973-76*. ERIC Clearinghouse.

Beech, G (ed) *Computer Assisted Learning in Science Education*. Pergamon, Oxford.

Black, J (1969) *Computers for Education*. CET Working Paper No 1. Councils and Education Press, London.

Coleman, M (1978) Micro-computer systems: revolution or revolt? *Computer Education* No 30, Nov 1978.

Coulson, J E (ed) (1962) *Programmed Learning and Computer-Based Instruction. Proceedings of Conference.* Wiley, London.

Eisele, J E (1971) *Computer-Assisted Planning of Curriculum and Instruction.* Educational Technology Publications, Englewood Cliffs, New Jersey.

Evans C (1979) *The Micro Millenium.* Viking Press, New York. Feigenbaum, E A and Feldman, J (1963) *Computers and Thought.* McGraw-Hill, New York.

Fielden, J and Pearson, P K (1978) *The Cost of Learning with Computers.* Council for Educational Technology.

Hickey, A E (1974) *Research Guidelines for Computer-Assisted Instruction.* Albert E Hickey Associates, Newburyport, Massachusetts.

Hills, P (1981) *The Future of the Printed Word.* Open University Press, Milton Keynes, UK.

Hooper, R (1977) *The National Development Programme in Computer-Assisted Learning.* CET, London.

Hooper, R and Toye, I (eds) (1975) *Computer-Assisted Learning in the United Kingdom.* Councils and Education Press, London.

Howe, J A M and Ross, P M (1981) *Microcomputers in Secondary Education.* Kogan Page, London.

Hoye, R E and Wang, A C (eds) (1975) *Index to Computer Based Learning.* Educational Technology Publications, Englewood Cliffs, New Jersey.

Hsido, T C (ed) (1977) *World Encyclopaedia of Computer Education and Research.* Science and Technology Press Inc, Washington DC.

Huntingdon, J F (1979) *Computer-Assisted Instruction Using BASIC.* Educational Technology Publications, Englewood Cliffs, New Jersey.

Jones R (1980) *Microcomputers: Their Uses in Primary Schools.* Council for Educational Technology, London.

Lippey, G (1974) *Computer-assisted Test Construction.* Educational Technology Publications, Englewood Cliffs, New Jersey.

Kemmis, S *et al* (1979) *How Do Students Learn: Evaluation of NDPCAL.* University of East Anglia, Norwich, UK.

National Development Programme in Computer Assisted Learning (1975) *Two Years On: Report of the Director.* Councils and Educational Press, London.

NCAVAE (1977) *Computer Educational Aids and Resources for Teachers.* NCAVAE Visual Education Book Service, London.

NDPCAL Technical Reports. The following reports were published by the National Development Programme in Computer Assisted Learning, UK, during 1976-77. All are available from NDPCAL, 37/41 Mortimer Street, London W1N 7RJ.
  TR 1 *Problems of implementing computer managed learning* D Hawkridge
  TR 2 *The NDPCAL – origins and starting point* R Hooper
  TR 3 *Making claims for computers* R Hooper
  TR 4 *Computers and sacred cows* R Hooper
  TR 5 *Terminals for CAL – problems and possibilities* Dr P Osmon
  TR 6 *An introduction to computer graphics* B Scott
  TR 7 *The human factors aspect of the student/terminal Interface in CAL systems* V Cook
  TR 8 *Co-ordination of development of computer based curriculum material* R Miles
  TR 9 *An approach to measuring the cost of CAL* J Fielden
  TR 10 *Computerised question banking systems* Dr C Byrne
  TR 11 *Simulation and modelling in CAL* D Tawney
  TR 12 *Legal aspects of computer programs for education* B Cornish

TR 13 *The cost of conventional university teaching* P Pearson
TR 14 *CAL in higher education – the next ten years* R Hooper (ed)
TR 15 *Educational computing in the local authority – the next ten years*
   R Hooper (ed)
TR 16 *Computer managed learning in the 1980s* N Rushby (ed)
TR 17 *TechnologiCAL – report of the working party on computer technology in
   the 1980s* K Knight (ed)
TR 18 *Computers in military training in the 1980s* R Mile.

Nelson, T (1977) *The Home Computer Revolution*. Distributors, South Bend,
Indiana.

Papert, S (1980) *Mindstorms*. Basic Books, New York.

Rushby, N (1979) *Introduction to Educational Computing*. Croom Helm, London.

Rushby, N (ed) (1981) *Selected Readings in Computer Based Learning*. Kogan Page,
London.

Seidel, R J and Rubin, M (eds) (1977) *Computers and Communications,
Implications for Education*. Academic Press, New York.

Shepherd, I D H, Cooper, Z A and Walke, D R F (1980) *Computer Assisted
Learning in Geography*. Council for Educational Technology, London.

Sledge, D (ed) (1979) *Microcomputers in Education*. Council for Educational
Technology, London.

Sleeman, D and Brown (1980) *Intelligent Computer Tutors*. Academic Press.

Summers, M K (1978) Microprocessors in the Curriculum and the Classroom, *British
Journal of Educational Technology*, Vol 9, No 5.

UCODI (1971) *File on the Computer Education in Germany*. UCODI, Batiment Sc
16B, 1 rue du Compas, 1348 Louvain la Neuve, Belgium. 2 vols.

16. Films and audiovisual packages concerned with educational technology

(a) Films and videotapes

British Council (CETO/CEDO) (1965/70). Series of 16mm films on techniques of
film and TV production:

Who Does What	20 minutes
Basic Shots	17 minutes
Cut or Mix	18 minutes
People Talking	20 minutes
Still Pictures on Television	28 minutes
Superimposition	27 minutes
Using Lenses (I & II)	37 minutes

Available from British Council Production Unit, Tavistock House South, Tavistock
Square, London WC1.

British Council and Doordarshan (Indian) Television Service *A Communication
Strategy for Development*. Colour, 16mm. Running time 28 minutes. A film about
the SITE experiment. For details contact the British Council Publications
Department, 65 Davies Street, London W1.

British Council *Not Extra To You: The Overhead Projector*. Colour, 16mm.
Running time 25 minutes. for details contact the British Council Publications
Department, 65 Davies Street, London W1.

COI for the Department of Education and Science *Patterns of Learning*. 16mm. For
free hire, contact the District Central Film Library.

Open University (1977). Series of audiotape/videotape/videocassette presentations describing the methods used in planning, writing and producing OU course materials:

General Subjects in Multi-Media Teaching Systems. Audio, 30 minutes.
Arts, Social Science, Education in Multi-Media Teaching Systems. Audio, 60 minutes.
Humanities in Multi-Media Teaching Systems. Videotape/cassette, 30 minutes.
Mathematics in a Multi-Media Teaching systems. Videotape/cassette, 30 minutes.
Science and Technology in a Multi-Media Teaching System. Videotape/cassette, 60 minutes.
Science and Technology in a Multi-Media Teaching System. Videotape/cassette, 60 minutes.
Social Sciences and Education in a Multi-Media Teaching System. Video, 60 minutes.

Open University Marketing division, Walton Hall, Milton Keynes.

A Programmed Aproach to Environmental Studies in the Primary School. Commissioned by the National Council for Educational Technology. For deails of hiring, contact the National Audio-Visual Aids Library, Paxton Place, Gipsy Road, London SE27. For details of purchase, contact CET, 160 Great Portland Street, London W1.

Programmed Learning. Commissioned by the Royal Navy. Technicolor, 16mm. Running time 31 minutes. Suitable for teachers, training management and learners, as an introduction to PL. Enquiries to Stewart Film Distributors Ltd, 82-84 Clifton Hill, London NW8 0JT. 01-624 1238.

The Systems Approach to Training. Commissioned by the Royal Air Force. For details of availability, contact Ministry of Defence EdS2C (RAF), Adastras House, Theobalds Road, London WC2.

(b) AV packages

British Council (1976) Radio Training Kits – tapes, slides and printed materials, describing various aspects of scripting/production of educational radio:

1 *Sound*
2 *The Studio*
3 *The Illusion of Reality*
4 *Writing for Talking*
5 *Dialogue and Drama*
6 *Music in Educational Radio*
7 *The Producer at Work*
8 *Editing*
9 *Teaching English by Radio*
10 *Using Radiovision*

British Council Production Unit, Tavistock House South, Tavistock Square, London WC1.

NCET *Support Materials for Courses in Educational Technology.* Five multi-media packages for courses organizers running courses in educational technology. The packages are flexible to allow the introduction of organizers' own material where appropriate. Films, OHP transparencies, tapes, slides and printed materials covering the following:

(a) educational objectives
(b) criteria for the selection of methods and resources
(c) management of resources
(d) characteristics of media
(e) evaluation.

A detailed leaflet is available from CET or from other distributors, EFVA and Scottish Film Council, 16-17 Woodside Terrace, Charing Cross, Glasgow C3.

Perrott, E *et al* (1975) *Self-Instructional Microteaching Course – Effective Questioning*. Guild Sound & Vision, Peterborough.

Scottish Educational Film Association (1973) *A Resources Centre...is a State of Mind*. SEFA, Glasgow.

Journals Relevant to Educational Technology

Compiled by **Rodney Battey, MA, MA (Ed)**, *Senior Lecturer in Materials Technology/Learning Resources at Middlesex Polytechnic*

(a) Major journals devoted to educational technology (English language)

American Educational Research Journal. American Educational Research Association, 1230 17th St NW, Washington DC 20036.

British Journal of Educational Technology. 3 times a year. Editor Dr G D Moss. Official journal of the Council for Educational Technology, 3 Devonshire Place, London W1.

Educational Communication and Technology: A Journal of Theory, Research and Development (formerly *AV Communication Review*). Articles on research aspects of educational technology, research and book reviews. Association for Educational Communication and Technology, 1126 16th St NW, Washington DC 20036.

Educational Technology. Monthly. Editor Lawrence Lipsitz. Theory and application of technology in education and training, new equipment, training and materials, all aspects of educational media and materials. Educational Technology Publications Inc, 140 Sylvan Ave, Englewood Cliffs, NJ 07632.

Improving Human Performance. The official research journal of the NSPI. Editor Philip Tiemann, NSPI. 1126 Sixteenth St, NW, Suite 315, Washington DC 20036.

Instructional Science. An international journal. Published quarterly by Elsevier Scientific Publishing Company, PO Box 211, 1000 AE Amsterdam, The Netherlands.

Journal of Educational Psychology. Official journal of the American Psychological Association, 1200 Seventeenth St NW, Washington DC 20036.

Journal of Educational Television and Other Media. Educational Television Association, 86 Micklegate, York YO1 1JZ

NSPI Journal. Short articles and news items on instructional and performance technology. Editor Harold Stolovitch, 1126 Sixteenth St NW, Suite 315, Washington DC 20036

Programmed Learning and Educational Technology. Official journal of the Association for Educational and Training Technology. Quarterly. Kogan Page Ltd, 120 Pentonville Road, London N1 9JN.

Simulation/Games for Learning. The journal of SAGSET (formerly entitled *SAGSET Journal*). Quarterly, Kogan Page, 120 Pentonville Road, London N1 9JN.

Visual Education. 11 times a year. Editor R Hawkins. Official magazine of the National Committee for Audio-Visual Aids in Education, NCVAE, 254 Belsize Road, London NW6 4BY.

(b) Other useful English language journals (published elsewhere than North America)

Appropriate Technology. Quarterly. For those involved in development work. Intermediate Technology Publications Ltd, 9 King St, London WC2E 8HN.

Australian Photography. Monthly. Globe Publishing Co, Sydney, NSW.

BKSTS Journal. Monthly. The British Kinematograph Sound Television Society, 110/112 Victoria House, Vernon Place, London WC1B 4DJ.

British Educational Research Journal. Twice a year. British Educational Research Association. Carfax Publishing Company, Haddon House, Dorchester-on-Thames, Oxford OX9 8JZ.

British Journal of Teacher Education. 3 times a year. Methuen & Co Ltd, North Way, Andover, Hants SP10 5BE.

BUFC Newsletter. British Universities Film Council, 81 Dean St, London W1V 6AA.

CAL News. Computers in Education. Council for Educational Technology, 3 Devonshire St, London W1V 2BA.

Comparative Education. 3 times a year. Carfax Publishing Company, Haddon House, Dorchester-on-Thames, Oxford OX9 8JZ.

Compare: A Journal of Comparative Education. Twice a year. Carfax Publishing Company, Haddon House, Dorchester-on-Thames, Oxford OX9 8JZ

Computers in Education. Quarterly. Pergamon Press, Headington Hill Hall, Oxford OX3 OBW

CORE (Collected Original Resources in Education). 3 times a year. Carfax Publishing Company, Haddon House, Dorchester-on-Thames, Oxford OX9 8JZ

Development/International Development Review. Society for International Development, Palazzo Civilta' del Lavoro, 00144 Rome.

Education Equipment. 11 times a year. A controlled circulation journal, listing new products of interest to schools and colleges. Benn Publications Ltd, Sovereign Way, Tonbridge, Kent TN9 1RW.

Educational Research. The Journal of the National Foundation for Educational Research in England and Wales. 3 times a year. Links research and the classroom by offering up-to-date information on research findings for evaluation and discussion by teachers, planners and administrators. NFER Publishing Co Ltd, Darville House, 2 Oxford Rd East, Windsor, Berks SL4 1DF.

Epistolodidaktika – see *The Journal of Correspondence Education*

European Journal of Education. Quarterly. Institute of Education of the European Cultural Foundation. Carfax Publishing Co, Haddon House, Dorchester-on-Thames, Oxford OX9 8JZ.

European Journal of Science Education. Quarterly. English language with French and German summaries. Taylor & Francis Ltd, 10-14 Macklin St, London WC2 5NF.

Evaluation in Education. 3 times a year. Research reports on evaluation. Pergamon Press, Headington Hill Hall, Oxford OX3 0BW.

Evaluation Newsletter. Evaluation in higher education. Carfax Publishing Company, Haddon House, Dorchester-on-Thames, Oxford OX9 8JZ.

Forum. Quarterly review of the Council of Europe published in English, French, German and Italian; each issue includes a section about educational and cultural matters to which is also chiefly devoted at least one of the 4 yearly issues. Obtainable free of charge from Directorate of Education, Culture and Sport, Council of Europe, BP 431 F-67006 Strasbourg – Cedex.

Higher Education. The International Journal of Higher Education and Educational Planning, published bi-monthly by Elsevier Scientific Publishing Company, PO Box 211, 1000 AE Amsterdam, The Netherlands.

Industrial and Commercial Training, The Management of Human Resources. Monthly. All aspects of training and manpower development. Wellens Publishing, Guilsborough, Northants NN6 8PY.

Information. Bi-monthly. Research and developments in health and medical education. BLAT Centre for Health and Medical Education, British Medical Association, BMA House, Tavistock Square, London WC1H 9JP.

Inter Media. Every 2 months. International Institute of Communications, Tavistock House East, Tavistock Square, London WC1H 9LG.

International Journal of Man-Machine Studies. Academic Press Inc (London) Ltd, 24-28 Oval Rd, London NW1 7DX.

International journal of Mathematical Education in Science & Technology. Quarterly. Editors A C Bajpai and W T Martin. Taylor & Francis Ltd, Rankine Rd, Basingstoke, Hants.

International Review of Education. Quarterly. Unesco Institute for Education, Feldbrunen Strasse 58, D-2000 Hamburg 13.

Journal of Computer Education. Contact Mrs P Jackson, North Staffs Polytechnic Computer Centre, Blackheath Lane, Stoke-on-Trent.

Journal of Curriculum Studies. Quarterly. Taylor & Francis, 10-14 Macklin St, London WC2 5NF.

Journal of Correspondence Education (from 1982 incorporates *Epistolodidaktica*). Twice a year. European Home Study Council, c/o Keith Rawson-Jones (Honorary Secretary), Research & Development Committee, The Linguaphone Institute, Beavor Lane, London W6.

Journal of European Industrial Training (incorporating *European Training and Industrial Training International*). Training news, research and ideas. 198-200 Keighley Rd, Bradford BD9 4JQ.

Leadership and Organisation Development Journal. Quarterly. MCB Publications, 198 Keighley Rd, Bradford, Yorks BD9 4JQ.

Mediacult. Newsletter of the International Institute for Audiovisual Communication and Cultural Development, A-1030 Vienna, Metternichgasse 12.

Royal Air Force Education Bulletin. Editor Sqn Ldr G W Fraser. Recent educational and training developments mainly in the Royal Air Force. The Educational and Training Technology Development Unit, Royal Air Force School of Education, RAF, Newton, Nottingham NG13 8HL.

Screen Education. Quarterly. The Society for Education in Film and Television, 29 Old Compton St, London W1V 5PL.

Software: Practice & Experience. Monthly. Applied journal on computer software. John Wiley & Sons, Baffins Lane, Chichester, Sussex.

Studies in Educational Evaluation. 3 times a year. Covers large-scale assessment programmes. Pergamon Press, Headington Hill Hall, Oxford OX3 0BW.

Studies in Higher Education. Twice a year. Society for Research into Higher Education. Carfax Publishing Company, Haddon House, Dorchester-on-Thames, Oxford OX9 8JZ.

Technical Education Abstracts. Quarterly. Carfax Publishing Company, Haddon House, Dorchester-on-Thames. Oxford OX9 8JZ.

Telecommunication Journal. Monthly. Published in English, French and Spanish. International Telecommunication Union, Place des Nations, 1211 Geneva 20.

Training. Official Journal of The Institute of Training and Development. Monthly. Pitman Periodicals Ltd, 41 Parker Street, London WC2.

The Training Officer, Monthly. Marylebone Press Ltd, 25 Cross St, Manchester M2 1WL.

Trends in Education, 1966. Quarterly. 82p by post from HMSO. Subscriptions to: PO Box 569, Cornwall House, London SE1 9NH. Editorial: Department of Education and Science, Elizabeth House, York Rd, London SE1.

(c) Journals published in North America

AEDS Monitor. Association for Educational Data Systems, 1201 16th St NW, Washington, DC 20036.

Audio-Visual Communications. How-to-do-it information, general case studies, product information. 12 issues a year. 475 Park Avenue South, New York, NY 10016.

The Audio-Visual Equipment Directory: A Guide to Current Models of Audio-Visual Equipment. Annually. Sally Harickes, National Audio-Visual Association Inc, 3150 Spring St, Fairfax, VA 22031.

Audio-Visual Equipment and Production Directory. United Business Publications, 475 Park Ave South, New York, NY 10016.

Biomedical Communications. Bi-monthly. Medical education and equipment, darkroom and processing techniques. 475 Park Avenue South, NY 10016.

Curriculum Inquiry: An International Journal of Curriculum. Ontario Institute for Studies in Education, 252 Bloor St W, Toronto, Ontario M5S 1U6.

Development Communication Report. For those interested in development activities involving the communications media. Clearinghouse on Development Communication, 1414 22nd St NW, Washington, DC 20037.

Educational Marketer. Twice-monthly. Newsletter for executives in educational publishing, materials, and equipment companies. Knowledge Industry Publication Inc, 2 Corporate Park Drive, White Plain, NY 10604.

Educational Researcher. Research in education, government affairs and policy developments relating to research and education. American Educational Research Association, 1230 17th St NW, Washington, DC 20036.

EFLA Evaluations. Evaluations (on 8½ × 11 sheets) of 400 educational films per year. Educational Film Library Association, 43 West 61st St, New York, NY 10023.

EPIEgram. Recent developments in educational software and hardware. EPIE reports, analyses and evaluations of instructional hardware and instructional materials including textbooks, projected and recorded products. Educational Products Information Exchange Institute (EPIE Institute), PO Box 620, Stony Brook, New York, NY 11790.

ETV Newsletter. News of educational and instructional TV, software. C S Tepfer Publishing Co Inc, 51 Sugar Hollow Road, Danbury, CT 06810.

Film & Broadcasting Review. Bi-monthly. Reviews of all theatrical films, 16mm features and shorts, resource information for educators, educational TV highlights. Office for Film and Broadcasting, US Catholic Conference, 1011 First Ave, Suite 1300, New York, NY 10022.

GP Newsletter. ITV articles, programme and service announcements. Published monthly – September through May. Editor Richard L Spence, GP Newsletter, Great Plains National Instructional Television Library, c/o University of Nebraska-Lincoln, Box 80669, Lincoln, Nebraska 68501.

HeSCA Feedback. Published by Health Sciences Communications Association. Editor Corki (Gloria) Wilson. Information on association activities, activities in health sciences education and uses and availabilities of new media in the field. c/o MERP, Indiana University School of Medicine, 1100 W Michigan St, Indianapolis, IN 46223.

Home Video Report. Twice-monthly newsletter. Information about home video: cassettes, discs, programming hardware CATV, pay TV. Knowledge Industry Publications Inc, 2 Corporate Park Drive, White Plains, NY 10604.

Individualized Learning Letter. Addressed to administrators in planning and implemention of individualized programmes. TILL, Box 74, Huntingdon, NY 11743.

Instructional Technology. Applications of computers, CCTV and other new media resources in instruction, newsletter format. Girad Associates Inc, Box 455, Mt Arlington, NJ 07856.

Journal of Educational Research. Publishes reports of original research that have direct relevance to educational practice. 4000 Albemarle St NW, Washington DC 20016.

Journal of Educational Statistics. American Educational Research Association, 1230 17th St NW, Washington, DC 20036.

Journal of Educational Technology Systems. Baywood Publishing Co, 120 Marine St, Farmingdale, NY 11735.

Journal of Personalized Instruction. Editor Robert S Ruskin. Center for Personalized Instruction, 29 Loyala Hall, Georgetown University, Washington DC 20057.

Journal of the University Film Association. School of Communication, Agnes Arbold Hall, Room 633, The University of Houston, Houston, TX 77004.

Mass Media Newsletter. Ecumenical communications resource for leaders in churches, schools and community organizations. Reviews of current commercial cinema and other media. Published twice monthly (except monthly in June, July, August and December). Mass Media Ministries Inc, 2116 N Charles St, Baltimore, MD 21218.

NHSC News. Concerned with correspondence education. National Home Study Council, 1601 18th St NW, Washington DC 20009.

NICEM Newsletter. National Information Center for Educational Media, University of Southern California, University Park, Los Angeles, California 90007.

One to One. Journal of the International Congress of Individualized Instruction. Editor Dr R Witkus, Biology Department, Fordham University, The Bronx, NY 10458.

Pipeline. Twice a year, featuring articles and package reviews concerning computers in education. CONDUIT (University of Iowa), PO Box 388, Iowa City, IA 52244.

Recorded Visual Instruction. Annual catalogue (issued in autumn) describing ITV series and single programmes distributed by Great Plains National Instructional Television Library. GPN, c/o University of Nebraska-Lincoln, Box 80669, Lincoln, Nebraska 68501.

Resources in Education. Monthly. Research-related reports, documents of educational significance. Educational Resources Information Center, National Institute of Education, Washington DC 20208.

Review of Educational Research. Quarterly. Reviews of research literature bearing on education and some reviews of relevant research from other disciplines. AERA, 1230 17th St NW, Washington DC 20036.

Satellite Telecommunications Newsletter. Box 5254Y, Beverly Hills, CA 90210.

Technical Communication. Quarterly. journal of the Society for Technical Communication, 815 15th St NW, Suite 506, Washington, DC 20005.

Training. The Magazine of Human Resources Development, Lakewood Publications, 731 Hennepin Avenue, Minneapolis, MN 55403.

Videocassette and CATV Newsletter. In-depth analysis of the systems, markets and future of the video-cassette and video-disc, CATV, satellites, etc and a review of current events in the field affecting education, business and commerce, Martin Roberts and Associates, Box 5254, Beverly Hills, CA 90210.

Visual Literacy Newsletter. 12 times a year. Information on conferences, workshops, publications for visual literacy membership and articles relating to visual literacy. The International Visual Literacy Association, c/o Dennis Pett, Executive Secretary, Audio-Visual Center, Indiana University, Bloomington, IN 47405.

(d) Journals in languages other than English

Dutch

NIAM – Mediatiek. Nederlands Instituut voor Audio-visuele Media (NIAM), Swelinckplein 33, 2517 GN The Hague, Netherlands.

Onderzoek van Onderwijs (Education Research). Postbus 590 Pr Beatrixlaan 4281, Voorburg.

French

Direct: Monthly Review on the use of Modern Communication Technologies in Education and Development. Agence de Cooperation Culturelle et Technique, 19 Avenue de Messine, 75008 Paris.

Centre National de la Cinematrografie – Informations CNC, rue de Lucke, 75784 Paris.

Sonovision. 15 rue d'Aboukir, 75002 Paris.

German

Unterrichts Medien-Dienst. Padagogische Arbeistelle des DVV, 6 Frankfurt, Holzhausenstr 21.

Sehen & Horen. Bundesstaatliche Hauptstelle fur Lichtbild und Bildungfilm, A-1152 Vienna, Plunkergasse 3-5.

Hebrew

Bulletin for Education Technology. Israel Society for Instructional Technology, Tel Aviv, 43 Brodetsky Street.

Italian

Tecnologie Educative. Cento Nazionale Italiano Tecnologie Educative, via Marche 84, 00187 Rome.

Spanish

Medios Audiovisuales. Desengano 12, Madrid 13.

Directoria Latinamericano de Recursos Humanos en Tecnologia Educativa. OE, Proyecto Mult de Tecnologia Educativa, Centro de Venezuela, Apartado 1147, Caracas 101.

Revista de Tecnologia Educativa. Organizacion de los Estados Americanos, Centros de Chile, Proyecto Mult de Tecnologia Educativa, OEA, Casilla 16162, Correo 9, Santiago.

An Index to *Aspects of Educational Technology*

The Proceedings of the annual conference of the Association have been published every year since 1966. All these volumes except that for 1967 are known as 'Aspects of Educational Technology' and are available in print. The 1967 conference was held under the joint auspices of the then Association for Programmed Learning and the National Centre for Programmed Learning at the School of Education in Birmingham, and the resulting volume, 'Problems and Methods in Programmed Learning' was published by the NCPL.

The full titles and other information of the various volumes are as follows:

Aspects of Educational Technology I. Proceedings of the Loughborough Programmed Learning Conference, 1966. Eds Derick Unwin and John Leedham.

Problems and Methods in Programmed Learning. Proceedings of the APL/NCPL Conference, 1967. Ed M J Tobin, published by the National Centre for Programmed Learning, University of Birmingham.

Aspects of Educational Technology II. Proceedings of the Glasgow Programmed Learning Conference, 1968. Eds W R Dunn and C Holroyd.

Aspects of Educational Technology III. Proceedings of the First International Conference, held at Goldsmiths' College, University of London, 1969. Eds A P Mann and C K Brunstrom.

Aspects of Educational Technology IV. Proceedings of the 1970 APLET Conference held at Loughborough University. Eds A C Bajpai and J F Leedham.

Aspects of Educational Technology V. Proceedings of the 1971 APLET Conference held at the University of Newcastle-upon-Tyne. Eds D Peckham, A Cleary and T Mayers.

Aspects of Educational Technology VI. Proceedings of the 1972 APLET Conference held at the University of Bath. Eds K Austwick and N D C Harris.

Aspects of Educational Technology VII. Proceedings of the 1973 APLET Conference, held in Brighton. Eds R Budgett and J F Leedham.

Aspects of Educational Technology VIII: 'Communication & Learning'. Proceedings of the 1974 APLET Conference, held at the University of Liverpool. Eds J Baggaley, G H Jamieson and H Marchant.

Aspects of Educational Technology IX: 'Educational Technology for Continuous Education'. Proceedings of the 1975 APLET Conference, held at The City University, London. Eds L Evans and J F Leedham.

Aspects of Educational Technology X: 'Individualised Learning'.
Proceedings of the 1976 APLET Conference held at Dundee College of
Education. Eds J Clarke and J F Leedham.

*Aspects of Educational Technology XI: 'The Spread of Educational
Technology'.* Proceedings of the 1977 APLET Conference, held at the
University of Surrey. Eds P J Hills and John Gilbert.

*Aspects of Educational Technology XII: 'Educational Technology in a
Changing World'.* Proceedings of the 1978 APLET Conference held at the
Polytechnic of Wales. Eds David Brook and Philip Race.

*Aspects of Educational Technology XIII: 'Educational Technology Twenty
Years On'.* Proceedings of the 1979 AETT Conference held at the Sheffield
City Polytechnic. Eds G T Page and Q Whitlock.

*Aspects of Educational Technology XIV: 'Educational Technology to the
Year 2000'.* Proceedings of the 1980 AETT Conference held at The City
University, London. Eds Roy Winterburn and Leo Evans.

*Aspects of Educational Technology XV: 'Distance Learning and
Evaluation'.* Proceedings of the 1981 AETT Conference held at Robert
Gordon's Institute of Technology, Aberdeen. Eds Fred Percival and Henry
Ellington.

The following list gives a classified breakdown of all the titles of papers
published in these 16 volumes. It is hoped that the list will serve the
convenience of readers as an index as well as demonstrating the wealth of
material on all aspects of educational technology that is available in these
volumes. The classification system adopted is similar in type to those used
by the majority of the successive editors of 'Aspects', and when in doubt
papers have been classified following the original edition. The classification
categories used here are:

1. Overviews
2. Research models and measurement
3. Instructional design and development
4. Problems in programmed learning
5. Instructional media
6. Computers in education
7. Evaluation and assessment
8. Organization, management and dissemination
9. Training of educational technologists
10. Resource centres, distance and open learning
11. Lifelong education
12. The teacher and the learning process
13. Individual factors and learning
14. Applications in schools
15. Applications in special education and with the handicapped
16. Applications in tertiary education (including teacher training)
17. Applications in the armed forces, vocational and industrial training
18. Applications in medical health education
19. Applications in other specific subjects
20. Applications overseas and the transfer of educational technology.

While all articles from 'Aspects' are entered in the following pages, it is not
possible to make multiple entries: an article covering two (or more) themes

will appear only in the category to which it has primary relevance. It is always worth consulting several categories, therefore, when seeking sources of information and guidance.

1. Overviews

APL/NCPL

Professor E A Peel. *Programmed thinking.*

Aspects III

Sir Brynmor Jones. *Educational technology in tomorrow's world.* Dr C K Rouse. *A psychological look into the future of programmed learning.*

Aspects IV

G Hubbard. *Conditions for progress – an analysis of educational technology.*
J F Leedham. *Some views on the function of an association for programmed learning and educational technology in the future.*
P D Mitchell. *Educational technology: panacea or placebo?*
Lord Robens. *Realising the potential of educational technology.*

Aspects VI

K Austwick. *The message, the medium and post-literate man.*
Gary O Coldevin. *The impact of mass media upon the development of international orientations.*
R L Edwards. *Children in a global village.*

Aspects VII

John Annett. *Psychological bases of educational technology.*
Robert Glaser. *Intelligence, learning and the new aptitudes.*

Aspects VIII

C Cherry. *Teaching or learning? A critique of 'educational technology'.*
R M Cook. *Communication and learning: an ethological approach.*
T K Davies. *Educational technology at the crossroads: efficient message design or effective communication.*
G P Meredith. *Instruments and individuals.*

Aspects IX

L F Evans. *Concluding address – 'educational technology with a human face'.*
J Leedham. *Conference theme and presentation: 'educational technology for continuous education'.*

Aspects X

J G Morris. *Why individualized learning?*

Aspects XI

L R B Elton. *Educational technology – today and tomorrow.*

Aspects XII

W G Fleming. *The shared understanding of human action: a more appropriate goal for educational technology?*

Aspects XIII

T Boydell and M Pedler. *Educational technology and significant learning? (Workshop).*
J Green and A Morris. *Mapping the field of educational technology (Workshop).*
C J Lawless. *Information processing: a model for educational technology.*
J Leedham. *Staffing and consultancy: UNESCO enquiry into modern educational techniques.*
D Rowntree. *Educational technology to educational development – a bid for survival? (Workshop).*
D Walsh. *Evaluation: dialogue between education and technology (Workshop).*

Aspects XIV

P Boero, P Forcheri, F Furinghetti, E Lemut and M T Molfino. *Possible contributions of mathematics teaching for technological and social education.*
C Neville. *The potential of packaged learning for meeting changing demands for education and training.*

Aspects XV

E B Duncan and R McAleese. *Information retrieval in educational technology.*
J Nisbet. *Educational technology: its current impact. (Keynote address).*
J G Morris. *Final thoughts (Closing address).*

2. Research models and measurement

Aspects I

Annett. *Research strategies for a technology of teaching.*

Aspects III

E M Buter. *Educational technology and the problem of joining didactical theory and teaching practice.*
F J J Butler. *Towards a revised methodology of research in programmed instruction.*
I K Davies. *Some aspects of measurement in educational technology.*
M W Neil. *An operational and systems approach to research strategy in educational technology.*
R A Wheatley. *Measurement in programmed learning experiments – problems encountered and some possible solutions.*

Aspects V

M Roebuck. *Floundering among measurements in educational technology.*

Aspects VII

G O Coldevin. *A model for systematic television research.*

Aspects IX

P D Mitchell. *Operational research models applicable to educational technology for life-long learning.*

Aspects XIV

E A Soremekun. *Towards a new paradigm in education.*

Aspects XV

R R Begland. *An analytic model and instructional paradigm for training 'soft skills'.*

3. Instructional design and development

Aspects I

Cassels. *The development and production of mathetical programmes: a case study.*
Davies. *Mathetics – a functional approach.*
Gane, Horabin and Lewis. *Algorithms for decision making.*
Harless. *The two meanings of mathetics.*
Pigott. *The factor method: a programme planning technique.*

APL/NCPL

T Birkin. *Human information processing and the structuring of teaching materials.*

Aspects II

M R Eraut. *The design of variable input learning systems.*
D Rowntree. *Tutorial programming – an integrated approach to frame-writing.*
P J Tansey and D Unwin. *Simulation and academic gaming: highly motivatational teaching techniques.*
D Willoughby and D Le Hunte. *The application of mathetical analysis.*

Aspects III

P J Tansey and D Unwin. *Simulation in the school setting.*

Aspects IV

A Orantes. *A framework for defining instructional sub-systems.*
G H Wace, G R Simmonds and G L Smart. *Notes towards defining techniques of audio-visual programming.*

Aspects VI

Gary M Boyd. *The derivation of programmed lessons from recorded protocols.*
Mark Braham. *Natural organization and education.*
S Gilmore. *The construction and evaluation of a guided oral language situation.*
Michael Macdonald-Ross. *Behavioural objectives and the structure of knowledge.*
Michael Macdonald-Ross and Patricia Fleetwood-Walker. *Should the programmer be a subject matter expert?*
P David Mitchell. *The sacramental nature of behavioural objectives.*

Aspects VII

J Hartley, P Burnhill and S Fraser. *Typographical aspects of instructional design.*
D Redfearn. *An application of queueing theory to the design and management of programmed learning.*
D Rowntree. *Which objectives are most worthwhile?*
T G Wyant. *Syllabus analysis.*

Aspects VIII

P Burnhill and J Hartley. *Psychology and textbook design: a research critique.*
G R Catlow. *The use of project network analysis in course design.*

B T Dodd, R J G LeHunte and C Sheppard. *Decision making in instructional design.*
B O'Hare. *The design of learning packages in the Royal Air Force.*
J C Richardson. *The design, production and use of learning packages in remedial mathematics.*

Aspects IX

R N Brown and J Cowan. *Scouting for poise: a search for a balanced strategy of curriculum development.*
P Burnhill, J Hartley, S Fraser and M Young. *The typography of college prospectuses: a critique and a case history.*
D Langdon. *Interactive instructional designs.*
D Langdon. *Construct lesson plan.*

Aspects X

J Cowan. *Must self-instructional materials be firmly structured and directed towards lower-level objectives?*
B S Furniss, C R McHugh, and J R Parsonage. *An effective strategy for the production of self-instructional materials.*

Aspects XI

B W Vaughan. *The application of a modified operational research technique in the design of curricula. Systematic Curriculum Design (SCUD) Technique.*
M S Yadav and R Govinda. *Evolvement of an instructional strategy for teaching educational evaluation.*

Aspects XII

C F A Bryce and A M Stewart. *Design and production of self-instructional learning packages in biochemistry using the Philips PIP System.*
H I Ellington, F Percival and E Addinall. *Building science-based educational games into the curriculum.*
J Hartley and K L Davies. *Searching tables in the dark: horizontal vs vertical layouts.*
P A Kirschner and H J van der Brink. *The effect of adjunct question position, type and the presence or absence of feedback on learning from a video-taped lesson.*

Aspects XIII

E W Anderson. *The design, development and assessment of a learning programme for part-time adult education.*
L M Bray. *Self-instruction for hotel and catering skills (Workshop).*
H I Ellington, F Percival and E Addinall. *Simulation-games and case studies – some relationships between objectives and structure.*
H I Ellington, F Percival and E Addinall. *'Power for Elaskay' (Workshop).*
L F Evans. *Packaging-a workshop.*
J Hartley and M Trueman. *Some observations on producing and measuring readable writing (Paper and workshop).*
L Landa. *Psychological troubleshooting diagnostics as a basis for deeper adaptive instruction.*
R J LeHunte. *Training design for manager skills.*
P D Mitchell. *A micro-analytical procedure to improve instructional materials.*
A J Romiszowski and B Atherton. *Creativity and control – neglected factors within self-instruction programme design.*
D Rowntree. *Developing a self-instructional course on how to develop self-*

4. Problems in programmed learning

Aspects II

I Dolejsi. *On the problems of 'purposefully wrong manipulation' of programmed texts.*
J J P Ellams. *The development of a student attitude questionnaire for use in programmed learning investigations.*
H Kelbert. *Modelling the programmed learning process.*
L N Landa. *The construction of algorithmic and heuristic models of thinking activity and some problems in programmed learning.*
R H Richardson and J I Allan. *What should be programmed?*

Aspects III

K Bung. *Phonetic intelligibility in programmed language instruction.*
H U Grundin. *Response mode and information about correct answers in programmed instruction: a discussion of experimental evidence and educational decisions.*
J Hartley and J Holt. *Teacher expectations and programmed learning.*
G Noble. *What instructional skills can intrinsic programmed instruction teach, with and without teacher implementation?*
J Shotter. *What can programmed minds do?*

Aspects IV

J Hartley and Janet Holt. *The effects of pre-testing on post-test performance following programmed instruction.*
C Holroyd, Rosemary Lever, Helen Kennedy, W R Dunn and R McG Harden. *Programmed instruction – individual or group presentation of audio-visual programmes? Report on a preliminary investigation.*

Aspects V

T N Davis. *Level of aspiration measures and order-sequence effects in program presentation.*

Aspects VI

J W Hamer, Anne Howe and A J Romiszowski. *Changes in the pattern of programmed materials available commercially in Britain.*

Aspects VII

R Schwarzer. *Can mastery learning be realized by programmed instruction?*

Aspects IX

A Mackie. *Consumer-orientated programmed learning in adult education.*

Aspects XI

C M Bateson, P G J Lewis. *Programmed learning applied to: (a) solving a 'numeracy' problem in training, (b) a group situation.*
J Leedham. *An examination of developments in programmed learning since 1968: reflections on the UNESCO Conference, Tiblisi, USSR 1976.*

Aspects XII

J Leedham. *Progress with programmed learning 1968-78: the development of the Longman Group Reading Programme.*

George Stenhouse and John Womersley. *Are educational technologists sufficiently hardware-orientated?*

Aspects VII

T S Allan. *Educational selection of media with particular reference to ETV.*
D G Hawkridge. *Media taxonomies and media selection.*
J F Leedham. *The video cassette: some experiences and an estimate of its potential for education.*
M A Tribe and D Peacock. *The use of simulated exercises (games) in biological education at the tertiary level.*

Aspects VIII

T S Allan. *The relevance of instructional systems design to ETV programme production.*
J P Baggaley and S W Duck. *Communication effectiveness in the educational media: three experiments.*
A W Bates. *Obstacles to the effective use of communication media in a learning system.*
G O Coldevin. *The differential effects of voice-over, superimposition and combined review treatments as production strategies for ETV programming.*
R Houlton. *What is a medium?*
R J Howland, A J Midson and R Williams. *Videotapes in laboratory classes: developments in an integrated approach to physiology teaching.*
R W Jones. *Applications and limitations of radio in schools.*
H Marchant. *Communicating by instructional film: a presentation strategy.*
G D Moss, R Maskill and A Morgan. *Practical teaching, the media and the Open University*
Sir J Pitman. *The importance of medium in the generation and maintenance of motivation in the learning of English as a foreign language.*
E Williams. *The application of interactive telecommunications systems to education.*

Aspects IX

M J Coombs. *Television learning: in search of a workable theory.*
S El-Araby and J Gould. *Audio video compositions: a pilot experiment.*
J Leedham. *The imaginative uses of closed circuit television in the training of staff and managers.*
B Turok and J S Daniel. *New uses of the telephone in adult education.*

Aspects X

E Phillips. *Development of keyboard skills teaching machines.*

Aspects XI

J A Bellamy. *Investigation of new techniques for teaching and learning using laser holography.*
V H C Evers, N Hazewindus. *Electronic media and home-based learning.*
J C Matthew. *PIP – a tape-film system.*

Aspects XII

A D Becker. *A survey and evaluation of teleconferencing.*
C M Bird. *A comparison of the effectiveness of teaching: (1) in the traditional classroom situation and (2) by cine film.*
Lt Comdr B A Brooking. *Ten years of closed circuit television in the Royal*

Navy.

J S Daniel. *Satellites in education: experimenting for ever?*

P A I Davies, J F Jarvis, J G Kelly, D T Rees and K R Webber. *An integrated learning system for technician education.*

P Hurst. *Levels of use of educational broadcasting in Britain and West Africa: a study of rejection of an innovation.*

E G M Jenkins. *The use of video-tape recordings as an aid to teaching in an undergraduate course.*

G Murza. *Microfiche: a new medium for audiovisual instruction.*

C Y Oh. *Teaching a graphics course through programmed instruction.*

W D Robertson. *The use of a communications satellite and interactive colour television in simulation teaching of fire suppression skills.*

A G Stephens. *A facility for self-paced instruction using tape/slide programmes.*

A M Stewart. *Appropriate educational technology.*

J Winfield. *Social perception: designing mixed-media instruction in a polytechnic.*

Aspects XIII

V R Belsey and J Wellington. *Songs and slides in the teaching of English as a foreign language (Workshop).*

F X Moakley. *The television phoenix at San Francisco State University.*

L Pettman. *Establishing a CCTV system (Workshop).*

F J Webb, with E Hudson, N Cooper, J T Mills, G Corfield and J Clarke. *Better tape/slide programmes for the amateur (Workshop).*

Aspects XIV

J J Andriessen, D J Kroon and K H J Robers. *Educational experiments with the videodisc.*

B Barnes. *How real is real? Simulation in context.*

R E Burns and W I Davisson. *The use of filmstrips and records, and computer-aided instruction (Workshop).*

H I Ellington, F Percival and E Addinall. *The potential role of games and simulations in science education.*

L J Lawler. *Educational television: the present and the future.*

J S Stoane. *A technique for OHP/tape lesson packages.*

Aspects XV

C F A Bryce and A M Stewart. *Multi-media multi-purpose: is the quality of the learning experience being well served by the use of educational media?*

G Coldevin and R M Bernard. *Learning from television: effects of presenter delivery style.*

P Copeland. *The educational significance of electronic media.*

J R L Dent. *Educational films: and now for something completely different – the new educational video programme.*

A McIntyre and R H Richardson. *Inter college research project on school broadcasting.*

E A Stuhler and S Mizra. *A cross-cultural study of the teaching effectiveness of the case method versus the lecture method of teaching in lecture-orientated environments.*

R N Tucker. *Questions about the uncontrollable element in audio-visual communication.*

6. Computers in education

Aspects I

Dodd. *Experiments with machine-like teaching at the undergraduate and*

management level.
George. *The development of computer-assisted instruction and problems of programming.*
Stolurow. *A computer-assisted instructional system in theory and research.*

Aspects II

W R Brokerick. *An approach to computer-aided learning.*
N S M Cox. *Operational requirements for computer time-tabling systems for schools.*
N S M Cox and J M Smethurst. *The role of the computer in educational libraries.*
B Dodd. *Computerising the programmed tutorial: preliminary trials of a progressive part system.*
B Dodd and W Laidlaw. *The development of a computer-assisted adaptive information system at the Programmed Instruction Centre for Industry.*
W R Dunn and D McGregor. *Assistance from the computer in the management of learning.*
D R Griffiths. *Computer-assisted instruction and the training of technical teachers.*
J R Hartley and D H Sleeman. *Teaching and evaluation logics in a computer-assisted learning system.*
A Hickey. *CAI in the States: a status report.*
J R W Hill and P W W Cavanagh. *Some explorations of the use of the ERE as an aid to teaching reading to adults.*
G Huggett. *A computer-based course for teaching operation and fault-finding of a communications transceiver.*
I R Keith and S Summersbee. *Computer-assisted instruction – a practical approach.*
P Lambert. *Computers and the educational system.*
N L Lawrie. *School timetabling by computer.*
P N Maddison. *Devising and using a business management gaming and simulation exercise.*
G L Mallen. *Recent developments in the theory and practice of adaptive teaching systems.*
M Nelson. *A computer aproach to the problems of schools with two sites.*
E Rees. *The Linwood Experiment: an experiment in computer-assisted feedback technique.*
D H Sleeman and J R Hartley. *The design and some possible uses of a computer-assisted learning system.*
Miss M Steadman. *IBM system 1500.*
L Stolurow. *CAI: problems and perspectives.*

Aspects III

W R Dunn, R McG Harden, C Holroyd, R Lover and A Lindsay. *Investigation of self-instructional materials in medical education.*
J D Fox. *Computer assisted language learning: a report on work in progress at Leeds University.*
J Gilligan. *Computers and individual instruction.*
J W Hamer and A J Romiszowski. *A computer-managed individualised remedial mathematics course at undergraduate level.*
Y Le Corre, H Bestougeff and R Jacoud (delivered by B Simonot). *Computer assisted instruction at the Faculty of Sciences, Paris.*
J-D Nicoud. *Computer-aided validation of skip-branching programmes.*
E Rees. *A cybernetic system for the administration of programmed material.*
P Woods, J R Hartley, K Lovell and D H Sleeman. *The teaching of arithmetic using a computer based system.*

C A Hawkins. *A survey of the development, application and evaluation of computer-based learning in tertiary education in the UK, the USA, the Netherlands and Canada.*
M Leiblum. *Structuring computer-assisted learning in a university environment.*
D W McCulloch. *The CAIPE Project – aims, development and assessment; Computer-Aided Instruction Programs in economics at the Northern Ireland Polytechnic.*
H F Rahmlow. *Opportunities and pitfalls in computer-based education networks.*
C van der Mast. *A modular CAI system.*

Aspects XIII

T R Black. *Computer-managed learning in a postgraduate service course.*
C F A Bryce and A M Stewart. *The application of random-access back projection in computer-assisted instruction.*
H S Butcher. *Computer-Assisted Instruction (CAI) and programmed learning in British Airways.*
A Cooper and F Lockwood. *The need, provision and use of a computer-assisted interactive tutorial system.*
A Roebuck. *Computer-based training for office tasks (Workshop).*
K Shaw. *Some educational uses of computers in UK schools.*

Aspects XIV

M H Aston and D A Walton. *The Hertfordshire Microcomputer Managed Mathematics Project.*
J W Brahan and G M Boyd. *The economical production of adaptable learning activity packages for computer/video-based education and training.*
H Butcher. *Applying programmed learning techniques to Computer-Assisted Instruction (CAI), and the use of Computer-Managed Instruction (CMI).*
E Clavering. *Non-literary stylistics: computer help for the student as writer.*
W J K Davies and M Needham. *Application of educational technology methods to the design and retrieval of information data bases.*
S Fisher, P Messer and Q A Whitlock. *Authorship technique in computer-based instructional programmes (Workshop).*
J F Huntington. *Technological developments and domestic applications of computer-based education.*
G Marante. *Cognitive activities related to student learning through computers.*
D W McCulloch. *The economics of computer-assisted instruction in UK higher education: choices for the year 2000.*
P A Messer and Q A Whitlock. *Computer-based training: the programmer's Problem.*
J D S Moore, J A Hawrylack and M J Kitchin. *The potential role of computer-managed instruction and computer-assisted instruction in the Royal Navy – an experimental evaluation.*
J D S Moore, J A Hawrylack and M J Kitchin. *An experimental evaluation of the potential role of CMI and CAI in the Royal Navy (Workshop).*
R Morris. *Using computer-assisted training to learn how to locate faults.*
N J Rushby. *Strategies for the introduction of computer-based learning.*
A Taylor. *Computer-assisted learning: clinical simulations for nursing.*

Aspects XV

J Megarry, N Smart and C Tomasso. *Microcomputers and Scottish education.*
N J Rushby. *Computer-based learning: what will we teach the teachers? (Workshop).*
D Wright. *Computer-assisted training in practice.*

7. Evaluation and assessment

Aspects I

Blake. *A procedure for the initial evaluation and analysis of linear programmes.*

APL/NCPL

PCL Croxton and L H Martin. *Progressive evaluation and the control of programmed class in degree courses.*

Aspects III

M G Stythe. *A study into the evaluation of courses in programmed learning, using student attitudes as a criterion of success.*

Aspects V

A Bell, W E Bains, B Farrimond, J Graham, J Hedley, T P Kenyon and E Oliver. *Objective testing techniques within a scheme of continuous assessment.*
G M Mills. *Criteria for assessing the optimum efficiency of teaching programs.*

Aspects VI

Bertram Banks. *The Kent Mathematics project – mode 3 assessment procedure.*
A W Bates. *The evaluation of broadcasting at the Open University.*
D E Billing and J R Parsonage. *The evaluation of conferences as educational experiences.*
B Bolton. *A preliminary investigation into the effects of a curriculum on intellectual abilities.*
R J Britton and G O M Leith. *An experimental evaluation of the effects of microteaching on teaching performance.*
John Cowan. *Student reaction to the use of detailed objectives.*
Michael Eraut. *Strategies for the evaluation of curriculum materials.*
N D C Harris. *An experiment to evaluate a multi-media course in mathematics.*
G C Hyde. *Validation of 'A Seaman's guide to the rule of the road'.*
Kamal Yousef Iskander. *Effectiveness of learning in general science using programmed learning and the traditional method.*
G M Mills. *The case for an O & M investigation of University teaching.*
G A B Moore and Gilbert Taggart. *Testing oral production in the language laboratory.*
D V Moseley and D Sowter. *The Hansel training machine: a new aid to (over) learning.*

Aspects VII

B Connors. *Objective testing at a distance.*

Aspects VIII

C J Byrne. *Assessment systems and student learning.*

Aspects IX

P J Hills, Mrs L Lincoln and L P Turner. *The formative evaluation of tape/slide guides to library instruction.*

Aspects X

D J Boud, W A Bridge and D Laurillard. *Teacher learning – can evaluation*

improve individualised courses?
G C Muldowney. *Monitoring of individual student achievement by means of standardised score profiles.*

Aspects XI

T M Blithe and L C Johnston. *Evaluation of a Keller Plan innovation in mathematics teaching.*
M J Clark, B W Imrie, L C Johnston and W G Malcolm. *A strategy for evaluating university courses with reference to large first-year classes in pure mathematics.*
C R Coles. *Gains and losses in a guided self-study engineering course: towards a problem-solving approach.*
N D C Harris and S Kirkhope. *An evaluation of the use of self-instructional materials in the library.*
J Hartley and A Branthwaite. *Course-work assessment: computer-aided decision making.*
J D S Moore. *Systematic evaluation in a large training organization.*
K Vaughan. *Evaluation of chemical card games as learning aids.*

Aspects XII

E W Anderson. *Some low-budget assessment procedures.*

Aspects XIII

C A Hawkins. *The evaluation of educational projects and programmes (Workshop).*
D C Moors. *A model for evaluating educational programmes.*

Aspects XIV

P Ellis. *Reliable short answer questions.*
E E Green. *Evaluating industrial training.*
R M Harden, C Stoane, W R Dunn and T S Murray. *Learning at a distance: evaluation at a distance.*
N D C Harris and J G Bailey. *Technology and evaluation in the year 2000.*
N D C Harris and J G Bailey; comments by A Ashman. *Technology and evaluation in the year 2000 (Workshop).*
A R Morgan, G Gibbs and E Taylor. *The development of educational technology: alternative perspectives on evaluation.*
J Pearson. *Education for a working life: an evaluation of City and Guilds foundation.*
D Williams and K Adderley; comments by H S Mathias. *Evaluation of educational development projects: before, during and after! (Workshop).*
D Williams and J Pearce. *Evaluation of educational development projects: before, during and after!*

Aspects XV

L C Barber, K J Adderley and M Randall. *Integrating evaluation with the learning of cashiering skills! problems and procedures.*
T. Becher. *Keynote Address (The role of evaluation in educational technology).*
C D Bell. *Evaluation resources for teachers (Workshop).*
R M Bernard, C H Petersen and R D Brown. *Evaluation through the aperture: an analysis of mediated observational techniques.*
M Ferraris, V Midoro and G Olimpo. *Validation processes for instructional systems.*

Aspects VII

J Cowan, J Morton and E Bingham. *An intermediate assessment of a developing learning unit.*

Aspects X

E M Buter and W Koorn. *Media and the change of attitude of future teachers.*
J Clarke. *The implications of implementing change for an institution of higher education.*
C Neville and J Coffey. *How can attitudes be changed? How can tutors be trained?*

Aspects XI

G M Boyd. *Contribution and appraisal networking as an educational technology.*
E M Buter. *The great shift – a perspective on the change of system-resistance to the spread of educational technology.*
G O Coldevin. *Educational media implementation: strategies for initiating change in formal learning environments.*
W C Hall. *The roles of tertiary teaching units in Australian universities.*
E S Henderson and M B Nathenson. *Case study in the implementation of innovation: a new model for developmental testing.*
R Hooper. *The dissemination and assimilation of educational innovation.*
A Logan. *Willing horse, camel and committee – a description of innovation in a college of technology.*
C R McHugh and J R Parsonage. *Educational technology – persuading the teachers.*
P D Mitchell. *An epidemic model of the dissemination of educational technology.*
P Waterhouse. *Systems for classroom management.*
I J Winfield. *Staff resources and innovation – open learning for polytechnic teachers.*

Aspects XII

D G Hawkridge. *The propagation of educational innovations.*

Aspects XIII

K J Adderley, J Pearce, J Tait and D Williams. *Time off for innovation.*
A J Romiszowski. *The management of large-scale instructional technology projects (Workshop).*
J Scobbie and R McAleese. *Course planning teams: the roles of participants (Paper and workshop).*

9. Training of educational technologists

Aspects I

Roebuck. *The application of programmed learning techniques to the organization of courses, with particular reference to courses on programmed learning.*

Aspects IV

E M Buter. *Educational technology applied to courses in educational technology.*

Aspects V

P D Mitchell. *The professional development of educational technologists.*

10. Resource centres, distance and open learning

Aspects VIII

J Clarke. *A carrel system for an institution for higher education.*

Aspects IX

J Cowan. *Scale effect, and its relevance for resource-based learning.*

Aspects X

G Manwaring. *Self-instructional biology – a resource centre for individualised learning.*
A G M Tonkin, J Richardson. *The achievement of training objectives through resources.*

Aspects XI

D Butts and J Megarry. *Teaching educational technology at a distance.*

Aspects XII

A L Barker and E G Bingham. *Encouraging freedom in learning: implications for cataloguing and retrieval of resource materials.*
P J Hills. *Librarians' needs in relation to teaching and learning in higher education.*

Aspects XIII

D P Ely. *The dynamics of an information system for educational technology.*
D P Ely. *Using the ERIC system (Workshop).*
B Green. *Flexistudy – further education college-based distance learning with face-to-face tutorials (Workshop).*
B Holmberg. *Distance study in educational theory and practice.*
J Megarry. *Home environment and learning – educational technology at a distance (Paper and workshop).*
P Noble. *Providing environments for resource-based learning in colleges of further education.*

Aspects XIV

D Dicks and G Coldevin. *Emerging communications technology in Canada: the challenge to conventional educational systems.*
B Green. *Flexistudy: from pilot scheme to national network.*
P Noble. *Open systems for open colleges from 1980.*
J Twining and C Ward. *Distance learning for technicians.*
C Ward and J Twining. *Distance learning for TEC: pacing and aspects (Workshop).*
D T Wynne and R M Adamson. *Distance learning within a large organization.*

Aspects XV

D J Boud. *Independence and interdependence in distance education: responsive course design.*
M Brophy and B A C Dudley. *Evaluation of distance teaching: a criterion sampling approach.*
D Butts. *Distance learning and broadcasting (Keynote address).*
M Cameron, A Fields, S H Kennedy and G S C Wills. *A new development in distance teaching – the Cranfield management resource.*
L R B Elton. *Academic staff development through distance learning.*

W Fyfe. *The production and evaluation of materials for a distance learning course.*
B Green and P Noble. *Deisgning evaluation of flexistudy (Workshop).*
C S Hannabuss. *The impact of independent and open learning on UK libraries since 1970.*
B Holmberg. *A typology of university distance education.*
A C Jones and T O'Shea. *Evaluation methods in distance computer-assisted learning.*
P D Mitchell. *Evaluating alternative strategies for allocating limited resources to develop a tele-education system.*
P Noble and B Green. *Designing evaluation of flexistudy.*
E Scanlon. *Evaluating the effectiveness of distance learning: a case study.*
J S Stoane, D Mayho and C Stoane. *Answers at a distance (Workshop).*
C Stoane and J S Stoane. *Answers at a distance.*
J Twining. *Distance learning for technicians.*
R S Zimmer. *The relational glossary: a tool for effective distance learning.*

11. Lifelong education

Aspects IX

E W Anderson. *Life-long objectives in a college of education.*
G M Boyd. *The importance and feasibility of 'transparent' universities.*
M Braham. *The idea of continuous education.*
L R B Elton. *Mature students – OU and non-OU.*
L F Evans. *Unconventional aspects of educational technology in an adult education programme.*
N C Farnes, R McCormick and J A Calder. *A proposed system for mass continuing education.*
G Hubbard. *Keynote address: perspectives for life-long education.*
S M Kay, S O'Connell and S Penton. *A teaching laboratory for continuing education.*

Aspects XIV

W D Clarke and M Devine. *Educational technology applied to retirement education.*
M Kirchmayer. *Does adult education need specifically designed textbooks, teaching strategies and materials?*
A Kirkwood. *Who's continuing education?*

12. The teacher and the learning process

APL/NCPL

C Buckle. *Relations between attainment of component skills, retention, and transfer.*
P Hodge. *A proposed model for investigating the instructional process: the relationship between learning theory and educational practice.*
G O M Leith. *The place of demonstration in teaching practical and verbal skills.*

Aspects II

K H Flechsig and K Heipcke. *Didacometric model-building and its relevance to the interpretation of instructional outcomes.*
H P R Hodge. *A systems approach to education: cyclical systems in teaching.*

Aspects III

G C Boyce and M E Sime. *The variable of 'attention', and its effects on learning.*
Address from Professor B F Skinner. *Contingency management in the classroom.*

Aspects IV

V Kulic. *The psychological interpretation of the concept of feedback in learning and problem solving.*

Aspects V

K Bung. *Abstract automata as models of verbal behaviour.*

Aspects VII

D D Pratt. *Understanding selective perception: a key to providing readiness for learning.*

Aspects VIII

P D Mitchell. *The ubiquity of positive feedback in educational cybernetics.*
D Rowntree. *Two styles of communication and their implications for learning.*

Aspects IX

S Gilmore. *Some aspects of 'modelling' in the microteaching context.*

Aspects XII

C R Coles and W G Fleming. *Understanding learning: a case study in student and staff development.*
R A Sutton. *Identification of educational needs: diagnostic testing.*
D M Wharry. *Analysing lecture styles.*

Aspects XIV

E S Harri-Augstein, R Beard and G Crosby; comments by A R Wiliam. *Learning-to-learn by reading (Workshop).*
P Lefrere, J Dowie and P Whalley. *Educating for justified uncertainty.*
G D Moss. *Why do we not teach students to solve problems?*
C Stoane. *Educational technology in the affective zone: is it possible?*
L F Thomas and E S Harri-Augstein. *Learning-to-learn by reading: towards a conversational technology.*
L F Thomas and E S Harri-Augstein. *Construct, reflect, converse and act (Workshop).*

Aspects XV

B Alloway. *Reappraisal of graphical learning techniques (Workshop).*

13. Individual factors and learning

Aspects I

Davis and Leith. *Some determinants of attitude and achievement in a programmed learning task.*

Aspects II

D Evans, R E Ripple and D Treffinger. *Programmed instruction and productive thinking: a preliminary report of a cross-national comparison.*
G O M Leith. *Learning and personality.*
B Wilcox. *Creativity and programmed learning: a pilot study.*

Aspects III

C K Basu, P Cavanagh and C Jones. *A comparison of the difficulties and distastes of students studying programmes in a correspondence and in a classroom situation.*
T N Davis and C E Wilkins. *Convergent and divergent thinkers in the programmed learning situation.*
A F Greer. *Personality and programmed learning.*

Aspects IV

P Cavanagh and C Jones. *Ability and its relationship to achievement.*

Aspects V

Sheila M Firmin and C C Webb. *Pacing schedules, personality type and learning performance.*

Aspects X

E U Heidt. *Media and the individual learner: trait-treatment interaction and the concept of supplantation.*

Aspects XI

J Cowan. *Individual approaches to problem-solving.*

14. Applications in schools

Aspects I

Austin. *Future development of programmed learning in schools.*
Beard. *Programmed reading – experimental work with the slow learner.*
Clarke. *The development and use of linear programmed instruction in a rural primary school.*
Greenwood and Widlake. *A language scheme for teaching English to immigrants.*
Kemp. *Innovations in the assessment of programmed instruction.*
Leedham. *A summary of research and development with programmes and machines in Leicestershire since 1960.*
Milan and Bernath. *The use of programmed learning in grammar for 11-year-old pupils.*
Noble. *An experimental attempt to integrate programmed instruction with classroom instruction.*
Thornhill. *What future has programmed learning in British schools?*
Worthy. *Punchboards and linear programmes in grammar school biology teaching.*

APL/NCPL

D Austin, C Mortimer and P Swallow. *The Ovenden Project.*
B Banks. *School experiments in the use of programmed tapes.*
N Beard. *Initial programme writing techniques for primary age and the slow learner.*
J Clarke. *The use of programme systems in the development of the integrated day in a primary school.*
J J G Clarke and D I Colwell. *The Westlain Project.*
J Hamer. *Programmed learning in schools.*
P J Hills. *The use of programmed learning in the attainment of objectives connected with modern chemistry courses in schools.*
B Wilcox. *Some promising applications of programmed learning to the teaching of science.*

Aspects II

B Banks. *An experimental auto-instructional course in mathematics.*
F Butler and P Cavanagh. *The role of the teacher in theory and practice in classroom programmed instruction.*
J Clarke. *The use of programmed systems in the development of the integrated day in the primary school.*
G Della-Piana and M Hogben. *Research strategies for maximising the effectiveness of programmed reading.*
R Eikeboom. *The application in a programmed Latin grammar of some data from learning psychology.*
K Payne. *Social factors in the classroom.*
H Schuffenhauer. *A complex experiment in the application of book programmes in the general schools of the German Democratic Republic.*

Aspects III

B Banks. *An experimental auto-instructional course in mathematics.*
J Clarke. *A systems approach to aspects of primary education.*
T Draisma. *Programmed learning for the isolated teacher.*
J Huskisson, D Packham and A Cleary. *Pre-reading experiments with the Touch-Tutor.*
C K Kefford. *A multi-media approach to environmental studies in the primary school.*
J Leedham. *The use of programmed closed circuit television at Loughborough.*
A P Mann and M B Broadley. *An integrated teaching unit.*
D J Reid and P Booth. *The work of the Nuffield Individual Learning Project in elementary biology.*
J Waller, M Tobin and L Biran. *An investigation into the use of audio visual programming in the primary school.*

Aspects IV

P S Adey. *Programmed learning and modern science education in Barbados.*
E Glynn, J P Pearce and A S Willott. *A simple mobile feedback classroom.*
A Mackie. *Visual explanation and the role of understanding in motivating children to learn.*
M Roebuck. *Factors influencing the success of programmed materials in under-equipped classrooms and inadequately staffed schools.*

Aspects V

P J Gayfer. *The extended use of programmed texts in preparing students for external examinations.*
J Gilligan, W Hazelton and W Kaye. *The Ridgewaye School Computer-Managed Instruction System.*
M E O Hughes. *A teaching method for school mathematics.*
Marian Liebmann, A Mackie and C Glover. *Writing programs for unstreamed classes.*
A Magnhagen. *Making local audio-visual software.*
Josephine S Maguire. *Systematic concept teaching to pre-readers.*
J S Nichol. *Programmed learning in the primary school.*
E Rees. *Model making for the analysis of teaching situations.*
M Roebuck and J McCormick. *Programmed materials as an adjunct to radio broadcasts.*
R E Ulrich, G J Alessi and M Wolfe. *The Learning Village: an alternate approach to traditional education.*

Aspects VI

W J K Davies and Marjorie Needham. *Learning systems techniques applied to a large-scale educational problem.*
C Reynolds. *Individual learning in schools. A course for GCE 'O' level chemistry.*
J D Tinsley. *Syllabuses and methods for computer education in schools.*
B W Vaughan. *The application of the operational research technique of network analysis to primary mathematics.*

Aspects VIII

J Leedham. *The development of a programmed reading system for primary education.*

Aspects X

K F Grace. *Individualised learning in science.*

Aspects XI

H I Ellington, N H Langton and M Smythe. *The use of simulation games in schools – a case study.*
J K Gilbert. *The Nuffield 'Working with Science' Project and its evaluation.*
E E Green and O O McKay. *Scientific discovery at the elementary level.*
E Hunter. *Language games for reading progress.*
M Needham, W J K Davies and S Leevers. *Individualized learning centres: a pragmatic approach to the development of a cost-effective and flexible way to provide remedial help.*

Aspects XIII

B Banks, A J Larcombe and A Tourret. *The development of the Kent Mathematics Project (Paper and workshop).*
D W Daly. *Can Keller Plan work in schools?*
N D C Harris and P J Watts. *Evaluation of the Schools Council Avon/Bath University Modular Courses in Technology Project (Paper and workshop).*

Aspects XIV

B Banks. *Kent mathematics project in the future.*
C H Bedwell. *The application of technology to aid the investigation and remediation of the under-achieving child.*

Aspects XV

R M Bottino. *Programmable pocket calculators as didactic aids in Italian upper secondary schools.*
C D J Waters and N L Lawrie. *Use of television equipment in Scottish secondary schools.*

15. Applications in special education and with the handicapped

Aspects I

Meredith. *Principles and methods of analytical programming with special reference to the remedial treatment of dyslexia.*

Aspects II

M Freedman. *The application of programmed learning to blind children (Abstract*

only).
Vera Wanless. *Programmed learning and maladjusted children.*

Aspects V

C C Cunningham. *The development of software for handicapped children.*
W J K Davies and M Needham. *Programmed assessment of learning difficulties in sub-normal and normal children.*
H P R Hodge and L D Bain. *Problems and procedures in the development of structured materials for special schools.*
D V Moseley. *A remedial program for severely subnormal pupils with and without the talking typewriter.*
D A Thompson. *Multiple-choice teaching machines and multiply-handicapped children.*

Aspects X

F McKee. *Audio-visual social education material for use in Glasgow with mentally handicapped pupils of secondary age.*

Aspects XIV

C Stoane. *Educational technology in special education.*

Aspects XV

M J Cox. *A trial course in basic programming and mathematics using CAL for a group of maladjusted boys.*
R Phillips and J Stirling Phillips. *A method for teaching the deaf to read and write.*

16. Applications in tertiary education (including teacher training)

Aspects I

Hogg. *The use of programmed learning with second-year university students.*
Unwin and Spencer. *The use of programmed instruction for revision purposes with technological undergraduates.*

APL/NCPL

T Davis. *Programmed learning and the student teacher.*
G M Mills. *Undergraduate attitudes to programmed learning.*

Aspects II

C K Basu, P Cavanagh and C Jones. *A comparative study of the use of programmed modern mathematics in correspondence and classroom situations.*
A W Davidson and H V Swann. *'Principles of valuation' – the introduction of programmed instruction into a correspondence course.*
J Goodwin. *Curriculum presentation at the technical level in forestry.*
G H K Hewlett. *Programmed learning in electrical engineering degree courses.*
D E Hoare and Maureen M Revans. *Achievement of educational objectives by programmed learning.*
E Stones. *An experiment in the use of programmed learning in a university with an examination of student attitudes and the place of seminar discussion.*
K A Stroud. *The development, organisation and administration of programmed learning at undergraduate level.*

Michael Tribe. *Designing an introductory programmed course in biology for undergraduates.*
T G Wyant. *Learner controlled self instruction.*

Aspects VII

D C B Teather, K Hardwick and J C Collins. *A case study of the development and use of teaching programmes in life science undergraduate courses.*

Aspects VIII

L R B Elton. *An analysis of aims of self-instructional methods in undergraduate science courses.*
J Morton, E Bingham and J Cowan. *A free format engineering course based on pre-recorded learning material.*

Aspects IX

P J Hills. *Self-teaching in university courses.*

Aspects X

E G Bingham. *Skills for the occasion.*
J A Bowden. *Independent learning of laboratory techniques.*
M G Cornwall. *Student-directed project-centred study: an approach to the truly individualised curriculum.*
D W Daly and W R Dunn. *An alternative approach to learning in undergraduate mathematics.*
L R B Elton and V Hodgson. *Individualised learning and study advice.*
F Morgan. *'One by one together' – a study of the individualisation of learning in a college of advanced education in Australia.*
G Wilkinson. *Towards an effective utilisation of learning packages in institutes of higher education.*

Aspects XI

E G Bingham. *Free format timetabling revisited.*
B C Fisher. *Teaching developments in a first-year mechanical engineering course.*
N Fjällbrant. *The need for library user orientation and the design and development of material and methods to meet this need.*
E E Green and S H B Christensen. *Introductory statistics: a simplified approach.*
C Kasipar, S Thaitrong and T G Wyant. *Practice teaching and teacher training at the Thai-German Technical Teacher College, King Mongkut's Institute of Technology, Bangkok, Thailand.*
W E McCavitt. *A study of some results of an educational media course within a teacher preparation program.*
R Wild and E McQuade. *A case study in the design and evaluation of a Unit on Waveform Analysis.*

Aspects XIII

E E Green. *Making large group instruction effective: a case study.*
P J Hills and R B Moyes. *The learning environment in chemistry: the contribution of the Educational Techniques Subject Group of the Chemical Society.*
R J McDonald. *Teaching adults in higher education (Workshop).*
W P Race. *An objective approach to teaching physical chemistry.*
P Scholl. *Mediated self-instruction: its history and continuing development at the University of Connecticut.*
A Wood. *A modular system of self-instruction in educational technology within a course of teacher training.*

Aspects XIV

B Alloway. *Criteria for the design of educational technology courses.*
D M Beach. *Utilizing educational technology in teacher training: preliminary implications.*
C Bird. *The structure of educational technology courses for student teachers in further and higher education.*
B Hollinshead; coments by K Adderley. *Learning materials for in-service training (Workshop).*
D Kozlowski and L Brillhart. *Media applications at an Illinois community college.*
M A Lezer. *Learning by tram.*
N Lougher. *The technology of teaching: art or science?*
R McAleese. *The impact of technology on higher education.*

Aspects XV

C Neville and R F Windsor. *The role of the educational technologist in the in-service training of teachers in the new micro-electronics-based technologies.*
W P Racc. *'Help yourself to success' – improving polytechnic students' study skills.*

17. Applications in the armed forces, vocational and industrial training

Aspects I

Jeffels. *Programmed techniques and their use in apprentice training.*
McGaulley. *Mathetics in industrial and vocational training.*
Normington, Babb, Jowett and Holroyd. *Programmed learning in local government. The large-scale use of programmed learning in the West Riding Fire Service.*
Pollock. *The preparation of a programme to train boiler operators.*
Stavert. *Programmed instruction in the Royal Naval Electrical School.*

APL/NCPL

R Amswych. *An investigation into the use of tape-recorded programs for craft training.*
P Cavanagh and C Jones. *An evaluation of the contribution of a programme of self-instruction to management training.*
B Dodd. *The correctable systems approach applied to re-training of steel-making teams.*
C Hall and R Fletcher. *A new training course for GPO telephonists.*
K Holme and D Mabbs. *Programmed learning – an expanding discipline (some case studies).*
J Horton and C Holt. *Programmed methods of arithmetic revision in a Naval new entry training establishment.*
A Knight. *The writing and validation of a complete electronics course.*
A Romiszowski. *A survey of the use of programmed learning in industry during 1966.*
H Stancliffe and D Hilton. *Some developments in programmed learning in the Army.*
G Stavert. *Human factors in programmed instruction.*

Aspects II

P J Edney. *Design and production of a systems approach to clerical training.*
B D Hilton. *Development of a diagnostic test to enable maximum use to be made of an available mathematics programme at the Army School of Education.*

A Jeffels. *Engineering apprentice training: programmed learning integrated with skill development.*
T O Jones. *Iron and steel industry: programmed learning with junior operatives.*
D Kitchen. *Office training in BEA: transfer of verbal learning to performance.*
A Malach. *Programmed learning, teaching machines and driver education.*
G Mellis and W R Dunn. *Shipbuilding industry: programmed learning at Fairfields (Glasgow) Ltd.*
A Romiszowski. *The use of programmed learning in industry.*
G S Stavert, R E B Budgett and J D S Moore. *The construction and testing of a programme in elementary English for the Royal Navy.*
C A Thomas. *Six years of programmed learning in the RAF.*

Aspects III

J E Beck. *A survey of the problems encountered by a number of industrial and commercial users of programmed instruction.*
R E Budgett and J D S Moore. *Audio-programming for marine engineering training in the Royal Navy.*
P N Cullingford. *Cross-conceptual teaching techniques as applied to trainees on Zambia Railways.*
J M Foy and G D H Leach. *8mm film loops as aids to productivity.*
A H Gibson and S L Morse. *Application of instruction technology to the training of personnel in the Canadian Armed Forces.*
D Kitchen. *Programmed instruction in management training.*
A Peters, F J A Voets and J Clark. *Programmed instruction as a tool for promotion.*
J M Pollock. *Training estimating engineers.*
J M Ventosa. Potential applications, customers and uses of programmed instruction courses, in industry and business.

Aspects IV

D W Clary. *Initial feasibility trials into the cost-effective uses of CCTV in Army training.*
I K Davies. *Change and innovation: a model for modifying the organisation of teaching and learning.*
B Dodd and H Hudson. *An application of the Sheffield System of Programming to traditional skill training.*
C W Dunnett *Audio-visual training aids for sonar operators.*
P G C Everett. *A programmed audio-visual typing course.*
A J T Green. *Programmed learning in the heavy chemical industry: operator training.*
H D Main. *The illustrated teaching program.*
S L Morse. *Educational technology and the behavioural objective.*
F Soukup. *Teaching machines and language teaching.*
T Spencer. *An experimental investigation into the effectiveness of CCTV as a medium for teaching weapon training.*
B Stejskal. *On classification of programmes presented by teaching machines and computers.*
B Stejskal, T Gottheiner and F Soukup. *Teaching conversation on a teaching machine.*
B Whitehead and E Williams. *Programmed learning – a technique of application.*

Aspects V

A Bano. *The role of programmed learning in industrial training.*
E M Buter. *The Austrian Ski-School: a near perfect model for educational technologists.*

training package.
E J Pritchard. *The application of educational technology for in-factory training in the printing and packaging industries.*

Aspects XII

J R S Bulford, A R G Tallis and P W J Howard. *Some applications of educational technology in agricultural training.*
C H Mason. *Utilization of the programmed learning technique in management development.*
J M Moffatt. *MAVIS: a case history of educational technology in industry.*
D M Tyrrell. *Design of package training materials for accountancy firms.*
K H Westley. *Programmed learning in the footwear industry.*

Aspects XIII

R M Adamson. *A systematic approach to the future of educational technology (Workshop).*
P J Edney. *A technology for job mobility through training and education (Workshop).*
Maj J R J Goose and Maj P T Nolan. *Twenty years on – the development of instructional technology in the British Army.*
D R F Hammond and P L Wilson. *Use of an optical mark reader in Army selection.*
S N Marson. *Programmed instruction – promise, propagation and progress.*
F X Moakley. *The American Military Educational Technology Complex: focus, research and development.*
Lt Cdr J D S Moore and Lt Cdr M J Kitchin. *An evaluation of the Royal Navy training system and implications for future development.*
P R Symes. *From panacea programme to peripatetic package.*
I Townsend. *Come into my parlour, said the spider...*

Aspects XIV

R Brown, J R Foster, B T Lusher, F Shaw and S Ward. *The higher education industrial training interface: panel session.*
E T Brueck and S T McKay; comments by J R S Bulford. *Future development of in-company training packages (Workshop).*
J E Hills. *Educational technology helps the unemployed.*
B J Hurn, B D Hilton, M Easby, B Drinkall and N J Rushby. *Innovation in military training: panel session.*
M A Lezer and W Veugelers; comments by J Pearson. *The Work-Experience Project in Holland (AEL-Project) (Workshop).*
D C Moors and K L Ozman. *Work samples as aids to vocational counselling.*
P J Phillips. *Training technology in the army in the 1980s.*

Aspects XV

P W J Howard. *Use of structural communication with film for the training of agricultural skills.*

18. Applications in medical health education

Aspects I

Kind. *The use of programmed learning in health education.*

Aspects II

D C Coull, A J M Fraser, H P R Hodge, R D Weir and J Crooks. *The*

J Gale, B C Jolly and M Devine. *Choice and design of an individual learning package: audiotape and booklet.*
V Graves. *Tape/slide in individual learning for medical topics.*
C Heath. *Individualising and updating in the pharmacology teaching laboratory.*
R W Kind, J Leedham and H Robson. *Patient counselling and the general practitioner.*
G Lloyd. *Learning to care for patients through audit of the medical record.*
L Lodewick, R Lulofs and H Schmidt. *An individualised learning system for interviewing techniques.*
S Marson and I Townsend. *Individualised learning in nurse education – past, present and future.*
T L Pilkington. *Filmstrip/tape programme for continuing in-service training in long-stay hospitals.*

Aspects XI

C R Coles. *Course designing: some suggestions following observations of undergraduate medical courses.*
C Evans and H C Price. *The doctor/patient interaction or consultation – can the computer assist in this dialogue?*
E E Green. *The development of self-instructing materials for diagnostic radiology.*
G D Moss, D K Roach and R Hammond. *The evaluation of a self-instructional zoology course.*
E D Prentice, W K Metcalf and N F Metcalf. *Development and evaluation of individual learning systems in the anatomical sciences.*
I Townsend and J Heath. *Is educational technology infectious?*

Aspects XII

C R Coles and B Mountford. *Relevance in medical education: an evaluation of students' introduction to clinical medicine.*
P Fieldhouse and M Shaw. *Applications of educational technology to dietetic education.*
P M J Hancock. *Training family planning field-workers by behaviour modelling.*
A Taylor. *Simulation in health education.*
A C L Zelmer and A E Zelmer. *Applications of educational technology for community health workers in developing countries.*

Aspects XIV

V Sistek and J Harrison. *A use of audio-visual methods in anatomical instruction.*

19. Applications in other specific subjects

Aspects I

Gaines. *Teaching machines for perceptual-motor skills.*
Gardner. *Programming the ability to recognize complex 'meaningful' noises.*
Gedye. *A teaching machine programme for use as a test of learning ability.*

APL/NCPL

K Bung. *Problems of task analysis for language programming.*
A P R Howatt. *The cyclical principle in foreign language programming.*
G Hubert-White. *Programmed instruction for physical training.*
R B Moyes. *An organisation for programmed learning in chemistry.*
P Widlake. *A taxonomy of objectives for reading programmes.*

Aspects XV

W P Race and R Vaughan-Williams. *'Graph-it' – a package for teaching graphical skills.*

20. Applications overseas and the transfer of educational technology

Aspects I

Rademacker. *Programmed instruction in Germany.*
Edwards. *Programmed learning in the Soviet Bloc countries.*

APL/NCPL

K A Keil. *An inquiry in Bavaria concerning programmed learning.*
D Müller. *Five stages of development of programmed instruction in Germany – a critical review.*

Aspects II

Brigitte A Rollett. *Developments in programmed instruction: proceedings of the VIth International Symposium on Programmed Instruction and Teaching Machines – Munich, March 1968.*
J K Bunyard. *The use of programmed learning in the Northern States of Nigeria.*
D G Hawkridge. *Programmed learning and problems of acculturation in Africa.*
D D Müller. *The present situation of programmed instruction in the Federal Republic of Germany with special consideration of existing programmes.*

Aspects IV

Luciana Fontanà. *The employment of programmed learning in Italy.*

Aspects V

S El-Araby. *Operating language laboratories in a developing country.*

Aspects VI

R D Bell. *Planning of technical courses for agriculture in the Northern States of Nigeria.*

Aspects VII

P J Conradie. *The trend and extent of educational technology in South Africa.*
S El-Araby. *British and American intelligibility for non-native students of English: a language laboratory experiment.*
T A Ilyina. *The development of the research work on programmed instruction in the USSR.*

Aspects VIII

A Hancock. *Communication and learning: applications to the development process.*
G H Jamieson. *Instructional innovation: a field study in functional literacy.*

Aspects IX

G O Coldevin. *The mass media with particular reference to television as an instrument of continuous education among Canadian Eskimos.*

ERIC: The Educational Resources Information Center

ERIC (Educational Resources Information Center)
National Institute of Education *(Central ERIC)*, Dissemination and Improvement of Practice Program, 1200 19th Street NW, Washington DC, 20208

ERIC stands for the Educational Resources Information Center, an information system in existence since 1966 and currently sponsored by the National Institute of Education, within the US Department of Education. Its function is to provide users with ready access primarily to the English language literature, both published and unpublished, dealing with education.

The organization of ERIC consists of a central government office (establishing policy, funding, and monitoring the entire system), and 16 Clearinghouses, each responsible within the network for acquiring significant educational literature within a particular subject area for analysis and processing (cataloguing, indexing and abstracting). Resulting information is fed into the ERIC system, which comprises: a central editorial and computer facility, which maintains the whole ERIC database and prepares the abstract journal *Resources in Education (RIE)* and other products; a central *ERIC Document Reproduction Service (EDRS)*, which prepares microfiches and can also provide a copying service for the great bulk of documents and journal articles announced in *RIE* and the *Current Index to Journals in Education (CIJE)*; and a commercial publisher who produces *CIJE*, the ERIC *Thesaurus*, and other ERIC publications.

In conjunction with these three main activities, ERIC also offers computer on-line retrieval and search services into its bibliographic database; the purchase of computer-compatible magnetic tapes of this database; information analysis products (research reviews, knowledge syntheses, and state-of-the-art studies); and question-answering services.

The exact number of Clearinghouses has fluctuated over time in response to the shifting needs of the educational community — there are currently sixteen. These are listed below, together with full addresses, and brief scope notes describing the areas they cover.

ERIC Clearinghouse on Adult, Career, and Vocational Education
Ohio State University, Center for Vocational Education, 1960 Kenny Road, Columbus, Ohio 43210
Career education, formal and informal at all levels, encompassing attitudes, self-knowledge, decision-making skills, general and occupational

knowledge, and specific vocational and occupational skills; adult and continuing education, formal and informal, relating to occupational, family, leisure, citizen, organizational, and retirement roles; vocational and technical education, including new sub-professional fields, industrial arts, and vocational rehabilitation for the handicapped.

ERIC Clearinghouse on Counselling and Personnel Services
University of Michigan, School of Education Building, Room 2108, Ann Arbor, Michigan 48109
Preparation, practice, and supervision of counsellors at all educational levels and in all settings; theoretical development of counselling and guidance; use and results of personnel procedures such as testing, interviewing, disseminating, and analysing such information; group work and case work; nature of pupil, student, and adult characteristics; personnel workers and their relation to career planning, family consultations, and student orientation activities.

ERIC Clearinghouse on Elementary and Early Childhood Education
University of Illinois, College of Education, Urbana, Illinois 61801
Pre-natal factors, parental behaviour; the physical, psychological, social, educational, and cultural development of children from birth through the primary grades; educational theory, research, and practice related to the development of young children.

ERIC Clearinghouse on Educational Management
University of Oregon, Eugene, Oregon 97403
Leadership, management, and structure of public and private educational organization; practice and theory of administration; pre-service and in-service preparation of administrators, tasks, and processes of administration; methods and varieties of organization, organizational change, and social context of the organization. Sites, buildings, and equipment for education; planning, financing, constructing, renovating, equipping, maintaining, operating, insuring, using, and evaluating educational facilities.

ERIC Clearinghouse on Handicapped and Gifted Children
Council for Exceptional Children, 1920 Association Drive, Reston, Virginia 22091
Aurally handicapped, visually handicapped, mentally handicapped, physically handicapped, emotionally disturbed, speech handicapped, learning disabilities, and the gifted; behavioural, psychomotor, and communication disorders, administration of special education services; preparation and continuing education of professional and para-professional personnel; pre-school learning and development of the exceptional; general studies on creativity.

ERIC Clearinghouse on Higher Education
George Washington University, One Dupont Circle, Suite 630, Washington, DC 20036
Various subjects relating to college and university students, college and university conditions and problems, college and university programmes. Curricular and instructional problems and programmes, faculty, institutional research. Federal programmes, professional education (medical, law, etc), graduate education, university extension programmes, teaching-learning, planning, governing, finance, evaluation, inter-institutional arrangements, and management of higher educational institutions.

ERIC Clearinghouse on Information Resources
Syracuse University, School of Education, 130 Huntington Hall, Syracuse, New York 13210
Materials dealing with the management and dissemination of information in the fields of education, library science, and information science; research, development, delivery, and evaluation of information and instructional technology; personnel, personnel development, strategies, systems, procedures, materials, and equipment used in these areas. Included are the following specific topics: libraries, learning resource centers, information science, instructional design, development and evaluation, systems analysis, community information systems, instructional media, information transfer, mastery learning, simulation and gaming, programmed instruction, individualized instruction, and information brokering. The Clearinghouse is also concerned with the delivery of information and instruction through media: television, computers, radio, films, microforms, holography, and other audiovisual devices.

ERIC Clearinghouse for Junior Colleges
University of California, Powell Library, Room 96, 405 Hilgard Avenue, Los Angeles, California 90024
Development administration, and evaluation of public and private community junior colleges. Junior college students, staff, curricula, programmes, libraries, and community services.

ERIC Clearinghouse on Languages and Linguistics
Center for Applied Linguistics, 3520 Prospect Street NW, Washington DC 20007
Languages and linguistics, instructional methodology, psychology of language learning, cultural and inter-cultural content, application of linguistics, curricular problems and developments, teacher training and qualifications, language sciences, psycho-linguistics, theoretical and applied linguistics, language pedagogy, bi-lingualism, and commonly taught languages including English for speakers of other languages.

ERIC Clearinghouse on Reading and Communication Skills
National Council of Teachers of English, 1111 Kenyon Road, Urbana,
Illinois 61801
Reading, English, and communication skills, pre-school through college.
Educational research and development in reading, writing, speaking, and
listening. Identification, diagnosis, and remediation of reading problems.
Speech communication — forensics, mass communication, interpersonal
and small group interaction, interpretation, rhetorical and
communication theory, instruction development, speech sciences, and
theatre. Preparation of instructional staff and related personnel in these
areas. All aspects of reading behaviour with emphasis on physiology,
psychology, sociology, and teaching. Instructional materials, curricula,
tests and measurement, preparation of reading teachers and specialists,
and methodology at all levels. Role of libraries and other agencies in
fostering and guiding reading. Diagnostic and remedial services in school
and clinical settings.

ERIC Clearinghouse on Rural Education and Small Schools
New Mexico State University, Box 3AP, Las Cruces, New Mexico
88003
Education of Indian Americans, Mexican Americans, Spanish Americans,
and migratory farm workers and their children; outdoor education;
economic, cultural, social, or other factors related to educational
programmes in rural areas and small schools; disadvantaged of rural and
small school populations.

**ERIC Clearinghouse for Science, Mathematics, and Environmental
Education**
Ohio State University, 1200 Chambers Road, Third Floor, Columbus,
Ohio 43212
All levels of science, mathematics, and environmental education;
development of curriculum and instructional materials; media application;
impact of interest, intelligence, values, and concept development upon
learning; pre-service and in-service teacher education and supervision.

ERIC Clearinghouse for Social Studies/Social Science Education
855 Broadway, Boulder, Colorado 80302
All levels of social studies and social science; all activities relating to
teachers; content of disciplines; applications of learning theory,
curriculum theory, child development theory, and instructional theory;
research and development programmes; special needs of student groups;
education as a social science; social studies/social science and the
community.

ERIC Clearinghouse on Teacher Education
American Association of Colleges for Teacher Education, One Dupont
Circle, NW, Suite 616, Washington, DC 20036
School personnel at all levels; all issues from selection through pre-service

and in-service preparation and training to retirement; curricula; educational
theory and philosophy; general education not specifically covered by
Educational Management Clearinghouse; Title XI NDEA Institutes not
covered by subject speciality in other ERIC Clearinghouses; all aspects of
physical education.

ERIC Clearinghouse on Tests, Measurement, and Evaluation
Educational Testing Service, Princeton, New Jersey 08540
Tests and other measurement devices; evaluation procedures and
techniques; application of tests, measurement, or evaluation in educational
projects or programmes.

ERIC Clearinghouse on Urban Education
Box 40, Teachers College, Columbia University, 525 W 120th Street,
New York, New York 10027
The relationship between urban life and schooling; the effect of urban
experiences and environments from birth onward; the academic,
intellectual, and social performance of urban children and youth from
grade three through college entrance (including the effect of self-concept,
motivation, and other affective influences); education of urban, Puerto
Rican and Asian American populations, and rural and urban black
populations; programmes and practices which provide learning experiences
designed to meet the special needs of diverse populations served by urban
schools and which build upon their unique as well as their common
characteristics; structural changes in the classroom, school, school system,
and community and innovative instructional practices which directly affect
urban children and youth; programmes, practices, and materials related to
economic and ethnic discrimination, segregation, desegregation, and
integration in education; issues, programmes, practices, and materials
related to redressing the curriculum imbalance in the treatment of ethnic
minority groups.

Other network components

Mr Robert Chesley, Head, **Educational Resources Information Center**
(Central ERIC), National Institute of Education, Washington, DC 20208

ERIC Processing & Reference Facility
4833 Rugby Avenue, Suite 303, Bethesda, Maryland 20014

ERIC Document Reproduction Service
PO Box 190, Arlington, Virginia 22210

Oryx Press (commercial contractor for *CIJE* publication)
2214 North Central Avenue, Encanto, Phoenix, Arizona 85004

The Network of Programmed Learning Centres

Chairman: N E Allen, Engineering Industry Training Board, 9 Park Road, Barnstone, Nottingham NG13 9JF

Secretary: B S Alloway, Educational Technology Centre, The Polytechnic, Huddersfield HD3 3BP

The Network is an organization of bodies working in the field of programmed learning and educational technology — educational technology defined as technology of education, rather than simply the use of audiovisual media. It is an autonomous body working in collaboration with other organizations wherever possible, and has close links with AETT (formerly APLET).

Aims of the network
To provide constant interchange of information and ideas among its members, through its organizations and by means of regular meetings.
To encourage the evaluation of pre-structured material and objective description of such material in standard form.
To make available to others information about services and facilities available from its members.
To encourage the setting up of further centres.

Membership

Membership is open only to units or organizations, and there are two grades:

Full membership: full members must (a) be either units or centres actively engaged in programmed learning/educational technology work and offering at least some services outside their immediate school or college; or non-commercial bodies with a special interest in the development and organization of educational technology which could contribute to the development of work by centres; (b) be individual or corporate members of AETT; (c) on request of the Standing Committee and at least annually, on a standard form, provide up-to-date information about their organization, the services it offers, the research/development work it undertakes other than private consultancy, and any material it publishes.

Corresponding membership: corresponding members must be an educational and/or industrial body. They will receive notice of meetings, reports of lectures and details of any centres likely to be of interest to them. They will be eligible to attend any meeting of the Network but not to vote.

Membership fees are currently £8 (full) and £4 (corresponding).

Activities

With AETT (formerly APLET), the NPLC runs regional conferences at various places. It holds three to four general meetings a year, publishes a Bulletin and Special Interest Papers, and maintains an information service, to enable members to be in contact with each others' activities. Members are provided annually with a pack of detailed information about all the centres within the organization. Enquiries about the Network should be addressed to the Secretary.

Full members

Mr Norman E Allen,
Engineering Industry Training Board,
9 Park Road,
Barnstone,
Nottinghamshire NG13 9JF

Mr B Alloway,
Educational Technology Centre,
Faculty of Education,
Huddersfield Polytechnic,
Holly Bank Road,
Lindley,
Huddersfield HD3 3BP

Mr W M Barber
Training & Education Dept,
TSB,
PO Box 3, Keens House,
Andover, Hants SP10 1PG

Mr Rodney Battey,
Programmed Instruction Centre,
Middlesex Polytechnic,
Bounds Green Road,
Bounds Green,
London N11 2NQ

Dr J R Calder,
Moray House College of Education,
Holyrood Road,
Edinburgh EH4 8QA

Dr W D Clarke,
Director,
BLAT Centre for Health and Medical
    Education,
BMA House,
Tavistock Square,
London WC1H 9HP

Mr Richard Cole,
Central Training Branch,
Home Office,
Whttington House,
19-30 Alfred Place,
London WC1E 7EJ

Mr J K Darby,
The Polytechnic, Wolverhampton,
Faculty of Education,
Wolverhampton WV3 9DX

Mr W J K Davies,
County Programmed Learning Centre,
c/o St Albans College of Further
    Education,
Hatfield Road,
St Albans,
Herts AL1 3RJ

Mr M Edmundson, HMI,
60A High Street,
Harpenden,
Herts AL5 2TS

Educational Technology Unit,
Coventry College of Education,
Kirby Corner Road,
Kirby,
Coventry

Mr D J Enoch,
Engineering Training Department,
BBC,
Wood Norton,
Evesham,
Worcestershire WR11 4TF

Mr P Everett,
North Worcestershire College,
Burcot Lane,
Bromsgrove,
Worcestershire

Mr Douglas Fagan,
Home Office Unit for Educational
    Methods,
Fire Service Technical College,
Moreton-in-Marsh,
Gloucestershire GL56 0RH

Mr J R Foster,
Napier College,
Colinton Road,
Edinburgh EH10 5DT

Mr P J Gayfer,
Department of Educational Technology,
Clydebank Technical College,
Kilbowie Road,
Clydebank,
Glasgow,
Dumbarton G81 2AA

Mr Jon Green,
525 Willoughby House,
Barbican,
London EC2

Mr G L Hall,
CITB,
Bircham Newton,
Kings Lynn,
Norfolk

Mr J E Hills,
Education Unit,
Coventry Technical College,
The Butts,
Coventry CV1 3GD

Mr R P Hoare,
Centre for Educational Technology,
Trent Polytechnic,
Clifton,
Nottingham NG11 8NS

Mr E Howarth,
Department of Educational Technology,
Plymouth Polytechnic,
Hoe Centre,
Notte Street,
Plymouth

Dr J F Leedham, OBE,
3 Kingsbury Avenue,
Evington,
Leicester LE5 6ND

Mr Peter G J Lewis,
Course Design Section,
Royal Engineers Training Development
    Team,
Ravelin Building,
Brompton Barracks,
Chatham,
Kent

Mr A D Mackie,
Learning by Appointment Centre,
City of Bath Technical College,
Avon Street,
Bath,
Somerset

Miss Helen Mackie,
Programmed Learning Unit,
Department of Employment,
97 Tottenham Court Road,
London W1P 0ER

Mr C J Meek,
AV Workshop,
Teachers Centre,
Baillie Street,
Rochdale,
Lancs OL1G 1MW

Lt Cdr R D Nicholas,
RNSETT,
HMS Nelson,
Portsmouth,
Hants PO1 3HH

Mr Kenneth Parker, HMI,
DES,
London House,
New London Road,
Chelmsford,
Essex

Mr J P Pearce,
Educational Technology Centre,
Brighton Polytechnic,
Falmer,
Brighton BN1 9PH

Mr D T Rees,
Dean of Faculty of Science and
    Technology,
Gwent College of Higher Education,
Allt-yr-yn Avenue,
Newport,
Gwent NPT 5XA

Mrs W R Rumsay,
Learning Resources Centre,
Windsor and Maidenhead College,
Boyn Hill Avenue,
Maidenhead,
Berks

Mr T R Sands,
Bradford College,
Great Horton Road,
Bradford BD7 1AY

Mr Bob Sawyer,
Queens College,
1 Park Drive,
Glasgow G3 6LP

Secretary,
Audio-Visual Committee,
Oxford Polytechnic,
Wheatley,
Oxford OX9 1HX

Mr C Shettlesworth,
Department of English,
Faculty of Agricultural Business,
Mac Jog Institute of Agricultural
 Technology,
Chiangmai,
Thailand

Mr J K Sinclair,
Room E4,
Pathfoot Building,
University of Stirling,
Stirling FK9 4LA

Mr C H Teall,
Head of Dept Educational Resources,
South Thames College,
Wandsworth High Street,
London SW18 2PP

Mr I Townsend,
NHS Learning Resources Unit,
Sheffield City Polytechnic,
55 Broomgrove Road,
Sheffield S10 2NA

Mr A J Trott,
Bulmershe College,
Woodlands Avenue,
Earley,
Reading,
Berkshire

Sqn Ldr John Upham, RAF,
Programmed Learning Centre,
RAF School of Education,
RAF Newton,
Nottingham NG13 8HL

Mr J A F Waller,
91 Mount Drive,
Urmston,
Manchester M31 1QA

Miss Sue Ward,
Information Librarian,
BACIE,
16 Park Crescent,
London W1N 4AP

Major A C Watson, WRAC,
Learning Systems Section,
Army School of Training Support,
RAEC Centre, Wilton Park,
Beaconsfield,
Bucks HP9 2RR

Mr Q A Whitlock,
Department of Educational Services,
Sheffield City Polytechnic,
36 Collegiate Crescent,
Sheffield S10 2BP

Mr F R Wilmore,
34 Burton Street,
Melton Mowbray,
Leicestershire LE13 1LF

Mr R Wilson,
Centre for Educational Technology,
Preston Polytechnic,
Chorley Campus, Union Street,
Chorley,
Lancs PR7 1ED

Mr A Wood,
Learning Resources Unit,
Bolton College of Education (Technical),
Chadwick Street,
Bolton,
Lancs BL2 1JW

Members (above) listed by institution

United Kingdom

Clydebank Technical College	— Mr P J Gayfer
Coventry College of Education	— The Educational Technology Unit
Coventry Technical College	— Mr J E Hills
Department of Employment	— Miss Helen Mackie
Engineering Industry Training Board	— Mr Norman E Allen
Gwent College of Higher Education	— Mr D T Rees
Hertfordshire County Council Programmed Learning Centre	— Mr W J K Davies
Home Office	— Mr Richard Cole
Huddersfield Polytechnic	— Mr B Alloway
Middlesex Polytechnic	— Mr Rodney Battey
Moray House College of Education	— Dr J R Calder
NHS Learning Resources Unit	— Mr I Townsend
Napier College	— Mr J R Foster
North Worcestershire College	— Mr P Everett
Oxford Polytechnic	— Secretary, Audio-Visual Committee
Plymouth Polytechnic	— Mr E Howarth
Preston Polytechnic	— Mr R Wilson
Queens College, Glasgow	— Mr Bob Sawyer
RAF School of Education	— Sqn Ldr J Upham, RAF
Royal Engineers	— Mr Peter J G Lewis
Royal Navy	— Lt Cdr R D Nicholas
St Albans College of FE	— Mr W J K Davies
Sheffield City Polytechnic	— Mr Q A Whitlock
South Thames College	— Mr C H Teall
Stirling University	— Mr J K Sinclair
Trent Polytechnic	— Mr R P Hoare
Trustee Savings Bank	— Mr W M Baxter
Windsor and Maidenhead College	— Mrs W R Rumsay
Wolverhampton Polytechnic	— Mr J K Darby

Overseas

Mac Jog Institute of Agricultural Technology, Thailand	— Mr C Shettlesworth

The Work of ICETT (The Industrial Council for Educational and Training Technology Ltd)

The ever-increasing demand from industry worldwide for trained technologists has caused the member companies of ICETT (The Industrial Council for Educational and Training Technology Ltd) to reassess educational methods.

ICETT provides a co-ordinating function for four separate associations:

Association of Consultants in Education and Training (ACET)
Audio-Visual Aids and Allied Manufacturers' Association (AVAMA)
Engineering Teaching Equipment Manufacturers' Association (ETEMA)
ICETT Project Contractors' and Suppliers' Association (PACSA)

Each of these trade associations specializes in a particular aspect of education:

Consultancy in education and training (ACET)
Incorporates consultancy companies providing general advice, project analysis, development plans and personnel development programmes. Members include companies and individuals providing advice on engineering, science, medicine, agriculture and languages.

Audiovisual aids and systems (AVAMA)
Covers all aspects of the audiovisual field as applied to learning and training, including engineering, science, medicine, agriculture and languages. The companies are able to provide standard equipment and materials to meet the specialized needs of individual organizations.

Equipment for teaching technology (ETEMA)
Includes equipment and associated software for laboratory use in the training of professional engineers, technicians and craftsmen in the fields of chemical engineering, civil engineering, electrical and electronic engineering, mechanical engineering, marine and agricultural engineering.

Science, medical and agricultural teaching apparatus is also embraced for use in the teaching of professional scientists, medical and agricultural personnel and technicians, including research, para-medical occupations and other related activities.

Project contractors and suppliers (PACSA)
Provides organization, supply, finance and advice on all large educational and training projects.

ICETT supplies central service functions and provides specialized aid and assistance mainly through the British Electrical and Allied Manufacturers' Association (BEAMA) and the Electronic Engineering Association. ICETT provides a forum for opinion in the educational and training technology industry as a whole. From the outset, the association has emphasized the importance of standardization, both nationally and internationally; it seeks to maintain fair and equitable contract practices; and it brings members' products and services to the attention of those concerned with learning and teaching throughout the world.

Membership of ICETT embraces British companies, firms, associations and individuals concerned with educational, technical and commercial matters relating to the design, manufacture, production, publishing, marketing and servicing of technological products and services, involving the provision of consultancy and supplies at all levels, including large-scale projects, for education and training throughout the world.

In practical terms, the work of ICETT involves the provision of information and services to its member companies, to assist them in enlarging the market for the industry's products, both at home and overseas.

Thus, the combined expertise of British educational and training equipment, materials and service companies is available through one organization. All over the world the emphasis is on education and training. Educating personnel including engineers and technicians for tomorrow now forms a major part of most countries' investment programmes, and the success of this investment depends on planning. To meet this need the foremost British educational equipment and service companies have come together in a common organization so that administrators, educationalists and teachers have easy access to the wealth of British expertise in education and training.

Specialist companies within ICETT are ready to help meet any requirement in educational planning, curriculum design, construction, training equipment or materials. Through the ICETT organization, teachers and training staff from home and abroad can be put into direct contact with manufacturers, publishers, producers, distributors, project contract suppliers, systems consultants and architects. ICETT provides a personal link with relevant government departments, national and international educational agencies and organizations.

ICETT has close ties with the British Overseas Trade Board, the British Council, the Council for Educational Technology for the United Kingdom, the Crown Agents, and the Manpower Services Commission.

The main function of each member association of ICETT is to promote the prosperity and progress of the industry and the member companies. Each negotiates and confers, either individually or collectively, with the European Commission, International Lending Agencies, including the World Bank, government departments, Confederation of British Industry (CBI) and with user organizations. A lively contact is maintained with other trade associations, both at home and abroad.

Courses in Educational Technology and Associated Subjects in the United Kingdom

Courses are arranged in two sequences:
1. those leading to recognized qualifications (college or national);
2. other (eg short) courses

1. Courses leading to qualifications

Courses leading to the National Diploma in Educational Technology, formerly offered at the **National Audio Visual Aids Centre,** are now under the joint aegis of the CET/CNAA and are (or shortly will be) available at a number of centres throughout the UK. Each centre will offer its own unique course, within the framework of the general aims and objectives. Further details of locations of offering centres can be obtained from:

J W Davies,
Council for Educational Technology,
College of St Mark and St John
Derriford Road,
Plymouth,
Devon

University College of Wales, Aberystwyth
Department of Education,
Cambrian Chambers,
Cambrian Place,
Aberystwyth SY23 1NU

College Diploma in Educational Technology; MEd (Wales) in Educational Technology; Diploma in the Advanced Study of Education (with a special option in Educational Technology)

University of Bath
Claverton Down,
Bath BA2 7AY

MEd; PhD (both in Educational Technology)

City of Birmingham Polytechnic
Department of Educational Studies,
Westbourne Road,
Edgbaston,
Birmingham B15 3TN

Polytechnic Diploma in Learning Resources

University of Birmingham
Department of Educational Psychology,
Faculty of Education,
Ring Road North,
PO Box 363,
Birmingham B15 2TT

BPhil (Ed) in Educational Technology; Diploma in Educational Technology

University College, Cardiff
University College,
PO Box 78,
Cardiff,
South Wales
(Contact: The Registrar)

MEd in Educational Technology; MEd in Educational Broadcasting and Distance Education

Cartrefle College see North East Wales Institute

City & Guilds of London Institute (CGLI)
46 Britannia Street,
London WC1X 9RG

Various colleges throughout the country offer courses leading to the City & Guilds of London Institute Certificate in Educational Technology. Details of the colleges can be obtained from the Institute (address as above)

City University
Centre for Educational Technology,
London EC1V 4PB, *jointly with*
Hatfield Polytechnic
Education Department,
Hatfield,

Herts AL10 9AB *and with*
University of Surrey
Institute for Educational Technology,
Guildford,
Surrey GU2 5XH

*Diploma in Teaching and Learning in
Higher Education*

Coventry Technical College
Butts,
Coventry,
West Midlands CV1 3GD

*Technology (City & Guilds 730);
Educational Technology (two years)
(City and Guilds 731)*

Dorset Institute of Higher Education
Cranford Avenue,
Weymouth,
Dorset DT4 7LQ

*University of Southampton Diploma in
Advanced Educational Studies*

Dundee College of Education
Gardyne Road,
Broughty Ferry,
Dundee DD5 1NY

*Postgraduate Diploma in Educational
Technology (CNAA); Postgraduate
Diploma in Educational
Technology – Distance Learning
(CNAA)*

Dundee College of Technology
Bell Street,
Dundee DD1 1HG

*College Diploma in Educational
Technology*

Garnett College
Downshire House,
Roehampton Lane,
London SW15 4HR

*Diploma in Educational Technology
(University of London)*

University of Glasgow
Institute of Educational Studies,
Glasgow
(Contact: The Administrative Assistant)

*MEd in Curriculum Development and
Educational Technology*

The Hatfield Polytechnic
PO Box 109,
College Lane,
Hatfield,
Herts AL10 9AB

Postgraduate Diploma in Applied

*Educational Studies (CNAA);
Postgraduate Diploma in Teaching and
Learning in Higher Education (jointly
with the City University/University of
Surrey Institute of Education)*

**Highbury College of
Technology/Portsmouth Polytechnic**
Education Unit,
Highbury College of Technology,
Cosham, Portsmouth PO6 2SA

*National Diploma in Educational
Technology*

University of Hull
Institute of Education
173 Cottingham Road,
Hull HU5 2EH

*MA in Communication Learning
and Individual Differences in Education;
BA (Ed) Media in
Education/Educational Technology*

Jordanhill College of Education
76 Southbrae Drive,
Glasgow G13 1PP

*Postgraduate Diploma in Educational
Technology (CNAA)*

**University of London Institute of
Education**
20 Bedford Way,
London WC1H 0AL

*Diploma in Teaching and Course
Development (University of London)*

Middlesex Polytechnic
Bounds Green Road,
London N11 2NQ

*Diploma in Educational Technology
(CNAA) – commencing 1982 (jointly
with Southgate Technical College)*

Newcastle upon Tyne Polytechnic
Ellison Place,
Newcastle upon Tyne,
NE1 8ST

*Postgraduate Diploma in Educational
Technology (CNAA)*

North East Wales Institute
Cartrefle College,
Wrexham,
Clwyd,
North Wales LL13 9HL

*In-service BEd in Educational
Technology (University of Wales);
Diploma in Educational Technology*

Oldham College of Technology
Rochdale Road,

Oldham,
Lancashire OL9 6AA

*Electronics Servicing course for
mechanics with fourth-year option in
audio equipment (City & Guilds 224)*

Padgate College of Higher Education
Fearnhead,
Warrington,
Cheshire WA2 0DB

*BEd (Hons) in Audio Visual
Communications (University of
Manchester)*

Plymouth College of Art and Design
Drake's Circus,
Plymouth, Devon

*Diploma in Audio Visual Techniques for
Education*

Plymouth Polytechnic
Polytechnic Hoe Centre,
Notte Street,
Plymouth,
Devon

*MSc Diploma in Educational
Technology; Postgraduate Diploma in
Educational Technology (CNAA);
Polytechnic Diploma in Educational
Technology*

Portsmouth Polytechnic *see* Highbury
College

Sheffield City Polytechnic
Department of Education Services,
Collegiate Crescent,
Sheffield S10 2BP

*Postgraduate Diploma in Educational
Technology (CNAA)*

South Devon Technical College
Newton Road,
Torquay,
Devon TQ2 5BY

*Educational Technology (two years)
(City & Guilds 731); evening modular
course in Audio Visual Resources for
Teachers*

Southgate Technical College
High Street,
London N14 6BS

*Diploma in Educational Technology
(CNAA) (jointly with Middlesex
Polytechnic); audiovisual aid courses for
teachers; Audio Visual Aid Course for
Technicians (two years) (City & Guilds
736)*

South Thames College
Department of Educational Resources,
Wandsworth High Street,
London SW18 2PP

*National Diploma in Educational
Technology; College Diploma in
Learning Resources*

**The Suffolk College of Higher and
Further Education** Rope Walk,
Ipswich
SuffolkIP4 KT

*Educational Technology (two years)
(City & Guilds 731)*

**University of Surrey
Institute for Educational Technology**
Guildford,
Surrey GU2 5XH

*MPhil or PhD in Educational
Technology; MSc in Teaching and
Learning in Higher Education;
Postgraduate Diploma in Teaching and
Learning in Higher Education; Diploma
or the Practice of Education (in-service)*

University of Sussex
Education Area,
Falmer,
Brighton BN1 9RG

*MA (Curriculum Development – includes
educational technology and principles, at
School or FHE levels)*

Teesside Polytechnic
Educational Services Unit,
Borough Road,
Middlesborough,
Cleveland TS1 3BA

*Polytechnic Diploma (Advanced) in
Educational Technology*

W R Tuson College
St Vincents Road,
Fulwood,
Preston PR2 4UR

Diploma in Educational Technology

**West Sussex Institute of Higher
Education**
Bishop Otter College,
College Lane,
Chichester,
West Sussex PO19 4PE

*National Diploma in Educational
Technology*

University of York
Heslington,

York YO1 5DD

*MPhil or DPhil in Educational Studies;
MA in Applied Educational Studies;
Diploma in Educational Broadcasting*

2. Other courses in educational technology and associated subjects

Association for Educational and Training Technology
BLAT Centre for Health and Medical Education,
BMA House,
Tavistock Square,
London WC1

Seminars and conferences

Audio Visual Programmes Ltd
Studio AVP,
82 Clifton Hill,
London NW8 0JT

Short courses in communication and presentation for management

Bell and Howell Audio Visual Ltd
Alperton House,
Bridgewater Road,
Wembley,
Middlesex

One-day courses for projectionists (16mm projector)

British Association for Commercial & Industrial Education (BACIE)
16 Park Crescent,
London W1N 4AP

Training officer/Instructor courses; in-company courses; communication skills

The British Council
Courses Unit,
Media Department,
Tavistock House South,
Tavistock Square,
London WC1H 9LL

Courses in all aspects of educational technology, primarily to meet the needs of students from the developing countries

CTVC
Hillside,
Merryhill Road,
Bushey,
Hertfordshire WD2 1DR

Short courses in radio and television presentation techniques

Cybernetics Teaching Systems Ltd
89 Park Lane,
Castle Donington,
Derby DE7 2JG

Criterion referenced instruction

Dundee College of Education
Learning Resources Department,
Gardyne Road,
Dundee DD5 1NY

Various long and short courses in educational technology, including one by distance learning

Eastleigh College of Further Education
Chestnut Avenue,
Eastleigh,
Hampshire

Short courses for (a) office practice teachers; (b) workshop instructors

Educational Foundation for Visual Aids (EFVA)
Paxton Place,
Gipsy Road,
London SE27 9SR

Short courses on TV production and applications; film projection; the overhead projector; audiovisual techniques generally. Tailor-made courses can be arranged to run either at EFVA or in-house

Enlightenment Audio Visual Productions
St Catherine's
Botesdale,
Diss,
Norfolk IP22 1BP

Tailor-made seminars for managers on effective presentation

Guardian Business Services Ltd
21 John Street,
London WC1N 2BL
Public courses in the use of audiovisual aids and equipment

Huddersfield Polytechnic
Hollybank Road,
Lindley,
Huddersfield HD3 3BP

Educational technology, microteaching, interview techniques, counselling and guidance and general audiovisual production; courses for industrial trainers (by special arrangement)

Huntingdon Technical College
California Road,

Huntingdon,
Cambridgeshire PE18 7BL

*Short course in instructional techniques;
Further Education Teachers Course*

The Industrial Society
PO Box 1BQ,
Robert Hyde House,
48 Bryanston Square,
London W1H 1BQ

Seminars for training managers

**The Institute of Training and
Development**
5 Baring Road,
Beaconsfield,
Bucks HP9 2NX

*Seminars in training and diploma in
training management*

Lancashire College
Southport Road,
Chorley PR7 1NB

*Courses in educational technology,
courses in TV production; courses in
radio production; resource-based
language courses; seminars and
conferences connected with the media
and resource-based learning*

London Microfilm Bureau
42 Tanner Street,
London SE1.

*Diploma courses on micrographics
technology and its practical applications
to individual operations – for institutions
considering installing a microfilm
operation*

**Middlesex Polytechnic, Learning
Systems Group**
Bounds Green Road,
London N11.

*Various short courses in aspects of
educational technology including
programmed instruction, simulation and
gaming, design of learning resources,
use of video in training; curriculum
development and evaluation. Also
courses on computer graphics;
computers and microcomputers in
education*

National Audio Visual Aids Centre
see Educational Foundation for Visual
Aids

National Health Service
Learning Resources Unit,

Sheffield City Polytechnic,
55 Broomgrove Road,
Sheffield S10 2NA.

*Courses for nurse educators in the
production and use of resources in
teaching and learning*

Plymouth Polytechnic
Drake Circus,
Plymouth PL4 8AA.

*Various specialist short courses in
educational technology and educational
television*

RECALL Training Consultants
13 Wisteria Road,
London SE13.

*Workshops on educational technology,
in-company instructor training; working
languages: English, German, French,
Italian*

Saville Audio Visual Ltd
Salisbury Road,
York YO2 4YW.

*Organizes Video Schools which run
regular courses at venues in the north of
England. Courses include a one-day
'Introduction to Video' course and a
two-day course on 'Practical Video' for
the more advanced user*

Sheffield City Polytechnic
Department of Education Services,
30 Collegiate Crescent,
Sheffield S10 2BP.

*Workshop courses in the design and
development of learning resources and
active training methods – programmed
instruction, simulations and games, role-
play, case studies, tape/slide packages
(See also* National Health
Service *– above)*

Slough College of Higher Education
Faculty of Management,
Training Technology Division,
Wellington Street,
Slough, Berks.

*Courses in applications of educational
technology to industrial training*

South Devon Technical College
Newton Road,
Torquay,
Devon TQ2 5BY

*Evening modular course in Audiovisual
Resources for Teachers*

Southgate Technical College
High Street,
London N14 6BS

Audiovisual aid courses for teachers

South Thames College
Department of Educational Resources,
Wandsworth High Street,
London SW18 2PP

Short courses in audiovisual media and learning resources

Television Training Centre
23 Grosvenor Stret,
London W1

Diploma in Television Studies, Television Direction and Production

3M Visual Workshops
3M House,
PO Box 1,
Bracknell,
Berkshire RG12 1JH

Transparency Workshops

University Teaching Methods Unit
55 Gordon Square,
London WC1H 0NT

Courses and seminars for teachers in higher education

Conferences – National and International

The following list gives some organizations which hold regular annual or biennial conferences which may be of interest to readers. Details of conference dates and venues can be obtained from the organizers or from the press (the Editor is not able to supply them). The list is not exclusive and readers will find many useful occasional conferences mounted by other organizations, as well as further regular conferences.

Nearly all the organizations listed here are entered as *'Centres of Activity'* in Section 4; this list follows the sequence of categories in that Section.

International organizations

International Bureau of Education
Palais Wilson, 1211 Geneva, Switzerland
(Biennial International Conference on Education)

Aslib
(Association of Special Libraries and Information Bureaux)
3 Belgrave Square,
London SW1X 8PL

Eurodidac
World Association of Manufacturers and Distributors of Educational Materials,
Jägerstrasse 5,
4058 Basle,
Switzerland

ICII (International Congress for Individualised Instruction) *see* USA listing

IMC – International Micrographic Congress *see Centres of activity* entry

ISOD (International Society for Organisations Development)
International Secretariat,
12K Dubash Marg,
Fort Bombay,
India

International Training and Development Conference
Contact: Tom Japp,
Executive Chairman,
5 Sandyford Road,
Paisley,
Scotland, UK

Europe

European Association for Research and Development in Higher Education
Contact: Dr E A van Trotsenburg,
University Klagenfurt,
Universitatsstrasse-A,
9010 Klagenfurt,
Austria

European Bureau of Adult Education
see Netherlands

Middle East

Arab States Educational Technology Centre
PO Box 20147,
Safat,
Kuwait

Organizations in the United Kingdom

Action Learning Trust
45 Cardiff Road,
Luton,
Beds
(Contact: The Director)

Association for Educational and Training Technology
(Contact: The Administrator, AETT)
BLAT Centre for Health and Medical Education,
BMA House,
Tavistock Square,
London WC1

Association for the Study of Medical Education
(Two-day meeting)
150B Perth Road,
Dundee

Association of Teachers of Management
c/o Polytechnic of Central London,
35 Marylebone Road,
London NW1 5LS

BACIE (British Association for Commercial and Industrial Education)
26 D'Arblay Street,
London W1V 3FH

BALT (British Association for Language Teaching)
c/o Mrs E A Dyson,
Glanffrwd,
Fernbrook Road,
Penmaenmawr,
Gwynydd

BISFA (British Industrial and Scientific Film Association)
26 D'Arblay Street,
London W1V 3FH

BKSTS (British Kinematograph Sound & Television Society)
110 Victoria House,
Vernon Place,
London WC1

British Universities Film Council
Dean Street,
London W1V 6AA

Educational Television Association
86 Micklegate,
York YO1 1JZ
(Annual conference)

Industrial Council for Educational and Training Technology Ltd
Leicester House,
8 Leicester Street
London WC2H 7BN

The Industrial Society
Peter Runge House,
3 Carlton House Terrace,
London SW1Y 5DG

Industrial Training Research Unit
32 Trumpington Street,
Cambridge

National Association for Staff Development in Further and Higher Education
Redgrave House,
Macclesfield,
Cheshire SK10 4BW

National Education and Training Exhibition and Conference
RWB Exhibitions Ltd,
178-202 Great Portland Street,
London W1N 6NH

Network of Programmed Learning Centres (NPLC)
The Polytechnic,
Holly Bank Road,
Huddersfield HD3 3BP,
West Yorks

Society for Academic Gaming and Simulation in Education and Training
Centre for Extension Studies,
University of Technology,
Loughborough,
Leics LE11 3TU

Society for Education in Film & Television (SEFT)
29 Old Compton Street,
London W1V 5PL

Society for Research into Higher Education Ltd
c/o University of Surrey,
Guildford,
Surrey GU2 5XH

Standing Conference on Educational Development Services in Polytechnics
Dr P Griffin, Secretary,
Middlesex Polytechnic,
Bounds Green Road,
London N11 2NQ

Organizations in the United States

Adult Education Association of the USA
810 18th Street NW,
Washington DC 20006

American Educational Research Association (AERA)
1230 17th Street NW,
Washington DC 20036

American Society for Training and Development (ASTD)
Suite 305,
600 Maryland Avenue,
Washington DC 20024

Association for Continuing Higher Education
The University of Tennessee,
451 Communications Building,
Knoxville, TN 37916

Association for Educational Communications and Technology (AECT)
1126 16th Street NW,
Washington DC 20036

Association for Educational Data Systems
1201 Sixteenth Street NW,
Washington DC 20036

Association for Supervision and Curriculum Development
225 North Washington Street,
Alexandria, VA 22314

Association of Teacher Educators
1701 K Street NW, Suite 1201,
Washington DC 20006

Center on Evaluation, Development, Research
Phi Delta Kappa,
PO Box 789,
Bloomington, Indiana 47402

Georgetown University, Center for Personalized Instruction
Washington, DC 20057
(Annual conference)

HeSCA – The Health Sciences Communications Association
2343 North 115th Street,
Wauwatosa, WI 53226
(Annual conference; other meetings)

International Congress for Individualized Instruction
c/o Dr Ruth Witkus,
Biology Department,
Fordham University,
Bronx, New York 10458

International Council for Computers in Education
Dept of Computer & Information Science, University of Oregon,
Eugene,
Oregon 97403
(Co-Sponsors the annual National Educational Computing Conference

National Association for Core Curriculum Inc
407D White Hall,
Kent State University,
Kent, OH 44242

National Association of Educational Broadcasters
1346 Conecticut Avenue NW,
Washington DC 20036

National Audio Visual Association (NAVA)/NAVA Media Council
3150 Spring Street,
Fairfax, Virginia 22031
(Two annual conferences – one on AV hardware, one on AV software)

National Council on Measurement in Education
1230 17th Street NW,
Washington, DC 20036

National Society for Performance and Instruction (NSPI)
1126 Sixteenth St NW,
Washington DC 20036

Olympic Media Information (Annual Training Film Festival)
71 West 23rd Street,
New York, NY 10010

University Film Association
217 Flint Hall,
University of Kansas,
Lawrence, Kansas 66045

Other countries

Australia

Educare
Educare Exhibitions Pty Ltd,
PO Box 794 GPO,
Sydney, NSW 2001,
Australia
(Australasian International Education Exhibition and Conference)

Higher Education Research & Development Society of Australia
Contact: Geoff Foster,
Tertiary Education Institute,
University of Queensland,
Australia

Canada

AMTEC – Association of Media & Technology in Education
Contact: AMTEC,
Box 1410, Carleton University,
1233 Colonel By Drive,
Ottawa, Ontario K1S 5B6,
Canada

India

Indian Association for Programmed Learning and Educational Innovation
c/o National Council of Educational

Research and Training, Sri Aurobindo
Marg, New Delhi 110016,
India

Israel

**Israel Association for Instructional
Technology,**
12 Zemenhoff Street, Tel Aviv
(Annual Educational Film Festival)

Japan

**Jemex – Japan Educational Materials
Exhibition**
Jemex Office,
26 Nishikube Sakuragawacho, Shiba,
Minato-ku, Shiba, Minato-ku, Tokyo
105,
Japan

Netherlands

European Bureau of Adult Education
Nieuweg 4,
PO Box 367,
3800 AJ Amersfoort,
Netherlands

Poland

**Annual International Symposium on
Educational Technology**
Poznan University of Technology,
Politechnika, Poznanska Centre for
Educational Technology, Zaklad,
Kowych Technic Naucania,
ul Strzelecka 16,
61-845 Poznan,
Poland

Consultants in the Design of Courses and Materials – National and International

Expertise, in education and educational technology as in other fields, is becoming increasingly valuable, particularly at a time of rapid technological change and development. It is in this context that AETT is compiling a register of members qualified and willing to act as consultants, and thereby to offer a consultancy service worldwide; at present the list comprises some 50 names but is growing – for further details see the article by Andrew Trott on page 83. The Editor will be pleased to hear from any individual or organization that considers it can offer relevant services in education and educational technology – where appropriate, such information will be included in future editions of the *Yearbook*.

It is worth noting that the International Consultants Federation (see USA list) publishes a free annual *International Consultants Registry* which lists members and their expertise in some detail; this mostly relates to industrial training and business efficiency themes, but may be of interest to some readers. The symbol * before an entry signifies that this is a repeat of the 1980/81 entry, and that the request for updated information went unanswered. Such entries will be eliminated from future editions unless updated information is received.

The United Kingdom

Dr Mark L Braham
Sopers Farmhouse,
Capton,
Dartmouth,
Devon TQ6 0JE

Educational consultant, researcher and writer; founder and secretary-general of the International Association for Integrative Education (Geneva, Switzerland); concerned with the development of strategies and heuristic models for interdisciplinary studies; and with the philosophical aspects of educational technology and general systems theory

H Burns, BSc, LRIC, MIEnvSc, NAEE
Burnitec Services,
c/o 21 Templemore Road,
Oxton,
Birkenhead,
Merseyside L43 2HB

Further education; microcomputers with special reference to computer aided instruction

*Cadwell, Berger, Harrison & Simmons
18 Stoke Road,
Leighton Buzzard,
Bedford

Organization development and training for industry and commerce

The Centre for Business Simulation
63B George Street,
Maulden,
Bedford MK45 2DD

Instructional games and simulations

Ron Clements Associates – Training Consultants, 29 Paxton Gardens,
Woodham Lane,
Woking,
Surrey GU21 5TS

International specialist in management and staff development; sales and communication training

*Control Data Ltd (Education Services Division)
179-199 Shaftesbury Avenue,
London WC2 8AR

Computer training services, including

development and marketing of PLATO CBL

*Cybernetic Teaching Systems Ltd,
89 Park Lane,
Castle Donington,
Derby DE7 2JG

Daedal Training
20 Green Lane,
London SE20 7JA

Industrial training programmes and services

Department of Education Services *see* Sheffield City Polytechnic

Dundee College of Education, Learning Resources Department
Gardyne Road,
Dundee DD5 1NY

Short courses and consultancies for educational and training organizations

*F International Ltd
The Bury,
Church Street,
Chesham,
Bucks 4P5 1LB

Worldwide consultancy in CAL and CML

ASS Training Division
Nelson House,
Park Road,
Timperley,
Altrincham WA14 5AB

Management, supervisory and training courses

H & H Productions (AV Consultants)
Springbank,
65 East Kilbride Road,
Busby,
Glasgow G76 8HX

Production of audiovisual teaching aids; advice on staff training programmes

HRA Training and Development Ltd
5 Sandyford Road,
Paisley PA3 4HW

Consultancy in self-development, management development, and organisational development; in-company and public courses; word-processing and microprocessing training

*Heads
8 Redburn Street,
London SW3

Instructional materials, curriculum

design; special interest in developing countries

*Hodgson Myers Associates Ltd
103 Walton Street,
Oxford OX2 6EB

Consulting and design services for management and organization development. Special emphasis on methods of self-development, strategic management and use of workshops on real problems and decisions

*Inbucon Learning Systems
Preston House,
302-308 Preston Road,
Harrow,
Middx

Industrial Relations Services (Training) Ltd
67 Maygrove Road,
London NW6 2EJ

Specialist courses and conferences; in-company training based upon unique modules adapted for the particular needs of client companies, in the field of industrial relations and laws, industrial health etc

Insight Evaluation Centres Ltd
11 Royal Crescent,
Glasgow G3 7SL

A consulting and advisory organization working in the fields of personnel selection and development, including the use of minicomputers as an aid to using and scoring testing material

J Associates
PO Box 1,
Wincanton,
Somerset BA9 9LR

Production of AV aids, consultation, course design, tailor-made courses, effective use of television in training and presentations

Peter Jones – Personnel Services
88 Kennel Ride,
Ascot,
Berks SL5 7NW

All areas of personnel management and training needs, including contractual arrangements, recruitment and selection, psychological and aptitude testing, appraisal, management development, safety and welfare

Learning Systems Group
Middlesex Polytechnic at Bounds Green,
Bounds Green Road,
London N11 2NQ

Design and development of instructional materials; course analysis/evaluation; copyright and education

*Mills and Allen Communications Ltd
Broadwick House,
15-17 Broadwick Street,
London W1V 2AH

Consultancy and course development in computer-based learning

Mitchell Leslie International
The Priory,
Redbourn,
Herts AL3 7LZ

Specialists in technical training conducted overseas in the trainees' own languages. Suppliers of machinery equipment and apparatus to educational institutions worldwide

Peat, Marwick, Mitchell & Co
Management Consultants,
5th Floor,
1 Puddle Dock,
Blackfriars,
London EC4V 3PD

Educational costing systems

Alan Puzey, AIIP, Dip CINE
75 Lion Road,
Twickenham,
Middx TW1 4HT

Lecturing, consultancy and production in video and audiovisual aids; creating resources and materials, with a specialization in the field of educational and training materials. Specialist knowledge and practical experience of the Middle East audiovisual situation

*RECALL Training Consultants
13 Wisteria Road,
London SE13 5HW

Programme design, foreign language programming, designing users' instructions, graphic design and product design, algorithms, research. Working languages: English, German, Spanish, Italian, French

Sheffield City Polytechnic
Department of Education Services,
36 Collegiate Crescent,
Sheffield S10 2BP

Consultancy in learning design, production of instructional materials for education and training

Mike Sleight & Associates
34 Netherfield Road,
Sandiacre,
Nottingham

Performance technology; design, development and implementation of instructional materials; workshops on criterion referenced instruction, instructional module development, performance aids and implementing change in organizations

Slough College of Higher Education Training Technology Division
Wellington Street,
Slough,
Berks SL1 1YG

Training services and packages, consultancy for industry, commerce, public service and the armed services, in the UK and overseas

Supervisory Management Training Ltd
21 Green Lane,
London SE20 7JA

Supervisory/management training material in various media including video

Taba Training Associates Ltd
PO Box 5,
Holmfirth,
Huddersfield HD7 1XJ

Consultancy services in organization and personnel development

Tecmedia Ltd
5 Granby Street,
Loughborough LE11 3DU

Consultancy, design and production for education and training, both national and international; special interest in packaged learning with a strong emphasis on printed word. Developed the teacher inductors pack for the Microelectronics Education Programme

Walpole Training & Development Ltd
32 Redburn Street,
Chelsea,
London SW3 4BX

Consultancy and training services for trainers and personnel staff

F R Willmore, DipEdTech (B'ham),
34 Burton Street,
Melton Mowbray,
Leics LE13 1AF

Specializing in systems for practical engineering and technician training

The United States

*Bill Brooks Medical Learning Systems
333 West First Street,
Suite 111,
Elmhurst,
Illinois 60126

Borg-Warner Educational Systems
600 West University Drive,
Arlington Heights,
Illinois 60004

Course design and development

Conduit
100 Lindquist Center,
The University of Iowa,
PO Box 388,
Iowa City,
Iowa 52244

Computer-based instructional materials

*Courseware Inc,
10075 Carroll Canyon Road,
San Diego,
CA 92131

*Creative Universal Inc
Suite 1200,
Tower 14,
21700 Northwestern Highway,
Southfield,
Michigan 48075
(Contacts: Lawrence G Short, President; Bernie Masztakowski, General Manager)

*Curriculum Innovations Inc
501 Lake Forest Avenue,
Highwood,
Illinois 60040

Materials for classroom instruction

*Denoyer-Geppert Company
5235 Ravenswood Avenue,
Chicago,
Illinois 60640

Audiovisual materials and installations

*General Motors Education and Training Department
General Motors Corporation,
1700 West 3rd Avenue,
Flint,

Michigan 48502
(Contact: Thomas B Scobel, Manager, Instructional Development and Sales)

Carl H Hendershot EdD
4114 Ridgewood Drive,
Bay City,
Michigan 48707

Consultant in programmed instruction, education and training systems (methods, media and materials); compiler of the Hendershot Bibliography of Programmed Learning and Individually Based Instruction

*IPO Associates Ltd
Box 339,
Flourtown,
Pennsylvania 19031
(Contact: Gordon E Kutler)

*Information Resources Inc
Box 417,
Lexington,
Massachusetts 02173
(Contact: R E Horn, President)

International Consultants Foundation
5605 Lamar Road,
Washington DC 20016

A non-profit organization providing consulting services throughout the world to governments, universities, communities, industry and international organizations, in fields of organization and management, marketing, planning, agriculture, etc

*JRS Enterprises
121 S Murphy Street,
Sunnyvale,
CA 94086
(Contact: Jeff R Spalsbury, President)

Learn Incorporated
Mt Laurel Plaza,
113 Gaither Drive,
Mount Laurel,
NJ 08054

Study skills materials and courses (mainly on management themes); includes Speed Learning for reading skills

Performance Design Corp
No 1 Tysons Ofice Center,
Suite 202,
McLean,
Virginia 22102

Specializes in cost-effective solutions to

organizational performance problems, including the development of performance-based instruction and job aids

*Performance Systems Design
Chrysler Institute,
7650 Second Avenue,
Detroit,
MI 48202
(Contacts: Dennis J Deshares, Manager; Thomas R Zander, Ed Tech Supervisor; Norman C Irish, Research and Evaluation)

Pictorial Publishers Inc
PO Box 68520,
Indianapolis,
Indiana 46268
(Contact: Philip K Jones, Vice-President, Training)

Peter Pipe Associates
962 Chehalis Drive,
Sunnyvale,
California 94087

Consulting and materials for instructional systems

*Research for Better Schools, Inc
444 North Third Street,
Philadelphia,
Pennsylvania 19123
(Contact: John E Hopkins, Acting Executive Director)

SRI International
333 Ravenswood Avenue,
Menlo Park,
CA 94025
(Contact: Dr Marian S Stearns, Education and Human Services Research Center)

*System Development Corporation
2500 Colorado Avenue,
Santa Monica,
California 90406
(Contact: L Carter, Vice President)

Systema Corporation
150 North Wacker Drive,
Chicago,
Illinois 60606
(Contact: Jack R Snader)

Applications of instructional technology to sales and marketing

TPC Training Systems
1301 S Grove Avenue,
Barrington,
Illinois 60010

Specializes in maintenance training programs for many fields. Individual study is emphasized, as is practical application

*Vontech Inc
1354 Buffalo Road,
Rochester,
NY 14624

Design and manufacture of microcomputer-based training systems

Canada
*Harold D Stolovitch
4510 Kensington Avenue, Montreal,
Quebec H4B 2W5

Holland
*Associatie voor Organisatie Ontwikkeling
Duivenkamp 738,
3607 VD Maarssenbroek (The Association for Organization Development)

A group of independent consultants in organization development, working in a number of European countries

Norway
*Instituttet for Laereprogrammer A/S (ILP)
Sandakervn 56A,
Oslo 4
(The Institute for Learning Programmes Ltd)

Training consultancy, self-instructional materials

Spain
*Bedaux Espanola, SA
Dpto de Formacion,
Diagonal 618,
Barcelona 21

Learning and training systems, programmed learning, simulation games

Section 4: Directory of Centres of Activity

Introduction

As this Yearbook aims to enable the reader to locate and find details on institutions or organizations that may be doing work very similar to his or her own, it is important that the information herein should be as accurate and as up-to-date as possible. However, accuracy depends entirely upon information being returned by those institutions listed, which do not always oblige. For the sake of completeness, rather than immediately deleting out-dated entries, these have been left in their 1980/81 format but have been *identified by the symbol * before the name*. This both serves to alert the reader of possible inaccuracies and offers the last known address and details of the institution or organization concerned. Unless further information is received, such entries *will* be deleted from all subsequent editions of the Yearbook.

This Section consists of four main elements, some of which are subdivided:

International and Regional Centres of Activity:
    International centres – Major UN and associated organizations
                            Other UN organizations
                            Other organizations
    Regional centres – Africa
    Regional centres – Asia
    Regional centres – Europe
    Regional centres – Middle East
    Regional centres – South America

Centres of Activity in the United Kingdom:
    Institutions and organizations in further and higher education
    Teaching support services at other levels
    Other organizations with an interest in education and training

Centres of Activity in the United States:
    Institutions of higher education
    Other organizations

Centres of Activity Worldwide (listed by country)

International and Regional Centres of Activity

International centres

Major UN and associated organizations

IBE (International Bureau of Education), Palais Wilson, 1211 Geneva 14, Switzerland

Founded in 1929 as the first official international body for education, the IBE became in 1969 an integral part of Unesco – in terms of programme, staff and budget the Bureau is an element of Unesco's work in education, designed to serve all member states of the Organization. *Role of the IBE:* The IBE continues to work in Geneva, at the site it occupied before integration with Unesco. The activities also carry on the traditions created by its founders, Jean Piaget and Pedro Rossello, giving the Bureau its specificity within the framework of Unesco.

Essentially, the IBE is a centre of comparative education, responsible for studying problems of major importance to all member states, with a view to helping them to elaborate new solutions on a dynamic and long-term basis. This means that the education authorities in member states maintain contact with the IBE through the Council, the Unesco Secretariat or directly on an inter-institutional basis, in order to focus attention on common problems and to exchange experience and information through the IBE mechanism. One of Unesco's main goals is to work for the improvement of education systems through international co-operation; the IBE provides the information component that is so necessary to this programme, serving both the Organization and its member states as the central point for the gathering, analysis and dissemination of information needed for education reform. *International Conference on Education:* Started as early as 1934, this Conference is now biennial. It is convened by the Director-General of Unesco in uneven years, alternating with the sessions of Unesco's General Conference. It takes place in Geneva, and is organized by the IBE. *Comparative Studies:* The International Conference on Education serves as a priority for the IBE in gathering and analysing information. There is, however, a second line of enquiry, that of educational innovation. After an initial set of studies on this subject, the IBE was able in 1974 to launch the International Educational Reporting Service (IERS) with the help of extra-budgetary resources. The aim is to make available to educators in developing countries information about innovations in the structures, content, methods and materials of education. The Bureau has accordingly focused its information gathering, analysis and dissemination activities on developing the reporting service. *Documentation Services:* The most general and basic function of the IBE is to establish an adequate basis of information to meet the needs of educators in member states. This implies action in two directions: the development of a network of relationships between existing institutions, and the systematic improvement of documentation and information techniques at international level. With regard to the network, the IBE has developed contacts with a considerable number of national and regional centres around the world which are concerned with documentation, information and research in education. The record of these centres is issued in the *Directory of Educational Documentation and Information Services* (IBEDOC reference series), published every two years. A central part of the network comprises the four Unesco Regional Offices for Education in Africa (Dakar), the Arab States (Beirut), Asia (Bangkok) and Latin America (Santiago). The Documentation Centre of the IBE attempts to apply modern techniques to solving the problems of international communication in the field of education.

ICAO (International Civil Aviation Organization), 1000 Sherbrooke Street West, Montreal, Quebec, Canada H3A 2R2 (Contacts: Chief, Personnel Licensing and Training Practices Section; Chief, Field Training Section)

Pursuant to the provisions of Article 37 of the Convention on International Civil Aviation (Chicago 1944), ICAO adopts Standards and Recommended Practices (SARPS) amongst others for personnel licensing as Annexe 1 to the Convention. As guidance for the required training of aviation personnel, ICAO publishes the Training Manual, amplifying the SARPS of Annexe 1 and providing training practices to be used, and audio visual training aids as published in the ICAO Catalogue of Audio Visual Training Aids.

ILO (International Labour Organization), *see* International Centre for Advanced Technical and Vocational Training (below)

International Telecommunication Union, Place des Nations, CH-1211 Geneva 20, Switzerland (Contact: Secretary General of ITU, for the attention of the Head of Training Division)

Training activities include: application of systems approach to telecommunication training; consultation on determination of training needs and course development; assistance in establishing telecommunication training centres/schools/institutes; organization of seminars and workshops for developing countries; international co-operation and determination of standards for telecommunication training; catalogues of telecommunication training materials; a microfiche service of selected training documents; a reference manual for telecommunication training centres; and workshops for telecommunication instructors and course developers. Services are available to ITU member countries only.

International Centre for Advanced Technical and Vocational Training, Via Ventimiglia 201, 10127 Turin, Italy

Advanced training courses for (a) trainers, instructors, directors and supervisory staff of training institutions engaged in technical and vocational training; (b) middle and senior managers in private and public enterprises; (c) trade union officials; also production of training and learning multi-media packages; advisory services in educational technology; data bank in educational technology with question and answer service; field support missions, advisory services to projects, training projects; identification, planning and evaluation missions.

International Trade Centre – UNCTAD/GATT, Office for Training Activities, International Trade Centre, Palais des Nations, 1211 Geneva 10,

Switzerland (Contact: The Chief, Office for Training Activities, Division of Inter-regional Programmes)

Activities are principally tailor-made training and training consultancy for developing countries in the area of trade promotion. Research and development work concentrates on the strengthening of training institutions in developing countries through the training of trainers and the creation of locally adapted training materials.

In addition to the national and inter-regional work undertaken the Centre operates three sub-regional training units, one each in Central America and the countries of the Andean Group and one serving the African countries belonging to the CEAO.

Unesco, Section of Methods, Materials and Techniques of Education within the Division of Structures, Content, Methods and Techniques of Education, 7 Place de Fontenoy, 75700 Paris, France (Contacts: Henri Dieuzeide, France, Director of Division SCM; Etienne Brunswic, France, Head of Section MMT; Herbert Marchl, Germany; Wayne McLeod, USA; Masako Saulière, Japan; Gotcha Tchogovadze, USSR; Ann Whiting, UK, Demonstration Centre)

Within the framework of Unesco's activities, the principal task of the Section consists in promoting, developing and updating the use of educational technology which can favour the expansion and improvement of both in-school and out-of-school educational systems in the member states. The main orientations given to Unesco's programme may be listed as follows. *Normative action:* in particular the promotion of the free circulation of educational materials, also activities concerned with the better standardization of audiovisual equipment and software and the analysis of the functions, status and training requirements of specialists in educational technology. *Organization and management:* the programme also focuses on management and economics of educational technology: systems approach, costs of educational media such as use of computers in education, media resource centres, educational broadcasting, etc. *Educational industries:* efforts are being made towards the development of national and sub-regional industries and, in parallel, the reinforcement of the production and use of low-cost and appropriate techniques and materials in developing countries. *Communication techniques:* Unesco also pursues a programme dealing with the modernization of production and use of textbooks as well as the widespread application of mass media to education, in particular the organization of media-based distance teaching systems. *Intellectual co-operation:* between member states this is furthered through regional or sub-regional networks for educational innovation, seminars and studies, and training, with emphasis on self-instruction techniques.

*Unesco Institute for Education, Feldbrunnenstrasse 58, D 2000 Hamburg 13, Federal Republic of Germany (Contact: Kenneth Robinson, Head, Publications Unit)

The Unesco Institute for Education (UIE) is a research centre which has developed a particular interest in lifelong education, and is engaged in research into the content and quality of education at school level, ie education both in-school and out-of-school. UIE has sponsored over 120 multinational projects, surveys, studies, seminars or meetings on such subjects as the links between educational research and educational reform, on the problems of teacher education, on key subjects in the school curriculum, on theory and practice of pupil evaluation and guidance, on education for international understanding, on forms of adult education, on ways and means of education for leisure time, and since 1973 on lifelong education with particular reference to school curricula. It has become a specialized institution focusing on the qualitative aspects of education of permanent concern to educators in all countries, which demand constant research work which no one research institution can cover exhaustively. Regarding school-level education as the first systematic phase of a continuing, comprehensive and many-sided learning process, UIE has succeeded in outlining and developing an overall conceptual framework involving particular forms of analysis. *Research activities:* The research activities of the UIE, the major component of its programme, are supported by documentation and publication activities. The major areas of the current research programme include the relation of lifelong education to national systems of education, to school curriculum, to basic education, to teacher training, to evaluation and to research. The research work is carried out through projects of a theoretical, analytical or developmental character by national teams or individual scholars in co-operation with and co-ordinated by the UIE. A major characteristic of this programme is that each project focuses on a specific topic, and at the same time makes two further contributions. One of these is to clarify, validate and systematize the theoretical aspects of lifelong education. The other is to identify, appraise and develop those operational components which may contribute to its implementation. The documentation activities, primarily conceived as a support for the research programme of the UIE, are gradually developing into a clearinghouse service on lifelong education and its implications. Such information is made available to all interested professionals through the UIE's own bibliographical lists and the IBE's international documentation service. *Publications activities:* The publications activities, with over 120 recorded titles in three major series (International Studies in Education, Educational Research and Practice, Documents on Educational Research) include, since 1973, a series of UIE Monographs on lifelong education. Of its regular publications, the quarterly *International Review of Education* provides departments and institutes of education, teacher training institutions and professional readers, through its articles, commentaries and book reviews, with scholarly information on major educational innovations, research projects and trends all over the world. It is distributed in 75 countries. A full list of UIE's publications is available on request.

UNICEF Headquarters and Regional and Country Offices, Project Support Communications Service, Information Division, 866 United Nations Plaza, New York, NY 10017, USA (Contact: R R N Tuluhungwa, Chief of PSC Service; David Burleson, Senior Unesco Adviser to UNICEF, Focal Point, Educational Technology)

The purpose of the PSC Service is to ensure that UNICEF-assisted programmes and projects in developing countries include as part of their design and execution, essential communication dimensions, inclusive of interventions to support their objectives and facilitate behavioural change.

UNICEF provides global services through a regional system reaching 50 main offices and as many liaison points. The Regional and Country PSC networks each in their turn, or independently, provide services to all countries which they serve. In country programmes such communication components and services can take many forms – training, prototype production, planning, research, monitoring, evaluation, purchase of equipment, media material supplies or grants for consultants to develop curriculum, and aspects related to adult and community education and appropriate technology. This assistance can be given to a number of ministries which are concerned with the betterment of life for youth and children. Headquarters produces a PSC newsletter, issued quarterly. Recent information on development communication issues, research and innovative PSC activities in the field is regularly disseminated through this publication. UNICEF points to contact at Regional or Country levels are: Afghanistan: PO Box 54, Kabul; Bangladesh: PO Box 58, Dacca; Bhutan: UNICEF, c/o UNDP, Thimpu; Brazil: SBS – Ed Seguradoras, 70072 Brasilia, DF; Burma: PO Box 1435, Rangoon; Egypt: 7 Sharia Lazoghli, Garden City, Cairo; India: 11 Jorbagh, New Delhi; Indonesia: PO Box 202/JKT, Jakarta; Ivory Coast: BP 443, Abidjan; Kenya: PO Box 44145, Nairobi; Republic of Korea: Central Post Office, Box 1930, Seoul; Lebanon: PO Box 5902, Beirut; Nepal: PO Box 1187, Kathmandu; Nigeria: PO Box 1282, Lagos; Pakistan: PO Box 1063, Islamabad; Peru: Avenida Juan A Pezet, 1500 San Isidro, Lima; Sri Lanka: PO Box 143, Colombo; Sudan: PO Box 1358, Khartoum; Thailand: PO Box 2-154, Bangkok; Turkey: PK 407, Ankara; Zaire: BP 7248, Kinshasa; Zambia: PO Box 2810, Lusaka; Zimbabwe: PO Box 1250, Salisbury.

UNRWA/Unesco Department of Education, UNRWA Headquarters, Vienna International Centre, PO Box 700, A-1400, Vienna, Austria (Contact: Dr H Feridun, Director, UNRWA/Unesco Department of Education)

Provides education and training through the UNRWA education systems for children of Palestine Arab refugee families now living in Jordan, the West Bank, the Gaza Strip, Lebanon and Syria. *Publications:* general: an information brochure entitled *UNRWA/Unesco Department of Education, 1980/81,* and a Statistical Yearbook. For teacher training: instructional materials which include, among other things, self-study work assignments, working papers and guide notes and AV and CCTV media such as filmstrips, slides, charts, overhead transparencies, audio recordings and CCTV videogrammes. For vocational and school education: prototype instructional materials and guide notes.

United Nations Radio and Visual Services, DPI, New York, NY 10017, USA (Contact: Ms Daphne Brooke Landis)

The Radio and Visual Services Division of the UN's Department of Public Information produces and distributes films, photographs, wallsheets, picture sets, slides and radio programmes about United Nations activities and programmes. Films and other audiovisual materials are distributed throughout the world in a variety of ways, principally via a network of some 60 UN Information Centres. Films are available for loan from UN offices, and some educational and non-governmental organizations. They may be purchased from the UN or, in a number of developed countries, from selected educational film distributors. Other audiovisual materials are available free on request, in limited quantities, from UN Information Centres. UN audiovisual materials are produced in a number of languages and most films are available in English, French, Spanish and Arabic. A 16mm film catalogue is available on request.

*World Health Organization, 1211 Geneva 27, Switzerland (Contact: Dr M A C Dowling, Chief Medical Officer for Educational Communication Systems, Division of Health Manpower Development) Development of 'appropriate technology', health learning material, teaching/ learning methods, research into communication. Information on health learning materials, audio-visual media, equipment and packages. Publications: *Basic Techniques for a Medical Laboratory*, a manual for training laboratory personnel in developing countries, by E Levy-Lambert (revised new edition 1979), WHO; *Reference Material for Health Auxiliaries and their Teachers*, 1976, bibliography, WHO Offset Publication No 28 (new updated edition in preparation); *Teaching for Better Learning*, a guide for teachers of health staff, by F R Abbatt, WHO 1979; *Management of Obstetric Emergencies in a Health Centre*, by B Essex (experimental edition), 1978, WHO; *Diagnostic Flowcharts* and *A Manual for Teaching and Evaluating*; *Diagnostic Flowcharts*, by B Essex, 1978, WHO (available in limited numbers); *Illustration Bank*, simple line drawings on health subjects with English and French captions, 1974, WHO.

Other UN organizations with an interest in educational technology

Food and Agriculture Organization of the United Nations, Via delle Terme di Caracalla, 00100 Rome, Italy (Contact: Mr R Lydiker, Chief, Current Information Branch, Information Division)

*GATT (General Agreement on Tariffs and Trade), Centre William Rappard, rue de Lausanne 154, CH-1211 Geneva 21, Switzerland (Contact: John Croome, Director, External Relations and Information)

*International Atomic Energy Agency, Kärtnerring 11, A-1010 Vienna, Austria (Contact: Mr Georges Delcoigne, Chief, Public Information Section)

*IBRD (International Bank for Reconstruction and Development, World Bank Group, 1818 H Street, NW, Washington DC 20433, USA (Contact: Mr John E Merriam, Director, Information and Public Affairs)

International Labour Organization, 4 Route des Morillons, CH-1211 Geneva 22, Switzerland (Contact: Mr Kyril Tidmarsh, Chief, Bureau of Public Information)

*UNDP (United Nations Development Programme), One United Nations Plaza, New York, NY 10017, USA (Contact: Mr A Bruce Harland, Deputy Director, Bureau for Programme Policy and Evaluation)

UNEP (United Nations Environment Programme), PO Box 30552, Nairobi, Kenya (Contact: Information Service)

United Nations (High Commissioner for Refugees), Palais des Nations, CH-1211 Geneva 10, Switzerland (Contact: Miss N Mayadas, Chief, Counselling and Education Section)

*United Nations Industrial Development Organization (UNIDO), Lerchenfelderstrasse 1, A-1070 Vienna, Austria (Contact: Mr E J Strohal, Chief, Information Service)

*United Nations Institute for Training and Research, United Nations Plaza, New York, NY 10017, USA (Contact: Mr Berhanykun Andemicael, Special Assistant to the Executive Director)

*Vision Habitat (United Nations Visual Information Programme), 2075 Westbrook Mall, Vancouver, BC V6T 1WS, Canada (Contact: Mr Dario Pulgar, Room 218, Ponderosa B)

World Intellectual Property Organization, 34 Chemin des Colombettes, CH-1211 Geneva 20, Switzerland (Contact: Roger Harben, Director, Public Information Division)

World Meteorological Organization, PO Box 5, CH-1211 Geneva 20, Switzerland (Contact: G Obasi, Director, Education and Training Department)

The main features of activities in the field of education and training are the award of fellowships, the strengthening of regional meteorological training centres, the organization of suitable courses, seminars and workshops, the preparation of training publications, the undertaking of studies and surveys of training needs, the provision of advice and information on various aspects of education and training, and collaboration with other organizations in the field of education and training in WMO's areas of competence.

Other organizations

AIMAV (Association Internationale pour la Recherche et la Diffusion des Methodes Audio-visuelles et Structuro-globales) (International Association for the Study and Promotion of Audio Visual and Structural-Global Methods), University of Ghent, Faculty of Philosophy and Letters, Blandijnberg 2, 9000 Ghent, Belgium (Contact: Professor Dr M De Grève, Secretary General; Delegate for UK: Professor Christopher Candlin, University of Lancaster)

Studies theoretical and practical aspects of transcultural communication; publishes results; performs interdisciplinary research in linguistics; provides grants to underwrite media research in several universities all over the world; offers colloquia; forms working teams.

Aslib (Association of Special Libraries and Information Bureaux), 3 Belgrave Square, London SW1X 8PL, UK

Concerned with promoting the effective management and use of information of all kinds, Aslib's corporate members number more than 2000 in the UK and worldwide. Aslib provides consultancy relating to information management, and also advice on obtaining specific information. Professional activity is encouraged and members may use the Library (special collection on information management), purchase Aslib's publications (monographs, directories, research reports, and periodicals) and attend meetings and conferences.

Aslib runs a number of short courses on information work at all levels, details of which may be obtained from the Education Officer.

CEMAS (International Cooperative Alliance, Cooperative Education Materials Advisory Service), 11 Upper Grosvenor Street, London W1X 9PA, UK (Contact: The Project Officer, CEMAS)

The Advisory Service operates a clearinghouse and production unit for education and training materials for co-operative educational work in developing countries. It also operates from the Regional Offices of the International Cooperative Alliance for Asia (based in New Delhi, India) and for East and Central Africa (based in Moshi, Tanzania). Regional centres: ICA Regional Office and Education Centre for South East Asia, Bonow House, 43 Friends Colony, PO Box 3312, 110014 India (Contact: the Regional Director); ICA Regional Office for East and Central Africa, PO Box 946, Moshi, Tanzania (Contact: the Regional Director); Services (Regional Centres); Co-operative education and training programmes including the training of co-operative college lecturers and educational extension workers, training of various cadres of top-level employees and policy-makers of the co-operative movement. Publications include: *Participative Teaching Methods* – a guide with specimen exercises for co-operative teachers, 1978; *Explaining Annual Reports* – a guide on the use of annual reports and accounts as an aid to education, 1978; *Cooperative Education Radio Programmes* – a general guide with specimen scripts, 1978; *Case Writing Workshop*, including teacher's guide, 1977; *Correspondence Education* – a guide for planners, course writers and tutors with specimen lessons, 1977; *Cooperative Book-keeping* – a simple standardized system for developing countries (four manuals for marketing, consumers, thrift and credit and industrial co-operatives), 1976; *Society Operating Manual* – a guide with specimens on the preparation of operating manuals for agricultural and consumer co-operatives, 1977; *Basic Control of Assets* – a manual on prevention of losses in small co-operatives 1979; *A Cooperator's Dictionary* – a selection of co-operative and commercial terms with explanations, 1977; *Sources of Cooperative Information*, 1979.

Clearinghouse on Development Communication, 1414 22nd Street NW, Washington, DC 20037, USA

An international clearinghouse for materials and information on the application of the communications media to development problems of the Third World in education, agriculture, health, nutrition, family planning, literacy and community development. Operated by the Academy for Educational Development; supported by the Bureau for Science and Technology of the US Agency for International Development. Disseminates information through publications, films, videotapes, seminars and consultations on applications of communications technology. Maintains a mailing list of 7000 persons worldwide in the fields of education, communication and development. Publishes *Development Communication Report* quarterly. (*See also under Centres of Activity in the United States*)

The Clearinghouse on Development Communication should not be confused with the various educational clearinghouses operating nationally in the USA as part of the ERIC organization – see page 176.

Eurodidac (World Association of Manufacturers and Distributors of Educational Materials), Jägerstrasse 5, 4058 Basle, Switzerland (Contact: Mrs Christine Kalt-Ryffel, Director)

Organization of international Educational Materials Exhibitions (DIDACTA), accompanying events and special displays, information exchange by documentation services, organization of study meetings. Publications: *Forum*, published eight times per year.

FID (International Federation for Documentation), PO Box 30115, 2500GC The Hague, Holland

Promotes research and development in documentation – its organization, storage, retrieval, dissemination and evaluation in the fields of science, technology, social sciences, arts and humanities.

International Association for Integrative Education, *see* Dr Mark L Braham (page 253)

*ICEM (International Council for Educational Media) (Contact: The Secretariat, 29 rue d'Ulm, 75230 Paris, Cedex 05, France)

The objectives of the Council are: (a) to promote worldwide contacts among people professionally responsible for promoting production, distribution, research and the use of modern media in the member countries; (b) to provide an international channel for exchange of views and experience in the field of educational technology; (c) to promote a better integration of all modern media in education; (d) to promote the use of modern media in the classroom by the training of teachers and future teachers; (e) to improve the supply of modern media all over the world by practical projects of international co-production and exchange; (f) to keep contact with and advise industrial manufacturers of hardware and producers of software; (g) to keep member countries informed of developments in the field of educational technology; (h) to co-operate with other international organizations in promoting educational technology.

ICII (International Congress for Individualized Instruction) (Contact: Dr Ruth Witkus, Editor, ICII, Biology Department, Fordham University, Bronx, New York NY 10458, USA)

An AECT affiliate initiating and fostering co-operation among educators interested in broad aspects of individualized instruction, including those in the audiovisual category. Aims to assist members in adapting and adopting new instructional techniques or systems to improve learning. (*See also Centres of Activity in the United States*)

International Copyright Information Centre, *see* INCINC (below)

International Council for Computers in Education, *see under Centres of Activity in the United States*

*IFTC (International Film and Television Council), 1 rue Miollis, 75732 Paris, Cedex 15, France (Contact: Professor Mario Vendone, President); incorporates the **Commission for Media in Educational and Professional Development** (Contact: Peter Whittaker, President)

The Council is an international organization covering the whole field of film and television including the international organizations dealing with education. It liaises with Unesco, and its services include co-ordination and provision of information. Publications: *IFTC Newsletter; Educational Technology in European Higher Education* (Round Table, Grenoble 1974); *Media Studies in Education* (Unesco: No 80 'Reports and Papers published by Mass Communication').

*IIALM (International Institute for Adult Literacy Methods), PO Box 1555, Tehran, Iran (Contact: John W Ryan, Director)

The objectives of the Institute are to provide documentation and library services, research, training and information exchange on literacy and functional literacy programmes, particularly on methods, techniques and media used in adult education. Regular and periodic publications, papers, monographs and bibliographies are used. The Institute works in close co-operation with Unesco and the International Bureau of Education (IBE). It also maintains working relations with regional organizations in the developing world. In association with other agencies, it organizes seminars and workshops and assists in the preparation, publication and distribution of conference papers. Training is given to holders of United Nations and university grants. In-service training over periods of six months to a year is offered to between one and three candidates a year. All programme activities of the Institute are inter-related and mutually supportive. The Institute's library and documentation centre contains more than 6000 books and documents on literacy, adult education and allied subjects, classified according to a modified ERIC (Education Resources Information Centre) system. This facilitates precise identification and rapid retrieval. Nearly 200 educational journals are regularly received and close contacts are maintained with documentation services working in related fields.

IIIT (International Institute of Instructional Technology), US International University, 10455 Pomerado Road, San Diego, California 92131, USA

Established in 1972 at the US International University to give attention to instructional change, the Institute is concerned with the identification, development and implementation of instructional changes and procedures necessary to respond to defined needs of individuals. It co-ordinates a PhD programme in instructional technology at USIU.

*IMC (International Micrographic Congress) (Current address not traceable – Ed.)

A non-profit-making, tax-exempt, educational corporation supporting micrographic education, exchange information, publications, etc. Organizes yearly conferences and exhibits in different parts of the world. Membership consists of national microfilm associations and sustaining individual members. Lists of micro-publications and audiovisual materials are available.

INCINC (International Copyright Information Centre), c/o Association of American Publishers, 1707 L Street NW, Suite 480, Washington, DC 20036, USA

INCINC was created by Unesco to serve developing nations in their efforts to acquire translation and reprint rights to copyrighted works.

*ISOD (International Society for Organization Development/Sociètè Internationale pour le Developpement des Organisations), International Secretariat, 12K Dubash Marg, Fort Bombay 23, India (Contacts: Dr Jagdish Parikh, President; Peter C Shephard, Executive Director)

Research, education and consultancy in the development of human resources, organizations, communities or government enterprises; organization development – organizational communications; manpower planning and development; development projects – training consultants; economic and social development; entrepreneurship development – cross-cultural issues. Materials produced: international journal; surveys and research publications; conference proceedings, in cassette and published form; team development exercises; videotaped lectures; audiovisual training aids; psychological tests and instruments. Services offered include research and information exchange; research projects in social, educational and organizational subjects; organization of seminars, workshops and conferences on subjects relating to the development of organizations;

provision of advisory and consultancy services in management, human resources and organization development; development and validation of psychological tests for vocational/industrial/educational use; development of entrepreneurs for small-scale industry development in developing countries. Recent publications: *Organization Development International* (the official journal of ISOD); *A Survey into Cross-cultural Work Values among Managers in S E Asia*; *A Survey into the Use of Consultants in Malaysia*; *A Strategy for the Transference of Organization Development Technology between Cultures*.

*ITE (International Tape Exchange), University of Michigan Audio Visual Centre, 834 Ruddiman Avenue, North Muskegon, Michigan 49445, USA (Contact: Ruth Y Terry)

Assists educational institutions at all levels to exchange reel or cassette tape recordings with their counterparts throughout the world. No fees are paid by schools outside the United States.

Regional centres – Africa

*The Demonstration Centre for Educational Technology, The Unesco Regional Office for Education in Africa (BREDA), BP 3311, Dakar, Senegal.

Demonstration of and information on new methods, materials and techniques in the field of education, collection and exchange of audiovisual documentation, promotion and support of local efforts and local adaptation of audiovisual aids and methods; exhibitions of locally produced educational materials; participation in the promotion of the Network of Educational Innovation for Development in Africa (NEIDA); assistance and advisory services on the selection and use of audiovisual aids; technical studies and reports on hardware and software for projects with audiovisual components; updated documentation on available equipment and pedagogical materials, publications and reports. Duplication and dissemination of AV documents; exchange of information and materials. There is a possibility for small-scale training activities on initiation, practical use and maintenance of AV equipment; the Centre also co-ordinates seminars and regional meetings for national and international experts in educational technology. It has financial and technical facilities as support for operational projects soliciting assistance in this field.

ICA (International Cooperative Alliance), Regional Office for East and Central Africa, *see* CEMAS *under International Centres of Activity*

*SEPA (Science Education Programme for Africa), PO Box 9169, Airport, Accra, Ghana

Unesco Office of the Regional Communication Adviser, PO Box 30592, Nairobi, Kenya (Contact: Alex T Quarmyne)

The Office is responsible for the planning and execution of Unesco-supported communication projects in Africa, including the organization of courses in radio, television, film and print journalism; and experimentation in hardware applications and in broadcast programme development.

URTNA (Union of National Radio and Television Organizations of Africa), Secretariat General, 101 rue Carnot, BP 3237, Dakar, Senegal

URTNA is a professional body committed to the development of all aspects of broadcasting in Africa, and currently has a membership of 39 active and 11 associate members. It has no commercial aim. Its objectives are to promote, maintain and develop co-operation between members; to support in every domain the interests of radio and television organizations which have accepted its statutes and to establish relations with other such organizations or groups of organizations; to promote and co-ordinate the study of all questions relating to radio and television, and to ensure the exchange of information on all matters of general interest; to use its best endeavours to ensure that all its members honour the provisions of international and inter-African agreements in all matters relating to radio and television; and to co-ordinate and collaborate closely with member organizations in the coverage of national and international events.

URTNA offers four permanent services:

   (i) *General Secretariat* to handle overall co-ordination and administrative matters – address as above;
  (ii) *Technical Centre* (Contact: the Director), BP 39, Bamako, Mali;
 (iii) *Programme Exchange Centre* (Contact: the Director), PO Box 50518, Nairobi, Kenya;
 (iv) *Inter-African Centre for Rural Radio Studies – CIERRO* (Contact: the Director) to handle training in broadcasting matters. BP 385, Ouagadougou, Upper Volta.

Overall, the activities of URTNA cover: training and technical matters relating to broadcasting; programme exchange; copyright; radio and TV coverage of major international and inter-African events; studies on specific projects; satellite communication; rural communications; seminars, workshops and conferences; the URTNA prize programme contest; screening sessions; co-production activities; and publication of the *URTNA Review*.

Associate membership of URTNA is available to all public broadcasting organizations outside Africa.

Regional centres – Asia

ABU (Asia-Pacific Broadcasting Union), Secretariat, c/o NHK, 2-2-1, Jinnan, Shibuya-ku, Tokyo 150, Japan. Secretary General's Office: PO Box 1164, Jalan Pantai Bharu, Kuala Lumpur 22-07, Malaysia

Aids in the development of international radio and television programme materials, conducts staff training activities, performs research and facilitates and aids the production of educational films about member nations.

ACEID (Asian Centre of Educational Innovation for Development), *see* APEID (below)

AMIC (Asian Mass Communication Research and Information Centre), 39 Newton Road, Singapore 1130, Republic of Singapore (Contact: Daniel G Santos, Senior Programme Specialist)

A regional mass communication centre engaged in documentation, publication, research and training programmes. Target audience: communication policy-makers, planners, scholars and practitioners.

APEID (Asian Programme of Educational Innovation for Development), at the Office of the Secretariat: Asian Centre of Educational Innovation for

Development (ACEID), Unesco Regional Office for Education in Asia, 920 Sukhumvit Road, PO Box 1425, Bangkok, Thailand (Contact: Dr A Latif, Chief of ACEID)

In 1973 the Asian Programme of Educational Innovation for Development (APEID) was started. The unique characteristic of this programme is that it is planned and developed co-operatively by the participating Asian member states themselves, and the activities are carried out through the national centres offered for association with APEID by those member states. It represents a concrete expression of technical co-operation among developing countries. The activities and network of the programme are co-ordinated by the Asian Centre of Educational Innovation for Development (ACEID) which is an integral part of the Unesco Regional Office.

Educational technology is one of the areas of innovation under APEID whose activities also serve other areas of innovation, such as non-formal and alternative structures in education; administration and management of educational innovation; curriculum development; education of teachers, teacher educators and other educational personnel; science (including mathematics) and technology education; and vocational and technical education. The main thrust in the area of educational technology centres on training, development of low-cost and indigenous teaching devices and materials based on cost-effective techniques, and use of mass media for expansion of educational opportunities. Educational technology programmes are designed to contribute to universalization of education, integrated rural development, development of productive skills and better health and nutrition.

Modes of operation: Exchange and dissemination of information and materials; inter-project/inter-country study visits; mobile training for in-country workshops; attachments/internships; high-level personnel project study and seminars; technical working groups; training courses/workshops; field operational seminars; joint innovative projects.

Publications: Inter-country co-operation in educational technology: report, 1980, 62pp; *Production and utilization of educational broadcasting programmes: report,* 1980, 55pp; *Inventory: low-cost educational materials – how to make, how to use, how to adapt,* Vol 1, 1980, 158pp; *Low-cost educational materials: report,* 1981, 117pp; *Designing instructional materials for general education and teacher training: a portfolio of experiences in Asia and Oceania,* 1980, 320pp; *In-service teacher education: developing innovatory strategies and instructional materials: report,* 1980, 96pp; *Self-learning modules for teachers of science* (3 modules); *Preparing educational personnel: training methodologies based on locally available learning resources: report,* 1980, 47pp; *Vocational and technical education: development of curricula and instructional materials with focus on mechanical and civil/building subjects: report,* 1980, 112pp; *Vocational and technical education: development of curricula, instructional materials and physical facilities, and teacher training, with focus on electrical and electronic subjects: report,* 1981, 98pp.

ICA (International Cooperative Alliance), Regional Office and Education Centre for South East Asia, *see* CEMAS *under International Centres of Activity*

RECSAM (Regional Centre for Education in Science and Mathematics),
SEAMEO, Glugor, Penang, Malaysia (Contact: Mr Chin Pin Seng, Centre
Director)

RECSAM, the Regional Centre for Education in Science and Mathematics,
was established by the Southeast Asian Ministers of Education Organization
(SEAMEO) in May 1967 to help improve the teaching of science and
mathematics in member countries in order to lay a firm foundation for
meeting the scientific technical manpower needs for Southeast Asian
countries in the future. RECSAM undertakes the following activities:
innovative short-term training programmes for key educators in modern
methods of teaching science and mathematics, development of action-
research techniques, development of specific studies and innovative
instructional materials, development of simple techniques in apparatus-
making, using low-cost materials, organization and conduct of professional
seminars and workshops for educators in the region; gathering of
information and acting as a clearinghouse for science for member countries
on request; and promotion of indigenous efforts in curriculum development.
The Centre has produced a number of educational materials and manuals. It
issues the following publications: *Journal of Science and Mathematics
Education in Southeast Asia* (semi-annual); *RECSAM News* (quarterly).

SAIDI (Southeast Asia Interdisciplinary Development Institute), *see under
Centres of Activity Worldwide – Philippines*

SEAMEO – *see* RECSAM (*above*)

Unesco Regional Office for Education in Asia and the Pacific, 920
Sukhumvit Road, Bangkok, Thailand

The Regional Office was established in Bangkok in 1961 in co-operation with
the Government of Thailand and services 29 member states in Asia and the
Pacific region. Since 1976 the Office also accommodates the regional advisers
in social sciences and culture. The activities of the Office take the form of
advisory services, training programmes, regional meetings and seminars,
promotion of educational innovation through the Asian Programme of
Educational Innovation for Development, and educational documentation
and information services.

The training programmes consist of regional/sub-regional/national training
courses, study workshops, internships, and field operational seminars. There
are annual training courses in educational planning covering a group of
countries which are conducted in four phases: by correspondence tuition,
training workshops for face-to-face instruction, third country visit for
practical experiences and follow-up after returning home for continuing
professional growth. One-month internship and attachment programmes are
also held in population education.

*Office of the Regional Advisor for Social Sciences in Asia and the Pacific
(RASSAP):* The Office also sponsors cross-cultural research projects on vital
social problems. It has promoted a network of social science organizations in
the region called Association of Asian Social Science Research Councils
(AASSREC). Training seminars in social sciences are held on development,
nation building, research methodology, human settlements, and social
indicators.

*Office of the Unesco Regional Adviser for Culture in Asia and the Pacific
(URACAP):* The activities of this Office cover a wide range. The most

important are: (a) organization of training and seminars dealing with various aspects of cultures; (b) promotion of research and study on traditional as well as contemporary aspects of Asian and Oceanic Cultures; and (c) the preservation and restoration of the cultural heritage in the region.

Regional centres – Europe

Centre Européen pour l'Enseignement Supérieur (CEPES), Strada Stirbei Voda No 39, Bucharest, Romania (Contact: A Øfjord, Director)

CEPES was set up in 1972 to promote co-operation between the Unesco member states of the European region (geographical Europe, Canada, Israel and the US) in the field of higher education. Its main objective is to serve as an instrument within the framework of Unesco's contribution to the development of and innovations in higher education in Europe and to the reinforcement of European co-operation in this field. CEPES serves as a centre of information, documentation, liaison and exchange, in order to provide practical services not only to the national authorities of member states concerned with higher education but also to universities and all other bodies working in the higher education field. The role of CEPES is to carry out certain tasks of interest to member states and to stimulate activities among the states themselves. Although the Centre can be concerned in principle with all aspects of higher education, in practice its activities must be directed, as far as possible, to matters of common interest to all or to a majority of the member states of the European region. CEPES has, on the one hand, basic activities of a permanent nature, such as documentation, information and liaison and, on the other hand, thematic activities such as symposia and studies on specific subjects. The Centre publishes a quarterly bulletin *Higher Education in Europe* (English, French and Russian versions) and *New Acquisitions of the CEPES Library* (also quarterly). Through a network of Liaison Officers, CEPES keeps up contact with higher education circles in all European member states.

*****Centro Europeo dell'Educazione,** via del Vascello 25, Rome (Contact: Mario Fierli)

Eurodidac, *see under International Centres of Activity*

The European Home Study Council (EHSC), c/o Keith Rawson-Jones, Honorary Secretary, Research and Development Committee, The Linguaphone Institute, Beavor Lane, London W6

EHSC is an educational foundation whose membership comprises private (commercial) organizations, educational foundations and state organizations concerned with teaching 'at a distance'. The main area of activity is the organization of workshops twice a year (spring and autumn) on themes relevant to the field of distance education/correspondence education. Research projects in this area are also stimulated (cf EHSC/Lund two-way communications in distance education research programme). Publication: the EHSC journal *Epistolodidaktika*, published twice a year; in 1982 the journal will be renamed *The Journal of Correspondence Education, incorporating Epistolodidaktika*.

*****European Institute for Vocational Training,** 48 avenue de Villiers, 75017 Paris, France (Contact: M Jean Roux, General Delegate)

The Institute has representatives from the employers and trades unions of ten European countries.

Regional centres – Middle East

Arab Centre for Audience Researches (ACAR), *see under Centres of Activity Worldwide – Iraq*

The Arab States Educational Technology Centre (Affiliate of the Arab League Education, Cultural and Scientific Organization – ALECSO), PO Box 24017, Safat, Kuwait (Contact: A Jabbar Wali, Acting Director)

This Centre is a specialized agency set up to realize the following objectives: to increase the awareness in Arab countries of the importance of educational technology and upgrade the effectiveness of its use in the light of up-to-date requirements of the present era; to encourage Arab countries to establish departments or centres of educational media to prepare software suitable for the needs of their students; to provide expertise in the field to support educational media centres in the Arab world as they improve their services; to improve the skills and know-how of Arab specialists in the field through refresher courses and training programmes designed and administered by the Centre; to conduct research studies in the field on the regional level and encourage local authorities to design research that meets their needs; to co-ordinate media production among Arab countries to provide equipment and materials better in quality and more economical in price; and to strengthen the ties of co-operation between Arab experts in educational media and their counterparts in other countries to exchange ideas, research and experiences to improve production and use of educational media.

Future plans include training courses, seminars, and more effective research, co-ordination in the field of production offering consultation on the production and use of materials and providing national centres with standard specifications for software and hardware and other ambitious projects.

Regional centres – South America

*Associación Latinoamericana de Educación Radiofonica (Latin-American Association for Radio Education), Corrientes 816, Buenos Aires, Argentina

The aims of the Association are to research, promote and publicize all aspects of radio education, with particular reference to Latin-America and the work of member organizations and to act as a liaison body in all aspects of this work.

*Associación Latinoamericana de Teleducación (ALTE), Calle no 6-56 Of 403A, Apdo Aereo 4490, Bogota, Colombia

Promotes exchange of experience and expertise in uses of educational radio and television among 20 member countries. Publication: *Teleducación.*

Caribbean Regional Council for Adult Education (CARCAE), *see under Centres of Activity Worldwide – Trinidad and Tobago*

Centro Internacional de Estudios Superiores de Comunicación para America Latina (CIESPAL), *see under Centres of Activity Worldwide – Ecuador*

ILCE (Instituto Latinoamericano de la Comunicación Educativa) (Latin American Institute for Educational Communication), Apdo, Postal 94-328, Mexico 10, DF (Contact: Dr José Manuel Alvarez Manilla, Director)

ILCE was founded in 1956 and supported by Unesco and the Mexican Government. On 31 May 1978 the Latin-American and Caribbean countries signed a Co-operation Convention for ILCE's reorganization to provide leadership in educational communication and instructional technology in Latin-America. ILCE has as objectives regional co-operation in research; experimentation, production and distribution of AV materials; training of human resources in educational technology; the collection and distribution of AV materials and documents through the Centre of AV Documentation for Latin-America (CEDAL) and specific technical assistance in these fields on the member countries' requests. The library has a collection of 5000 volumes, and there is a bi-monthly publication *Sintesis Informativa*.

OREALC (Unesco Regional Office of Education for Latin America and the Caribbean), Casilla 3187, Santiago, Chile (Contact: Simón Romero Lozano, Director)

The Unesco Regional Office for Education in Latin America and the Caribbean, with Headquarters in Santiago de Chile, is one of the four regional offices (Africa, Latin America, Asia and the Arab States) through which Unesco carries out its decentralized programme in education throughout the various regions. The main functions of the Regional Office are: training and in-service training of educational personnel, advice to Member States in the region, technical support for projects in the region in which Unesco participates, information and documentation services, and the carrying out of studies and research on educational trends in the region. In addition to the *Boletín de Educación* (published every six months), a *Boletín bibliográfico* (monthly) and a *Boletín de informaciones estadísticas y análisis cuantitatico* (quarterly), the Regional Office publishes and distributes the working documents and the final reports of the meetings it organizes and the studies prepared in the framework of its Work Plan.

Proyecto Latinoamericano de Teleducación de la Fundación Konrad Adenauer (Latin-American Tele-education Project of the Konrad Adenauer Foundation), Apartado Postal 4951, Miraflores, Lima 18, Perú (Contact: Hugo Osorio M)

Co-operation of people through training, technical assistance and publications in tele-education throughout Latin America.

Centres of Activity in the United Kingdom

Centres of activity in the UK have been organized into three groupings:

1. Institutions and organizations in further and higher education;
2. Teaching support services at other levels;
3. Other organizations with an interest in education and training.

Institutions and organizations in further and higher education

University of Aberdeen Television Service, King's College, Aberdeen AB9 2UB (Contact: Alan Grimley, Director)

Established 1970 to provide television and film production services for the five faculties of the University in undergraduate teaching and research.

A one-year non-certificate Television Studies Course began for a two-year experimental period in October 1981.

Ballymena Technical College, Trostan Avenue, Co Antrim (Contact: R J Anderson)

Ballymena is a technical college providing all types of further education courses. It also co-ordinates the teaching of computer studies courses in all other schools and colleges within the area of the local education authority. The College Computer Centre provides a full processing and advisory service to schools and colleges within the local education authority area.

City of Bath Technical College Learning by Appointment Centre/ Programmed Learning Unit, Adult Education Department, Bath, Avon (Contact: Alan Mackie)

The Centre provides independent learning facilities over a range of topics and in a variety of media. A main area of development is in computer-assisted learning, both at the keyboard and 'at a distance'.

The Centre is the administrative base for the College's Open Learning programmes including Flexistudy, and for an internal 'correspondence' numeracy service using computer marked progress checks.

University of Bath

1. School of Education, Claverton Down, Bath BA2 7AY (Contacts: Professor K Austwick; Professor J J Thompson)

The School of Education in Bath is engaged, with the support of British Petroleum Company Ltd, in the preparation of teaching modules for general and business studies for school and college students. The School is also working with CET on evaluation, and provides a taught Master's degree course in educational technology, as well as facilities for research degrees in this area. Other topics of research interest include microelectronics in education.

2. Science and Technology Education Centre (Contact: Dr Eon Harper)

The Centre is an organization within the School of Education and carries out research development and consultancy in collaboration with members of the academic staff in the University. The functions include the application of educational technology in education at all levels. The Centre is a member of the Science and Technology Regional Organization (SATROS). Main activities include: research into readability, mathematical assumptions and conceptual assumptions in science, mathematics and other curricula; cost analysis of existing and developing curricula; evaluation of courses, laboratory and project work; encouragement and assistance in co-operative ventures between industry, commerce and education; development and evaluation of curriculum and industrial training material, specially aimed at long courses in education and technology; dissemination of experience, research and development through publications, in-service training, courses and seminars. A list of publications is available.

University of Birmingham

1. Department of Educational Psychology, Faculty of Education, Ring Road North, PO Box 363, Birmingham BI5 2TT (Contact: C F Buckle)

The Department of Educational Psychology offers post-experience courses at Advanced Diploma and BPhil(Ed) degree levels for practising teachers and lecturers. The courses are particularly concerned with the application of new psychological ideas to teaching and learning including the use of microcomputers in the school and the design of classroom or open learning materials.

Research degrees in this field are also available by full or part-time study.

2. Faculty of Medicine and Dentistry Educational Services Unit, The Medical School, University of Birmingham, Birmingham B15 2TJ (Contact: William G Fleming)

The role of the Unit is fourfold – consultancy, research into medical education, photographic and lecture theatre services.

University of Bradford Educational Development Service, Bradford, West Yorkshire BD7 1DP (Contact: Trevor Hearnshaw, Director)

The Service is responsible for supporting academic staff in their teaching and research. To achieve this, a comprehensive series of workshops and seminars are run each year in aspects of teaching and learning; and well equipped photographic, graphics and television units have been set up to assist staff in the preparation and production of a wide range of learning materials. The service works closely with the Library to ensure that students can use these materials for self-study.

Publications include articles and papers on the selection and use of audiovisual media, on teaching methods and on aspects of staff development.

Brighton Polytechnic Educational Technology Centre, Falmer, Brighton BN1 9PH (Contact: J Pearce)

The Centre possesses a wide selection of resources (film projectors, tape recorders, duplicators, copiers, teaching machines, programmed texts, resource files, etc). Students learn many of the basic skills from programmed assignment cards during an introductory course in educational technology.

The Centre is interested in programmed educational packages and has produced a number of these.

Bristol Polytechnic

1. Centre for Educational Services (CES), IE20, Bristol Polytechnic, Frenchay, Bristol BS16 1QY (Contacts: John Davidson or Trevor Habeshaw)

CES has the following terms of reference: to provide information and consultancy in the areas of course design and curriculum development; to develop a system of in-service staff development within the polytechnic; to advise departments in the purchase and use of AV equipment; to assist staff in the design and production of teaching materials; to act as a clearing house for information about innovatory activity within the polytechnic and to stimulate such activity.

2. Management Learning Productions (MLP), Room 3B10, Bristol Polytechnic, Frenchay, Bristol BS16 1QY (Contact: Brian Cawthray)

MLP are oriented towards the production of materials for management and business studies education. Their resource centre aims to provide a professional service making materials for and selling to educational establishments, local authorities and private business firms who are concerned with training, personnel and management development at all levels. On file are over 3000 ohp visuals and 2000 non-book items. Two bi-annual publications provide access to these materials – the *Management Teachers Handbook* and *Summary Papers on Management Subjects.*

Brunel University, Uxbridge, Middlesex UB8 3PH

1. Audio Visual Centre (Contacts: George Noordhof, Director; John Fanthome, Chief Engineer; Mrs Barbara New, Production Manager)

The primary purpose of the Centre has been to develop the use of television, audiovisual aids and photography in teaching in the University. The Centre operates a professional colour Television Studio, along with a mobile colour television unit. Recordings are made on Sony U-matic (broadcast standard) machines with interface editing facilities. Extensive videotape self-replay facilities for individual study are available in the University Library as well as departmental laboratories. Many of the television programmes produced by the Audio Visual Centre have been sold and distributed to other educational institutions, government bodies and industrial organizations. The Centre's facilities are also used by outside organizations for demonstrations, conferences and for the production of specialized educational and instructional videotapes. The Centre published a catalogue of video-recordings.

*2. Institute of Industrial Training (Contact: G P Ritterman, Training Adviser)

In addition to placement work, the Institute is engaged in the following activities: *Training Advisory Service:* a service to training officers in the private and public sectors on all matters relating to manpower planning, recruitment, selection and training, including advice on ITB matters and the implications of Government policy on company training matters. A regular discussion group for local training officers forms an adjunct to this service; *Short courses:* short residential courses for personnel managers and training managers on specialist aspects of the training function.

Bulmershe College of Higher Education, Bulmershe Court, Woodlands Avenue, Earley, Reading, Berks (Contact: A J Trott)

The College has a well-equipped resources and services area under the directorship of Mr L Giddins. College courses range from those of an introductory nature to those at second degree level, and carry awards from College certificate to degree. Educational technology units appear in the initial BEd(Hons) courses, the in-service BEd(Hons) course, the BA(Hons) and postgraduate and short courses for teachers. This Centre offers specialist advice, lectures, conferences and courses; and consultancy in the UK and abroad. Research interests include microteaching and the preparation of learning packages. Enquiries are welcomed from possible MPhil students.

University of Cambridge Computer Aided Teaching of Applied Mathematics (CATAM), Department of Applied Mathematics and Theoretical Physics, Silver Street, Cambridge CB3 9EW (Contacts: Dr Robert D Harding; John H Davidson)

CATAM was started in 1969 by lecturers in this department who found that computational analysis of certain problems in applied mathematics led to greater insight. CATAM aims to make this new mathematical tool available to undergraduate mathematicians, so that they may use it to improve their understanding of normal coursework. CATAM's approach calls for the students to write most of their own programs, apart from standard library routines. This in turn calls for a simple, reliable on-line computing system and system software, which the project staff aim to continue improving. Great emphasis is placed on the use of graphical displays, which enable the qualitative nature of mathematical results to be assimilated very rapidly. A list of publications is available on request.

University College, Cardiff, Centre for Educational Technology, 8 North Road, Cardiff CF1 3DY (Contact: Dr G D Moss, Director)

The Centre provides the College with a comprehensive teaching-support facility, including full production and design support for video and other productions. The senior staff of the Centre act as consultants on teaching problems within the College and are actively involved in curriculum development and the production of new learning materials for several teaching departments. The Centre also offers a variety of courses in communication skills to several departments and to outside organizations, and provides an option in Educational Technology in the MEd degree offered by the Faculty of Education. In addition it is now planned to offer a complete MEd (EdTech) programme in 1982 which will include options in distance education and educational broadcasting with particular reference to the needs of the Third World. Short specialist courses in educational TV and radio and in broadcast journalism will also be available in 1982.

Chelsea College (University of London) Educational Computing Section, Chelsea Centre for Science Education, Fulton Place, London SW6 5PR (Contact: R Lewis, Reader in Computer-Assisted Education)

Areas of activity are: 1. Educational computing, primarily computer-assisted learning; 2. Development of materials (written and computer-programmed) for use at secondary and tertiary level; 3. Computer software support to purchasers of the published materials; 4. Courses and lectures at Chelsea and other institutions; 5. Collaboration over CAL material development and research. Materials published include the revised *Chelsea Science Simulation*

Project (ten units) published by Edward Arnold (Publishers) Ltd; the revised *Computers in the Curriculum* packs, and new material in the sciences, mathematics and humanities will be published by Longman. Chelsea College has also been the base of *CUSC – Computers in the Undergraduate Science Curriculum* (produced in collaboration with University College London and the University of Surrey). (*See also* Schools Council *under Other organizations*).

Clydebank Technical College Department of Educational Technology, Kilbowie Road, Clydebank, Glasgow G81 2AA (Contact: Peter J Gayfer)

The Department offers the following services: PL by appointment; advice to local industry on training problems; liaison with local schools; photographic and graphic art services; 'packaged learning' production; and CCTV service. Research and development work is being undertaken on the use of learning packages in a variety of subject areas, but with particular accent on their use within machine-shop environments.

College of Librarianship Wales Media Services Unit, Llanbadarn Fawr, Aberystwyth SY23 3AS, Dyfed, Wales (Contact: T Evans, Director)

The College runs graduate and postgraduate courses in librarianship and information science. The MSU was created (i) to provide educational technology support for the College; (ii) to support media courses at the College; (iii) to advise library organizations on media matters. The Unit makes teaching materials for the College and associated organizations, in the form of printed materials, slides, OHTs, tape/slide and videotape. College publicity material is designed and printed by the Unit. Resource support is provided for the College's media courses and special short courses are provided for continuing education in librarianship, information science and educational technology. The Unit consists of five departments: printing, design, photography, studio production and teaching support. Details of materials and publications are available on request.

Committee for the Training of University Teachers (Contact: Vice-Chancellors' Committee, 29 Tavistock Square, London, WC1H 9EZ)

The Committee for the Training of University Teachers was established in August 1981 under the auspices of the Committee of Vice-Chancellors and Principals to review the current provision for the training of university teachers and to ensure that universities are made aware of this provision. The Committee draws its membership from the Vice-Chancellors' Committee, the Association of University Teachers, the National Union of Students and, on an *ad hominem* basis, from among those involved in universities in local training arrangements. The Committee is serviced by the Secretariat of the Vice-Chancellors' Committee. It is the successor to the Co-ordinating Committee for the Training of University Teachers which was formed in 1972 and dissolved in July 1981.

Coventry (Lanchester) Polytechnic Learning Systems Development, Priory Street, Coventry CV1 5FB (Contact: Stephen Cox)

Consultancy and support is provided for the academic staff, including the provision of an induction course for new members of staff; a staff development programme of workshops and other activities; liaison and advice on educational development matters and the support and stimulation of innovatory activity within the Polytechnic. There are separate visual aids and television services available for use by staff, and an active Media Unit in the Polytechnic Library.

Coventry Technical College, Education Unit, Department of Management and Training Services, Butts, Coventry (Contact: J E Hills)

The Education Unit operates long and short courses for teacher training, instructor training and educational technology. There is also an overseas consultancy service.

Dorset Institute of Higher Education Teaching Resources Centre, Wallisdown Road, Poole, Dorset BH12 5BB (Contact: Mr L O Pettman)

The Centre is fully equipped with audio and colour video studios, graphics and offset printing units, photography and audiovisual sections. It has produced a number of materials relating to hotel catering and administration. The centre runs short courses for industry in the production and presentation of visual/audio media.

Dundee College of Education, Gardyne Road, Dundee DD5 1NY (Contact: the Principal)

The college, which has been equipped as a high-activity centre for the implementation of educational technology with the aim of providing student instructional material, provides courses leading to the award of the CNAA Postgraduate Diploma in Educational Technology. One of these CNAA courses is offered by distance learning methods with short residential periods in the college and lasts between two and four years. Students will be awarded the college Advanced Diploma in Educational Technology if they are unable to attend in-college sessions. The CNAA Postgraduate Diploma in Educational Technology is also provided (one year full-time).

Dundee College of Technology Audio Visual Unit, Bell Street, Dundee DD1 1HG (Contact: A M Stewart)

The Unit is responsible for the production of self-instructional materials in a variety of media made available in the learning resources area of the College library. Courses in educational technology, including a post-experience diploma course, are offered for practising teachers and training officers.

University of Dundee Centre for Medical Education, Dundee DD1 4HN (Contact: Professor R M Harden, Director)

The Centre for Medical Education is the first of its kind in Britain. The Centre has a responsibility to help the faculty to improve undergraduate and postgraduate medical education. It is also an independent unit within the faculty carrying out its own programme of teaching and research. The work of the Centre is aimed not only at undergraduate students, but also at postgraduates and those engaged in continuing education. Activities include assistance to faculty; teaching; research and development including curriculum design, teaching methods, development of self-assessment techniques, and production of independent learning materials including printed and audiovisual formats. In addition, the Centre is engaged in exploring different approaches to learning; pioneering new approaches to continuing medical education; organizing courses and workshops for doctors from the UK and overseas; and providing a Medical Audio-Visual Aids Information Service (MAVIS), a Health Education Material Information Service (HEMIS), and a Medical Education Literature Retrieval Service. In the course of this work the Centre has produced and published a range of printed and audiovisual materials, and some study packages.

University of Edinburgh Department of Artificial Intelligence, Forrest Hill, Edinburgh EH1 2QI (Contact: Dr J A M Howe)

The Department of Artificial Intelligence exists to carry out research into the cognitive processes underlying such complex activities as seeing, interpreting natural language utterances, producing speech, problem solving and reasoning. It offers postgraduate courses in Artificial Intelligence, in part in conjunction with other departments such as Linguistics, Philosophy, Psychology and English Language; it also offers introductory and second level undergraduate courses. The principal research projects embrace problems in mathematical reasoning, automatic assembly, robot vision, man-machine interaction in natural language, applications of computers in education and in special education. Publications include: Howe, J A M, Ross, P M, Johnson, K, Plane, F and Inglis, R (1982) Teaching mathematics through programming in the classroom, *Computers and Education*, 6, 85-91; Howe, J A M (1980) Computers: a researcher's view, *Special Education: Forward Trends*, 7, 17-21; Howe, J A M (1981) Teaching handicapped children to read: a computer-based approach, *Proceedings of 3rd World Conference on Computers in Education* (Eds: Lewis and Tagg), North Holland; Sharples, N (1981) Microcomputers and creative writing in *Microcomputers in Secondary Education* (Eds: Howe and Ross), Kogan Page; du Boulay, J B H and Howe, J A M (1981) Re-learning mathematics through logo: helping student teachers who don't understand mathematics in *Microcomputers in Secondary Education* (ibid).

University of Exeter, The Teaching Service Centre, Streatham Court, Rennes Drive, Exeter (Contact: Donald Bligh)

The Centre provides Academic, Graphic and Technical Services for staff and students of the University including consultation and back-up for teachers, and study skills counselling and occasional workshops for students. Media presentations are also produced. *Contact:* The Centre has been asked by the Council for Educational Technology to establish a national telephone information service on research and developments in teaching and learning in higher education. It aims to put enquirers in touch with relevant persons in other institutions. *TEARS – The Exeter Abstract Reference System:* Primarily established as a service for Exeter University, the service is pleased to pass on information to other institutions. Information retrieval systems are maintained on research into Higher Education and on films available for hire.

University of Glasgow

1. Department of Education, 4 University Gardens, Glasgow G12 8QJ (Contact: W R Dunn)

Research and development projects include: (i) computer-assisted learning applications in medicine, mathematics, physics and teacher training; (ii) the production and implementation of resources to stimulate the development of the early communication skills of the profoundly handicapped, and the multi-handicapped deaf; (iii) the development of techniques for the assessment of practical skills, communication skills, problem-solving and attitudes; (iv) the development of techniques for the assessment of professional competence and distance learning techniques to promote professional competence.

The Department of Education offers courses leading to the MEd (Curriculum Development and Educational Technology) and the MPhil (Curriculum Studies).

2. Basic Mathematics at University Level Project, Mathematics Department, University of Glasgow, Glasgow G12 8QW (Contact: Professor J Hunter, Director)

Computer program exchange.

The Hatfield Polytechnic Centre for Educational Development, PO Box 109, Hatfield, Herts AL10 9AB (Contact: Trevor Jones, Senior Lecturer)

The teaching and practice of educational technology in its widest sense forms an integral part of the work of the Centre for Educational Development. The BEd degree for serving teachers includes an option in educational technology, and the Postgraduate Diploma in Applied Educational Studies is concerned with the systematic analysis, design and evaluation of curricula, teaching, learning and assessment methods. Educational services including audiovisual media services are provided for staff of the Polytechnic, and where possible curriculum development advice and support is given to staff of other colleges.

Hatfield Polytechnic is also the base of the CHESS (Computers in Higher Education Software Scheme) program exchange scheme (*see* CHESS *under Other organizations*)

Huddersfield Polytechnic Department of Education, Queensgate, Huddersfield, HD1 3DH (Contact: Dr D E Newbold, Head of Department)

The Department of Education at the Polytechnic is interested in the development of computer-assisted learning projects. A 380 Z machine is at present being used by students in their final year to assist them in developing learning packages. Access to the ICL 2960 Computer is encouraged.

The Department is closely involved in regional developments for the Government-supported MEP proposals. Education in the role of the 'Computer in Society' is a component of many degree courses at the Polytechnic. CAL is seen as an important element in teacher education at all levels, both initial and in-service.

Imperial College (University of London), the CEDAR Project (Computers in Education As a Resource), Imperial College Computer Centre, Exhibition Road, London SW7 2BX (Contact: N J Rushby, Director)

The broad aim of the CEDAR Project is to encourage and facilitate the development and effective use of educational computing within Imperial College, the University of London, and elsewhere. The Project supports teaching staff by providing an information service and demonstration facilities, by developing and implementing educational computer programs and by assisting with educational development and training. The Project has developed an information and advisory service, whence teachers in the College and from other organizations can get assistance with computer-based and computer-managed learning. Although developed for the College itself, the information service, which is unique in the UK, has been made generally available to other educational and training organizations in the UK and abroad. The Project has strong links with similar organizations abroad, particularly in France, Holland, West Germany, USA, Canada and the Soviet Union. It is therefore able to draw on a very wide range of expertise and paint a broad picture of the CAL scene. The advisory and information services provided by CEDAR may be divided into four categories: The *enquiry service* is founded on two databases held on the main College computer, which hold details of books, reports and papers on computer-based learning and related topics, and details of computer-assisted learning packages available in the UK. These catalogues are published in microfiche together with a keyword in context (KWIC) index, and can be searched on-line using a computer terminal and a simple enquiry program. Many of these books and reports are held in the *CEDAR collection in the College Library*, and are available on loan to members of the College and other libraries. The enquiry service is supported by *personal advice* from members of the College Computer Centre who have had considerable practical experience of computer-based learning and can relate the techniques to a variety of learning problems. CEDAR organizes a *programme of seminars and colloquia* on various aspects of educational computing. The seminars, given by guest speakers from the United Kingdom and overseas, are open to all interested parties. Over the past two years the Project has become deeply involved in providing training for both teachers and trainers on the use of computer based learning. Publications include: CEDAR (1981) *The CEDAR Project*, Imperial College London; many selective bibliographies on CBL and related topics and a number of papers particularly in the area of introducing CBL into the institution. A complete list is available on request.

Jordanhill College of Education, 76 Southbrae Drive, Glasgow, G13 1PP (Contact: G H Kirkland, Head of AV Media Department)

The College's areas of activity are the teaching of educational technology at pre-service and in-service levels of teacher training, and resource production and technical services are offered to all college departments. Distance learning materials are produced for CNAA Diploma in Educational Technology, also a wide range of resource material covering all varieties of non-print media.

University of Keele Department of Psychology, Keele, Staffordshire (Contact: J Hartley, PhD)

Research carried out at Keele University concentrates on two main areas: (i) the layout and design of instructional text; and (ii) teaching and learning in a university context.

Lancashire College, Southport Road, Chorley PR7 1NB, Lancs (Contacts: David J Herd, Principal; Pete E Darnton, Tutor in Educational Technology)

A Local Authority College concerned exclusively with high intensity short courses. Relevant activities include courses in Educational Technology; courses in TV production; courses in radio production; resource-based language courses; seminars and conferences connected with the media and resource-based learning. Full production facilities for radio, TV and AV presentations are available. Materials produced include TV films, sound tapes and tape/slide presentations produced to order for a wide range of industry, Public Service and Education Authorities; ELT training materials; language learning packages; distance learning packages on a variety of subjects.

Lanchester Polytechnic, *see* Coventry (Lanchester) Polytechnic

Leeds Polytechnic Educational Technology Unit (ETU), Calverley Street, Leeds LS1 3HE (Contact: W C Chavner)

The ETU is seen as a major factor in the Polytechnic's Educational Development Programme. Its purpose is to stimulate innovation in teaching and learning. It operates as a central service agency for the teaching staff providing equipment for teaching purposes (including a full colour TV studio set-up), runs educational development workshops for academic staff, and works on a consultancy basis with them. The Unit is not a constituent part of any faculty but, like the Library, is a major central service and is funded centrally by the Polytechnic.

University of Leeds, Leeds LS2 9JT

1. Audio-Visual Service (Contact: Dr J R Moss)

The Audio-Visual Service is a unified central service created in 1977 from the former Photography and Television Services, for the creation of television, film and photographic materials. Its prime purpose is to support teaching, learning and research at the University, and it is also increasingly concerned with the hire or sale of its resources to outside bodies, and the production of commissioned materials.

2. Computer Based Learning Unit (Contact: J R Hartley)

The Computer Based Learning Unit was set up by the Research Councils in 1969, and took part in the National Development Programme in Computer Assisted Learning which was funded by DES from 1972 to 1977. It has also received research grants and linked studentships from the Social Science Research Council. The Unit provides service teaching via computer-based materials to a variety of departments within the Social Science, Biological Science, Chemistry, and Medical Faculties. Research interests embrace: educational psychology, cognition, problem-solving, and artificial intelligence which is related to learning processes. Several full-time and part-time students are working in these areas. Recent work is exploiting the use of microcomputers in Secondary and Higher Education. A list of publications and materials is available on request.

CALCHEM (Computer Assisted Learning in Chemistry) programme exchange scheme is based at Leeds University

Leicester Polytechnic, PO Box 143, The Newarke, Leicester LE1 9BH

1. Centre for Educational Technology and Development. The Centre is engaged in the following activities:

Educational development services, media production services, teaching services, technical support services. Two campuses are involved.

The staffing comprises three academics, a secretary, two graphic designers, and eight technical staff. From time to time the staff is complemented by academic staff officially seconded to the Centre whole or part-time under the Leicester Polytechnic Internal Secondment Scheme. This innovation involves staff who wish to explore in depth a certain facet of their teaching, free from the pressures of teaching itself.

The Centre has recently opened a small but high quality TV studio, and a series of programmes are initially being made on staff development, dealing with such topics as teaching/learning strategies, evaluation, media production and the curriculum. Programmes may be purchased and a list of available material is supplied on request. Any member of staff may commission a programme, the priority being material made specifically for teaching purposes. Wherever appropriate, it is the Centre's policy to make this of a kind and quality suitable for wider distribution.

Other publications of the Centre which may be purchased include two instruments for evaluation: (a) *The Students' Feedback Questionnaire* and (b) *The Tutor's Self-Evaluating Questionnaire.* Details/prices of these supplied on request.

The Centre has a recognized teaching function. Courses and seminars are mounted for staff, and contributions are made to the BEd degree, MA Graphics (Information Design), and Cert FE course for serving teachers. A popular innovation has been a special course on communication techniques for students on many degree courses who need presentation skills as part of their curriculum.

A major function of the Centre is the Media Production Unit, a large workshop under the supervision of a highly qualified graphic designer: here staff may make, with or without assistance, a large variety of teaching media. This also incorporates an information unit, library of educational technology, and self-study area. A further important function of the Centre is to monitor the purchase, use and location of audiovisual equipment throughout the Polytechnic: while policy is generally to decentralize this into the Schools, certain specialized facilities are retained in the Centre.

2. Computer Centre (Contact: A Dawson, Information and Advisory Officer)

The Computer Centre provides services to support those aspects of educational computing that can benefit from the use of centrally managed facilities. The prime aim of the Centre is to support teaching within the Polytechnic. Support for research programmes is considered next in importance, followed by assistance with running programmes for educational administration.

The main computer system is based upon a Burroughs B6700 which can be accessed via the batch system, the Cafeteria Batch System or the terminal system. Twenty-four terminals are located in three laboratories, including six graphics terminals and other graphics facilities which are well used for computer aided learning, design and analysis.

The Computer Centre also has over 50 PET microcomputers, located in three PET laboratories and the library, which are heavily used for introducing computing to beginners. An increasing range of other microcomputers are also becoming available. As well as this hardware the Centre maintains a library of over 500 computer programs, for both B6700 and micros, which serve as teaching and research aids in a wide variety of subjects. A full list and brief description of all these is given in the *Software Catalogue Index.* An information sheet is available for the great majority of programs, giving details of the purpose and use of the program and an example. For the large and heavily used programs and packages and the main programming languages a user guide is also available, and so far about 70 user guides have been produced. To complement and support the range of hardware, software and documentation the Centre supplies a comprehensive news service, an advisory service, a programming service and a range of general and specific training courses which can be tailored to meet the particular needs of any group within the Polytechnic. A full description of all the Centre's equipment, facilities and services, and a list of available documents, is given in the *User Guide to Services.*

*University of Leicester, Centre for Mass Communication Research,
104 Regent Road, Leicester LE1 7LT (Contact: Professor J D Halloran)

The Centre's research programme focuses on the study of mass communication as a social process and the mass media as social institutions, both in the UK and abroad. Graduate students may read for an MPhil, MA or PhD. The Centre is also the headquarters of the International Association for Mass Communication Research.

University of Liverpool

1. The Department of Communication Studies, Chatham Street, Liverpool L69 3BX (Contact: G W H Leytham, Director)

The Department (initially the Audio-Visual Aids and Programmed Learning Unit) offers ten undergraduate courses in Communication Studies, and provides facilities for postgraduate research. Linguistic, psychological, sociological and media aspects of human communication are being studied. A full list of publications, including earlier research papers in educational technology, may be obtained on application to the Director. The Department continues to provide photographic and television services in monochrome and colour, and has produced a large number of videotapes, films, tape-slide programmes, slides, etc for teaching purposes.

2. School of Education, Abercromby Square, PO Box 147, Liverpool L69 3BX (Contact: Professor E Stones)

The whole field of educational studies is covered. A large and wide-ranging range of optional fields of studies is offered at Master's level with the provision of flexible scheduling and different forms of course make-up. Particular use of educational technology is made in the MEd options concerned with psychopedagogy (Professor E Stones). Programmed instruction is used and taught; CCTV is used extensively in microteaching, supervisor training and in the study of classroom interaction and interpersonal behaviour. Microteaching is also used in many of the PGCE courses.

University of London

(The following are central services of the University; centres of activity within Colleges are listed under Imperial College, Queen Elizabeth College, Queen Mary College, University College London.)

1. Audiovisual Centre, 11 Bedford Square, London WC1B 3RA (Contacts: Michael Clarke, MA, Director; R H Bradley, MBE, Chief Engineer; Patricia M Gulliford, Secretary)

Areas of activity are production of films, videotapes, sound tapes, tape-slide sequences and photographs, in association with the teaching staff of the University; design and production of associated print materials; information on audiovisual materials and methods; advice and assistance in communication problems in teaching or research; design of systems for TV production, AV equipment in teaching spaces, etc; assistance and co-operation with institutions producing their own AV materials; distribution, by sale, of the University's AV products. The activities of the Centre are limited to the schools, institutes and activities of the Federal University of London, and to institutions with which it has academic involvement; and to other co-operative activities with, eg, international agencies and public bodies, where academic institutions of the University are already active.

2. University Teaching Methods Unit, 55 Gordon Square, London WC1H 0NU (Contact: Allan Schofield)

The Unit's activities include: the provision of short courses and workshops which bring together teachers from a wide variety of disciplines to discuss common problems and develop skills in aspects of teaching such as lecturing, running seminars and tutorials; the provision of a venue for informal study groups on such topics as project work, the evaluation of teaching and interdisciplinarity; and the initiation of research and development activities in the areas of teaching and student assessment and the design and evaluation of courses. The Unit has an interest in educational planning, and consequently in various aspects of administration and management. Recently it has become increasingly concerned in helping institutions provide their own staff training and development programmes. As part of the University of London, UTMU will assist departments or individuals within the University on any educational procedure. Consultancy is also available to other institutions of higher education, although large-scale assistance usually cannot be provided because of the limited resources of the Unit. A resource centre housing a wide variety of training materials is at present being established. As an outcome of its training activities, UTMU has produced a number of publications of which the most recent are *Improving Teaching in Higher Education, Evaluating Teaching in Higher Education, Issues in Staff Development, Women in Higher Education, The Changing University, The Efficiency and Effectiveness of Teaching in Higher Education* and *Studies in Course Design.* A full list is available. From October 1978, UTMU has run a postgraduate diploma course in *Teaching and Course Development in Higher Education.* The course is available on both a full- and part-time basis, and applicants must have been employed as a teacher in a university or similar institution for the equivalent of at least one year full-time.

*Loughborough University of Technology

1. The Centre for the Advancement of Mathematical Education in Technology (CAMET) (Contact: Professor A C Bajpai)

Activities include: the review of mathematics curricula in higher education to meet the changing requirements of modern technology; the interpretation of the content of syllabuses with respect to the specific needs of applied scientists and technologists (the term 'applied scientists' includes students of biology, physics, chemistry, the social sciences, economics, etc); the development of educational techniques, in particular the use of educational technology in the teaching of mathematics for applied sciences and technology in institutes of higher education; liaison with schools in easing the transition from schools to university-level mathematics, particularly for students of applied sciences and technology; study of the use of computer-assisted instruction in the teaching of mathematics to engineers and scientists; much work in the study of the impact of school curricula being taken in the contents of the new A-level courses, their growth and development and the possible application of 'modern mathematics' in engineering and science; and investigation of the use of mathematical models in the teaching of mathematics to applied scientists. A number of materials have been produced and details are available on request.

2. GAPE (Geographical Association Package Exchange) is based at Loughborough University, Department of Geography – *see under Other organizations*

MUPCET (Midlands Universities and Polytechnics Committee on Educational Technology) (Contact: Dr C Tory, Chairman 1981/83, AVA Service, University of Leicester)

The Committee meets three times a year to exchange information and ideas and to discuss developments in audiovisual media and methods.

City of Manchester College of Higher Education, Hathersage Road, Manchester M13 0JA (Contact: J McCartney)

The College offers basic courses in audiovisual media methods to all students; microteaching with postgraduate courses and some other courses; the learning resources centre comprises multi-purpose workshops, small TV studio, sound recording studio and darkrooms.

Manchester Polytechnic Staff Development and Educational Methods Unit, Bracken House, Charles Street, Manchester M1 7DF (Contact: Miss B Hollinshead, Head of Staff Development Unit)

The Unit is responsible for staff development of existing and newly appointed staff. It covers a wide range of activities, is charged with developing the application of new educational activities in the Polytechnic, eg distance learning, Prestel in education, and with encouraging research in educational activities in the Polytechnic. The Unit has a number of major sponsored research projects. It also has a brief which relates to colleagues in FE and HE in the North, and holds workshops and conferences for such colleagues on a nationwide basis.

Methodist College Belfast, Physics Department, 1 Malone Road, Belfast BT9 6BY (Contact: Dr Martin Brown)

The Department took part in the CAMOL (Computer-Assisted Management of Learning – project of NDPCAL (Reference: *Physics Education* 14 (1979) 14). The Physics Department is developing computer-managed learning systems in O and A level science, including the use of videotapes and tape/picture material. It offers advice and a material exchange service to those working in or considering entering the field of open learning in science at this level. Independent learning units covering the A level physics syllabus with computer-generated individual comments on multiple choice questions.

Middlesex Polytechnic Learning Systems Group, Bounds Green Road, London N11 2NQ (Contacts: Rodney Battey, Bounds Green; Anne Howe, Bounds Green; Chris Osborne, Bounds Green)

The Learning Systems Group is part of the Learning Resources facilities of the Polytechnic. It is co-ordinated with the other learning resources, libraries, computers and media. Within the Polytechnic the Group has undertaken a wide range of activities. These include (i) dissemination of information within the Polytechnic to do with innovations and research in the fields of teaching and learning method. Seminar/workshops are held to illustrate innovation/research; a Learning Resources Bulletin is circulated; (ii) advice and consultancy to teaching staff on course curriculum development; (iii) advice about copyright, and assistance in obtaining copyright clearance; (iv) assistance in the development and production of new course materials;

(v) short courses in new teaching and learning methods for teaching staff; (vi) Study Skills programmes for students, and assistance to courses which wish to design and run their own 'Learning to Learn' courses; (vii) short courses and consultancy projects for industrial and other organizations in the preparation of materials and the running of special courses on aspects of Educational Technology; (viii) a Learning by Appointments service using programmed and other self-instructional materials is available to students of the Polytechnic. The service can also be made to people from other institutions; (ix) general research development projects, some sponsored by external agencies, including (a) repertory grid analysis for self-evaluation of teaching ability, (b) evaluation of TEC programmes in colleges, (c) computer-based diagnostic testing for EFL Visual communication development; investigation into the educational potential of PRESTEL and other viewdata systems.

Moray House College of Education Programmed Learning and Audiovisual Centre, Holyrood Road, Edinburgh (Contact: Dr J R Calder)

The College provides programmed texts, slides, filmstrips, overhead transparencies, cassettes, etc on free loan to Scottish schools, and assists teachers in overhead transparency and slide-making, etc.

Napier College of Commerce and Technology, Colinton Road, Edinburgh EH10 5DT

1. Learning Resources Unit (Contact: J R Foster)

The main activities and services provided by the Centre at Napier College are: Learning-by-Appointment (open five days per week); SCOTEC courses for the Higher Certificate in Audio-Visual Technology and Photography, both full-term and day release; training of College staff in the design and implementation of learning packages; production of materials to aid individualized student learning and aids for the classroom lectures.

2. Mathematics Laboratory Project (Contact: John A Hampton, Mathematics Department)

The Mathematics Department (in which the MATLAB Computer Assisted Learning Project is based) offers a range of Service Mathematics courses where the MATLAB material is used to aid the understanding of concepts or assist with data manipulation. MATLAB may be viewed as a sophisticated calculator with provision for producing graphs and manipulating matrices and statistical data. Current development includes establishing MATLAB on a PET microcomputer. The program is mounted on a CTL Modular I and Prime 550, and accessed via ASR 3.3 teletypes. Publications relating to the use of the MATLAB package include: *Teacher Guide; Student Manuals.* Details of publications describing the project are available on request.

National Extension College, *see under Other organizations*

New University of Ulster, Educational Computing Laboratory, Education Centre, Coleraine (Contact: H F McMahon, Senior Lecturer in Education)

The Education Centre provides first degree courses in education and communications and in-service Diplomas, Masters' and research degrees in education. The Educational Computing Laboratory provides a focus for those teaching and research staff and students engaged in developing and evaluating applications of computing to teaching and administration in both schools and higher education institutions. Major areas of expertise and experience are: the development and application of computer-managed learning systems to both in-house and distance education courses; development and evaluation of microcomputer systems for the implementation of computer-assisted learning in schools and colleges; trial and evaluation of teletext, viewdata and telesoftware systems in their application to education development and trial of computer-based systems for record-keeping, assessment and administration. Research into student learning in computer-based learning systems. The Laboratory provides some evaluation and consultancy services, and houses the Northern Ireland Regional Information Centre for the UK Microelectronics Educational Programme.

Newcastle upon Tyne Polytechnic (PETRAS), Pandon Building, Camden Street, Newcastle upon Tyne NE1 8ST (Contact: Joanna Tait, Head of PETRAS)

PETRAS is a central academic service department whose purpose is to promote in the Polytechnic an awareness of the opportunities and need for innovation and development in teaching and learning methods, and to provide a range of services which encourage and enable academic staff to implement changes and new approaches in this field. Encouragement, advice, and practical assistance in introducing new/revised methods of teaching and learning, and curriculum structures is the key service provided by PETRAS, and to which all its other services relate. Other activities are participation in Polytechnic Working Parties on, eg, Open Learning Systems and Recurrent Education; advice and support on developments in teaching and learning for local schools and colleges in the region; video, audio, photographic, microfiche, word-processor, typesetting, and related graphic design services; introductory programme for new academic staff; specialized seminars for academic departments, faculties, and the Polytechnic as a whole on issues such as: resources in teaching, small group teaching, open learning systems, use of AV equipment, microelectronics, and TV presentation courses; and a CNAA Postgraduate Diploma in Educational Technology (part-time). Materials and publications produced include printed advice on operating a number of basic items of AV equipment, and on study skills; videotapes; mixed media kits on *Child Abuse* and *Microelectronics*; and a series of items on *Microelectronics Education*.

University of Newcastle upon Tyne, Audiovisual Centre, Newcastle upon Tyne, NE1 7RU (Contact: R S Gilder)

The Centre is concerned with the design and production of effective audiovisual media for the whole University, for the regional hospitals and the postgraduate medical centres. The range of materials extends from simple graphs, charts and record photographs on the one hand to films, television programmes and teaching displays on the other. Many of the teaching packages are distributed nationally.

North East Wales Institute, Cartrefle College, Wrexham, Clwyd LL13 9HL (Contact: Dr J O Clarke, Head of Resources)

The Resources organization provides a wide range of media services including reprographic, photographic and television facilities. Educational technology, media and resources courses are provided for Institute students from the UK and overseas, for serving teachers and for special groups from the local community. Educational media advisory and production services are used by personnel in local government, hospitals, industry and schools.

North Staffordshire Polytechnic Computer Education Group, Computer Centre, Blackheath Lane, Stafford ST18 0AD (Contact: H E W Jackson, Chairman)

The Group is an informal organization for teachers and others interested in the use of computers in teaching in educational establishments. The annual subscription is £5 for UK members and £10 for overseas members. The subscription entitles members to three copies of the journal *Computer Education* per year, issued termly. In addition, the Group has 33 local branches based throughout the UK.

Northern Universities Working Party for Co-operation in Educational Technology (Contact: Angela J Bogg, Secretary, NUWPCET, University of Manchester Institute of Science and Technology, PO Box 88, Manchester M60 1QD)

The Working Party has not met recently, and may (temporarily?) be considered as being in abeyance.

University of Nottingham, University Teaching Service, School of Education, University Park, Nottingham NG7 2RD (Contact: Dr George Brown)

The University Teaching Service provides a service to all members of staff interested in developing their teaching. Courses and workshops on various topics and themes are organized, and advice on making films and videotapes and other audiovisual materials is given. There is also a consultancy service for students with learning difficulties and courses are run for students who wish to develop their methods of study. Most of the courses and workshops are technologically based. Small-group activities in conjunction with videotape feedback are used extensively in courses on explaining, lecturing, small-group teaching, tutorials, counselling and interview training. Further details are available from Dr George Brown.

The Open University

1. Committee on Communication Technology, Walton Hall, Milton Keynes, MK7 6AN (Contact: J K Hargreaves, Secretary)

The Committee promotes developments in and the use of communication/ information technology for distance learning.

Two projects are computer-based: *Cyclops* is an audiovisual system based on the conventional television set, standard audio cassettes, and microcomputer technology. It uses the facts that microcomputers can process pictorial information in digital form, and that this information can be stored on an audio cassette or sent along a telephone line. The Cyclops terminal can be used as a Prestel terminal, or as a colour graphics terminal for computer-assisted learning. Terminals can also be linked directly in 'electronic blackboard' mode, and a light pen used to 'write' on the television screen. The terminal can also be used in an 'electronic tape-slide' mode to replay sound and animated diagrams from a standard audio cassette. There is a big brother of the Cyclops terminal called the Cyclops studio. This allows the user to draw graphics and diagrams and store them on audio tape or computer systems. Cyclops is being used throughout one Open University region for teleconference tutorials, and will also be used at 1982 and 1983 Summer Schools.

Optel is a viewdata system that has been developed at the Open University. It runs on Digital Equipment DEC-20 computers, and offers a number of advanced features, such as page names, keyword retrieval, and automated help for information providers. It is being piloted in one Open University region and also used around the campus. If the trials go well, it is expected that Optel will be used as part of the distance teaching system, especially in the areas of educational administration and educational guidance. (Contact: Dr P Bacsich, Senior Project Manager, Information Technology)

Two projects involve tutoring by telephone, and research is carried out into tutoring techniques and educational effectiveness. (Contact: Ms B Robinson, OU Nottingham Regional Office)

An educational teleconference network using dedicated lines and loud-speaking equipment is also planned. (Contact: Professor J J Sparkes, Faculty of Technology)

2. Institute of Educational Technology, Walton Hall, Milton Keynes, Bucks, MK7 6AA (Contact: Professor David Hawkridge, Director)

The Institute is an academic unit within the Open University. Its staff advise course teams of the University, carry out course evaluation, and conduct a wide range of studies on the University's operations. Its activities are financed (1981) by about £1 million of the University's funds, plus funds from external sources for particular projects. The current bibliography is available free on microfiche and publications of the Institute may be ordered via the Director's Office. Visits to the Institute may be arranged via the University's office of Information Services. Other services of the Institute may be obtained through the University Secretary on a fee basis. Individual members of staff may act as private consultants and may be approached direct. In general, the Institute's work is for the benefit of the University.

Oxford Polytechnic, Educational Methods Unit (EMU), Headington, Oxford OX3 0BP (Contact: Mr Graham Gibbs)

Initially an audiovisual support service for part of the Polytechnic, the Unit is now the central AV resource and operates TV and graphics services as well as the provision and maintenance of basic AV equipment and materials. Consultancy to and training of both lecturers and students in teaching and learning methods started in 1980. There is a staff of 13 on two sites, 11 of whom are technicians with one senior lecturer and one principal lecturer, who teach for one-fifth of their time. The Unit's main activity is the day-to-day provision of basic AV equipment and materials, while it also provides TV production and a graphics service.

Academic services include evaluation, consultancy workshops, short courses and one-year (120 hour) compulsory initial training for new lecturers. Lecturers are seconded to EMU to undertake educational development activities. The Unit runs study skills courses, and individual study counselling. Publications include: *The Efficiency of the Lecture as a Teaching Method; Overhead Projector Handbook;* numerous collections of papers by lecturers on specific topics (eg study skills), numerous confidential evaluation reports; and *Teaching News* (twice-termly news sheet).

Plymouth Polytechnic, Learning Resources Centre, Drake Circus, Plymouth PL4 8AA (Contact: I D Sidgreaves, Head of LRC)

Courses are housed in newly adapted accommodation, including media workshops and colour studio. The teaching unit is part of the Learning Resources Centre of the Polytechnic and also houses the Devon County Schools Television Service. Courses include CNAA Diploma (one year full-time), Polytechnic Diploma (one term part-time) and National Diploma (two years part-time). All courses are based on projects produced to meet students' own needs.

Preston Polytechnic Centre for Educational Technology, Corporation Street, Preston, Lancs PR1 2TQ (Contact: D H Ormerod, Head of Centre)

The Centre offers courses and consultancy in all aspects of educational technology to staff and students of the Polytechnic and to schools, industry, the public services, etc within the region. Comprehensive production services are maintained in video, 16mm film, print, tape/slide, etc and the staff of the Centre are involved in research and development projects related to the use of the media in education and instruction in schools and industry.

Queen Elizabeth College (University of London), Campden Hill Road, London W8 7AH (Contact: for CAL – Brian Meek, Computer Unit; for other media – EAR Unit)

A college within the Faculty of Science with a special interest in computer-assisted learning, but also active in other media such as video and tape-slide. CAL programs are used and under development both for interactive terminals and for personal microcomputers; there is particular activity in the Biochemistry Department and a Physics and Computer Science CAL Laboratory. In other media there are Learning Aids Centres in Chemistry and Physics and an Educational Aids and Resources Unit serving the whole college.

Queen Mary College (University of London), Faculty of Engineering, Mile End Road, London E1 4NS

1. Computer Assisted Teaching Unit (Contacts: Dr P R Smith, Director; Mr C Sadler, Manager)

CATU was set up in 1973 to provide a computer-based teaching facility for the Faculty of Engineering at Queen Mary College. From 1973 to 1977 it was also the base for a national project under the auspices of the National Development Programme in Computer Assisted Learning. The project, known as the Engineering Science Project, involved the collaboration of ten departments of engineering in six tertiary educational institutions and resulted in the development of some 60 CAL packages in engineering. Main activities are now the development and implementation of computer-based teaching packages in aeronautical, electrical, electronic, civil, mechanical and nuclear engineering.

2. Engineering Science (CAL) Program Exchange (Contacts: Dr P R Smith, Director; Co-ordinator to be appointed)

The Engineering Science Program Exchange (ESPE) was set up in 1978 with support from the Council for Educational Technology in order to make available to the academic engineering community computer-assisted learning packages, developed by the Engineering Science Project of the 1973-77 National Development Programme in Computer Assisted Learning. The

Exchange also seeks to encourage co-operation and discussion between academic engineers by the issue of a periodic newsletter and the organization of occasional seminars on topics related to computer-based education. Main services provided: packages (computer readable source and full supporting documentation) are available in aeronautical, chemical, civil, electrical, electronic, mechanical and nuclear engineering topics; provision is made for exchange or purchase of packages (details available from the Co-ordinator); assistance and advice on computer-assisted learning package development is available to members of the Exchange. Contact the Exchange Co-ordinator for details of package titles, leaflets describing briefly the content and aims of packages, specification of documentation requirements for packages to be accepted into the Exchange, costs of membership and package handling charges.

University of Reading Academic Support Centre, Whiteknights, Reading RG6 2AP (Contacts: Mr D F L Pritchard, Director; Zoology, Dr E Johnson; Physiology and Biochemistry, Dr A G Stephens; Classics, Dr J G Landels)

The Centre purchases and services educational technology equipment within the University and advises on the use of such equipment. Slide tape and programmed materials have been developed and are in use in the Zoology, Physiology and Biochemistry and Classics Departments.

Robert Gordon's Institute of Technology, Educational Technology Unit, St Andrew Street, Aberdeen AB1 1HG (Contact: Dr H I Ellington)

The Unit is responsible for educational technology activities in RGIT and acts as a development centre for science-based educational games and simulations.

Royal Air Force School of Education, *see Other organizations*

Royal Military College of Science Electrical and Electronic Engineering Department, Shrivenham, Swindon (Contact: C A Sparkes)

A computer-assisted learning system was set up in the Electrical and Electronic Engineering Department in early 1975 to support undergraduate courses in electrical engineering and control systems. The System was enhanced, with funding from the NDPCAL programme, from late 1975 to the end of 1977. The project investigated the cost-effectiveness of the use of CAL in a service establishment and carried out transfer of CAL material from one establishment to another. The CAL system uses a PDP 11/40 processor, supporting three student stations, and running under RT11 MU Basic or RSX11M. Each student station consists of an Alpha-numeric terminal and a Graphics terminal with hard copy facilities. Documentation for each CAL package is provided for student use and for transfer.

Royal Navy School of Education and Training Technology, *see Other organizations*

SCEDSIP (The Standing Committee on Educational Development Services in Polytechnics) (Contact: Trevor Habeshaw, Chairman, Centre for Educational Services, Bristol Polytechnic, 1E 20 Coldharbour Lane, Bristol BS16 1QY)

SCEDSIP was established in 1974 to improve the effectiveness of educational development services in polytechnics. It collects and disseminates information, runs bi-annual conferences, organizes regional activities and publishes bulletins and occasional papers and a *Register* containing details of educational development service provisions in all the mainland polytechnics. (The third edition of the *Register* was published in October 1981.) While the SCEDSIP network was initiated within the polytechnic sector of advanced further education, it has welcomed to its various activities representatives and interested participants from other sectors, and it is its policy to extend and strengthen these links. To 'join' SCEDSIP involves attending its conferences and workshops, whether they are held at a national or regional level and where possible participating in, and contributing to, the activities generated under the SCEDSIP banner. This is the only requirement, though it is recognized that the levels of participation in SCEDSIP activities will vary with the interests of the individuals and the attitudes of their employing institutions. In establishing the organization, a network for the exchange of information and ideas has been established and the conferences provide the opportunities needed to diffuse and evaluate these ideas, which are the lifeblood of the organization. SCEDSIP acts as a publishing house for wider dissemination of innovatory ideas, and details of this can be obtained from the Secretary, Penny Griffin, c/o Middlesex Polytechnic. Other information about SCEDSIP can be obtained from its pages on PRESTEL by keying *226/ and then 226.50 et seq. SCEDSIP has a Publications Sub-Committee under the Chairmanship of Trevor Habeshaw of Bristol Polytechnic, to whom copy for future publications should be sent. It also has a Conference Sub-Committee whose Chairman, Stephen Cox of Coventry (Lanchester) Polytechnic will be happy to give further information about future programmes. A list of SCEDSIP publications is available from Derek Ormerod, Preston Polytechnic, Centre for Educational Technology, Union Street, Chorley, PR7 1ED.

University of Salford, Salford M5 4WT

1. Audio-Visual Media Section (Contact: Dr A I R Wiliam)

This Section is a service unit with overall responsibility for audiovisual equipment in the University. It offers courses of instruction in the use of audiovisual media as well as media production services.

2. Professional Development Programme (Contact: Dr E Wilde, Department of Mathematics)

The programme is concerned with the introduction to academic staff of appropriate educational methods and philosophies whilst preparing them to cope with continual changes occurring in their working environment as a result of social, economic and academic pressures. Mechanisms used for this include courses, workshops, seminars and discussion groups.

Sheffield City Polytechnic Instructional Technology Unit, Department of Education Services, 36 Collegiate Crescent, Sheffield (Contact: Quentin Whitlock)

The Unit continues much of the work of the former Programmed Instruction Centre for Industry at Sheffield University. Its main function is to encourage the use of individualized methods of learning in vocational education and training. The Unit's main activities are (i) regular courses in aspects of educational technology including (a) a two-part course on developing self-instructional programmes, (b) case studies and role plays, (c) CCTV production (in-company versions of these courses are available on request); (ii) development of learning materials for industry and the classroom; and

(iii) research into applications of educational technology. The Unit has published a variety of packages for industry and education, in the series PAVIC productions.

Southampton University, Department of Teaching Media, Southampton SO9 5NH (Contacts: W J Allen, Director; R E B Budgett, Administrator)

The Department is one of four in the Faculty of Educational Studies and contributions are made to the MA(Ed) degree course amongst others. A major contribution is made to the University's programme for Academic Staff Development and help is available to individuals or departments wishing to improve their teaching methods. Support for education and training activities in the Wessex Health Region is also provided. The Department is carrying out research and developmental work in academic staff development programmes, in teaching/learning methods, in student study skills and in the evaluation of learning materials.

Production and audiovisual service sections include photography, graphic design, medical art, audio-recording, display, 16mm film and tape-slide programme production. There is also a CCTV studio with facilities for production (in colour), microteaching and similar exercises, video-editing and dubbing. Most of the Department's 16mm films, television and tape-slide programmes on medical subjects are available from the Rank Film Library, Oxford Educational Resources and Concord Films Council; the remainder on a variety of other subjects including particularly, careers in engineering, industrial archaeology, safety and the use of Library collections are available from the Department (list on application).

South Thames College Department of Educational Resources, Wandsworth High Street, London SW18 2PP (Contact: C H Teall, Head of Department of Educational Resources)

The Department runs in-service courses for teachers and initial training courses for audiovisual technicians. A Diploma in Learning Resources course is offered on a one-year full-time or two-year part-time basis. The National Diploma in Educational Technology course operates in a distance learning mode. The short courses unit arranges courses for education and industry either internally in the College or based in schools, teachers' centres or clients' own premises. The course programme includes audiovisual media, resources management, design of learning materials, media workshops and closed circuit television. There are specialist facilities for graphics, photography, reprography, film making and television.

University of Strathclyde, Adviser in Educational Methods, Alexander Turnbull Building, 155 George Street, Glasgow, G1 1RD (Contact: Dr Alex Main)

Activities include staff development – the Adviser's office acts as focus for staff training and development activities; study guidance – the Adviser is responsible for general study guidance service to students; there is a Study Centre with individual viewing facilities and wide range of books and materials on study methods; individual counselling is available; the University has produced videotape materials on aspects of study skills; and research and development – the Adviser's office offers an advisory service to staff undertaking educational development projects within their own discipline.

University of Surrey, Guildford, Surrey GU2 5XH

1. Institute for Educational Technology (Contact: L R B Elton, Head of
Institute and Professor of Science Education)

The Institute is concerned with research and development in teaching and
learning in higher and secondary education. It offers a number of courses on
teaching and learning in higher education, including a Diploma in the
Practice of Higher Education which uses distance learning methods. This is
available to teachers in higher and further education both in Britain and
abroad. Students may register with the Institute for MSc, MPhil and PhD.
Further details and a list of publications are available from the Institute.

2. Computer Assisted Learning – A University Service – project (Contact:
T F Goodwin, Director, Computing Unit)

University of Sussex

1. Reginald M Phillips Research Unit, Falmer, Brighton (Contact:
Dr W J Watts, Director)

The Unit is concerned with research in educational technology, with special
reference to the education of deaf and other handicapped children. The
research undertaken includes problems of human learning, conceptual
development, psycholinguistics, curriculum development and media
organization.

2. Teaching and Learning Support Programme, Falmer, Brighton (Contact:
Dr Eric Hewton, Convener)

At the University of Sussex the Education Area provides a range of MA in
Education courses, for Teachers in all sectors of education, on both a full-
time and part-time basis. Some courses, such as Curriculum Development in
Schools; Curriculum Development in Higher and Further Education; and
Curriculum Evaluation, Planning and Management in the Context of
National Development, are concerned with the process of curriculum design,
development and evaluation across all disciplines. The curriculum is viewed
from several disciplinary perspectives and is studied in its organizational and
cultural context. Other courses, such as Education and Society; Language,
the Arts and Education; and Educational Policies and Decision-Making,
focus upon a particular aspect of the educational process and subject it to a
rigorous analysis from the standpoint of two or more disciplines. In all
courses the aim is to encourage professional development of teachers
through: reflecting upon and discussing their own experience; studying ideas,
concepts and theories which offer challenging alternative perspectives from
which to analyse this experience; and engaging in the search for solutions to
or clarification of problems and issues which they regard as important in
their own sphere of work.

Enquiries should be addressed to: The Admissions Secretary (IYE), The
Graduate Studies in Education Office, Education Development Building,
University of Sussex, Falmer, Brighton BN1 9RG

Trent Polytechnic Nottingham Centre for Educational Technology, Clifton,
Nottingham NG11 8NS (Contact: R P Hoare)

The Centre offers educational technology courses for students of CertEd,
BEd; a software production service, photographic, audio-tape and CCTV;
and information and advice for local teachers. The Centre is also carrying

out research and development work in tape/slide presentations and learning systems design.

Ulster Polytechnic Educational Technology Unit, Shore Road, Newtownabbey, Co Antrim BT37 0QB, Northern Ireland (Contact: G M Wilkinson, MA BSc DipEd ACP, Head of Unit)

The Unit promotes educational technology in the areas of course design, staff teaching, student learning, teaching/learning resources, relevant information provision and research. It teaches educational technology on certain courses in the Polytechnic and provides an external consultancy service in educational technology.

University College London, Department of Physics and Astronomy, Gower Street, London WC1E 6BT (Contact: Dr J McKenzie)

The Department was involved in the Development Project 'CUSC' (Computers in the Undergraduate Science Curriculum) funded by NDPCAL, based at University College London and run in collaboration with Chelsea College and the University of Surrey. The present main function is to develop and consolidate the use of interactive computer graphics as an enhancement of the teaching and learning of science, primarily at undergraduate level.

University Teaching Methods Unit, *see* University of London

University of Warwick Department of Psychology, Coventry CV4 7AL (Contacts: Professor J Annett; Mr G R Kiss)

The Department has a strong interest in training and educational technology and especially the use of microcomputers in training and education research. Research projects include work for SRC and SSRC and Manpower Services Commission on the acquisition and retention of skill and the use of microprocessors in psychological research.

*Windsor and Maidenhead College Learning Resources Centre, Boyne Hill Avenue, Maidenhead, Berks (Contact: Wendy R Unwin)

The Centre includes a 'Learning by Appointment' centre which offers courses by programmed texts and by machines, and also language courses. Short courses on audiovisual aids are also offered.

Wolverhampton Polytechnic Central Program Exchange, Wolverhampton WV1 1LY (Contact: A J Powell)

The Central Program Exchange is associated with the Council for Educational Technology. Its function is to provide a centre for the exchange of computer programs applicable in education, with special emphasis on software development for use on microcomputers in schools.

In parallel with this is the project 'Pertinent Concepts in Computing', the purpose of which is to develop self-teaching multi-media modules to assist in computer science education (contact: Mr G Wilday).

*Wythenshawe College, Moor Road, Manchester M23 9BQ (Contact: Peter L Smith, Learning Resources Area)

The College offers the following services: Audiovisual Technician's Certificate, CGLI Course 736 Part I, full- and part-time; short courses for industry and local government in the use of audiovisual equipment and the preparation of the related materials; remedial/revision using PL texts and machines in a variety of subjects, at present for College students only; and microteaching CCTV (education and industry).

Teaching support services at other levels

Advisory Unit for Computer-based Education *(see* Hertfordshire County Council, Advisory Unit for Computer-Based Education)

Avon County Resources for Learning Development Unit, Bishop Road, Bishopston, Bristol BS7 8LS (Contact: the Director)

This was a four-year project (1974-78) continuing the work of the Nuffield Resources for Learning Project, and was jointly funded by Avon County and the Department of Education and Science. The Unit is now administered by Avon County. Its work is organized within a number of clearly defined programmes. Each programme involves co-operative making of resources, consultancy, and in-service education. There is a strong emphasis on styles of classroom management using a wide repertoire of methods and media.

Bexley Teachers' Centre, Lamorbey Park, Burnt Oak Lane, Sidcup, Kent DA15 9BY (Contact: Miss Ann Cronin, BSc, Warden)

Background local support service and provider of In-Service Education for teachers in the Bexley London Borough. Activities include local curriculum development, in-service courses, information service, reprographic services, AVA loan service.

Central Region, Education Department, Viewforth, Stirling, Scotland (Contact: J K Sinclair)

The Region provides an advisory service and in-service courses for teachers in primary, secondary and further education establishments within the local authority's area. The Resources service includes a limited production facility.

Chiltern Consortium, *see under Other organizations*

Cornwall Resource Centre, Cornwall County Council, Old County Hall, Truro (Contact: Mrs J M Key)

Existing, and future, stocks of software materials will soon form part of a fully integrated, multi-media project collection service, in addition to the present loan system. The Centre also operates a radio and TV back-up recording service, and provides information and advice for schools. Its workshop supplies them with an installation and repair facility for their hardware.

Educational Foundation for Visual Aids (EFVA), The National Audio-Visual Aids Centre and Library, Paxton Place, Gipsy Road, London SE27 9SR (Contacts: G C Marchant; Heads of appropriate departments)

The National Audio Visual Aids Centre was established to provide educationists with a centralized and authoritative source of information and advice on all practical problems associated with the use of audiovisual resources in education and training. The activities at the Centre are part of the many services organized by the EFVA to promote and advance the effective use of audiovisual aids.

The Technical Sales and Service Departments: the supply, maintenance and repair of audiovisual equipment is undertaken by these departments through the network of regional and area centres at Bristol, Birmingham, Leeds and

Preston, Crawley, Doncaster, Nantwich, Newhaven, Penrith, North and South Humberside, and at London. Experienced staff can give practical advice on the supply, installation and performance of equipment. By its policy of bulk purchase, the sales department is able to offer a wide variety of equipment at discounted prices. Local education authorities and other organizations can also enter into servicing contracts at advantageous rates.

The Training Department: provides information and instruction on the application and potential of audiovisual media in teaching and training and organizes regular courses on television production and applications, film projection, the overhead projector and audiovisual techniques generally. Tailor-made courses can be arranged to run either at the Centre or in-house. The hire of video and other audiovisual equipment, and a three-camera colour television studio can be arranged through the Training Department.

Publications Department: responsible for publishing booklets and leaflets produced by the EFVA, including the catalogue of 16mm films in the National Audio-Visual Aids Library and catalogues of Filmstrips, Slides, Kits and Overhead Projector Transparencies. Books from other publishers are also available through the mail order section.

The National Audio-Visual Aids Library: houses one of the largest collections of educational and training films for hire or loan. Special borrowing schemes are available to local education authorities. The Film Library for Teacher Education is maintained at the Library. NAVAL also offers for sale 16mm films, videotapes, filmstrips, slides, kits, overhead projector transparencies, wallcharts and other audiovisual resources. Catalogues are available.

(*See also* Training and Educational Systems Testing Bureau *under Other organizations*)

Graves Medical Audio-Visual Library, *see under Other organizations*

Havering Educational Computer Centre, Tring Gardens, Harold Hill, Romford, Essex RM3 9QX (Contact: Mr W R Broderick)

The Centre provides an educational computing service for schools and colleges in the London Borough of Havering and investigates ways in which the computer can be applied in education. The Centre provides computing service for schools allowing pupils and teachers to run their own programs; provides computing service for schools allowing pupils and teachers to run programs from a central library; researches, develops, implements and supports computer-assisted learning and computer-managed learning programs; and provides administrative computing service for in-school administration. The Centre has produced the Havering Computer-Managed Learning System including courses and tests in the following areas: Mathematics, English, Physics, Chemistry and Biology, and has published the *JIIG/CAL Careers Education and Guidance System* (in conjunction with Dr S J Closs, Department of Business Studies, University of Edinburgh).

Hertfordshire County Council

1. County Programmed Learning Centre, c/o St Albans College, St Albans, Herts (Contact: W J K Davies, Director)

The Centre exists to investigate and to develop the techniques of individualized learning and the systems approach to education in their widest sense, to build up knowledge and experience in the practical uses of these techniques in both education and industry, and to make the results of its work available to interested people. It acts as a learning resource centre and is particularly concerned with remedial work and industrial training, for which it provides a consultancy service.

2. Mid Herts Teachers' Centre, *see* CET Prestel Education Umbrella Service *under Other organizations*

*3. Advisory Unit for Computer-Based Education, Endymion Road, Hatfield AL10 8AU (Contact: Dr W Tagg)

The Hertfordshire Computer Managed Mathematics Project (HCMMP) originated from an investigation at Hatfield School, Hertfordshire, into the use of a computer-managed system within a first-year all-ability mathematics course. In 1972 money was injected into the scheme by the National Development Programme in Computer Aided Learning (NDPCAL) and by Hertfordshire County Council. Funding from NDPCAL ceased with the end of that programme in 1977, by which time HCMMP had established itself within the 12 development schools in Hertfordshire and three schools in a 'transfer' experiment in the Inner London Education Authority. HCMMP is a mathematics project that offers two learning packages: ESYMRK – an approach to teaching a course of mathematics, when the pupils are in mixed ability lower secondary school classes, and SAM – an arithmetic testing scheme that diagnoses, for the teacher and pupil, areas of arithmetic where the pupil is encountering conceptual problems. Both packages are serviced by their own computer marking, routing and record keeping/reporting systems, which are offered as a technological aid to the teacher. Currently, assisted by a Department of Industry grant, the project is being implemented on a disc-based microcomputer with mark sense card input. The system can be operated in a school in two ways: (a) batch mode (between 6 and 24 hour turnround); (b) cafeteria mode (immediate turnround). All aspects of the project are centred on the Advisory Unit for Computer-Based Education and all information is available from the Unit.

Inner London Education Authority Central Library Resources Service: Centre for Learning Resources, 275 Kennington Lane, London SE11 5QZ

The Central Library Resources Service, part of the ILEA Learning Resources Branch, provides central reference, information and loan services to schools and colleges throughout the ILEA and support for all ILEA staff. The ILEA Education Library is based at the County Hall (London SE1). As well as a large book stock and a growing collection of periodicals relevant to education, the library displays all learning materials produced by the ILEA Learning Materials Service. At the Centre for Learning Resources, the Reference Library and Information Service has a major reference collection of materials for use in the classroom and library resources centre, and is fully equipped with appropriate audiovisual equipment so that visitors can preview them. An information hotline (01-735 8202) provides information about these, and other, resources. The CLRS Loans Division, which includes the ILEA Film and Video Library, makes a wide range of materials available for use within ILEA educational establishments. ILEA staff may borrow materials through the CLRS Loans Division.

NAVAC/NCAVAE (National Committee for Audio Visual Aids in Education), *see* EFVA (*above*) *and* Training and Educational Systems Testing Bureau *under Other organizations*

*Portsmouth Teachers' Resource Centre, Olinda Street, Portsmouth, Hants PO1 5HP (Contact: Ray Tingley, Organizer)

The Centre offers in-service training and curriculum development; media resources design, production and distribution; county resources loan service; equipment loan and service workshop facilities; and media management advice and training.

*Rochdale Teachers' Centre, Baillie Street, Rochdale, Lancs (Contact: C J Meek)

Services offered by the Centre are instruction in PL techniques; production of materials; T working groups (specific enquiries welcomed); and hard and software resources/AVA. The Centre is also carrying out research and development work on the Rochdale Programmed Learning Project (maths, English) (prim), Syncrofax programmes, and research into the educational use of CCTV.

Southend Teachers' Centre, Area Education Office, Civic Centre, Southend-on-Sea SS2 6ER (Contact: Bernard Crix, Warden)

Part of Essex County Council's network of centres for in-service education, offering short courses for teachers; various publications of professional and local interest; reprographic services; equipment loan scheme; information and advisory service.

*Surrey County Council Media Resources Centre, Glyn House, Church Street, Ewell, Epsom, Surrey KT17 2AR (Contact: Peter Turner)

The Surrey Programmed Learning Project is concerned with the development of learning systems and materials. The central core of materials is composed of branching and linear programmes, together with ancillary workbooks and texts, prepared by ESL Bristol Ltd for use on the Auto Tutor Teaching Machine and the Superviewer equipment. In addition, a production specialist works directly with teachers in schools on original materials and can make use of the technical facilities and staff of the Media Resources Centre for production support in a variety of formats.

*Tayside Education Committee PL Unit, Ancrum Road Primary School, 45 Ancrum Road, Dundee (Contact: Mrs Ann Lickley)

The Unit provides an advisory service for teachers, and students in-training, who are involved in initiating change through curriculum development, and the production of structured learning materials. Its general aim is to facilitate the implementation of educational technology through the provision of in-service courses and lectures, workshop facilities, and software editing and overseeing services. There is a close liaison between the Unit and the local College of Education (staff and students), and in-service courses for teachers are run within the Unit by Mrs Lickley.

Visual and Aural Aids Teaching Centre and Film Library, 65/67 Hanworth Road, Hounslow, Middlesex TW3 1UD

The Visual and Aural Aids Teaching Centre and Film Library is administered by Hounslow and serves the schools and other educational establishments of nine outer London boroughs. It offers the following services: *educational advice* – the Visual and Aural Aids Adviser is available to give individual advice concerning the use of audiovisual equipment. He is also pleased to give professional advice to the Borough Officers concerning the provision of equipment; *technical advice* – various items of mechanical and electronic equipment and models having subsequent modifications, are tested by the Technical Officer. He will also give advice concerning the installation of equipment and the wiring of schools. This is particularly important when considering installations such as public address systems, closed-circuit television, etc; *purchase of equipment* – a list of recommended equipment is compiled, based on educational usefulness, technical reliability, ease of operation, and price. The Administrative Assistant will give information on what equipment is recommended and where it can be obtained. Headteachers and teachers may visit the Centre by appointment to view equipment; *teacher training* – teachers may visit the Centre by appointment for training in the use of all types of audiovisual equipment, receiving individual attention from appropriate staff. The Centre also provides courses in the operation of equipment, its educational function and the use of materials. These are usually held at the Borough's Teachers' Centres (the Warden will have details), but can also be held at individual schools when no suitable course is available at the local Teachers' Centre and when sufficient staff will support the course; *16mm film/video library* – the Library contains over 1600 titles, mostly on 16mm film, but with an increasing number on VHS videocassette (120 titles – May 1981); *other services* – emergency service – Radio, Schools Broadcasts and Radiovision; Slide copying service – from teacher's original slide: slides made from original opaque material. Copyright clearance the school's responsibility.

Other organizations with an interest in education and training

Aslib, *see International Centres of Activity*

***Action Learning Trust,** 45 Cardiff Road, Luton, Beds (Contact: Charles Simeons, Director)

The Trust was set up as an educational charity in 1977 to consolidate and be a focal point for Action Learning (pioneered by Professor Reginald Revans). Action Learning involves the solving of real problems requiring an urgent solution through exchange of personal experiences between the learners. The Trust aims to provide a platform for all involved in Action Learning; exchange and dissemination of information; a reference library of books, pamphlets and cuttings on the subject. The first of a number of Conferences was promoted by the Trust in June 1979. Publications include a Monthly Bulletin, a Quarterly Newsletter, and sundry articles by members of the Trust.

***Agricultural Training Board,** Bourne House, 32-34 Beckenham Road, Beckenham, Kent (Contact: the Director)

Air Transport and Travel Industry Training Board, Staines House, 158-162 High Street, Staines, Middlesex TW18 4AS (Contact: Mr Westbrook, Public Relations and Information Adviser)

Army School of Training Support, Wilton Park, Beaconsfield, Bucks (Contact: the Commanding Officer)

The Army School of Training Support provides the Army with courses, applied research and development, and consultancy in the field of the systems approach to training. Emphasis is placed upon the derivation of training objectives through job analysis, course design based on selection of instructional objectives, and the validation of training and instruction. The School is divided into departments dealing with training development, instructor training, audiovisual aids, closed-circuit television, learning systems and the provision of a training consultancy service to the Army.

Association for Educational and Training Technology (AETT), BLAT Centre, BMA House, Tavistock Square, London WC1

For full information about AETT, *see* the article on page 10.

Association for the Study of Medical Education (ASME), 150b Perth Road, Dundee

ASME provides a forum for communication and a focus of ideas for those concerned with medical education. It publishes a series of booklets on medical education and the Journal *Medical Education*. It also organizes occasional conferences.

Association of Computer Units in Colleges of Higher Education, *see* CHESS (*below*)

*BACIE (British Association for Commercial and Industrial Education), 16 Park Crescent, London W1N 4AP (Contact: Christine Watkins, Head of Information Services)

BACIE is a voluntary educational charity. Its services cover the whole range of vocational training through (i) the Training Department, which provides short courses, seminars and conferences on training topics and tailor-made in-company courses; (ii) the Information Department, which answers members' queries in the field of training and further education, including information about external courses, training aids and training films; and (iii) the Publications Department, which produces a growing range of handbooks and training manuals, together with the *BACIE Journal* issued monthly except for August.

BALT (The British Association for Language Teaching), c/o Mrs E A Dyson, Glanffrwd, Fernbrook Road, Penmaenmawr, Gwynedd

BALT was founded in 1962 as the Audio-Visual Language Association. The change of name in 1977 reflects the broadening of its aims and activities. BALT branches arrange weekend or evening meetings on topics of interest and concern to language teachers, from new materials and methods to issues currently the subject of local or national debate. At these meetings, local BALT members meet many speakers who are expert practitioners in their field; each branch is directly represented at every BALT Executive Committee meeting, so that each member can inform and influence the Association in its work. The Association publishes *The British Journal of Language Teaching*.

BLAT Centre for Health and Medical Education, BMA House, Tavistock Square, London WC1H 9JP (Contact: Dr W D Clarke, Director)

The British Life Assurance Trust for Health Education, founded in 1966, is the joint creation of the British Medical Association, the Life Offices' Association, and the Associated Scottish Life Offices. To a large extent, the Trust represents the common ground that lies between medicine and insurance, and which exists because both have an interest in promoting the further education of the medical profession, and the general public, in the fields of preventive medicine and health. Working mainly through the medium of educational technology, BLAT seeks to promote this further education by encouraging individuals and institutions to introduce new ideas and materials into their teaching. Over the years the work of BLAT has been greatly assisted by the support of the Nuffield Foundation and the World Health Organization. WHO designated BLAT 'a Collaborating Centre for Educational Technology' so that it functions at an international level, especially in the developing countries of the Third World. The research and teaching functions of BLAT have resulted in a large number of publications in the form of books, journal articles, conference papers and learning materials. The main emphasis has been placed upon assisting teachers to develop methods and materials which promote individual/independent learning. A list of current research projects and publications for sale is available on request. The service function of BLAT takes the form of the provision of information – the operation of both a film library and a reference library consisting of books, periodicals and learning materials in all formats. The main vehicle of information is a bulletin called *Information*. The film library catalogue contains 900 titles. An audiotape recording and duplicating service, a photographic service, a printing service and TV recording facilities are available for the use of teachers in health and medical education; teachers in other fields are also assisted whenever possible.

Dr Mark L Braham, Sopers Farmhouse, Capton, Dartmouth, Devon TQ6 0JE

Educational consultant, researcher and writer; founder and secretary-general of the International Association for Integrative Education (Geneva, Switzerland); concerned with the development of strategies and heuristic models for interdisciplinary studies; and with the philosophical aspects of educational technology and general systems theory.

British Broadcasting Corporation, Engineering Training Centre, Wood Norton, Evesham, Worcs WR11 4TF (Contact: D G Enoch, Head of Training Section, Technical Operations)

Occasional CCTV courses are open to non-BBC staff. For dates and details, contact the Head of Engineering Training Department at the above address. Feedback classrooms and programmed texts are being used and development work is under way on individualized learning. Links with other organizations are welcomed in these areas. Programmed texts dealing with fundamental electrical/electronic principles are available for sale to other training organizations. Full details and an explanatory leaflet are available on request.

British Council Media Group, 10 Spring Gardens, London SW1A 2BN (Contact: A B Edington, Head)

The British Council exists to provide a wider knowledge of Britain and the English language abroad and is responsible for the development of educational and cultural relations between Britain and other countries. The British Council also acts as agent for the administration of HMG's Educational Aid Programme. The British Council's Media Group is charged with the promotion of the more effective use of radio, television and audiovisual media for developmental and educational purposes. This is done through (1) the identification and provision of British specialists to undertake short and long-term assignments in various aspects of media advice, training and application; (2) advising on and arranging training at British institutions in the various disciplines of media work; and (3) the provision of information on all aspects of media hardware and software. Publication: *Media in Education and Development* (formerly *Educational Broadcasting International*), a quarterly journal concerned with all aspects of media use.

The British Educational Research Association, c/o Dr S Delamont (Membership Secretary), University of Cardiff, PO Box 78, Cardiff CF1 1XL

The Broad aim of the Association is to encourage the pursuit of educational research and its applications for both the improvement of educational practice and for the general benefits of the community. In particular, the Association seeks to further the communication of educational research findings to all interested in the theory and practice of education, both within the educational system and in the community at large; promote co-operation among research workers in various disciplines working in the field of education; provide a professional framework for the critical discussion of problems and methods in educational research; and improve the training of, and facilities for, educational research personnel, so that their skills may be of maximum benefit to the community. Membership of the Association, which is generally on an individual basis, is open to all persons interested in educational research, and who are engaged in furthering the broad aim of the Association. At present there are some 400 members from varied locations who are, or have been, specialists in academic disciplines which can focus on educational problems.

British Industrial and Scientific Film Association (BISFA), 26 D'Arblay Street, London W1V 3FD (Contact: Colonel Keith Bennett, Director)

The Association of companies, organizations and individuals in industry, commerce, science and education with the producers and distributors of films, videotapes, slide and filmstrip programmes for all business purposes. Activities include festivals for films, videotapes and slides, conferences and meetings. Publishes specialized film catalogues and information sheets. Publicity and contacts (UK and overseas). Monthly magazine.

British Universities Film Council, 81 Dean Street, London W1V 6AA (Contact: Elizabeth Oliver, Director)

The Council is a representative body for universities and other institutions of higher education. Its objects are to encourage the production, use and study of audiovisual media, materials and techniques for degree-level teaching and research, and to provide a forum for the exchange of information and opinion in this field. The Council's Information Service deals with enquiries relating to the production, availability and use of audiovisual materials in higher education. A small reference library, a major collection of film catalogues and a file of appraisals on audiovisual materials currently available in the UK are maintained. Member institutions receive a free copy of the Council's major publications. These include the catalogue *Audiovisual Materials for Higher Education* which lists appraised materials currently available from a number of sources in the UK. The *Newsletter* appears three times a year. The *Higher Education Learning Programmes Information Service (HELPIS) Catalogue* lists audiovisual materials made in UK institutions of higher education. A series of source books is published (Pergamon Press). The Council is responsible for the Higher Education Film Library which is intended to provide an outlet for degree-level films and videocassettes which might not otherwise be accessible to teachers. Apart from regular activities such as conferences and screenings, the Council has established an Audio Visual Reference Centre, and an *Information Service Subscription* costing £15 per annum (including some publications) is available.

Carpet Industry Training Board, Eagle Star House, Alderley Road, Wilmslow, Cheshire SK9 1NX (Contact: B Hague)

The Carpet Industry Training Board offers advice based on the needs of the carpet industry. The training material is specific to narrow fields of application.

Central Programme Exchange, *see* Wolverhampton Polytechnic

Centre for Advanced Television Studies (at Fantasy Factory Video Ltd), 42 Theobalds Road, London WC1X 8NW (Contacts: John Hopkins, Sue Hall)

CATS publishes about 20 titles on video and film available by mail order plus *Portapak-based video production – foundation course* a training course for distance learning with professional supervision, produced for Unesco. Fantasy Factory Video is a non-profit video centre part-funded by the Arts Council of Great Britain and the British Film Institute, and provides information and advice, a reference library, video editing and production services.

Centre for Information on Language Teaching and Research (CILT), 20 Carlton House Terrace, London SW1Y 5AP

The Centre is open to individuals and organizations concerned with modern languages and their teaching. Its library has about 25,000 volumes, over 350 periodicals, a classified collection of documents and theses, and a special section which houses audiovisual and recorded language-teaching materials and has facilities for listening and viewing. A register of research in progress is maintained covering work on language, linguistics and particular languages, as well as language learning and teaching. Specialist staff answer individual enquiries, receive pre-arranged group visits and assist at courses and conferences by arrangement.

The Centre produces numerous publications, a catalogue of which is available on request.

Ceramics, Glass and Mineral Products Industry Training Board, Townsend House, 160 Northolt Road, Harrow, Middlesex HA2 0EF (Contact: Miss S M Sheen)

The main areas of activity are company manpower planning and training systems, management and supervisory development, technician and craft training (particularly in the engineering, road transport and plant maintenance areas), safety and industrial relations.

The Board has sponsored six training films on various aspects of safety at work.

*Chemical and Allied Products Industry Training Board, Staines House, 158-162 High Street, Staines, Middlesex TW18 4AT (Contact: D T Hardie, Manager, Health and Safety Training)

The Board has sponsored a number of major research projects on aspects of management and organization development and related implications for training. It co-operates with a number of outside organizations in setting up symposia, conferences and training courses, and produces a range of related

publications including training guides, research studies, articles,
recommendations, and a Training Development Bulletin which reports its
activities.

**CHESS (The Association of Computer Units in Colleges of Higher
Education),** Hatfield Polytechnic, Hatfield, Herts AL10 9AB

The Computers in Higher Education Software Scheme (CHESS) has
produced a short list of programmes, primarily for Higher Education but
with some programs suitable for sixth-form work. The topics covered are
accountancy, economics and business studies.

Chemistry Society, *see* Educational Techniques Subject Group of the
Chemistry Society (*below*)

Chiltern Consortium, Wall Hall, Aldenham, Watford, Herts

The Consortium was established in 1970 by five Colleges of Education in
Bedfordshire, Buckinghamshire, and Hertfordshire. In 1974 the Brent
Education Advisers joined the Consortium, followed by the Bedfordshire
Advisers in 1977. The present members are Bedford College of HE,
Bedfordshire Advisers, Brent Advisers, Buckinghamshire College of HE, and
Hertfordshire College of HE. The Consortium is governed by a Management
Committee comprising the Principal of each member establishment, and a
senior Education Officer from each of the LEAs financing the Consortium;
there is also a Consultative Panel of educational technology advisers and
lecturers from the member establishments. The unit is based at Wall Hall and
is administered by Hertfordshire County Council.

The main function of the Chiltern Consortium is to produce learning
material for applications in Higher Education, with a particular emphasis on
in-service teacher training. All projects are commissioned by lecturers and
advisers in member establishments and range from simple lecture support
material to multi-media packages designed for individual or group learning.
A speciality of the unit is the production of structured video programmes
edited from recordings of actual situations recorded on location.

A Members' Catalogue lists all items available to Consortium Members free
of charge. These include all programmes produced by the Consortium, a
selection of videotapes produced by other Consortia and Open University
television programmes recorded under licence. Additions to the catalogue are
publicized termly in the Consortium newsletter *Preview.* An educational
advisory service is provided for members seeking assistance with the selection
of appropriate Chiltern Resources Library materials for their courses.

A selection of Consortium programmes is available to educational bodies
throughout the UK and overseas. These are listed in an External Catalogue
available free to all enquirers. For borrowers who are not Consortium
Members, the Management Committee has approved a scale of hire charges
to help defray production and administration costs.

*Civil Service College Learning Resources Centre, Sunningdale Park, Ascot,
Berks SL5 0QE (Contacts: Rob Adamson; David Wynne)

The Learning Resources Centre was established in 1977. Its main functions
are to provide self-study facilities for use in conjunction with college courses;
administer a 'learning by appointment' scheme for new writers of self-
instructional material in the Civil Service; provide departments with
information on self-instructional and educational technology, and produce

materials for use in the Civil Service College and elsewhere in the Civil Service. Various materials related to Training of Trainers, Self-Instructional and Educational Technology techniques, office procedures, numeracy and effective written communication have been produced.

Clothing and Allied Products Industry Training Board, 10th Floor, Tower House, Merrion Way, Leeds LS2 8NY (Contact: Roy P Weldrick, Information Services Department)

Commonwealth Secretariat Education Division, Marlborough House, Pall Mall, London SW1Y 5HX (Contact: Director, Education Division)

The Secretariat encourages Commonwealth co-operation in education, including educational media and book development, through conferences, seminars, workshops, publications, and the exchange of information. Information and Advisory services are offered to Commonwealth countries and institutions on education and training programmes and on educational technology. Consultants for Commonwealth developing countries, specialist staff for their institutions, and third-country training for their personnel are provided by the Commonwealth Fund for Technical Co-operation. Publications include reports, commissioned studies and handbooks on educational topics.

Construction Industry Training Board, Training Services, Bircham Newton, near Kings Lynn, Norfolk

CITB gives advice on all aspects of training technology, especially programmed learning and related techniques for application in the industry. CITB also develops and publishes a wide range of training materials including self-instruction texts and packages to meet specific training needs.

Co-operative College, *see* International Co-operative Training Centre

Cotton and Allied Textiles Industry Training Board, 10th floor, Sunlight House, Quay Street, Manchester (Contact: Information Officer)

Council for Educational Technology, 3 Devonshire Street, London W1N 2BA (Contacts: Geoffrey Hubbard, Director, Jill Coates, Information Officer)

The Council was established by the Government in October 1973 in response to the recommendations of an official working party representing a wide range of educational and training interests. It replaced, and took over the resources of the former National Council for Educational Technology (established in 1967). The Council is an autonomous body, deriving most of its financial resources from government departments. Most of its members are appointed as representatives of organizations, associations and authorities concerned with education or occupational and vocational training. Assessors are appointed to the Council by government departments with a similar interest in education and training. The Council's activities include co-ordinating and facilitating the work of organizations providing specialist or regional services in educational technology; acting as a focal point for the dissemination of information and advice; assisting in identifying the requirements of various sectors of education and training for services and materials in educational technology and arranging for these needs to be met; and initiating development programmes and studies of educational innovations. A list of free and priced publications is available on request.

The CET also operates the Prestel Umbrella for Education and Training

(Contact: Mrs Mary Hope at CET), which is based at the Burleigh Teachers' Centre, Wellfield Road, Hatfield, Herts AL10 0BZ (Contact: The PRESTEL Editor)

CET leases pages to educational and training organizations so that they can put information on to PRESTEL. CET assists with the design, inputting and updating of frames. The service is non-profit-making and the aim is to offer the use of this new technology at the lowest possible rate to a wide range of organizations. The cost per frame is £19 plus VAT. The service includes: advice on the structure and content of database; editing and design; inputting and updating; indexing on PRESTEL and PRESTEL directories; daily retrieval and postage of response frames; monthly frame access counts.

Directorate of Training, 162-168 Regent Street, London W1R 6DE (Contact: Mrs P A D Tickle)

The Directorate, which is part of the Training Services Division (TSD) of the Manpower Services Commission, operates in conjunction with the Industry Directorate and the Training Opportunities (TOPS) Directorate of the TSD across the whole spectrum of UK training and research with the operating brief of helping to bring about improvements to the effectiveness and efficiency of the national training effort. Its activities are separated into eight departments as follows: Commercial and Business Training; Training for Safety and Health at Work; Training Information; Management Development and Industrial Relations; Occupations and Topics based on Technology and Science (young people); Psychological Services; Training Research and Surveys; Trainer Training and Training Methods. (*See also* Training Services Division (*below*))

Distributive Industry Training Board, MacLaren House, Talbot Road, Stretford, Manchester M32 0FP (Contact: H Webb, Information Director)

In the field of educational technology the Board offers a training advice service by its field force, a number of half-day, one-day and three-day courses, and an extensive range of publications including films, video programmes and slide/talks as well as course manuals, etc. The Board also has a team of careers information officers, operating regionally.

ETEMA (Engineering Teaching Equipment Manufacturers Association), Leicester House, 8 Leicester Street, London WC2H 7BN

The British system of engineering education is world famous for its emphasis on instructional laboratory work and practical training. A consequence has been the development of a unique industry concerned with the design and manufacture of specialized equipment, apparatus and materials for use in the teaching of engineers and technicians. Most of the principal companies in this industry are members of ETEMA. Each member company has extensive links with the academic and training world and is familiar with all aspects of engineering teaching, both in the UK and abroad. Comprehensive back-up services are provided: instructional literature, student software, suggested syllabuses and laboratory/workshop design examples are available for the whole range of subjects with which members are concerned. ETEMA is affiliated to the Industrial Council for Educational and Training Technology (ICETT) – see below.

The Educational Techniques Subject Group of the Chemical Society
(Contact: Dr D H Maass, Department of Chemistry and Applied Chemistry,
University of Salford, Salford M5 4WT)

The Society has two main aims: to provide up-to-date information to
teachers and trainers on the methods, techniques and materials available for
chemical education; and to originate new materials for use in chemical
education.

Educational Television Association, 86 Micklegate, York YO1 1JZ (Contact:
Patricia Kelly, Administrator)

The Educational Television Association brings together institutions and
individuals using television and other media for education and training. The
Association is generally recognized as the major organization representing
the views of those whose experience is in the creation of audiovisual material
and the employment of the media for educational purposes. Member
institutions include Universities, Polytechnics, Colleges, LEAs, Schools,
Training Boards, Broadcasting organizations, the Armed Services, as well as
commercial and industrial organizations, in the United Kingdom and
elsewhere. The Association provides a forum for the exchange of experience
and information on all aspects of the production and use of television at all
levels of education and training. It encourages high production and technical
standards and promotes research and evaluation into the use of the medium.
It fosters contact at management level between units on such matters as
staffing, training, technical installations, etc. It liaises with organizations in
all areas of educational media development both in the United Kingdom and
internationally and speaks authoritatively on behalf of its members on
policies affecting the development of educational television. Activities and
services now offered to members include the *Journal of Educational
Television*, the annual conference on educational television and regional
meetings throughout the year, the Directory of Members (under revision),
the Newsletter of the Association, published quarterly, the ETA Awards
scheme, and access, through the Executive Committee, to related
organizations and to the Association's own Technical Liaison Committee,
Design Liaison Committee, Research Group and other expert sub-
committees.

*Electricity Supply Industry Training Committee, The Electricity Council, 30
Millbank, London SW1P 4RD (Contact: D Williams, Chief Training Officer)

The earlier work of the ESITB in producing programmed texts and other aids
has been supplemented by the production of such training aids as a training
package on basic safety and an audiovisual presentation on the work of the
ESITB. Electricity boards have welcomed this contribution to the effective
implementation of training, and more work is in progress, an example being
the preparation of a range of training materials related to the industrial
relations training recommendation.

Employment Relations Ltd, 62 Hills Road, Cambridge CB2 1LA (Contact:
David Rigglesford, Resource/Administration Manager)

Employment Relations Ltd, previously known as the Industrial Relations
Training Resource Centre, is an independent company sponsored by the
Manpower Services Commission and provides a range of information and
advisory services, most of which are available free of charge. The Company's
primary purpose is to provide a national focus for activity in the field of

management training, especially in industrial relations. To meet this objective, the Company has a staff of experienced practitioners working on the development of training materials which are used by companies throughout the UK. Current training programmes include such titles as *Collective Bargaining, An Introduction to Negotiation* and *Industrial Relations and the Supervisor.*

The Company houses a comprehensive collection of video, film and audiovisual material, publications, case studies, examples of company practice and reference materials covering all aspects of industrial relations training. Thus visitors can inspect under one roof almost the entire range of training materials available in the UK, as well as receiving guidance from the Company's staff in their use and appropriateness to any particular organization. In addition, the Company publishes a free quarterly journal, *Topics*, which reviews recent acquisitions to the library as well as developments in the field of industrial relations training. Through close working relationships with academics and practitioners in the field, the Company can provide information about recent research and developments which may not be otherwise available, as well as evaluative references to consultants across the range of industrial relations activity. The Company also acts as a catalyst for initiating new ideas and approaches to the improvement of industrial relations and management training through seminars and conferences held from time to time around the UK.

Engineering Industry Training Board, PO Box 176, 54 Clarendon Road, Watford, Herts WD1 1LB (Contact: Mrs M Holmes)

The Board's four major objectives are to:
- (a) help the industry to secure key aspects of the training situation in the engineering industry;
- (b) help companies to identify, plan and make the most effective provision for other training necessary to achieve their own corporate aims;
- (c) help bring about an improvement in the deployment and use of manpower in the industry as a whole;
- (d) provide training facilities and information best provided for the industry as a whole rather than by individual companies.

Its main training activities are:
- (a) operator training;
- (b) craft and technician training;
- (c) technologist training;
- (d) professional engineers;
- (e) management and supervisor training;
- (f) commercial and administrative occupations;
- (g) training of industrial training staff;
- (h) mechanical and electrical engineering construction industry.

The Board has produced an extensive range of training materials, including self-instructional manuals for craftsmen and operators and instructor guides and training recommendations. A publications list is available from the Board.

*Food & Drink Industry Training Board (Northern Ireland), ITB House, Glenmount Road, Church Road, Newtownabbey BT36 7LH (Contact: Mr R Patterson, Board Secretary)

The Board was set up in 1969 under the Industrial Training Act (Northern Ireland) 1964. Its objectives are to (i) ensure an adequate supply of properly trained men and women at all levels of industry; (ii) secure an improvement in the quality and efficiency of industrial training; and (iii) share the cost of training more evenly between companies in the industry. In order to achieve its objectives the Board operates a Levy Remission and Grants Scheme enabling companies to try and qualify for a maximum of 110 per cent of levy assessed in remission and grants. To enable companies to take full advantage of this, the Board provides a training advisory service through which individual companies are given guidance and assistance in planning and implementing the training programme through a systematic approach. It also provides a number of courses where there appears to be a specific need or to update companies on new legislation, etc. A number of other training services are also provided directly by the Board. These include management and supervisory development schemes, training in hygiene, safety, sales, office and business, fork lift truck and driver training.

Food, Drink and Tobacco Industry Training Board, Barton House, Barton Street, Gloucester GL1 1QQ (Contacts: for publications or publications list – A Calvert, Publications Editor; for all other enquiries – J T Newton, Secretary and Deputy Director)

The Board's main area of activity is a training review, advice and grants service to companies in the food, drink and tobacco industries in Great Britain. This service is restricted to companies which are 'in scope' to the Board. The Board has produced training packages and a full list of its publications is available.

*Footwear, Leather and Fur Skin Industry Training Board, 29 Birmingham Road, Sutton Coldfield, West Midlands B72 1QE (Contact: J Edgar, Chief Executive)

The Board produces a range of job descriptions and training recommendations for industries 'within scope'. A publications list is available.

Foundation for Teaching Aids at Low Cost (TALC), Institute of Child Health, 30 Guilford Street, London WC1N 1EH (Contacts: Professor David Morley; Mrs Barbara Harvey)

This Foundation is concerned with providing low-cost teaching aids, particularly sets of slides with full descriptions, which will help in teaching health care in developing countries. Some of the sets of slides are also appropriate for use in industrialized countries. Requests for price lists of sets of slides and books should be addressed to: Mrs Barbara Harvey, TALC, PO Box 49 St Albans, Herts AL1 4AX.

*Foundry Institute Training Committee, 50-54 Charlotte Street, London W1 (Contact: O G Wheeler, Secretary)

Furniture and Timber Training Board, 31 Octagon Parade, High Wycombe, Bucks (Contacts: A R Searle, Technical and Production Training Services Manager; C K McGivern, Management Development Manager)

The Board's areas of activity are technical and production training within the furniture and timber industries; and management training and development. It has produced a number of films and a list of these and other publications is available.

Geographical Association Package Exchange (GAPE) (Contact: David Walker, Department of Geography, The University, Loughborough, Leics LE11 3TU)

GAPE is a Geographical Association Project which exists to promote computer-assisted learning in geography. It acts as a forum for the exchange of information and publishes computer programmes relevant to geography teaching.

Graves Medical Audio-visual Library, 'Holly House', 220 New London Road, Chelmsford, Essex CM2 9BJ

A postal library service of medical and paramedical audiovisual material, mainly in the form of audiocassettes and slides. A catalogue containing over 1200 titles is available on request.

*HELP(P) Higher Education Learning Project (Physics) Contact: Jon Ogborn, Chelsea College Centre for Science Education, Bridges Place, London SW6 4HR)

HELP(P) is a working alliance of teachers in universities and colleges, initially in physics but increasingly involving teachers in other related subjects, who are concerned with the quality of their teaching. HELP(P) aims to help teachers by promoting discussion and exchange among them. The Project has published four books and has developed networks of people interested in several kinds of teaching problem. It is planned that this activity will continue, supported by local and national meetings, and by information circulated by its newsletter.

Home Office Unit for Educational Methods, Moreton-in-the-Marsh, Glos GL56 0RH (Contact: Head of Unit)

The Unit was established in 1968 to provide educational and training material for local authorities' fire brigades. Its terms of reference were expanded in January 1975 and the Unit now offers consultancy and production services in most aspects of educational technology to Home Office departments.

Hotel and Catering Industry Training Board, Ramsey House, Central Square, Wembley, Middlesex HA9 7AP (Contact: M H McDougall, Senior Information Officer)

Training related to operations and management in the Hotel and Catering Industry is the Board's main area of activity. It has produced numerous training packages.

The Industrial Council for Educational and Training Technology Ltd (ICETT), Leicester House, 8 Leicester Street, London WC2H 7BN (Contact: J M Wright, Chief Executive and Secretary)

ICETT worldwide areas of activity; its membership, co-ordinated through the Association of Consultants in Education and Training; the Audio Visual Aids and Allied Manufacturers Association; the Engineering Teaching Equipment Manufacturers Association; and the Project Contractors and Suppliers Association; embraces British companies, firms, associations and individuals concerned with the design, manufacture, production, publishing, marketing and servicing of technological products and services, involving the provision of consultancy and supply at all levels and including large-scale projects, for education and training throughout the world (see page 186).

Industrial Relations Training Resource Centre, *see* Employment Relations Ltd

The Industrial Society, Peter Runge House, 3 Carlton House Terrace, London SW1Y 5DG

The Society is a leading British advisory and training body in man management and industrial relations. The Society's practical services include in-company advice and training courses and conferences, information, publications, audiovisual programmes and a quarterly magazine.

Industrial Training Boards: ITBs are listed individually throughout this section.

Industrial Training Research Unit, Lloyd's Bank Chambers, Hobson Street, Cambridge (Contact: Dr E Belbin)

The Industrial Training Research Unit is supported mainly by a five-year rolling grant from the Manpower Services Commission to conduct authorized and commissioned research into problems related to industrial selection and training: 1. team skills management; 2. test design and validation (i) trainability assessments, (ii) job disposition analysis, (iii) high grade tests for managers; 3. development of self-organized learning and autonomous working groups; 4. study of instructor effectiveness; 5. training for the transition from school to work. Seminars are organized on 1, 2(i) and 2(iii) above.

The Institute of Chartered Accountants in England and Wales, PO Box 433, Moorgate Place, London EC2P 2BJ (Contact: E T Brueck, Training Officer)

The ICAEW is a professional institute concerned with the education, training, examination, regulating admission and the work of Chartered Accountants. The training activities include the provision of a comprehensive training advisory and consultancy service on student training and the provision of courses, particularly for updating and for continuing education. The Institute's Training Services Section develops training packages for accountants and their staff, designed for group training and home study. A comprehensive range of material is available including audio and video cassettes; publications catalogue available on request from the Professional Development Services Department.

Institute of Medical and Biological Illustration, 27 Craven Street, London WC2N 5NX (Contact: N Pearce, Department of Medical Illustration, Royal Gwent Hospital, Newport, Gwent NPT 2UB)

The Institute of Medical and Biological Illustration was founded in 1968, to bring together all those professionally engaged in audiovisual communication in the life sciences. Its function is to stimulate the study and application of all aids to communication in medicine and biology – by advising on the use of such aids, by improving the knowledge of those producing and using them, and by acting as a qualifying body. Publications are *IMBI News*, house journal, circulated every two months, and *The Journal of Audio Visual Media in Medicine*, published quarterly by Update Ltd.

The Institute of Training and Development, 5 Baring Road, Beaconsfield, Bucks HP9 2NX

The Institute is an independent, voluntary association of members engaged in training and vocational education at all levels, in industry, commerce, administration and the public services. Its aims are to represent training and the interests of the professional trainer, to promote the development and application of training, and to set and maintain high levels of knowledge, skill and performance for training staff. The qualifications awarded by the Institute are the Certificate in Training and Development and the Diploma in Training Management.

The benefits of membership include giving weight and authority to the Institute as representative of the profession, recognition of individual professional standing, access to the information and appointments services, participation in local branch activities and preferential rates for attendance at conferences, seminars and other national Institute meetings. The journal *Training*, published 11 times a year, is issued free to all members.

Full details of membership and the services offered, and the regulations governing the Certificate in Training and Development and the Diploma in Training Management, may be obtained from the above address.

International Co-operative Training Centre, Co-operative College, Stanford Hall, Loughborough, Leics (Contact: The Education Officer, Administration and Services)

Training courses of three months' and nine months' duration are offered in the management of co-operative organizations in LDCs.

A substantial element of the course content is 'training for trainers'; the College has excellent training, video and closed circuit TV facilities. (*See also* CEMAS *under International Centres of Activity*)

*International Correspondence Schools, Intertext House, 160 Stewarts Road, London SW8 (Contacts: A Spencer; B Usher)

Over 500 different correspondence courses are available, covering business, electronics, accountancy, plus a wide range of general and leisure subjects. Specialist industrial training services are also available.

Iron and Steel Industry Training Board, 190 Fleet Street, London EC4A 2AH (Contact: R Duncan, Director)

Knitting, Lace and Net Industry Training Board, 4 Hamilton Road, Nottingham (Contact: P J Dennis, Information Officer)

Local Government Training Board, 4th Floor, Arndale House, Arndale Centre, Luton LU1 2TS (Contact: E Hayes, Information Officer)

The overall aim of the Board is to influence local authorities in England and Wales and all other relevant bodies to ensure that training, to the required standard and quantity, is provided for local government employees. Some of the methods used to achieve this aim include.

(a) acting as a source of professional training advice and, where appropriate, assistance, to all bodies concerned with training and examining local government employees;

(b) obtaining and disseminating all information on manpower, developments in training and related issues;

(c) issuing training recommendations and other material, including training packages based on analytical studies and research, and giving advice and assistance in support;

(d) setting and recommending training standards and systems of assessment, and implementing these for specific groups of employees.

Man-Made Fibres Producing Industry Training Board, Langwood House, 63-81 High Street, Rickmansworth, Herts WD3 1EQ (Contact: The Administration Officer)

The Board stimulates, monitors and advises on industrial training and related further education within the man-made fibres producing industry.

Manpower Services Commission, *see* Directorate of Training (*above*) *and* Training Services Division (*below*)

Merchant Navy Training Board, 30-32 St Mary Axe, London EC3A 8ET (Contact: R C Matthew, Secretary)

The Merchant Navy Training Board is the central organization for the discussion of all matters affecting training and education in the Merchant Navy. It formulates the industry's training policies and liaises with statutory bodies. It comprises representatives of employers, employees, educationalists and government assessors and mainly operates through sections concerned with specialist areas and sponsors relevant research projects. The Board issues training bulletins and produces films.

MICE, c/o Dr Morfydd Edwards, Polytechnic of the South Bank, Borough Road, London SE1

This computer program exchange group comprises teachers working on software development. It is building up a library of programs mainly concerned with teaching computer appreciation and computer studies, which can be made available to interested parties.

Microelectronics Education Programme (MEP), Cheviot House, Coach Lane Campus, Newcastle upon Tyne NE7 7XA (Contact: Richard Fothergill, Director)

See article on page 75.

*Mills & Allen Communications Ltd, Broadwick House, 15/17 Broadwick Street, London W1V 2AH (Contact: Ian Inglis)

Mills & Allen Communications is a wholly owned subsidiary of Mills & Allen International. The company is one of the largest publishers on PRESTEL, the Post Office viewdata system, as well as being involved in other forms of electronic publishing and computer-based information systems. The company is also active in computer software – the Systems Division is concerned with developing programmes for dialogue applications and other mass-user computing. Products include software tools for preparing Computer-Based Training, courseware, ie programmes designed to teach a wide range of topics. Mills & Allen Communications are actively involved in promotion of computer-based learning techniques as a valuable aid, particularly within the training functions of business organizations both large and small, and are currently engaged in two major programmes in this area. The first, funded by the Training Services Division of the Manpower Services Commission, is to establish a number of pilot projects in computer-assisted training in various business environments to demonstrate the viability of computer-based techniques. The second programme, receiving funding under the Software Products Scheme administered by The National Computing Centre, is to develop an authoring system to enable non-programming training staff to create computer-based training courses.

MUSE Software Exchange Scheme, Freepost, Bromsgrove, Worcs B61 7BR (Contact: Charles Sweeten)

MUSE (Mini and Microcomputer Users in Secondary Education) offers, to members only, packages developed by members (frequently practising teachers) covering mainly mathematics, statistics, some chemistry and computer applications.

National Association for Staff Development in Further and Higher Education, Redgrave House, Prestbury, Macclesfield, Cheshire SK10 4BW (Contact: Dr F D Bacon, FRSA)

The Association represents the special interests of staff development officers and other teachers (including local authority advisers) concerned with staff development and in-service education in both maintained and non-maintained sectors of further and higher education (including training departments in the public service, business and industry). The Association disseminates information to its members, and holds at least two conferences a year on topics of prime importance to its members. It provides advice, assistance and general services and information for its members and opportunities for the progression of fresh ideas, as well as fellowship with colleagues and advising and assisting them in their projects and improving their impact in their own establishments. It is particularly concerned to disseminate information regarding all changes and developments in the management of learning, including those arising from rapid technical developments. The Association publishes a journal (March and September).

The National Audio-visual Aids Library, see Educational Foundation for Visual Aids (EFVA) *under Teaching support services*

National Committee for Audio-Visual Aids in Education; The National Audio Visual Aids Centre, see (EFVA) *and* Training and Educational Systems Testing Bureau (*below*)

The National Computing Centre Ltd, Oxford Road, Manchester M1 7ED (Contact: Manager, Training Development)

The National Computing Centre Ltd is a non-profit-distributing organization financed by industry, commerce and government. It is dedicated to promoting the wider and more effective use of computers throughout the economy. In realizing its objectives, the Centre gives information and advice; provides education and training; promotes standards and codes of practice; co-operates with, and co-ordinates the work of, other organizations concerned with computers and their use; and publishes training materials and books.

Training packages currently available include the following: Basic Computing Concepts (V) for clerical staff; Computing for Managers (V); COBOL Programming (V); Filetab Learning Module; Structured FORTRAN (V); Business BASIC; Introduction to Data Processing; Programming Techniques and Practice; The Implications of Computing Technology; Systems Analysis Training Library. (Note (V) indicates that the package includes video programmes on cassette.)

National Centre for Developments in Nurse Education, Sheffield City Polytechnic, 55 Broomgrove Road, Sheffield S10 2NA (Contact: Mrs Jean Heath, Information Officer)

The Unit, funded by the Department of Health and Social Security since 1972, has the following functions in regard to nurse education: to administer an information and consultancy service to promote the application of educational technology to nurse education; to produce materials in areas of special need; to conduct short courses for nurse educators on developing curricula and to conduct evaluative research on use of educational technology in nurse education.

National Extension College, 18 Brooklands Avenue, Cambridge CB2 2HN (Contact: Executive Director)

The College was founded in 1963 to develop improved methods of home-based adult education. Its activities include correspondence courses, study packs, flexistudy courses, television-based courses, outreach work with young unemployed, and basic skills materials for young unemployed.

National Foundation for Educational Research in England and Wales (NFER), The Mere, Upton Park, Slough, Berks SL1 2DQ (Contact: Alfred Yates, Director)

The NFER is an independent research institute carrying out empirical research in education and educational psychology. The Foundation investigates problems of the public education system at all levels in England and Wales, and collaborates on a national and international basis with other educational and research bodies. Membership is institutional (corporate and affiliate) and both members and Board of Management are very widely representative of organizations from the public sector in England and Wales. Current information concerning educational research projects in the UK is obtainable from the Educational Research Data Bank. *Tests:* the Test Department of the NFER-Nelson Publishing Company (Darville House, 2 Oxford Road East, Windsor, Berks SL4 1DF), sells educational, clinical and occupational tests, and advises on their use and construction. It is also concerned with the research standardization and evaluation of tests and assessment procedures. A Test Library is maintained, which incorporates the test collections of the BPS and NIIP. *Statistical services:* these offer access to data processing and computer centre facilities at moderate cost and are consulted about the analysis of projects being conducted by members of other organizations and individual teachers. The following publications are available from the NFER-Nelson Publishing Company: Research Reports, *Register of Educational Research in the United Kingdom, Eudised R and D Bulletin,* the journal *Educational Research* published three times a year, and a newsletter, *Educational Research News,* published twice yearly. The following are available through NFER Information Services: the '*Research in Progress*' series and other reports, mostly of an interim character, issued by our Projects; *Research Information Brochures,* and Project Newsletters.

National Health Service, Learning Resources Unit, *see* National Centre for Developments in Nurse Education

National Reprographic Centre for Documentation, Hatfield Polytechnic, Bayfordbury, Hertford, Herts SE13 8LD (Contact: A M Hendley)

The Centre is concerned with organizations and individuals interested in reprographic and micrographic techniques in further education, industrial training, libraries and information units, colleges of education and universities. A quarterly journal and special publications are produced. Services offered by the Centre are the testing and evaluation of reprographic equipment, seminars and courses on specific applications of micrographics and word processing.

The Network of Programmed Learning Centres (NPLC), The Polytechnic, Holly Bank Road, Huddersfield HD3 3BP, West Yorks (Contact: Bernard Alloway, Secretary)

Details of the Network and its membership are included in full on page 187.

*Northern Ireland Training Executive, ITB House, 33 Church Road, Newtownabbey BT36 7LH

Paper and Paper Products Industry Training Board, Star House, Potters Bar, Herts (Contact: Mrs Helen Wardle, Editor and Communications Adviser)

The Board specializes in day-to-day advice to individual establishments within scope of the Board (1550 establishments employing approximately 170,000 people); direct training in the form of courses and seminars for managers, supervisors and trade union representatives; published advice – recommendations, guides and guidelines. A publications list is available.

Peat, Marwick, Mitchell & Co, 5th Floor, 1 Puddle Dock, Blackfriars, London EC4V 3PD (Contacts: J Fielden; P K Pearson)

A professional management consultancy practice, whose main activities are consultancy services in management and organizational studies, financial evaluations and analyses and data processing and microprocessor studies; and development and provision of training seminars for senior staff on financial subjects and microprocessor applications. Evaluation studies of educational technology, computer-assisted learning and educational microprocessor applications have been prepared. The organization has produced a series of case studies on costing educational innovation (CET copyright) as follows: *The Costs of Education in the UK* by P K Pearson, CET 1977; *The Cost of Learning with Computers* by J Fielden and P K Pearson, CET 1978; *Costing Educational Practice* by J Fielden and P K Pearson, CET 1978, and *The Cost of Innovating and Change in Education*, PLET Vol 15, No 1, February 1978.

Petroleum Industry Training Board, Kingfisher House, Walton Street, Aylesbury, Bucks HP21 7TQ (Contact: Information Unit)

The Board provides advisory services to the petroleum industry and supplies direct training service at the Offshore Training Centre (comprising fire, drilling and production training) together with other courses where these are not otherwise available to the industry.

Details are also available from the Offshore Training Centre, Forties Road, Montrose, Angus DD10 9ET.

Prestel Education Umbrella Service, *see* Council for Educational Technology

Printing and Publishing Industry Training Board, Merit House, Edgware Road, London NW9 (Contact: John Baxter, Head of Communications Unit)

The PPITB was set up in 1968 and operates from a head office and five regional offices. It deals with, through the means of a committee structure and a permanent staff of 160 people, the following areas of activity: national newspapers; regional newspapers; general printing; periodical publishing; book publishing; general publishing; newsagencies; photography screen process printing and display; reprography; letterpress blockmaking and engraving. Major elements in this current training strategy include the development of staff at all levels to meet the demands of change, both in terms of technology and competition. At management level this involves courses, case studies, training packages and in-company specialist work. On the shop floor, it means the first-year integrated course for production workers giving a broad base on which further training and retraining can take place in-company using a modular system of unit training enabling the trainee to train precisely for the job to be done. Emphasis is also placed on supervisor training and on encouraging companies of all sizes to adopt a planned, systematic approach to training, derived from present and future commercial needs. A publications list is available.

Road Transport Industry Training Board, Capitol House, Empire Way, Wembley HA9 0NG (Contact: Information Centre)

The Board specializes in the production of imaginative and up-to-date training aids and kits for managers and trainers, and in the application of systems thinking to the analysis and solution of management problems. Leaflets describing its various techniques can be obtained from the Board, as can details of its instructional materials.

Royal Air Force School of Education, RAF Newton, Nottingham NG13 8HL (Contact: The Officer Commanding)

The School was established in 1948 to provide induction training for education officers and assistants entering the Service. Since then, responsibilities have expanded and now the School's overall aim is to improve the standard of training throughout the RAF. To achieve this aim the School organizes and conducts courses in support of RAF training and education, offers advice and consultancy, and provides specialist services for the Ministry of Defence in the administration of examinations and in research and development in the fields of educational and training technology. The major courses run by the School are Management of Training, Education Officers' Orientation, TV Familiarization, Instructional Techniques, Command and Staff Tutor Training, English Language for Overseas Students, Flight Simulator Instructor Training, and Presentation Techniques. Advice and consultancy is provided in the areas of Training Design and Management, Instructional Techniques, Packaged Learning, CAL/CML, Resources/Media, and Assessment Techniques. The School also publishes the RAF Education Bulletin.

Royal Army Educational Corps, *see* Army School of Training Support

Royal Military College of Science, *see Institutions and organizations in further and higher education*

Royal Naval School of Educational and Training Technology, HMS Nelson, Portsmouth, Hants (Contact: The Commander)

The RN School of Educational and Training Technology is the Lead School for educational and training technology in the Royal Navy. It provides training for RN, RM and WRNS personnel in the management, design and execution of education and training, including the use of CCTV. It also provides advice and assistance to MOD(NAVY) and to all Naval Commands and establishments on matters concerning educational and training technology and carries out research and development projects in support of the Naval Training System as required by the MOD. The School is a centre for the evaluation of Computer Based Training (CBT) as applied within the Royal Navy and also maintains a CODAP-based facility for the execution of occupational and other analyses.

*Rubber and Plastics Processing Industry Training Board, Brent House, 950 Great West Road, Brentford, Middlesex (Contact: D R Small, Public Relations Officer)

The Board has produced several slide/tape programmes.

The Schools Council Computers in the Curriculum Project, Educational Computing Section, University of London, Chelsea College, 552 Kings Road, London SW10 0UA (Contact: Mrs Sophie McCormick, Project Co-ordinator and Information Officer)

The first computer-assisted learning work at Chelsea College, the Chelsea Science Simulation Project, began in 1969 and was supported by a Shell grant. The Computers in the Curriculum Project developed from this and has been supported by the Schools Council since 1973. Additional funding is now provided by the Microelectronics Education Programme. The Project aims to investigate and evaluate the use of CAL in secondary schools across the curriculum and to provide new learning materials.

The Project operates nationally and support from LEAs, advisers and teachers has enabled subject writing groups to be established throughout the country. These regional groups are involved in the development and production of new material in the sciences, mathematics, the humanities, languages and craft design technology. The Central team at Chelsea co-ordinates the regional work, provides secretarial and programming support and advises on the style of programs and documentation for publication. It also organizes the school trials of new materials and has established a lecture service and training scheme now being taken over by the MEP.

The Project is undertaking the revision of published material to take into account the new facilities available on microcomputers and to produce programs easily adaptable for a variety of machines by writing the newly developed Library of routines.

Publications include the *Chelsea Science Simulation Project* published by Edward Arnold (1975-77) (10 packs); *Computers in the Curriculum Packs in Biology* (1978), *Chemistry* (1978), *Economics* (1978), *Geography* (1979), *Home Heating* (1979) and *Physics* (1978), published by the Schools Council; and the *Software Library of Routines* published by Schools Council (1981). To be published in 1982: second editions of currently published material, and new materials in the sciences, economics, geography, history and mathematics.

The Scottish Council for Educational Technology, 74 Victoria Crescent Road, Glasgow G12 9JN (Contacts: Richard N Tucker, Senior Assistant Director; James W Mackechnie, Information Officer)

The Council's area of activity is the promotion of educational technology in its widest sense to all levels of education, industry and commerce, and its services include information service, advisory service, Scottish Central Film Library, preview and sales service, and technical service. Educational technology is supported through research, promotion and development, courses, conferences, exhibitions, etc. Details of publications are available on request.

*Scottish Film Council, 16 Woodside Terrace, Glasgow G3 7XN. SFC is a division of the Scottish Council for Educational Technology (Contacts: R B Macluskie, Director; J Brown, Assistant Director)

SFC is responsible for the promotion of film culture in Scotland, forming a counterpart to the British Film Institute. SFC's activities include promotion of film study in education; development of regional film theatres; support for the film society movement, amenity cinema, etc; assistance to amateur/ independent film makers and promotion of video; archival activities, etc. SFC can provide information and advice on a wide range of concerns in film, especially cultural concerns. SFC has published *Video in Scotland*, a survey of video facilities in Scotland, and *Vale Television*, a report on the experiment of local television broadcasting which took place in Dumbartonshire in 1976.

Scottish Microelectronics Development Programme (SMDP), c/o Scottish Council for Educational Technology (no information supplied by SMDP)

*Shipbuilding Industry Training Board, Raebarn House, Northolt Road, South Harrow, Middlesex (Contact: M E R Bulloch, Information Officer)

The Board has produced three programmes available for firms in the industry and, if stocks allow and if the applicant has a genuine need for them, to 'outsiders'.

Society for Academic Gaming and Simulation in Education and Training (SAGSET), Centre for Extension Studies, University of Technology, Loughborough, Leics LE11 3TU (Contact: the Secretary)

SAGSET was founded in 1970 to encourage and develop the use of games and simulations in all areas of education and training in which they are suitable. Membership is open to anyone who is interested in the techniques. SAGSET assists communication between simulation/gamers working in different subject areas and at different levels, between theoreticians and practitioners, research workers and producers, and computer-based and 'manual' simulation/gamers. It achieves these aims by means of publications, conferences and an enquiry service. The principal publication is *Simulation/ Games for Learning*, a quarterly periodical which carries articles on the use, design and evaluation of simulation and games, reviews of games, simulations and books, abstracts of research and news about courses and conferences. It is edited by Fred Percival, Glasgow College of Technology, to whom all editorial correspondence should be addressed. Members also receive *SAGSET News*, which provides information about the Society's activities, a calendar of courses and conferences, lists of references, and can be used as a notice board for members to get in touch with groups having similar interests. Subscription and membership enquiries should be sent to SAGSET's Secretary at the permanent address given above. The Society runs an Annual Conference, usually in September. Proceedings from the 1975 conference onwards are available under the series title *Perspectives on Academic Gaming and Simulation*. In addition, short courses and one-day workshops are sponsored. The enquiry service tries to meet members' needs for information, contacts and advice. SAGSET also publishes specialized lists of books and materials available in various subject areas and is the sole distributor in Europe for the Stadsklev handbooks listed below. Since its foundation in 1970, SAGSET has built up a growing membership and network of contacts both in the UK and abroad. It has informal links with the International Simulation and Gaming Association (ISAGA), with the North American Simulation and Gaming Association (NASAGA) and with APLET itself. It is also a participating body in the Council for Educational Technology. Its publications include *Simulation/Games for Learning* (edited by F Percival), published quarterly by Kogan Page; *Aspects of Simulation and Gaming* (edited by J Megarry, 1977), an anthology of Volumes 1-4 of SAGSET Journal, published by Kogan Page; *Academic Gaming and Simulation in Education and Training* (edited by G I Gibbs and A Howe, 1975), published by Kogan Page; *Handbook of Simulation Gaming in Social Education, Parts I and II* (by R Stadsklev, 1974 and 1975) published by University of Alabama/SAGSET; *Perspectives on Academic Gaming and Simulation* (series title of annual conference proceedings), published by Kogan Page. So far, the volumes available are Nos 1 and 2 (Communication, Computer Basis and Education – proceedings of the 1975 and 1976 Conferences); No 3 (Training and Professional Education – proceedings of the 1977 Conference); No 4 (Human Factors in Games and Simulations – proceedings of the 1978 Conference); No 5 (Simulation and Gaming for the 1980s – proceedings of the 1979 Conference); and No 6 (Games and Simulations: the Real and the Ideal – proceedings of the 1980 Conference).

Society for Research into Higher Education Ltd, University of Surrey, Guildford, Surrey GU2 5XH. NB: The Society is not part of Surrey University though located there. (Contacts: Sally Kington, Publications Officer; Rowland Eustace, Administrative Officer)

The Society's areas of activity are research in further and higher education, publication of monographs, conference proceedings, seminar papers, registers of research, abstracts, journal. Services offered include seminars, conferences, working parties on specific aspects of further and higher education; newsletter; information dissemination.

*System Research Ltd, Woodville House, 37 Sheen Road, Richmond, Surrey (Contact: Professor G Pask)

System Research Ltd is an organization for research in cybernetics and the behavioural sciences.

The Test Agency, Cournswood House, North Dean, High Wycombe, Bucks (Contact: Mrs Phyllis Morgan)

The Agency's areas of activity are psychological testing for industry and education; sale of tests for industry, education, and paediatric assessment. Tests are also published. Courses are offered in selection testing; personality assessment; vocational guidance (testing and interviewing); personnel selection; aptitude testing; and advice on the use of tests. Recent publications include *Shapes Analysis Test; Electrical and Electronics Test; Factored Aptitude Series;* and *Life Style Questionnaire.*

Training and Educational Systems Testing Bureau (Test Bureau), Office and Laboratory, Vauxhall School, Vauxhall Street, London SE11 5LG (Contact: A M Crocker)

Training and Educational Systems Testing Bureau was formed by the National Committee for Audio Visual Aids in Education to continue the audiovisual aids equipment evaluation testing programme carried out by its

Technical Information Service when NCAVAE ceased operating in March 1981.

TEST Bureau is an independent limited guarantee company with charitable status, which provides a wide range of advisory and technical consultancy services. Local education authorities are a large group which benefits from the service, but many industries and businesses also subscribe to receive Technical Reports which cover a wide range of audiovisual equipment. Distributed once every two months, the reports, together with a newsletter, *Technical News*, give users and those purchasing equipment up-to-date information on current AV products and topics. There is an annual subscription for Technical Reports with *Technical News* and packages including consultancy are also available on an annual subscription basis to suit individual requirements.

*Training Services Division, 162-168 Regent Street, London W1R 6DE (Contact: Andrew Demian, Directorate of Training/Information)

The TSD is an executive arm of the Manpower Services Commission. It provides training services for individuals, principally through the Training Opportunities Scheme; it provides services for industry through the Industrial Training Boards; and it has extensive research and development commitments in pursuit of its general aim of improving the national training system. Services offered are information services on research in training and related areas; publications; occasional seminars, conferences, etc on selected topics; and advice and support for research and development work in selected fields. Publications are many and varied. A full list is available from the above address. (*See also* Directorate of Training (above))

Wool, Jute and Flax Industry Training Board, Butterfield House, Otley Road, Shipley, West Yorks BD17 7HE (Contact: R Broadbent, Manager, Central Training Services)

The Board's objectives are to encourage and assist companies in scope to identify and meet their own training needs to enable them to maintain a high level of efficiency through the effective use of manpower. In part, this is achieved through the development of training courses, systematic training schemes, publications and visual aids. Lists of publications and other materials are available.

Glasgow College of Technology Learning Resources Centre, Cowcaddens Road, Glasgow, G4 0BA (Contact: Dr F Percival, Learning Systems Adviser)

The Learning Resources Centre at the College has a policy role of providing a central agency for improving teaching and learning methods throughout the College. The Centre is a central agency within the College for the purchase, repair and maintenance of the whole range of audiovisual equipment, and it also operates an educational television service. It assists departments or individual staff who may wish to develop self-instructional approaches and materials. In addition, short courses and workshops on a range of educational technology-related topics are run for College staff. As the Learning Resources Centre is a relatively recent innovation in the College its full range of possible activities, and mechanisms for their implementation, are still a matter of discussion.

Centres of Activity in the United States

Centres of Activity in the USA have been organized into two listings:

1. Institutions and organizations in higher education;
2. Other organizations with an interest in education and training.

As elsewhere in the Yearbook, the symbol * before an entry indicates that it has not been updated since the 1980/81 edition.

Institutions and organizations in higher education

The American College, Zimmerman Adult Learning Laboratory, 270 Bryn Mawr Avenue, Bryn Mawr, PA 19010 (Contact: Dr Richard E Lincoln, Vice-President, Learning Systems Division; Dr Harold F Rahmlow, Vice-President, Graduate Center)

The general functions of the Laboratory are applied research and development at professional adult education level, using an instructional technology approach. Research and development also consists of designing new instructional materials for distance teaching. Completed to date are a new study guide format with an accompanying manual for subject matter experts, an instructor's manual with an accompanying guide for its development by subject matter experts, and student and instructor handbooks of general and course specific information. A current project is the application of document design research to improve further the learning effectiveness of the College's educational informational offerings. The College engages in computer-based education research and development activities. Materials and publications include computer-based courses in economics, accounting, mathematics of life insurance, and research methods – all of which have been developed. Details are available from the College.

University of Arizona, College of Education, Tucson, AZ 85721 (Contact: Dr Raymond Klein, Professor, Secondary Education Media)

Activities include the use/application of educational technology, radio, television and instructional systems.

*Auraria Media Center (serving Community College of Denver-Auraria, Metropolitan State College, and University of Colorado at Denver), 11th and Lawrence Streets, Denver, CO 80204 (Contact: Dr Ray L Anderton, Director, Auraria Media Center)

Activities include media production, television, instructional development, evaluation and selection, media librarianship, and research.

Boston University

1. Center for Educational Development in Health, 53 Bay State Road, Boston, MA 02215 (Contacts: Ascher J Segall, MD, Director; Hannelore F

Vanderschmidt, PhD, Associate Director)

Activities include teacher training in medicine and public health, curriculum and course design for the training of polyvalent health workers in developing countries, design of courses in continuing education, validation of curriculum for family and preventive medicine, workshops in systematic course design for the health fields – curriculum design, evaluation of training programmes, design of instructional activities and materials.

2. Boston University, School of Education, 605 Commonwealth Avenue, Boston, MA 02215 (Contact: Dr Gaylen B Kelley, Professor of Education, Chairman, Program in Educational Media and Technology, Division of Instructional Development)

Academic programs at the MEd, CAGS and EdD levels in School Librarianship and Instructional Technology. Program prepares participants for roles in public schools, college and universities, business and industrial training and biocommunications. Course modules include the areas of materials evaluation and selection, information storage and retrieval, media librarianship, production of various media/materials including television, graphics and photography, use/applications of instructional technology, microcomputer applications in education, instruction and training, multimedia design and programming and facilities and environmental design for media and technology. Programs also include academic work in communication theory, instructional systems design, research design and curriculum theory. Approximately 100 students at EdD level, 150 at MEd and 30 at CAGS levels.

*University of Bridgeport, Bridgeport, CT 06602 (Contact: Dr David M Silverstone, Director, Audio Visual Center, Professor, Educational Administration)

*1. Audio Visual Center

Campus services, including programming, production and scheduling of instructional and educational television and community cable television; graphics and photography; the usual line of audiovisual projectors – slide, film, etc; consultation with faculty; in-service training; audio specialization including speech compression; planetarium instruction; and a wide range of other services. The Center offers training in television to journalism and communication students.

*2. College of Education Media Center

This group is an extension of the AV Center, serving only the College of Education.

University of California

1. Educational Media Resources, San Francisco, CA 94143 (Contact: Peter Ng, Director)

Educational television production and service, still/motion photography, medical illustrations and graphics. Media services include educational broadcasting, audiovisual programming, self-instructional media uses, and classroom audiovisual support.

*2. UCLA Media Center, 405 Hilgard Avenue, Los Angeles, CA 90024 (Contact: Andrea L Rich, Director, Instructional Development)

*3. Lawrence Hall of Science, Berkeley, CA 94720 (Contact: Arthur Luehrmann, Associate Director)

The Lawrence Hall of Science is an organized research unit of the University of California at Berkeley. LHS conducts research, curriculum development and public service programmes in the general field of science education. It also operates a public science centre with interactive science exhibits, classes, films and lectures. The LHS Computer Group conducts a major public programme in computer education. It operates an 80-terminal time-sharing computer system. Half the terminals are located in schools in the San Francisco Bay area. The others are used at LHS to conduct classes and workshops where individuals or visiting school groups learn to use and to programme computers. A new project takes a dozen microcomputers out to schools every day and conducts similar classes at their locations, up to 50 miles away. Altogether there are about 40,000 annual enrolments in all computer education activities. Finally, LHS acts as programming contractor for a project to produce CAI material for deaf students.

*4. University of California, Davis, CA 95616 (Contact: Dr Charles L Nearing, Director, Instructional Media)

*5. University of California, Santa Barbara, CA 93106 (Contacts: Dr David Outcalt, Dean, Instructional Development; Stanley Nicholson, Instructional Consultant; Dr Joseph J Sayovitz, Director, Learning Resources)

*California State University, Center for Instructional Media, 6000 J Street, Sacramento, CA 95819 (Contact: Dr Charles J Vento, Associate Director)

Instructional design: efforts are being made to redesign entire courses, with the help of a responsible faculty. The new courses will be used either on a class basis or in study carrels on an individual viewing basis. Several are being made and/or planned on videotape. The Center operates a fully equipped production facility.

Catholic University of America, School of Education, Washington, DC 20064 (Contact: Dr Joseph A Tucker, Co-ordinator, Center for Educational Technology)

Programmed instruction, instructional design, computer-assisted instruction, use/application of educational technology, educational systems.

*Coastline Community College, 10231 Slater Avenue, Fountain Valley, CA 92708 (Contacts: Bernard J Luskin, President, Coastline Community College; Peter Van der Haeghen, Director, Learning Systems & Services, Coastline Community College)

Coastline offers classes in over 150 community sites and on broadcast TV. The college has received full accreditation from the Western Accrediting Association and has been recognized by the British Open University Centre for International Co-operation and Services as one of the 23 major institutions of higher education in the world successful in 'learning at a distance'. Coastline provides academic (degree) and non-academic courses in a range of subjects and maintains an independent study programme for co-ordinated instructional systems, which distributes instruction via open broadcast television and radio, closed-circuit television, newspapers and the mail. The television design department of the college provides design expertise and production. Included in the services offered are instructional media services, counselling, guidance/academic advice, vocational training, CETA training, instructional design and development, staff development for full-time and part-time staff, library services, lecture series, student activities programmes, etc.

University of Colorado

1. Educational Media Center, Stadium Building, Boulder, CO 80309

Activities include Master's degree programme; radio, television, programmed instruction, research, materials evaluation and selection, media/librarianship. Includes the *National Center for Audio Tapes* (NCAT) – *see under Other organizations*

2. University Computing Center, 3645 Marine Street, Campus Box B-45, Boulder, CO 80309 (Contact: Robert Edgerly, Director)

Provides instructional and research computing facilities for the four campuses of the University of Colorado. In addition to providing computing hardware network communication and a library of computer software, the Center provides training and assistance to faculty members and students. Seminars or short, non-credit courses are offered each semester, and computing assistants are employed by the Center to answer user questions. Batch and time-sharing service is provided to campuses at Boulder, Denver, and Colorado Springs, Colorado. Time-sharing on each campus is provided on an appropriate minicomputer, while large-scale scientific research is supported by a Cyber 170/720 at Boulder. Extensive mathematical, statistical and data base applications are employed by undergraduate, graduate, faculty and staff users.

Columbia University: Microcomputer Resource Center – *see* Microcomputer Resource Center *under Other organizations*

Commonwealth Center for High Technology/Education, *see under Other organizations*

University of Connecticut

1. University Center for Instructional Media and Technology, Storrs, CT 06268 (Contact: Dr Phillip J Sleeman, Director)

The Center is organized into the following ten divisions: Administrative Services Division, Graduate Academic Program Division, Instructional Development Division, Telecommunications Division, Graphics Division, Self-instructional Division, Film Library Division, Learning Resources Division, Technical Division, Instructional Media Facility – School of Social Work Division.

*2. Health Centre Library, Learning Resources Centre, Farmington, CT 06032

The Health Centre Library offers a free audiovisual loan service for nurses in the State of Connecticut.

*University of Delaware, Instructional Resources Center, East Hall, Newark, DE 19711 (Contact: Donald E Nelson, Director)

*Eastern Kentucky University, Division of Instructional Media, Richmond, KY 40475 (Contact: George L Pfotenhauer, Director)

East Texas State University

1. Department of Educational Media and Technology, Commerce, TX 75428

The Master of Science with a major in Educational Technology, the Master of Science in Library Science, and a Doctor of Education with a major in Educational Media and Technology are offered by the department. A campus wide service operation provides practical experiences for students.

2. Computer Assisted Instructional Facility, East Texas Station, Commerce, TX 75428

The facility contains over 300 programs, and provides faculty members with a large assortment of supplementary material. A full-time staff assists faculty, staff and students with problems that might occur. The CAI materials include programs in many academic areas. Bachelor and Master of Science degrees may be earned in the Computer Science department.

Florida State University

1. College of Education, 305 Stone Building, Tallahassee, FL 32306 (Contact: Dr Walter Dick Jr, Instructional Design and Development)

The College offers the following courses: graduate programmes in instructional design and development, leading to a Master's degree in educational media or instructional systems and to the Doctoral degree in instructional systems.

2. Learning Systems Institute, Tallahassee, FL 32306 (Contact: Dr Robert M Morgan, Director)

Applying technology and research to improve education, engaging in developmental research about all phases of education and providing training and technical assistance to educational agencies and institution specialities are systems analysis for educational planning, instructional design and development, educational evaluation, military and industrial instructional systems development, and technical assistance for overseas education and for developing countries. Individualized instruction, mastery learning, multi-media instruction, computer-based and computer-managed instruction, audiovisual medical education, educational uses of radio and television, are all special interests. The Institute's Center for Needs Assessment and Planning conducts research and development in needs assessment, system planning, and evaluation relative to organizations, and offers training for Master's and Doctoral students.

Fuller Theological Seminary, *see under Other organizations*

Georgetown University, Center for Personalized Instruction, Washington, DC 20057 (Contacts: J Gilmour Sherman; Robert S Ruskin; Ronald Lazar)

The Center was established in 1973 to provide help to college teachers who want to use individualized instruction in their classes. It holds institutional workshops on campuses in the US and overseas, as well as regional workshops open to individual teachers. It also sponsors an annual national conference on personalized instruction and provides speakers for various types of meetings. Its purpose is to serve teachers interested in individualized instruction who want to get the best possible start in this field. The Center's major workshops last from two to six days and are intended to prepare a teacher fully to give his or her own PSI course. A list of publications is available on request.

University of Illinois

1. Center for Instructional Research and Curriculum Evaluation (CIRCE), 1310 S Sixth, Champaign, IL 61820 (Contact: Dr Robert E Stake, Director)

The Center for Instructional Research and Curriculum Evaluation (CIRCE) was officially organized in 1964 as a service and research agency within the College of Education, University of Illinois at Urbana-Champaign. This agency brought together a number of activities which in the previous 20 years operated informally from the office of the University Examiner, the Bureau of Educational Research, the office of the Illinois Statewide High School Testing Program, and other college offices. Some of the interests of CIRCE members are: building evaluation models, instrumentation, field studies, collection of literature, and professional training in measurement and evaluation. They help federal and state agencies and professional organizations to design evaluation plans and to evaluate curricular projects. Many visitors, both long-term and short-term, are hosted by CIRCE. They come from many countries – recently, in particular, from Australia, Great Britain, Iceland, India, Sweden – as well as the United States. Weekly informal seminars are held, where faculty members and graduate students have the opportunity to present ideas and to obtain feedback through discussion. Occasional other seminars and workshops are presented as well, which attract participants from around the world. CIRCE provides service, instruction, and research on problems of educational programme evaluation. Consultation on evaluation designs, interpretation, and personnel development are aimed at large organizations and agencies. Materials and publications: details are available on request.

2. Computer-based Education Research Laboratory, 252 Engineering Research Laboratory, Urbana, IL 61801 (Contact: Professor Donald L Bitzer, Director)

The Laboratory is responsible for research and development as well as operation of the PLATO computer-based education system at the University of Illinois at Urbana-Champaign. The University of Illinois PLATO system (CERL) has approximately 1200 graphics terminals attached to Cyber computers. The CERL system can communicate electronically with many of the other PLATO systems now in existence worldwide. The Laboratory develops system software and hardware for the current system, does research on advanced systems, and carries on some curricular development (much curricular development is carried out by PLATO users outside CERL). Main services provided include consulting with authors of curricular materials, documentation on-line and off-line, and help with communications options. Materials and publications produced are too numerous to list – they include thousands of hours of curricular materials written in the TUTOR language for graphics terminals.

3. Media Services, Normal, IL 61761 (Contact: Dr John Sharpham, Director)

Media Services is a division of the Faculty and Instructional Development Program at Illinois State University. Media Services includes a fully equipped Learning Resource Center, an Equipment/Materials Distribution unit, Graphic, Audio and Television production facilities. A library of audiovisual materials is available for loan and equipment is available for practice use by faculty and students.

Indiana University

1. Audiovisual Center, Division of Development and Special Projects (DDSP), Room 235, Student Services Building, Bloomington, IN 47405 (Contact: Dr Thomas M Schwen, Director and Associate Professor)

DDSP is one of the largest instructional development offices in an American university. In a typical year the office is involved in up to 40 development projects, ranging from major, multi-year curriculum development efforts to intensive short-term projects focused on a particular problem or instructional question. In addition, the office regularly engages in application-oriented research into questions of theoretical interest to instructional developers, and publishes research reports and technical papers. A typical year also includes numerous short-term consultancies both within and outside the University. Recent development projects include *Associate Instructor Training*, current programmes offering training in classroom techniques for beginning college instructors have been surveyed, and a number of techniques adapted for incorporation into on-going course development projects; *Ballet:* DDSP assists the client in the development of instructional films designed to increase the analytical skills of future dance instructors. A comprehensive evaluation plan to assess the content validity and instructional effectiveness of the films as well as their potential acceptability among dance professionals is currently being designed; *Introductory Chemistry Laboratory:* a course has been developed which teaches experimental methods in chemistry by use of algorithm-based instructional modules. Revision based on a comprehensive formative evaluation has been completed; *Pediatrics Models Evaluation:* personnel from DDSP are working with medical school faculty to evaluate a series of models designed to teach correct procedures in the care of neonates. To date, the project has focused on a model designed to teach correct performance of radial arterial punctures; *Helping Networks in Academic Settings:* this project seeks to identify and map associations which members of faculty use either to provide or receive help concerning teaching. Those naturally occurring helping networks may be important units in the instructional change process. Applications of this project include (i) the development of new indices for assessing the effectiveness of helping organizations, and (ii) establishing new means for disseminating information concerning teaching; *Academic Advising Analysis:* this project investigated some types of information used by academic advisers in predicting probable student success in a particular course. Ultimately, this information will be of use in developing an empirically based technique for improving the academic advising process.

2. Center for Innovation in Teaching the Handicapped (CITH), School of Education, 2805 E Tenth Street, Bloomington, IN 47401 (Contact: Dr Melvyn I Semmel, Director)

CITH focuses on research and development projects designed to enhance the skills and understanding of people who work with handicapped children. The ultimate goal of the Center is the improvement of the academic status and social acceptance of the handicapped. In pursuit of this goal, CITH has integrated research, development and demonstration activities to generate a broad range of training materials and services designed to improve the competencies of people who work with handicapped children in American schools.

3. Center for Visual Literacy, *see under Other organizations*

International University, *see* IIIT *under International Centres of Activity*

University of Iowa

1. Center for Education Experimentation, Development and Evaluation, University of Iowa, 218 Lundquist Center, Iowa City, IA 52242 (Contact: Dr Lawrence M Stolurow, Director)

Controls the rights of the PLAN* system (Program for Learning in Accordance with Needs), a computer-managed instructional system by means of which both teachers and students are able to create individualized programmes of study in language arts, mathematics, science and social studies; and also of the Mastery Centre™ (a remedial math and reading system).

2. Iowa Regional Computer Center, *see under Other organizations*

3. CONDUIT, *see under Other organizations*

*Ithaca College, Ithaca, NY 14850 (Contact: Dr John Keshishoglou, Dean, School of Communications)

Activities include programmed instruction, production of various media/materials, instructional design, educational broadcasting.

*Kent State University, College of Education, Kent, OH 44242 (Contact: Dr Marie McMahan, Professor of Curriculum and Instruction, Director, Instructional Resources Center)

*University of Kentucky, Center for Professional Development, College of Education, Lexington, KY 40506 (Contact: Dr Frank V Colton)

The Center for Professional Development is the service and outreach unit of the College of Education, University of Kentucky. In addition to providing internal services to the College, the Center provides direct services to schools, colleges and other agencies with educational missions. The Center facilitates the use of College and University resources in three general thrusts: (1) educational research and development; (2) continuing education; (3) other educational services. Details of publications are available on request.

University of Maine at Orono, 12 Shibles Hall, Orono, ME 04469 (Contact: Dr Edward P Caffarilla, Associate Professor of Education, Director of Instructional Systems Center)

Instructional development, production of various media/materials, research, instructional design, materials evaluation and selection.

Michigan State University

1. Learning and Evaluation Service, 17 Morrill Hall, East Lansing, MI 48824 (Contact: Dr Lawrence T Alexander, Director)

Consults with faculty on improvement of instruction; conducts research on teaching/learning processes; conducts teaching laboratory; provides test design and scoring services; produces hard-copy and mediated guides on various topics and procedures related to instructional design, development and evaluation; consults with faculty, individually and in groups; conducts seminars and workshops; analyses instructional procedures; maintains system for student ratings of instruction; maintains facility for machine-scoring tests and summarizing results; performs instructional analyses; conducts training programmes for graduate teaching assistants. Recent publications: Davis, R L, Alexander, L T and Yelon, S L (1974) *Learning System Design*, McGraw-Hill, NY; Davis, R L and Alexander, L T (1977) *Guides for the Improvement of Instruction*, MSU, East Lansing, Michigan; and Yelon, S L (1977) *A Teacher's World*, McGraw-Hill, NY.

2. Non-Formal Education Information Center, 513 Erickson Hall, College of Education, East Lansing, MI 48824 (Contact: Joan M Claffey, Director)

The Center co-ordinates a worldwide network of programme planners, practitioners and researchers concerned with the generation and use of knowledge about non-formal education and development. Started in 1974 and funded through a contract with the United States Agency for International Development. Main activities include publication of a newsletter, *The NFE Exchange* (three times a year, in English); library on non-formal education; training workshops; programmes of information relating to women in development; and responses to requests from network participants (over 4500 people in 145 countries are in contact with the Center).

The University of Michigan, Center for Research on Learning and Teaching, 109 East Madison, Ann Arbor, MI 48109 (Contacts: Wilbert J McKeachie, Director; Janet H Lawrence, Associate Director)

The Center is charged with providing service to faculty in the area of instructional and faculty development and the conducting of research on instructional effectiveness and innovation. It offers workshops for faculty and teaching assistants, faculty and course evaluation, program evaluation, and teaching assistant training. Research has involved the following: PSI, CAI, course evaluation, program evaluation, dissemination of instructional innovations, and student development.

University of Mid-America (UMA), Box 82006, Lincoln, NE 68501 (Contact: Donald R McNeil, President)

A consortium of 11 Midwestern state universities which develops and distributes instructional materials using mass communications technology and other media materials for use in educational programmes at a distance. UMA's current plans call for the development of a nationwide, independent, accredited degree-granting institution that will serve working adults, especially those interested in part-time education. It will be known as the American Open University.

Minnesota Educational Computing Consortium, *see under Other organizations*

University of Minnesota, Curricular and Instructional Systems, College of Education, 178 Pillsbury Dr SE, Minneapolis, MN 55455 (Contact: Dr Robert D Tennyson, Chairman)

MA degrees are offered in curriculum systems, instructional technology, instructional design, computer-based systems; a specialist certificate in general curriculum supervision is also available. DPhil degrees are offered in curriculum systems, instructional design, instructional technology, computer-based systems, staff development and instructional research. Materials produced include courseware in computer- and video-based programmes of study, research publications – *Management of Computer-Based Instruction*, pictorial support and specific instructions as design variables for children's concept and rule learning, *The Teaching of Concepts, Content Structure and Management Strategy*, etc. Services offered include a nationally recognized faculty; opportunities for internships in public schools, business, industry and health science; technical assistance and resources for design of research and development projects; an instructional system laboratory housing a wide range of educational technology and media resources; and professional courses needed for certification at media supervisor, media generalist and audiovisual director levels.

*University of Nebraska, Department of Anatomy, University of Nebraska Medical Center, 42nd and Dewey Street, Omaha, NE 68105 (Contacts: Ernest D Prentice, PhD; William K Metcalf, MD)

Development and evaluation of auto-instructional learning systems in the anatomical sciences; development and evaluation of anatomy teaching aids; instructor training for teachers in the basic and clinical sciences.

*University of Nebraska – Lincoln, Lincoln, NE 68588 (Contacts: Dr Wesley C Meierhenry, Professor of Education, 61 Henzlik Hall; Brandon Whistler, Director of Media Design Center, 122 Henzlik Hall; Dr Robert E Stepp, Professor of Education, 301 Barkley Center)

Use/application of educational technology, production of various media/ materials, instructional systems. Media services are offered.

State University of New York

*1. Faculty of Educational Studies, New Media Lab and Programmed Instruction Center, 210 Baldy Hall, Amherst, NY 14260 (Contact: Dr Taher A Razik)

Activities centre around the following components: programmed instruction centre; media facilities – video production, film production, audio production, slide and other projected images; graphic productions – support services for the media production; software development – preparation of instructional materials from the above activities. A list of publications is available on request.

2. Department of Computer Science, Plattsburgh, NY 12901 (Contacts: Dr Stewart A Denenberg; Dr Kenneth W Loach)

The Department is responsible for computer science education. It has a programme of development of CAI software and author languages and development of semantic network software and CAI tutorials.

3. Department of Technology and Society, College of Engineering and Applied Sciences, Stony Brook, NY 11794 (Contacts: Ludwig Braun; Thomas T Liao)

Faculty members of the Department of Technology and Society (DTS) are involved in various aspects of educational technology. Professor L Braun heads a centre, Laboratory for Personal Computers in Education, and has been active in educational computing for the past 15 years. Professor T Liao co-edits the *Journal of Educational Technology Systems* and is in charge of Master's programme on instructional technology. A major focus of DTS is science and engineering education, and the department has developed curriculum materials in the areas of technology, engineering and applied mathematics, and computer-based instructional materials. Services include undergraduate minor in technology and society, Master's in Applied Science with two areas of concentration: technology assessment and instructional technology; National Co-ordinating Center for Curriculum Development (a minorities-in-engineering programme).

*University of North Carolina, Department of Education, Wilmington, NC 28401 (Contact: Dean R Spitzer, Assistant Professor, Co-ordinator of Instructional Technology)

Instructional design, educational technology, media production, economics and consumer education materials, workshops, teacher education programme.

North Carolina Educational Computing Service, *see under Other organizations*

Northeastern University, 360 Huntington Avenue, Boston, MA 02115 (Contact: Mina B Ghattas, PhD, Director of Office of Learning Resources)

Use/application of educational technology, programmed instruction, instructional systems, instructional design, media production; the development and use of interactive video and computer-assisted (CAI) lessons.

University of Northern Iowa, College of Education, Cedar Falls, IA 50614 (Contact: Dr Ernest K Dishner, Head of Department of Curriculum and Instruction)

Programmed instruction, instructional systems, research, use/application of educational technology, instructional design consultation, computer-assisted and computer-managed instruction, media production, instruction design and development consultancy.

Ohio State University

1. Computer Based Instruction, Office of Learning Resources, 124 West 17th, Columbus, OH 43210

University-wide responsibility for planning, co-ordinating, and implementing computer-based education in the 18 colleges of the University. The efforts of the central staff focus on overall planning for the computer-based education needs of the University community. The staff provide intensive and continuing consultation with faculty members in the analysis and design of computer-based education programmes. The development and implementation of these programmes are the responsibility of the faculty members and their respective colleges. The central staff conduct faculty development seminars and sponsor discussions and symposia of interest to the faculty. A complete re-write of the operating system has allowed the implementation of CWIII code with less computer overhead and central processing unit cycles. The implementation of this product has enabled it to increase the total number of terminals available on the system without increasing the size of the central processor.

2. The National Center for Research in Vocational Education, *see under Other organizations*

University of Oregon, *see* International Council for Computers in Education *under Other organizations*

Pennsylvania State University

1. College of Education, University Park, PA 16802 (Contact: Paul W Welliver, Professor of Education)

Activities include systematic instructional development; computer-based instructional systems; theory, research and media use; administration of media; undergraduate courses in instructional media and technology; masters' and doctoral programmes in educational technology.

2. Laboratory for Human Performance Research, No 11 Laboratory Building, University Park, PA 16802 (Contact: E R Buskisk, Director)

The Laboratory is engaged in education and research related to human applied physiology and ergonomics with a special emphasis in exercise physiology.

*3. Department of Business Administration, Middleton, PA 17057 (Contact: Dr Joseph P Yaney, Chairman, Department of Business Administration)

Activities include self-instructional systems; learning analysis for industrial and commercial organizations, organization development research; research and contract development of instructional materials; evaluation programmes; feasibility studies.

University of Pittsburgh, Learning Research and Development Center, Pittsburgh, PA 15260 (Contact: John Aug, Director of Administrative Services)

Research on learning and instruction, involving 77 professional researchers and graduate research assistants, and focusing on basic knowledge and learning skills, learning environments and social processes, evaluation research, and computer-based instruction. A publications list is available.

Purdue University

*1. Education Building, 112 West Lafayette, IN 47907 (Contact: Carolyn I Whitenack, Professor of Education, Chairman of Media Sciences Curriculum)

Research, computer-assisted instruction, instructional systems, use/application of educational technology, materials evaluation and selection, Master's degree programme.

2. Office of Instructional Development, School of Humanities, Social Science and Education, West Lafayette, IN 47906 (Contact: Dr John Feldhusen or Dr James Russell, Co-Directors)

Activities include research on college teaching, consultation with individual faculty, workshops, consultation about course design and development, course evaluation.

3. Educational Psychology Section, Purdue University, SCC-G, West Lafayette, IN 47909

Rochester Institute of Technology, One Lomb Memorial Drive, Rochester, NY 14623 (Contact: Dr Lawrence Belle, Associate Professor, Director of Instructional Development)

Activities include instructional development and design for courses and curriculum; objectives, instructional strategies; computers in instructional processes; evaluation; career development and evaluation.

*University of Rochester, Rochester Clearinghouse on Self-Instructional Materials for Health Care Facilities, River Campus Station, Rochester, NY 14627

Information clearinghouse, some bibliographic assistance and service.

*Rutgers University, Graduate School of Library and Information Studies, 4 Huntington Street, New Brunswick, NJ 08903 (Contact: Dr Craig N Locatis)

Conducts programmes in educational media, offers courses in instructional development and evaluation, conducts research and evaluation studies in the area of instructional technology. The faculty have produced independently materials in the areas of educational media, management, evaluation and information science. These include workshop materials for instructional television, design of simulation and clinical evaluation for health science faculty.

San Diego Mesa College, Independent Learning Center, 7250 Mesa College Drive, San Diego, CA 92111 (Contact: Dr Curtis J McCarty)

Created in 1974, the Independent Learning Center is a student and faculty service facility. It provides individualized learning experiences to students wishing to improve academic skills, augment in-class activities and/or delve more deeply into a particular subject area.

Faculty members may use the ILC to design, produce, evaluate, and/or select materials for their students to use or for their own use in classroom instruction. In addition, there is a computing facility with word processing capability for faculty development use.

The Learning Center also offers one unit of transferable credit to students who are assigned here by instructors for specific learning activities which are supplementary to those courses currently taught by the instructor. These courses are listed as 296 in the catalogue and schedule under the various departments which offer them. Enrolment is concurrent with the instructor's course.

San Francisco State University, Audiovisual and Instructional Television Center, 1600 Holloway Avenue, San Francisco, CA 94132 (Contact: Dr Francis X Moakley, Director)

University resource for acquisition, distribution, production, development and maintenance of audiovisual and instructional television materials and equipment. Founded in 1922. The Center has recently developed a 35-channel cable system for video, audio and data distribution; operates a cable channel reaching over 60,000 homes in San Francisco; owns a satellite receiver for programme reception and distribution; supports the University Learning Center with video, audio and data links; has extensive PVTR cameras (colour) and video editing ensembles; has on-line video disc distribution system, and is starting experiments in video text services.

The Center's main activities include: *Production:* video modules, programmes and courses; slides, audio tapes and tape slide programmes. Complete facility for graphics production, slide duplication and document copying; two multi-media image display systems for programme display and development; *Instructional systems and instructional product development:* uses a two-tiered approach to instructional development; conducts workshops and consults with faculty on class, module, and course development; other tier involved with instructional product development; materials produced to support instructional systems goals; *Learning center:* provides planning, media, and technical support of the University Learning Center. The Learning Center is supported by a cable TV system, conventional media such as film and filmstrips, and contains a media production centre for audio, video, film and data. Post-production facilities include two ¾ inch editing systems; *Resources:* provides a range of media, equipment, and portable television equipment, and holds a video, film, videocassette and video disc library; *Television:* operates the University cable system to over 300 instructional spaces; uses mobile colour studios; televises campus information/message service 24 hours daily; Program Channel 35 on the city cable network; uses a satellite receive station for programme acquisition. Majority of work in and with colour equipment.

San Jose State University, Instructional Resources Center, Washington Square, San Jose, CA 95192 (Contact: Dr Ron J McBeath, Director, Instructional Resources Center)

The Instructional Resources Center at the University serves 20,000 students and 1500 faculty members. The Center co-ordinates the Faculty and Instructional Development Office, Audiovisual Services, Instructional Television Services and Electronic Learning Laboratories, and has been involved with several projects related to the integration of media and curriculum. Through these projects, ten self-paced learning laboratories have been developed in teaching departments, with over 2000 students using them each week.

The Faculty Self-Appraisal and Development Programme has been a major project over the last six years. The hypothesis is that if faculty are helped to identify their own professional needs they will voluntarily work with specialist consultants or resource materials to improve their professional competencies. After the development of a self-appraisal form, self-instructional modules were produced on setting objectives, preparing lectures, constructing objective tests, conducting item analysis, measuring student attitudes, constructing and scoring essay tests, improving faculty-student relationships, self-paced learning, discussions and performance testing. The modules are in a text-workbook format and are complemented with a videotape on lecturing and tape/filmstrips on self-paced learning. The materials are being used in more than 400 universities interested in staff or professional development.

University of Southern California, School of Education, Department of Instructional Technology, Phillips Hall 801, Los Angeles, CA 90007

Research, instructional design, instructional systems, simulation/gaming, programmed instruction, computer-assisted instruction, information storage and retrieval, materials production. The Department offers a Master's degree programme in instructional technology.

Southern Illinois University at Carbondale, Educational Media Program, Department of Curriculum, Instruction and Media, Carbondale, IL 62901 (Contact: Dr Doris C Dale, Professor, Co-ordinator)

Activities include research, production of various media/materials, media librarianship, use/application of educational technology, instructional systems, simulation/gaming, Master's degree programme, PhD degree programme.

University of South Florida, The College of Education, Tampa, FL 33620 (Contact: Dr Thomas C Wilson)

Instructional design, media design and implementation, courses, consultancy services. Materials produced include journal publications, audiovisual materials.

*Southern University, PO Box 9714, Southern Branch Post Office, Baton Rouge, LA 70813 (Contact: Dr Henry Wiggins, Director of Department of Communications and Instructional Technology)

Research, instructional systems, simulation/gaming, instructional design and materials production, Master's degree programme.

Stanford University, The Institute for Communication Research, Stanford, CA 94305 (Contact: Professor S H Chaffee, Director)

Operating as the inter-disciplinary research division and PhD training arm of the Department of Communication at Stanford University, the Institute has undertaken projects on international communication, communication and health, new information technology and on developmental communication and attitude change. It is responsible for the research training and experience of advanced students in communication. A list of publications is available.

Syracuse University

1. **Center for Instructional Development,** 115 College Place, Syracuse, NY 13210 (Contact: Dr Robert M Diamond)

The Center is a support agency to the entire institution charged with working with all schools and departments in the improvement of instruction. Staff include specialists in instructional design, evaluation, testing and media production. A list of publications is available on request.

2. **Instructional Design, Development and Evaluation Program,** School of Education, Syracuse, NY 13210 (Contact: Dr Phillip Doughty, Chairman)

Founded in 1948, the Program (formerly called the Department of Instructional Technology) is a graduate level academic programme which emphasizes the study and application of technology in planning, implementing and evaluating instruction. It offers graduate degrees and undertakes materials development and consultancy.

3. **University Consortium for Instructional Development and Technology,** *see under Other organizations*

Temple University, Department of Educational Media, Philadelphia, PA 19122 (Contact: Dr Donald Fork)

Two graduate programmes leading to both the Master's and Doctorate degree in educational media. The programmes are designed to produce individuals capable of planning and implementing programmes which employ instructional technology to enhance the interaction of teaching and learning throughout the field of education. Laboratory experience is offered in the production of graphics, visual materials, photography, motion pictures and instructional television.

University of Tennessee, *see* Association for Continuing Higher Education *under Other organizations*

University of Texas at Austin, Research and Development Center for Teacher Education, Education Annex 3.114, Austin, TX 78712 (Contact: Dr Gene E Hall, Division Co-ordinator)

The Center is an institution with a national leadership role in educational research and development. One of its major goals has been to contribute to the improvement of educational practice through an increased focus of the Research on Concerns-Based Adoption (RCA) Project for the past seven years. This research has been carried out within the framework of the Concerns-Based Adoption Model (CBAM), a theory developed at the Center for explication and facilitation of change. Initial efforts have dealt with verification of major conceptual dimensions of the model (Stages of Concern About the Innovation, Levels of Use of the Innovation), and have explored how some of the key variables change over time and how they interrelate. Staff have, in addition, provided consultative services and technical assistance with research-verified tools and concepts to a wide variety of practitioners involved in facilitating or evaluating change efforts in diverse settings. Recently, research has examined Innovation Configurations (the various forms of an innovation that result when users 'adapt' it for their own use), and interventions used by change facilitators. A system for classifying levels and types of interventions (An Intervention Taxonomy) is being developed. Present research is focusing upon the effects of various line administrators and other change facilitators as they intervene on the change process. A set of elementary school principals have been the focus of the present large-scale study. Continued research based on the model will provide a rich base for change process facilitation, management and evaluation that in combination will enable that process to be more effective, efficient and personalized. Center and RCA Project publication lists are available upon request.

*University of Utah, Department of Educational Systems and Learning Resources, Salt Lake City, UT 84112 (Contact: Dr James G Buterbaugh, Chairman)

Undertakes research and development, with a particular interest in self-instructional materials. The Department offers graduate teaching programmes.

*University of Virginia, Department of Curriculum and Instruction, School of Education, Charlottesville, VA 22903 (Contact: Dr Donald H Shoemaker, Professor of Education)

Activities include instructional design, use/application of educational technology, production of various media/materials, graduate teaching programme.

University of Wisconsin

1. Educational Communications Division, PO Box 413, W1 53201 (Contact: Theodore Steinke, Director)

The functions of ECD are to acquaint faculty and staff with the new technology available to higher education; demonstrate the available material and equipment; show successful uses of various media; help faculty keep abreast of contemporary trends in the instructional field; and foster liaison between the educational community and commercial producers of instructional materials. ECD on the University campus offers outstanding media production resources including: broadcast quality colour television facilities for studio and on-location production; professionally-equipped art and visual design studios; a full range of professional photographic capabilities; and computer-based learning centres. Publications include the *Index to Computer-Based Learning*, a computer-generated publication (updated every two years and internationally distributed).

*2. Wisconsin Center for the Analysis of Individualized Instruction, 225 North Mills, Madison, WI 53706 (Contacts: M Vere De Vault; G Thomas Fox Jr)

Assistance in the analysis, design and development of individualized instruction with special reference to the appropriate integration of technology and humanism.

3. University of Wisconsin-Stout, Learning Resources, Menomonie, WI 54751 (Contact: Dr D P Barnard, Dean of Learning Resources)

Activities include media retrieval services, instructional technology services, broadcast TV production, academic computer services and media technology (instruction). Graduate Teaching programmes are offered.

4. Wisconsin Center for Education Research, *see under Other organizations*

Other organizations

*Academy for Educational Development Inc, 680 Fifth Avenue, New York, NY 10019 (Contacts: Alvin C Eurick, President and Chief Executive Officer; Joseph S Iseman, Secretary)

Non-profit-making organization established to stimulate, develop, co-ordinate, plan and improve programmes in education and communications.

*Adult Education Association of the USA, 810 18th Street NW, Washington, DC 20006

An annual conference. The AEA seeks to 'further the concept of education as a process continuing throughout life'. Publications: *Lifelong Learning: The Adult Years; Adult Education; Handbook of Adult Education*; and others.

Agency for Instructional Television, Box A, Bloomington, IN 47402

A non-profit-American-Canadian organization established in 1973 to strengthen education through television and other technologies. AIT develops joint programme projects involving state and provincial agencies, and acquires and distributes a wide variety of television and related printed materials for use as learning resources. It makes many of the television materials available in audiovisual formats. AIT's predecessor organization was National Instructional Television. There are regional offices in the Washington DC, Bloomington, and San Francisco areas.

Agency for International Development (AID), US International Development Co-operation Agency, Bureau for Science and Technology, Office of Education, Washington, DC 20523

American Council on Education, One Dupont Circle, Washington, DC 20036 (Contact: J W Peltason, President)

Founded in 1918 and composed of institutions of higher education and national and regional education associations; the nation's major co-ordinating body for post-secondary education. Provides comprehensive leadership for improving education standards, policies, procedures, and services. Publications include *Higher Education & National Affairs* and *Educational Record*.

American Educational Research Association (AERA), 1230 17th Street NW, Washington, DC 20036 (Contact: William J Russell, Executive Officer)

AERA is an international organization of educators and behavioural scientists with an interest in research in education and the application of research to educational practice. Programmes of the Association are concerned with the improvement of scholarly inquiry related to education, the dissemination of research results to the research community and to practising educators, and the application of research to education in practice, in the interests of improving education. The Association is constituted in 10 divisions and more than 60 Special Interest Groups. Publications include *Educational Researcher* – news and feature magazine, monthly except for combined June/July and August/September issues; *Review of Educational Research* – quarterly; *American Educational Research Journal,* quarterly; *Journal of Educational Statistics* (co-sponsored with American Statistical Association) – quarterly; *Review of Research in Education* – annual, casebound; *Educational Evaluation and Policy Analysis* – quarterly;

Contemporary Education – A Journal of Reviews (first issue, Spring 1982) – quarterly. Information on cassette tapes series on developments in educational research is available upon request.

*American Federation of Information Processing Sciences Inc (AFIPS), 210 Summit Avenue, Montvale, NJ 07645

American Film Institute (AFI), John F Kennedy Center for the Performing Arts, Washington, DC 20566; and AFI Center for Advanced Film Studies, 2021 N Western Avenue, Los Angeles, CA 90027

A non-profit organization created in 1967 by the National Endowment for the Arts to preserve the heritage and advance the art of film and television, AFI preserves films and co-ordinates a national preservation effort; publishes the magazine *American Film* which goes to 112,000 members; exhibits programmes of film and television at the AFI Theater in the Kennedy Center; provides touring programmes of film and guest speakers; maintains a conservatory for the training of filmmakers; administers NEA funds for production grants to independent filmmakers; and otherwise serves as a national advocate for the art form, the artists, and the organizations that serve them. Publications include *American Film* (ten issues per year); *AFI Guide to College Courses in Film and Television; AFI Catalog of Motion Pictures: Feature Films 1921-1930* and *1961-1970*; the *Factfile* series (reference bibliographies on film, video, and television).

American Institutes for Research in the Behavioural Sciences, Box 1113, Palo Alto, CA 94302 (Contact: J C Flanagan, Chairman)

Activities include research on applications of educational technology, educational systems, individual differences, guidance, aptitude, interests, and related publications.

American Library Association (ALA), 50 E Huron Street, Chicago, IL 60614

Divisions include **American Association of School Librarians (AASL), American Association of College and Research Libraries (ACRL), Information Science and Automation Division (ISAD), and Library Education Division,** all at the above address. **Audiovisual Committee (for Public Libraries)** (Contact: Laura Murray, AV Services) **Metropolitan Toronto Library Board,** 789 Yonge Street, Toronto, Ontario M4W 2G8, Canada

American Management Associations, 135 West 50 Street, New York, NY 10020

The American Management Associations (AMA) is a not-for-profit educational membership organization conducting worldwide management training activities for more than 150,000 public and private sector executives annually. It also publishes business books, periodicals and multi-media films as well as audio and video cassette programmes, management briefings, surveys and research studies, and executive compensation reports. Its AMA/International division maintains European headquarters in Brussels (Management Centre Europe) and centres in Toronto, Mexico City and Sao Paulo, Brazil.

*American Medical Association (AMA), Department of Motion Pictures and Television, 535 North Dearborn, Chicago, IL 60610

Co-ordinates AMA audiovisual services to the medical profession, particularly with respect to loan of 16mm films.

*American National Standards Institute (ANSI), Sectional Committee on Instructional Audio-Visual Standards, 1430 Broadway, New York, NY 10016

*American Science Film Association (ASFA), Box 30305 Bethesda, Maryland 20014 (Contacts: Donald A Benjamin, President; Layton Mabrey, Secretary)

ASFA is devoted to the advancement of science, including the social sciences, through the use of motion pictures, television and other related media as tools of research, as means of communicating results of research, as instruments for education and training, as media for dissemination of technological information and for the public awareness and understanding of science and technology and their impact on modern society. Publications: *ASFA Notes* (bi-monthly).

*American Society for Cybernetics, 1025 Connecticut Avenue, NW, Suite 911, Washington, DC 20036

*American Society for Information Science, 1010 16th Street NW, Washington, DC 20036

Seeks to improve the information transfer process through research, development, application and education. Provides a forum for the discussion, publication and critical analysis of work dealing with theory, practice, research and development of elements involved in communication of information. Publications: *Bulletin* (bi-monthly); *Handbook & Directory* (annually); *Journal of the ASIS* (bi-monthly).

The American Society for Training and Development, Suite 305, 600 Maryland Avenue, SW, Washington, DC 20024 (Contacts: Carnie Ives Lincoln, President 1980-81; Curtis Plott, Executive Vice President; Darius Van Fossen, Assistant Secretary and Director of International and Society Affairs)

A non-profit national educational society representing persons involved in training and development in business, industry, education and government. It provides educational programmes and services to over 21,000 members in the form of a member inquiry service, seminars and institutes, research, regional conferences, a national conference and exposition, and the publication of a monthly journal, the *Training and Development Journal*, a national report newsletter which appears every three weeks, and a membership quarterly newspaper. Among the subjects of recent seminars and institutes are The Training Function, Designing Effective Training and Selecting Appropriate Methods, and a Training and Development Senior Symposium. The Society is represented by a network of nine geographical regions and over 125 chapters throughout the United States.

*Association for Computer-Based Instructional Systems, Box 70189, Los Angeles, CA 90070 (Contact: P Dean)

Exchange of information on computers in education. Publications: *Journal of Computer-Based Instruction*; *Annual Conference Proceedings*; *Newsletter*.

Association for Continuing Higher Education, The University of Tennessee, 451 Communications Building, Knoxville, TN 37916 (Contact: Dr William D Barton)

The Association for Continuing Higher Education (ACHE) is an association of institutions and individuals having a commitment to providing opportunities in higher education for adults in traditional and non-traditional programmes. ACHE is divided into nine regions and includes members from all over North America and some in Europe. It holds an Annual Meeting and publishes *Proceedings* – a summary of the discussions and papers presented at the annual meeting; *Continuing Higher Education* – a periodical, published four times a year; *'Five Minutes with ACHE' Newsletter* – published nine times a year (members only); and *Programs and Registrations* – a joint publication of ACHE and NUEA detailing statistics of members' activities.

Association for Educational Communications and Technology (AECT), 1126 Sixteenth Street, NW, Washington, DC 20036 (Contact: Howard B Hitchens, Executive Director)

A professional association for those concerned with the improvement of instruction through the effective use of media and technology, AECT is active in promoting standards for school media programmes at all levels of education as well as in the evaluation of school media programmes. AECT serves as an information clearinghouse and communications centre for its members. It works to improve the professional development of the media practitioner, the quality of the tools and materials used, and most importantly, the quality of the end product – instruction. Selected AECT committees are: Affirmative Action, Certification, Continuing Education, Definition and Terminology, Evaluation of Instructional Materials, Intellectual Freedom, Technical Hardware/Software Standards, and Program Consultation. AECT membership is open to anyone interested in the application of media and technology to education and training. Regular membership ($50) includes a subscription to *Instructional Innovator* magazine and the membership newspaper, *Ect Network*. Members also receive a discount on prices for AECT publications and registration fees at annual meetings. AECT has nine divisions as follows: (1) Division of Educational Media Management, c/o Carl Stafford, AV Center, Rm 64, Purdue University, West Lafayette, IN 47907; (2) Division of Computer and Information Systems, c/o Judith Meyers, Co-ordinator of Media Services, Lakewood Public Schools, 1470 Warren Road, Lakewood, OH 44107; (3) Division of Instructional Development, c/o Joseph Durzo, Forum Corp, 84 State Street, Boston, MA 02109; (4) International Division, c/o Fred Branscombe, 11 St Leonards Avenue, Toronto, Ontario, Canada M4N 1K1; (5) Media Design and Production Division, c/o Charles Vento, California State University, 6000 J Street, Sacramento, CA 95819; (6) Research and Theory Division, c/o Perrin Parkhurst, A-312 East Fee Hall, Michigan State University, East Lansing, MI 44824; (7) Division of Telecommunications, c/o Kathy Busick, Educational TV for Alaska, PO Box 1185, Juneau, AK 99802; (8) Industrial Training and Education Division, c/o Richard Scudder, Johns Manville, PO Box 5108, Denver, CO 80217; (9) Division of School Media Specialists, c/o Anthony Schulzetenberg, Center for Library and AV Education, St Cloud State University, St Cloud, MN 56301. AECT also sponsors an annual convention which features the largest display of educational technology materials, equipment, and services in the world. AECT publishes *Instructional Innovator* which comes out eight times a year, containing articles about the use of media and technology at all levels of education and training, as well as a quarterly journal of research and theory in educational technology entitled *Educational Communications and Technology Journal*, the quarterly *Journal of Instructional Development* and a membership newsletter. AECT also publishes books, films, and filmstrips on a variety of topics related to educational media. Recent publications are: *Guide to Microcomputers, Creating Slide/Tape Programs, Evaluating Instructional Materials, Media in Instruction: 60 Years of Research, Evaluating Media Programs: District and School, Professional Development and Education Technology, Educational Technology: A Glossary of Terms, Masters Degree Programs in Instructional Technology.*

Association for Educational Data Systems, 1201 Sixteenth Street NW, Washington, DC 20036 (Contact: Shirley Easterwood, Executive Secretary)

AEDS membership is open to all persons interested in learning more and keeping informed about current developments and directions in educational data systems and computer technology. An annual international conference is held to bring together key people from education and technical specialities. AEDS sponsors workshops on relevant topics and publishes three quarterly publications: *AEDS Bulletin*, a newsletter *AEDS Monitor*, containing short articles; and *AEDS Journal*, a technical journal. Conference proceedings are also published.

Association for Media-based Continuing Education for Engineers, Inc (AMCEE), 225 North Avenue, NW, Atlanta GA 30332 (Contact: John T Fitch, Executive Director)

AMCEE is a non-profit, tax-exempt association of engineering universities in the United States, all of which offer off-campus education via television and videotape. Most of the courses are at the graduate level, and most of the participants are practising engineers in local industry and government laboratories. AMCEE was formed to make the output of these regional programmes available nationally and internationally and to encourage the development of non-credit short courses, particularly for mid-career engineers. AMCEE publishes an annual catalogue of courses available from its members on videocassettes. (The 1981/82 edition lists 477 courses in 26 disciplines.)

*Association for Supervision and Curriculum Development, 225 North Washington Street, Alexandria, VA 22314 (Contact: Dr Gordon Cawelti, Executive Director)

ASCD is a professional education association open to all interested persons but compounded mostly of administrators, supervisors, teachers and professors. It focuses on curriculum, development, supervision and leader behaviour in education. The Association runs the National Curriculum Study Institute, and offers consultant and information services. It runs an Annual Conference. Publications include *Educational Leadership*, journal (eight issues a year); *News Exchange*, newsletter (eight issues a year); *Yearbook*. The Association also makes media presentations and produces four to six books a year (details on request).

*Association of Information and Dissemination Centres (ASIDIC), Box 8105, Athens, GA 30601 (Contact: Dr Daniel U Wilde, Director)

Composed of information centres representing industry, government, and academic institutions of the US, Canada and several other countries. Promotes applied technology of information storage and retrieval; shares member experiences through meetings, seminars and workshops; recommends standards for data elements, formats and codes; promotes research and development.

*Association of Media Producers (AMP), 1707 L Street NW, Suite 515, Washington, DC 20036 (Contact: Daphne Philos)

A non-profit-making international association of producers and distributors of educational audiovisual materials and those companies providing services to the industry.

*Association of Teacher Educators, 1701 K Street NW, Suite 1201, Washington, DC 20036 (Contact: Dr Robert J Stevenson, Executive Director)

The Association is a national, individual membership organization devoted solely to the improvement of teacher education for both school-based and campus-based educators. The Association holds an annual conference and offers occasional local 'clinics'. Publications: *Action in Teacher Education* (quarterly); *Newsletter* (six times a year).

Association of Visual Science Librarians (AVSL), c/o Mrs Pat Carlson, Southern California College of Optometry, 2001 Associated Road, Fullerton, CA 92631

Center for Research on Learning and Teaching, *see* University of Michigan

The Center for Visual Literacy, Indiana University, Bloomington, IN 47405 (Contact: Dennis Pett, Director)

Center on Evaluation, Development, and Research, Phi Delta Kappa, PO Box 789, Bloomington, IN 47402 (Contact: The Director)

The Center's mission has two parts: assisting members of Phi Delta Kappa in obtaining information from research, and improving understanding of and ability to participate in research, evaluation, and development work. Main activities are: TAFI (Teacher Appraisal for Improvement) Workshops (a structured one-day workshop on different ways to measure the quality of teaching); NSPER (National Symposia for Professionals in Evaluation and Research), a 2½-day conference held each autumn, focused on selected aspects of evaluation, research, and development; and invited presentations on evaluation, development, and research topics.

*Children's Television Workshop, 1 Lincoln Plaza, New York, NY 10023 (Contacts: Dr Edward L Palmer, Vice-President, Research; Fran Kaufman, Director of Information)

Activities include production of educational and informational television programmes with extensive research into the impact of television on children. Productions include 'Sesame Street', 'The Electric Company', 'The Best of Families' (TV series); newsletter, plus numerous international co-productions; research materials; numerous periodicals, books and a research bibliography.

Clearinghouses: ERIC Clearinghouses are described in full in Section 3

Clearinghouse on Development Communications, 1414 22nd Street NW, 5th Floor, Washington, DC 20037 (Contacts: Jill Merrick, Director; Heddy Reid, Editor; Judy Brace, Manager, Resource Center)

A centre for materials and information on important applications of communication technology to development problems, the Clearinghouse is operated by the Academy for Educational Development, a non-profit-making planning organization, and supported by the Science and Technology Bureau of the US Agency for International Development as part of its programme in educational technology and development communication. Publications: quarterly *Development Communication Report* which is available free of charge to developing countries by writing to the Clearinghouse; 'Project Profiles' which describes important communications and educational technology projects in developing countries in a succinct and standard format, available in English, Spanish, French and Arabic; occasional information bulletins covering one topic or project in depth.

*Commonwealth Center for High Technology/Education, 900 Washington Street, Wellesley, Massachusetts 02181 (Contact: Dr Douglas K Fulrath, Director)

The Commonwealth Center, a joint venture between the 10-campus Massachusetts State College System and Digital Equipment Corporation, was established in 1977 to link higher education with high technology firms for three reasons: to help fill the critical need for a technologically trained labour force (and to supply other consulting/educational services to high technology industries); to transfer technology across public and private sectors for improving education; to apply instructional/educational technology and media to areas of educational need.

CONDUIT, 100 Lindquist Center, The University of Iowa, PO Box 388, Iowa City, IA (Contact: Harold J Peters, Associate Director)

CONDUIT is a not-for-profit agency affiliated with The University of Iowa, and supported in part by grants from the National Science Foundation and the Fund for Improvement of Post-secondary Education. Its mission is to deliver proven computer-based instructional materials into the hands of educators. Current offerings include over 100 curriculum packages in 13 different disciplines, for use on large mainframes as well as microcomputers, each reviewed and tested before distribution for conceptual validity, instructional usefulness, and overall quality.

Main activities include research and development of effective, usable instructional computing materials; distribution of those materials; and research and development of authoring aids, programming standards, transfer guidelines, and evaluation tools. Services include the distribution of reviewed and tested instructional computing materials; aiding authors of these materials through assistance in development and distribution; research into design, development, style, packaging, evaluation; research into authoring aids, transferability. Publications include: *Pipeline*, a twice-yearly magazine available on subscription, which includes announcements of newly available instructional computing packages as well as timely articles of general interest to educators with respect to educational computing; *The CONDUIT BASIC Guide*, standards for writing transferable programs in BASIC based on comparison of the features of over 20 dialects; *The CONDUIT Author's Guide*, covering areas of design, development, style, packaging, and reviewing; *CONDUIT Abstracts*, including abstracts of each of the instructional computing packages currently available from CONDUIT; Reviewed and Tested Materials – over 100 instructional packages in 13 different disciplines.

Consortium of University Film Centres, c/o Audio Visual Services, 330 KSU Library, Kent, OH 44242 (Contact: Charles H Hunger, Executive Director)

The Consortium is an organization composed of the directors and senior staff members from approximately 50 of the major university film centres. There are associate and sustaining memberships available for those not associated with a university film centre and for commercial members. The general purpose of the Consortium is to improve the effective use of motion pictures by making films more accessible; fostering co-operative planning among universities and other organizations in the solving of mutual problems; gathering and disseminating information on improved procedures and new developments; reducing duplication of effort and waste of resources; and generating and co-ordinating research which may further these purposes and objectives. The Consortium membership meets twice a year, once in October and once in conjunction with the annual convention of the Association for Educational Communications and Technology (AECT). (The Consortium is not affiliated with AECT, but most of its members also belong to AECT so they have a pre-conference meeting.) Publications: *Guidelines for Producers and Distributors of Educational Films*, available direct from the Consortium. The Consortium has published numerous reports and studies for internal circulation on such subjects as film evaluation, job classifications and salaries, and copies of the various forms used in the conduct of film rental libraries. Several of these reports have found their way into various publications, but a bibliography is not available.

Council for Educational Development and Research (CEDaR), 1518 K Street NW, Suite 206, Washington, DC 20005

CEDaR is a clearinghouse and disseminator of information regarding activities and products of the following: Appalachia Educational Laboratory Inc, Charleston, West Virginia; CEMREL Inc, St Louis Missouri; Center for Educational Policy and Management, University of Oregon, Eugene; Institute for Research on Educational Finance and Governance, Stanford University, California; Center for Social Organization of Schools, The Johns Hopkins University, Baltimore, Maryland; Center for the Study of Evaluation, University of California (Los Angeles); The National Center for Research in Vocational Education, The Ohio State University, Columbus; Far West Laboratory for Educational Research and Development, San Francisco, California; Learning Research and Development Center, University of Pittsburgh, Pennsylvania; Mid-Continent Regional Educational Laboratory, Kansas City, Missouri; The Network, Merrimac, Massachusetts; Northwest Regional Educational Laboratory, Portland, Oregon; Research and Development Center for Teacher Education, The University of Texas (Austin); Research for Better Schools Inc, Philadelphia, Pennsylvania; Southwest Educational Development Laboratory, Austin, Texas; SWRL Educational Research and Development, Los Alamitos, California; and Wisconsin Research and Development Center for Individualized Schooling, University of Wisconsin (Madison).

*Curriculum Materials Clearinghouse, University Microfilms, 300 North Zeeb Road, Ann Arbor, MI 48106

Provides publishing service, information exchange and document dissemination for curriculum developers – a commercial service, associated with the ERIC Clearinghouse.

*The Division of Educational Technology, 3116 ROB/3, US Office of Education, Washington, DC 20202

The Division of Educational Technology is located in the Office of Libraries and Learning Resources in the Bureau of Elementary and Secondary Education. It administers three legislated programmes: the Special Projects Act – Educational Television and Radio Programming; Title II – Basic Skills Improvement, Sec 207, both under the Elementary and Secondary Education Act; and the Emergency School Aid Act – Educational Television and Radio. The Educational Technology Development Branch administers the Special Projects Act – Educational Television and Radio Programming. This programme awards competitive contracts for the development, production, evaluation, dissemination, and use of innovative educational television or radio programmes designed for broadcast and/or non-broadcast uses. Awards are made for a single year's duration; continuation awards for subsequent years are subject to satisfactory performance and availability of future appropriations. The overall objectives of this programme are to increase the quality of programmes available for learning through television in both formal and informal learning environments; provide for the secondary use and distribution of programmes during and after their broadcast phase; and prepare teachers and parents in the use of techniques which will help children understand the use of television for learning by relating it to the classroom and books. Integrated television series for minority and non-minority children are funded under the Emergency School Aid Act – Educational Television and Radio. Contracts and grants are awarded to public and private non-profit agencies for the development and production of children's integrated television and radio programming to improve the effectiveness of desegregation. There are separate regional and national television series competitions, and beginning in 1980 there will be a separate radio competition as well.

Educational Captioned Films, Selection and Evaluation Program, 814 Thayer Avenue, Silver Spring, MD 20910 (Contact: Salvatore J Parlato, National Co-ordinator)

The Programme is responsible for evaluating films for the US Government to purchase, caption, and distribute to schools and colleges serving the deaf. It is responsible for analysis of national curriculum priorities; recruitment and training of educators as film evaluators; and corresponding with the 120 participating film companies. Details of publications are available on request.

Educational Facilities Laboratories, 850 Third Avenue, New York City, NY 10022 (Contact: Mrs Ruth Weinstock; Alan Green)

Instructional technology, research, reporting and consulting on facilities planning and programme applications. Research, reporting, consulting on hardware and programmes: consulting services are extremely useful to educational institutions because of the organization's knowledge of 'who's doing what'; of 'what works, what doesn't work, and why'; of 'when technology makes sense and when it doesn't'; of the solutions it offers to new needs – for reaching off-campus students, for serving students better, for rationalizing the process of instruction, and for expanding the options for learners. It is now expanding its consulting services to institutions and communities outside the US. Among the many books and pamphlets produced are *The Impact of Technology on the Library Building* (1967); *Cables, Cameras and Schools* (1974); *New Spaces for Learning: The Design of College Facilities to Utilize Instructional Aids and Media* (1966); *Designing for Educational Technology – A Guide to Resources* (1970); *Design for ETV* (1960); *Communications Technologies in Higher Education* (1976); a series of profiles documenting experience of the use of technology in 21 colleges and universities (1979); and *Broadcasting and Adult Literacy – The British Experience/Implications for the US* (1981).

Research and reporting is supported by a grant from The Ford Foundation.

Educational Film Library Association, 43 West 61 Street, New York, NY 10023 (Contacts: Nadine Covert, Executive Director, EFLA; Judith Trojan, Evaluations Editor; Maryann Chach, Film Reference Librarian)

EFLA is a non-profit membership organization which serves as a national clearinghouse for information about non-theatrical 16mm films, video and other non-print materials. EFLA administers an independent evaluation programme to assist film libraries, audiovisual directors and educators in film selection, and sponsors the annual American Film Festival. EFLA's library maintains a reference collection of books, periodicals, and vertical files. Publications include: *Sightlines*, a quarterly magazine; *EFLA Bulletin*, a quarterly newsletter; *EFLA Evaluations*, 5 issues a year; *American Film Festival* guides (annual); plus a number of film lists.

Educational Media Producers Council (see NAVA Materials Council)

*Educational Products Information Exchange, EPIE Institute, 475 Riverside Drive, New York, NY (Contact: P Kenneth Komoski)

EPIE Institute was established as an educational consumers' co-operative in 1967. From its inception, EPIE's purpose has been to help school people to choose wisely from among the growing number of educational products and to help teachers make the most effective use of instructional materials and equipment. EPIE has no commercial ties and is supported by income from co-operating schools and colleges who are EPIE members/subscribers and by occasional non-restrictive grants and contracts from private foundations and public agencies. In 1975, EPIE was permanently chartered by the Regents of the University of the State of New York as an independent non-profit-making agency. In 1973, EPIE established the nation's only independent Educational Equipment Testing Laboratory, initiated with the help of a grant from The Ford Foundation and now supported by EPIE member schools and colleges. At the Laboratory, technicians rigorously test equipment for performance, durability and safety. The Laboratory also collects and analyses information on all types of equipment currently reported to EPIE by more than 100 schools and colleges. Participating institutions keep detailed maintenance records and report on the costs, in terms of time as well as money, of maintaining equipment and on performance ability and reliability. In 1974, with Lilly Endowment support, EPIE began a longitudinal study. The National Survey and Assessment of Instructional Materials (NSAIM). NSAIM gathers information from more than 24,000 elementary and secondary school buildings in all 50 American states on the selection and use of instructional materials. Results of the study began appearing in EPIE Reports in 1975 and are being distributed to EPIE members throughout the country. In 1974, EPIE began conducting workshops on analysing instructional materials. To date, more than 600 teachers and curriculum and media specialists have been trained in EPIE's highly structured, systematic method of materials analysis. In 1977, in response to requests from schools, EPIE began to offer a second type of training session: workshops on selecting instructional materials. The EPIE system of instructional materials analysis is used in these workshops to develop in materials selectors the skills needed for wise purchasing decisions. EPIE Institute provides a unique 'care-sharing' and 'cost-sharing' information service to educational consumers throughout the US, in Canada and other countries. The 'care-sharing' members/subscribers – state agencies, countywide districts and professional associations – sponsor workshops which EPIE conducts for teachers, curriculum co-ordinators and media specialists. EPIE-trained and certified analysts 'care-share' by contributing time to instructional materials analysis for *EPIE Reports*. The 'cost-sharing' members/subscribers, more than 2300 schools and colleges in the US, Canada and other countries, provide financial support for EPIE's on-going research and publications programme. Publications include *EPIEgram*: EPIE currently publishes a twice-monthly, October through June, educational consumers' newsletter called *EPIEgram* which delivers up-to-date information on instructional materials and equipment, as well as on new developments in education and on consumer issues. In autumn 1977, EPIE began publishing two versions of *EPIEgram*, one focusing on the needs of purchasers and users of instructional materials (*EPIEgram: Materials*), and one focusing on equipment (*EPIEgram: Equipment*). *EPIE Reports*: beginning in autumn 1977, EPIE increased the number of Reports published each year to eight (two each in autumn, winter, spring, and summer). An *EPIE Report* analyses either materials in use or available for teaching a particular subject, or laboratory test findings on a particular class of equipment. Reports also include user-based evaluations of materials and equipment.

Educational Resources Information Center (ERIC): ERIC is described, and the Clearinghouses listed, in Section 3.

Educational Technology Publications Inc, 140 Sylvan Avenue, Englewood Cliffs, NJ 07632

Publishers of *Educational Technology* (12 issues per year) and of numerous books and booklets, audio-cassettes and related media resources covering the field of educational technology. *Educational Technology*, published since 1961, is the world's leading periodical in this field, with a circulation of more than 80 countries. ETP also has over 200 books in print in the field of educational technology.

Educational Testing Service, Princeton, NJ 08541 (Contact: Donald L Alderman)

A non-profit organization which serves education through measurement, research and related activities; besides offering a wide variety of test services, ETS conducts research on a range of topics including human learning and development, programme evaluation, educational policy analysis, methodology and theory in measurement and statistics, and educational technology.

Far West Laboratory for Educational Research and Development, 1855 Folsom Street, San Francisco, CA 94103

Activities include educational research, development, evaluation and dissemination. Technical assistance and consulting services are available at cost. Publications include reports, studies, handbooks, audiovisual products, curricula, etc.

Fuller Theological Seminary, School of World Mission, 135 North Oakland, Pasadena, CA 91101 (Contact: Dr Paul E Pierson, Dean)

Courses in open education, extension training and programmed instruction: theological education by extension, programmed instruction, education in anthropological perspective.

Great Plains National Instructional Television Library, Box 80669, Lincoln, NE 68501 (Contacts: Paul H Schupbach, Director; Richard L Spence, Information Co-ordinator)

The Library identifies and acquires extant recorded instructional materials (videotape, film), then makes them available through duplication to educational institutions and educational television stations desirous of their use. Available on either a lease or sales basis. Many of the materials are also made available in 16mm film format. The bulk of the material is course-centred and classroom-structured.

Hendershot Bibliography, 4114 Ridgewood, Bay City, MI 48706 (Contact: Dr Carl H Hendershot)

Compilers and publishers of source books of individualized instruction, periodically updated by supplements; designers of self-teaching instruction. Current release entitled *Programmed Learning & Individually Paced Instruction-Bibliography*, fifth Edition with Supplements 1/6, two volumes, approx 800pp.

HeSCA – The Health Sciences Communications Association, 2343 North 115th Street, Wauwatosa, WI 53226 (Contact: Phyllis Duke, Associate Manager)

Originally known as CMT, the Council on Medical Television. Now broader in scope, it is composed of professionals interested in applying educational technology to the health sciences. Members select a functional section which best describes his/her prime interest, but may participate in the activities of all sections at the annual conference. HeSCA's main activities include the Annual Meeting which includes workshops for continuing education unit credit; media festivals in which members can enter and compete for cash awards; the Learning Resource Center, also at the annual meeting, in which media can be entered and viewed by other members. *Publications* available for sale at cost are a *Feedback Newsletter* (six issues per year); *The Journal of Biocommunication* (three issues per year); and membership includes complimentary subscriptions to Biomedical Communications & Video Systems. A special International Committee for members in Europe, Middle East and Far East is now being formed.

Health Sciences Consortium Inc, 200 Eastowne Drive, Suite 213, Chapel Hill, NC 27514 (Contact: Vera Pfifferling, Director, Special Projects)

The Health Sciences Consortium is a non-profit publishing co-operative of more than 50 health science institutions nationwide. Its primary goal is to facilitate the sharing of high quality educational materials.

Activities and services include publication of educational materials; consulting; faculty development workshops; instructional design; peer review. (*See also entry in Section 5.*)

HumRRO – Human Resources Research Organization, 300 North Washington Street, Alexandria, VA 22314 (Contact: Dr Saul Lavisky)

During its years of working to improve human performance, HumRRO scientists and technicians have engaged in research and development to solve specific problems in training and education, development, refinement, and instruction in the technology of training and education; studies and development of techniques to improve the motivation of personnel in training and on-the-job; research on leadership and management, and development of programmes to prepare men and women for leadership; criterion development, individual assessment, and programme evaluation in training and operating systems; measurement and evaluation of human performance under varying circumstances, and studies of how well individuals see, hear, act, and interact in different environments; organizational development studies, including such elements as performance counselling, group decision-making, management by objectives, and factors that impact upon organizational competence; and studies in, and development of, manpower information systems and the application of management science to personnel systems, including studies and analyses of procurement, use, performance, retention, and separation of military manpower.

*Industrial Audio-Visual Association, Box 656, Downtown Station, Chicago, IL 60690 (Contact: F Woldt)

Activities include development of standards for the audiovisual media industry.

Institute for Research on Educational Finance and Governance, CERAS 402, Stanford University, Stanford, CA 94305 (Contact: The Director)

The Institute for Research on Educational Finance and Governance (IFG) is a national research and development centre with a long-range commitment from the National Institute of Education and administered through the School of Education at Stanford University. IFG is devoted to a programme of policy-oriented research, dissemination and training on the finance and governance of education. The programme represents an attempt to provide a systematic and co-ordinated research attack on the information needs and major issues facing educational policy makers. It focuses particularly on issues of equity and efficiency with an understanding of the broad social and economic forces which are making increased demands on education, as well as the consequences of various alternatives being proposed in response to those demands. IFG also attempts to provide a national resource for research and dissemination on the origins, implementation, and consequences of various finance and governance arrangements in education, through an examination of their processes, outcomes and equity patterns.

The research programme is divided into six major areas. Participants in each of the major programmes are drawn from several disciplines, with a strong interest in the specific problem area being the major common bond. The major programme areas of research include: categorical grants in education; structures of educational governance and their alternatives; law and education; problems of legitimacy in the governance of education; post-secondary educational finance and governance; and policy communication in education.

Providing information is IFG's main service, as its main output is research. It is strongly committed to distributing the findings of its research and promoting a general knowledge of educational issues. An extensive programme of publications includes over 60 research papers annually, and a quarterly publication, IFG *Policy Notes*, which attempts to summarize and synthesize current research activity at IFG and to highlight its policy implications. Outcomes of conferences and seminars are also covered. On a periodic basis, IFG *Policy Perspectives* is published as an effort to focus in greater depth on the research and policy implications of a particular topic in a newsletter format. Publications are regularly sent to a mailing list of almost 3000. Groups and individuals may obtain access to the publications by sending their name and address for inclusion on the mailing list. All such requests should be sent to Sandra L Kirkpatrick, Assistant Director for Dissemination, who can also provide a cumulative list of publications with abstracts.

International Congress for Individualized Instruction Contact: Dr Ruth Witkus, Editor, ICII, Biology Department, Fordham University, Bronx, NY 10458)

The International Congress for Individualized Instruction meets annually and abstracts of papers presented at the Congress are published in its proceedings following the meeting. The Congress's Newsletter *One-to-One* is published quarterly and includes information in the area of research and evaluation into the effectiveness of various models of individualized instruction (PSI, audio tutorial, CAI, etc).

International Copyright Information Center, *see* INCINC *under International Centres of Activity*

International Council for Computers in Education, Department of Computer and Information Science, University of Oregon, Eugene, OR 97403 (Contact: David Moursund, President)

ICCE was founded in 1979 to work in the field of instructional use of computers at the pre-college level. It publishes a journal, *The Computing Teacher*. ICCE has about 6000 individual members and 14 organization members. It also publishes booklets and books of interest to educators involved in the instructional uses of computers. ICCE is one of the sponsoring organizations for the National Educational Computing Conference held each year in the USA.

International Institute of Instructional Technology, *see* IIIT *under International Centres of Activity*

*International Tape Exchange, 834 Ruddiman Avenue, North Muskegon, MI 49445 (Contact: Ruth Y Terry, Director of Publications)

Presents procedure and supplies lists of participants interested in exchanging cassette or reel tapes on a national and international basis: advises and consults with administrators and teachers on the preparation of programmes.

The International Visual Literacy Association, c/o Dennis W Pett, Executive Secretary, Audio Visual Center, Indiana University, Bloomington, IN 47405

Iowa Regional Computer Center (RCC), Weeg Computing Center, University of Iowa, Iowa City, IA 52242 (Contact: Judith R Brown)

The Iowa Regional Computer Center is a consortium of liberal arts colleges, founded in 1968, with the goal of improving the computer resources for all member institutions. The consortium has continued to share ideas and information through regularly scheduled co-ordinators' meetings and publication of the *RCC News*. RCC institutions share information on administrative and academic computer use. An updated list of professional activities involving computer use in teaching and research by the faculty at member institutions is being prepared. Some early work was done in the development of administrative data processing packages. Recently, instructional programs in the science areas were developed.

The University of Iowa provides computer resources and consulting to the member schools. Through co-ordinators' meetings, programs, information and ideas are shared. Several grant proposals for computer literacy and microcomputer projects are under development.

Joint Council on Educational Telecommunications, 1126 16th Street NW, Washington, DC 20036 (Contact: Frank W Norwood, Executive Director)

The Joint Council is a consortium of leading non-governmental associations and organizations in formal and informal education, library services and non-commercial broadcasting. It serves its members as a mechanism for dealing with emerging communications technologies and the formulation of public communications policies. The JCET maintains close and continuing contact with the Federal Communications Commission, the National Information and Telecommunications Administration, the National Aeronautics and Space Administration, the Department of Health, Education and Welfare, and with commercial and non-commercial communications entities.

Landa International Institute for Algorithmic Methods of Training and Simplification of Documents, Inc, 42-74 79th Street, Elmhurst, NY 11373 (Contact: Dr L Landa, President)

The Institute was formed in 1979 to serve the needs of academic and business communities in algorithmic methods of training and document simplification. The Institute has provided lectures, seminars and training courses for a number of government organizations and universities in the USA and Europe, as well as major corporations such as American Bankers Association, American Telephone & Telegraph, Carnegie Corporation, Control Data Corporation, Xerox Learning Systems and some others. It has also been involved in creation of algorithm based courses in different disciplines. Such courses allow to increase the efficiency of training manyfold. The algorithmic method of simplification of rules, regulations, laws and other documents allows one to speed up the process of rule comprehension and application up to 80 times. The Institute has developed a method not just for document simplification but teaching organizations how to do this.

Learning Research and Development Center (LRDC), *see* University of Pittsburgh

Microcomputer Resource Center (MRC), Box 18, Teachers College, Columbia University, New York, NY 10027 (Contacts: Karen Billings, Director; James Dunne, Associate Director)

The Microcomputer Resource Center provides services that include teaching, consultation, and information on the educational uses of microcomputers. The Center also conducts hardware and software evaluations as well as a continuing program in research and development. The instructional staff has extensive experience working with adults, children and computers. Workshops currently being offered by the Center include: Computer Activities for Children: Programming in LOGO; Computer Activities for Parents with Children: Home Computers – Educational Uses; Orientation to Microcomputers; Special Topic and Special Group Workshops. Other projects which the Center is currently involved in include in-service courses for teachers at their schools; software development; software evaluation; consultation to schools on the acquisition of computer materials.

Minnesota Educational Computing Consortium (MECC), 2520 Broadway Drive, St Paul, Minnesota 55113.

MECC is an organization created by the four public educational systems in Minnesota to co-ordinate and provide computer services to students, teachers and educational administrators throughout the state.

*Motion Picture Association of America, 522 Fifth Avenue, New York, NY 10036

The Association seeks to develop the educational and entertainment values of films.

National Association for Core Curriculum Inc, 407D White Hall, Kent State University, Kent, OH 44242 (Contact: Dr Gordon F Vars, Executive Secretary-Treasurer)

A membership corporation, registered in the State of New York, designed 'to promote the development of secondary school general education programmes variously known as core, common learnings, unified studies, block-time, etc'. At its annual conventions, teachers, administrators, curriculum specialists, and college professors share ideas and discuss problems relating to curriculum, methods, and teacher preparation for core and other types of humanistic inter-disciplinary programmes. Between meetings, members are kept informed of research and developments in the field through *The Core Teacher*, a quarterly newsletter. The Association also distributes films and videotapes about core teaching, and makes available bibliographies and curriculum guides. It also arranges for book discounts to members.

National Association of Educational Broadcasters, 1346 Connecticut Avenue, NW, Washington, DC 20036 (Contact: James A Fellows, President)

NAEB is a professional association of individuals either employed in or seeking to further the growth of public and educational telecommunications. The goal of NAEB is to promote and maintain a high standard of professionalism and to foster communication and interaction among working professionals. Activities include publications programme, annual convention, professional training seminars, policy and research studies, awards programme, local chapter support. Publications include *Current*, a twice monthly newspaper, and special studies as acquired and commissioned. *Current* carries the nation's most comprehensive listing of employment openings for non-commercial broadcasting and related fields.

National Audio-Visual Association (NAVA), 3150 Spring Street, Fairfax, Virginia 22031

NAVA is a national association of media hardware and media software producers and manufacturers, dealers, representatives and others involved with educational communications and information activities, services, and products. Annual Convention and Exhibit is held in January. Publications: *Audio-Visual Equipment Directory; NAVA News* (newsletter).

NAVA Materials Council (formerly Educational Media Producers Council, a council within the National Audio-Visual Association), 3150 Spring Street, Fairfax, Virginia 22031 (Contacts: Kenton Pattie, Senior Staff Vice-President; Terri Fawcett, Representative to the Council)

As a Council of 206 producers, publishers, dealers, agents and distributors of audiovisual programmes and materials, the NAVA Materials Council concentrates on projects which help improve the marketplace for audiovisual software and improve the professionalism and working knowledge of salespeople, managers and owners in audiovisual companies. An annual Software Conference is held every August. The Council also publishes on the themes of microcomputer software and copyright law.

National Audiovisual Center (NAC), General Services Administration, Reference Section, Washington, DC 20409

The National Audiovisual Center was created in 1969 to serve the public by making Federally produced materials available for use through distribution services, and by serving as the central clearinghouse for all US Government audiovisual materials. Through the Center's distribution programmes – sale, rental, and loan referrals – the public has access to audiovisual materials covering a variety of subjects. Major subject concentrations in the Center's collection include medicine, dentistry, and the allied health sciences; education; aviation and space technology; vocational and management training; safety; and the environmental sciences. Many of the Center's audiovisual materials are designed for general use, while others are designed for specific training or instructional programmes. The instructional materials are appropriate for classroom use or for self-instruction. To complement and increase the effectiveness of these audiovisual programmes, many are accompanied by printed materials such as teacher manuals, student workbooks, or scripts.

National Captioning Institute (NCI), 5203 Leesburg Pike, Falls Church, VA 22041 (Contacts: John E D Ball, President; Doris C Caldwell, Special Assistant to the President)

The National Captioning Institute (NCI), a non-profit and tax-exempt corporation, was established in 1979 to open the world of television for hearing-handicapped persons through its innovative closed-captioning service. 'Closed' captions (like subtitles on a foreign movie) appear only on specially equipped TV sets and, quite simply, enable viewers to read what they cannot hear. The new service is the first of its kind anywhere in the world.

A series of grants from the US Department of Education funded technical development of the system and its implementation by NCI. Federal funds are being rapidly phased out and supplemented by philanthropic grants as the innovative service grows toward a self-supporting financial footing.

The NCI has published numerous *Research Reports*, brochures and articles.

National Center for Audio Tapes (NCAT), c/o Educational Media Center, Stadium, University of Colorado, Boulder, CO 80309

NCAT receives tapes from colleges and universities, state departments of education and various government, commercial, school and private groups, and reproduces them for educational users throughout the country. Currently there are 15,000 titles available from NCAT on either open reel or cassette format. A cumulative catalogue is available for $4.50.

*National Center for Higher Education Management Systems, PO Drawer P, Boulder CO 80302 (Contact: Delma Oberbeck, Staff Associate)

Involved in the areas of research, development and improvement of higher education management.

The National Center for Research in Vocational Education, Ohio State University, 1960 Kenny Road, Columbus, OH 43210 (Contact: Robert E Taylor, Executive Director)

The mission of the National Center is to increase the ability of diverse agencies, institutions, and organizations to solve educational problems relating to individual career planning, preparation and progression. The National Center fulfils its mission by: generating knowledge through research; developing educational programmes and products; evaluating individual programme needs and outcomes; providing information for national planning and policy; installing educational programmes and products; operating information systems and services; and conducting leadership development training programmes. With a staff of over 300, the Center carries out its work through seven divisions: Development, Evaluation and Policy, Information Systems, Personnel Development, Research, Special Projects, and International. Funds for the National Center's activities are provided from contracts and grants from the US Department of Education, the National Institute of Education, other federal agencies, state departments of education, local school districts, private industry and business, non-profit institutions and organizations, and ministries of labour and education from around the world.

The National Center houses the most comprehensive collection of research materials on vocational education in the nation, over 50,000 volumes, and has operated The Educational Resources Information Center (ERIC) Clearinghouse on Adult, Career, and Vocational Education, sponsored by the National Institute of Education, since 1976. The Center also operates the Resource and Referral Service (RRS) also sponsored by the National Institute of Education. RRS is a service of the Research and Development Exchange designed to make the results of educational research more readily available to educational practitioners. A National Alliance of Postsecondary Education Institutions, A Consortium for the Development of Professional Materials, and an Alliance for Career and Vocational Education are all operated at the National Center through the support and participation of many institutions, state governments and local school districts. In the last three years the National Center has received over 45,000 requests for information from a variety of constituencies. Leadership development and professional training is offered through a National Academy and an Advanced Study Center.

The National Center publishes a wide range of research reports and publications on many different training sectors including vocational education, manpower training, apprenticeship, CETA, and others. It also publishes an annual report and a monthly newsletter, *Centergram*, that reaches over 80,000 vocational educators, administrators, and researchers. Additionally, several monthly or bi-monthly newsletters are disseminated as part of contractual obligations.

National Center for Visual Literacy, *see* Center for Visual Literacy

National Council on Measurement in Education, 1230 17th Street NW, Washington, DC 20036 (Contact: Dr William J Russell, Executive Officer)

NCME is a professional organization formed to service educators who are concerned with the practical use of various types of measurement in the instructional setting. Its main activities are disseminating useful information about sound techniques and instruments available for the measurement of individuals and groups; promotion of improvement of instruments, techniques and interpretive procedures through conduct of special studies or projects; providing the membership with current information exchange, through publications, national conventions and area meetings.

*National Education Association (NEA), 1201 16th Street NW, Washington, DC 20036 (Contact: Terry Herndon, Executive Director)

NEA advances the interests of the profession of teaching and promotes the cause of education.

National Information Centre for Education Media, *see* NICEM

National Institute of Education, 1200 19th Street NW, Washington, DC 20208

A separate agency within the Department of Health, Education and Welfare with a major interest in educational research and development. NIE sponsors the ERIC Clearinghouses.

*National Medical Audiovisual Center (NMAC), 1600 Clifton Road NE, Atlanta, GA 30333

*National Micrographics Association, 8719 Colesville Road, Silver Spring, MD 20910 (Contact: O Gordon Banks, Executive Director)

Education in the field of micrographics and interfacing technologies, standards development in micrographics. Publications: *Journal of Micrographics* (bi-monthly); *Buyer's Guide* (annually); numerous consumer and reference series publications, audiovisuals.

*National Public Radio, 2025 M Street NW, Washington, DC 20036 (Contact: Ms Linda E Brown, Director, Promotion and Public Affairs)

National Public Radio represents a network of non-commercial radio stations, engaged in public service broadcasting, including educational broadcasting. The organization produces and distributes programmes as well as representing public radio at the national level.

National Research Council, Board on Telecommunications-Computer Application, 2101 Constitution Avenue, Washington, DC 20418 (Contact: Dr R B Marsten, Executive Director)

Since 1970 the Board on Telecommunications-Computer Applications has provided telecommunications-information support services to a consortium of Federal departments and agencies, the Interagency Committee on Telecommunications Applications (ICTA), under a basic contract that has been renewed annually. Currently the ICTA consists of the following members: the Departments of Commerce (Chairman); Housing and Urban Development; Energy; Transportation; US Postal Service; National Science Foundation; and National Aeronautics and Space Administration. The services provided by the Board for its sponsors have included, primarily, the conduct of studies on important subjects related to the sponsors' missions, but also the following: organizing symposia on significant topics in telecommunications/information technologies and applications, sponsoring visits to US research facilities, hosting briefings by experts from the US and abroad, and collecting and disseminating information on significant US and foreign telecommunications/information developments. The goal of these activities is to keep the sponsors aware of significant developments that could be useful in furtherance of their missions. Reports of the Board are available from the US Department of Commerce, National Technical Information Service.

National Society for Performance and Instruction (NSPI) (formerly National Society for Programmed Instruction), 1126 Sixteenth Street NW, Washington, DC 20036 (Contact: Kay Schaeffer, Executive Director)

NSPI has, as its primary purpose, the advancement of education and training through the collection, development and diffusion of information concerned with the process of developing instructional materials. This process involves a systematic design of instructional materials through successive approximations until the learning reaches optimum relevance and efficiency. The Society has about 2000 members and 20 local Chapters. Originally, NSPI was formed to gather and disseminate information on programmed instruction. Over the years, since the Society was established, their goals have been expanded to include the entire educational and instructional field along with most aspects of human performance. During this same period, the educational and instructional art technology has made remarkable progress. NSPI members and supporters have been responsible for a large share of this progress through their applied research and practical experience. Today NSPI is the only professional inter-disciplinary organization where researcher, programmer, classroom instructor, industrial trainer and hardware people talk to each other and learn from each other. The Society publishes the *Performance and Instruction Journal*, a magazine with ten issues per year.

These publications serve as a forum for basic and applied research in educational and training technologies. The Chapters represent one of the major opportunities for obtaining and providing information about preparing high quality instructional materials. The dialogue and activities in these local groups are continuous throughout most of the year and provide members with an opportunity to interact with others who are concerned with the process of developing instructional materials and programmes. The Chapters are intended for individuals rather than organizations. The advantages of joining a Chapter depend on the specific Chapter. In general, Chapters offer contact and collaboration with other professionals in the local region and/or in specialized fields.

National Society for the Study of Education (NSSE), 5835 Kimbark Avenue, Chicago, IL 60637

National Video Clearinghouse Inc, PO Box 3, Syosset, New York 11791 (Contact: Arnold Menis, Director of Marketing)

The Clearinghouse will serve as a national comprehensive reference centre for all video programme software information in all video-cassette and video-disc formats. Using computer technology, the Clearinghouse will assemble computer information about all video programming available for home, institutional, broadcast and cable users in all present and future formats. The comprehensive information will include a title-by-title analysis based on programme descriptions, subject category areas, producers, stars/hosts, distributors, and price per use per format. The information will be updated monthly and made available through various printed publications, including *The Video Source Book, The Home Tape/Disc Guides,* the *Video Newsletter*, and the *Video Index*. The Clearinghouse will also operate the Video Hot-Line – a toll-free national telephone information centre with complete up-to-date information about all video programmes in all tape and disc formats. The first edition of the *Video Source Book* already contains many thousands of pre-recorded video programmes; it is also available in a UK edition.

The NETWORK, Inc, 290 South Main Street, Andover, MA 01810 (Contacts: David P Crandall, EdD., Executive Director; David Max McConkey, Director)

The NETWORK, Inc, is a private, non-profit educational service and research organization. Founded in 1969, its main focus is to provide support for school improvement efforts. Its services are provided through competitively won grants and contracts from the federal and state governments, local school districts, and foundations. The NETWORK provides consultation, training, technical assistance, materials, and research to schools, other educational institutions, and numerous other public and private agencies. A publications list is available on request.

*The Network for Continuing Medical Education, 15 Columbus Circle, New York City, NY 10023

A bi-weekly video-cassette service is provided by the Network in the US for practising physicians to use as part of continuing education activities.

*NEXUS, American Association for Higher Education, 1 Dupont Circle, Washington, DC 20036

NICEM – National Information Center for Educational Media, University of Southern California, University Park, Los Angeles, CA 90007

The National Information Center publishes educational indexes of non-print media available on today's market. Their data base includes approximately 500,000 entries. Each entry contains a brief synopsis of the material.

North American Simulation and Gaming Association (NASAGA), c/o Dr W T Nichols, Box 100, Westminster College, New Wilmington, PA 16142

North Carolina Educational Computing Service (NCECS), Box 12035, Research Triangle Park, NC 27709

The North Carolina Educational Computing Service (NCECS), a division of The University of North Carolina General Administration, is the central organization for a network of 56 institutions in North Carolina, including 13 campuses of The University of North Carolina and the General Administration, 11 private colleges and universities, 17 community colleges and technical institutes, and 12 high schools. NCECS was established in 1966 as a retailer of computing service. It purchases machine time from the Triangle Universities Computation Center (TUCC) and other suppliers, and distributes that time, together with training, consulting, information services, and data communication facilities. During the past year NCECS has greatly expanded its microcomputer activities and has introduced support services for stand-alone microcomputers. NCECS has developed intelligent terminal software and provides training, consulting, evaluation of hardware and software, microcomputer discount arrangements, and other information for microcomputer users. A new computer-based message and 'bulletin board' system will facilitate the exchange of information. In addition to supplying computing services, NCECS supports curricula by providing access to its library of computer-based instructional materials and by offering workshops for training faculty to use this library. NCECS is a charter member of CONDUIT, a national consortium that distributes high quality computer-based curricular materials.

NCECS, which is an original member of EDUNET, a national computing network sponsored by EDUCOM, is also one of 35 university computer centres serving as suppliers to EDUNET. More importantly, NCECS, through its membership in EDUNET, provides customers with access to the facilities of all EDUNET suppliers. NCECS customers typically use EDUNET for specialized services not available on the local machines at TUCC.

Northwest Regional Educational Laboratory, 300 SW Sixth Avenue, Portland, OR 97204 (Contact: Robert R Rath, Executive Director)

The Laboratory aims to assist education, government, community agencies, business and labour in improving quality and equality in educational programmes and processes by: developing and disseminating effective educational products and procedures; conducting research on educational needs and problems; evaluating effectiveness of educational programmes and projects; providing training in educational planning, management, evaluation and instruction; serving as an information resource on effective educational programmes and processes. Its work is carried out in 20 programmes administered through five divisions: *(a) The Evaluation, Research and Assessment Division* assists agencies in resolving their educational problems through the application of appropriate evaluation, assessment and research techniques; *(2) The Instructional Improvement Division* conducts long-term programmatic research and development in selected substantive areas, including computer technology; *(3) The Multicultural Education Division* promotes equal learning opportunities for children regardless of their cultural and linguistic background, sex or race; *(4) The Planning and Service Co-ordination Division* provides problem-solving services to educational agencies; *(5) The Division of Independent Programs* houses other special long-term projects.

The Laboratory's work in educational technology has three major aspects: selection and installation of equipment; research and feasibility studies; and curriculum development. The Laboratory's *Products and Services Catalog* describes available materials including: general: *Annual Report; Northwest Report* newsletter; educational technology; *MicroSIFT* newsletter; *Introduction to Data Processing; Relevant Educational Applications of Computer Technology; The Computer in Educational Decision Making; Computer Applications in Instruction.*

*Olympic Media Information, 71 West 23rd Street, New York, NY 10010 (Contact: Watt Carroll, President)

Serves schools, libraries and the business community as a clearinghouse for audiovisual (non-print) information and evaluation. Publishes subscription services. Systematic collection and dissemination of audiovisual data and evaluations. Develops and maintains mailing lists for audiovisual distributors. Organizers of the Annual Training Film Festival. Publications include *Educational Media Catalogs on Microfiche*; *Training Film Profiles*; *Hospital/Health Care Training Media Profiles*; *Educational Trading Post & Swap Mart*.

*PLAN – Program for Learning in Accordance with Needs, *see* University of Iowa, Center for Education Experimentation, Development and Evaluation

Public Service Satellite Consortium, Suite 907, 1660 L Street, NW, Washington, DC 20036 (Contacts: Polly Rash, Director of Marketing; Dr Elizabeth L Young, President; Robert A Mott, Executive Vice-President; Dr Louis A Bransford, Vice-President, Planning and Development)

PSSC is an international non-profit organization, with members in the US, Canada, Australia and the South Pacific. Through the National Satellite Network, PSSC transmits educational programmes to specialized audiences. It provides technical co-ordination and assistance to organizations using satellite communications and acts as a co-ordinating body with federal agencies, non-federal public service organizations, communications-related groups and the communications industry. Telecommunications consultancy is available to non-profit organizations and the consortium acts as a clearinghouse for information on public service uses of telecommunications. Through its newly incorporated for-profit subsidiary, Services by Satellite (SatServ), PSSC now provides similar services to corporate clients. Publications include a monthly newsletter, Report to Members, and *Teleguide: A Handbook for Video-Teleconference Planners*, published in 1981. PSSC also holds an annual conference, of which audio-cassette tapes are available, and workshops.

Research for Better Schools Inc, 444 North Third Street, Philadelphia, PA 19123

Research, development and dissemination activities on the applications of reading, mathematics, career education, and citizen education in elementary and secondary classrooms. Assists schools, school districts and state education agencies in improving both instructional and managerial functions. Various research reports, curriculum materials, descriptions of systems and surveys. Most of these are available through ERIC Clearinghouse. A full catalogue of publications is available.

SWRL Educational Research and Development, 4665 Lampson Avenue, Los Alamitos, CA 90720 (Contact: Dr Richard E Schutz, Executive Director)

SWRL was established in 1966 as a Regional Educational Laboratory and operates within a long-term special institutional relationship with the US Federal Government. The National Center for Bilingual Research is a unit of SWRL and operates within a co-operative agreement with the National Institute of Education. SWRL conducts other R&D within its areas of expertise through grants and contracts with private concerns, education agencies, and government agencies within the US and internationally. It is concerned with design and development of: instructional systems; training systems; testing systems; management information systems; electronic data systems; programme implementation systems; media delivery systems; and technical assistance systems.

SWRL activity covers the range of research, development, evaluation, training, technical assistance, policy analysis, and programme implementation. Multi-disciplinary inquiry is conducted by a staff of 200 that includes expertise in linguistics, psychology, social sciences, information sciences, mathematics, fine arts, and all specializations of professional education.

SWRL distributes print-based, media-based, and computer-based product systems and publishes technical reports and professional papers.

*The Simulation and Gaming Association (SAGA), 4833 Greentree Road, Lebanon, OH 45036

Society for Applied Learning Technology, 50 Culpeper Street, Warrenton, VA 22186 (Contact: Raymond G Fox, President)

The development of international projects to advance and improve the standards of educational technology. Publishes *Journal of Educational Technology.*

Society for Computer Simulation (Simulation Councils Inc), PO Box 2228, La Jolla, CA 92038 (Contact: Charles A Pratt, Executive Director)

SCS is the only technical society devoted primarily to the advancement of computer simulation, modelling, and allied technologies. It has worldwide membership and a network of regional Simulation Councils that cover the US, parts of Canada, the UK, and other foreign countries. Publications: *Simulation* (monthly); *Simulation Councils Proceedings* (semi-annual series); *Annotated bibliographies of simulation.* Details of publications available on request.

*System Development Corporation, 2500 Colorado Avenue, Santa Monica, CA 90406

The Corporation conducts many media-related research and evaluation survey projects.

*Television Information Office of the National Association of Broadcasters, 745 Fifth Avenue, New York, NY 10022 (Contact: Roy Danish, Director)

Provides reference, information and bibliographical services; publicizes programmes of special interest; conducts research on public attitudes toward TV; issues publications on the structure and operation of the industry; produces AV materials for its sponsor TV networks, groups and stations.

*TEXT – Africa, 135 North Oakland, Pasadena, CA 91101 (Contact: F L Holland, Project Director)

Production of programmed textbooks for theological education by extension, with particular reference to Africa. Several workshops on programmed learning and other educational subjects are on offer.

University Consortium for Instructional Development and Technology, School of Education, Syracuse University, Syracuse, NY 13210

A consortium of six institutions of higher learning, promoting and providing training materials, consultants and analysis and design skills for programmes of instructional development in public schools, colleges and universities and training agencies in the US, and a variety of educational agencies and institutions in other countries.

*University Film Association, 217 Flint Hall, University of Kansas, Lawrence, KS 66045 (Contact: Dr Peter Dart, President, Department of Radio-TV-Film)

The University Film Association is a professional association of people with the following common purposes: furthering and developing the potentialities of the motion picture medium for purposes of instruction and communication throughout the world; encouraging the production of motion pictures in the various educational institutions; engaging in the teaching of the art and science of motion picture production techniques, film history, criticism, and/or related subjects; serving as a central source of information on film instruction and film production by educational institutions; and providing means for the sharing of ideas on the various activities involved in teaching film courses, in producing and distributing motion pictures and allied materials. The Association holds an Annual Conference, and members include film teachers and students, producers, business firms and educational institutions. Publications: *Journal of the University Film Association* (quarterly); Vice-President's Newsletter *Digest* (several times a year); *UFA Membership Directory.*

*University Film Study Center, 18 Vassar Street, 20B-120, Cambridge, MA 02139

Non-profit-making organization which co-ordinates and supports the study of film and TV in universities; provides resources for research, study programmes, festivals, symposia. Publications: *Newsletter* (a quarterly production).

WVNET (West Virginia Network for Educational Telecomputing), 837 Chestnut Ridge Road, Morgantown, WV 26505 (Contact: Rita Saltz)

Provides computing services in support of instruction, research, and administration to all State-supported institutions of higher education in West Virginia. This includes hardware, software and software support, documentation, training, consulting services, etc. Available resources include large-scale processors, minicomputers, and microcomputers as well as national network connections. Individual activity centres exist on each member institution campus, to a greater or lesser degree, with centralized and co-ordinative expertise available at a 'host site'. While most materials are particular to the needs of the West Virginia's institutions of higher education and computer-using communities, a newsletter of more general interest (including mention of materials, publications and selected activities) is available on request.

*Western Educational Society for Telecommunications, University of Nevada, Reno, NV 89557 (Contact: Wendell H Dodds, President)

Association of specialists in educational television, library science, audiovisual instruction in public and private educational institutions in Western states. Publications include *West Telemeno* (bi-monthly).

Wisconsin Center for Education Research, 1025 West Johnson Street, Madison, WI 53706 (Contacts: Marshall Smith, Director; Laurence Weber, Public Information)

The Wisconsin Center for Education Research seeks ways to help educators deal with individual differences among students (such as motivation and ability) and with group differences (such as cultural background and sex).

Studies are divided into four areas: learning and development, instruction and classroom organization, school organization and administration, and social policy. Special attention is given to the use of microcomputers in research and school practice. The Center is a non-teaching department of the school of education at the University of Wisconsin-Madison and is supported primarily by the National Institute of Education.

Centres of Activity Worldwide

Editor's note: where there are numerous entries for one country (eg Australia, Canada), they have been listed under two headings:
1. Institutions of further and higher education;
2. Other organizations with an interest in education and training.

As elsewhere in this edition, the symbol * before an entry indicates that it has not been possible to update the 1980/81 entry.

AFGHANISTAN

*National Science Centre, Ministry of Education, Kabul (Contact: Juma Gul Karimi, Director General)

The Centre was established in 1970 as a Department of the Ministry of Education. Of the total staff, 40 professional staff members are Centre-based and divided among the different departments. In addition there are 50 to 60 provincial supervisors, responsible to the National Science Centre and the Provincial Education Centres. The main functions of the Centre are secondary maths/science curriculum development and material production; design and production of school science equipment; in-service training of science supervisors and teachers; conducting research related to the above fields; and the development and implementation of curricula and syllabi for the School Science Laboratory Technicians School. The Centre is divided into the following departments: Mathematics, Physics, Chemistry, Biology, Environmental Education, Research, Workshop, and Administration. The Centre produces textbooks, teachers' manuals and study kits relevant to the above subjects.

ALGERIA

*Centre Audio Visuel, de l'Université de Constantine (Audio Visual Centre of the University of Constantine), Route d'Ain el Bey, Constantine (Contact: M Meriche Messaoud, Director)

ARGENTINA

Asociación Argentina de Educación a Distancia, Corrientes 4595 3°A, 1195 Buenos Aires (Contact: Lic Roberto Enrique Bulacio)

The AAED is a private non-profit organization of professionals as well as institutions, which carry out activities connected with teleducation. It was formed in 1979, and is dedicated to the development of distance education so that it contributes to the enrichment of the individual and equal opportunities for all; and to the integration of and collaboration with other Argentine, Latin American and international organizations in the same field. It is supported financially by the monthly dues of its members and by the sale of publications, courses and consultancy as well as donations. Members include professionals belonging to both state and private universities, to the public administration, private enterprise and the Catholic church.

Association Latinoamericana de Educación Radiofónica, *see under Regional Centres of Activity – South America*

Centro Nacional de Tecnologia Educativa (National Centre for Educational Technology), Tinagasta 5268, Capital Federal (Contact: Estela Saenz de Mendez)

The Centre started in 1948, first as a Department of Radio and Audio Visuals, with several functions that continue today, such as training teachers, preparing and lending materials to schools and investigating new methodologies. Main activities today are television, video-cassettes and radio, covering the whole country. Seminars for people involved in teaching, especially directors and supervisors, are conducted in conjunction with OAS project on Educational Technology. Publications include a range of materials including teachers' notes, etc. A catalogue is available.

Centro Provincial de Technologia Educativa de Santa Fe (CPTE), 9 de Julio 1532, 3000 – Santa Fe (Contact: Lermo R Balbi, Director; Ivonne Schneider, Deputy Director, Head of Planning/Programming Department)

CPTE was established in 1968 as the provincial Public Radio and TV Centre, but took on additional roles to become CPTE in 1973. Its responsibilities now include helping to tackle problems of educational development through the application of scientific and technical approaches and media. It is concerned, through its various departments (planning; research; production; training and validation – for teachers as well as CPTE personnel; etc), to identify problems, develop responses, and design, evaluate and produce educational materials to meet needs. CPTE is fully aware, however, of the importance of seeking to change educational *attitudes* rather than just develop new teaching materials, and runs many training workshops and correspondence courses for teachers (particularly those making use of CPTE's educational radio broadcasts and other materials). Its publications include a *Catalogue of AV Materials* as well as printed training material.

Departamento de Tecnologia Educativa y Educacion Permanente (Department of Educational Technology and Lifelong Education), Cordoba y Laprida, 6° piso, 3100 Parana (Entre Rios) (Contact: Roberto Ronchi)

A government organization which seeks to incorporate educational technology into the education system as a means of overcoming its problems and meeting its needs. At present concentration is on the training of educators in all aspects of educational technology, and production of non-conventional teaching materials.

Dirección de Información y Tecnologia Educativa, Diagonal 73 n° 1910, La Plata (1900), provincia de Buenos Aires (Contacts: Director: Sra Brígida Alcántara; Jefe Departamento Documentación: Sra M. del Carmen Crespi; Jefe Departamento Información: Sra Irma González)

This Centro de Documentación e Información Pedagógica y Museo Pedagógico (at present *Dirección de Información y Technología Educativa)* was created for the establishment and development of basic educational information and specific technology as a means of help to the teaching-and-learning process. It also provides professionals involved in education métier with documentation and information advice. DITE has three departments, Documentation, Information and Technology, of which the latter is responsible for the production of radio and TV programmes, films and audiovisual material relevant to the teaching-and-learning process. Its publications include the *Revista de Educación y Cultura* (quarterly) and the *Resena Informativa* (monthly), plus various bulletins and a children's educational newspaper.

Instituto de Cultura Popular (INCUPO), Rivadavia 1275, – 3560 Reconquista, Santa Fe

A private, non-profit-making, Christian-oriented organization with the aim of broad-based adult education and the promotion of educational development opportunities in rural areas of North Argentina. To this end, it works through the mass media, notably radio programmes on health, the family and basic literacy for a general audience; it also operates via printed materials and offers courses in training, personal and community development.

*Universidad Nacional de Lujan, Centro de Educacion a distancia, Bartolome Mitre 707, 6700 – Lujan (Prov Bs As) (Contact: Professor Enrique Valls)

The Centre is concerned with the production of teaching and learning aids at various levels and in various formats, using educational technology and non-conventional teaching/learning media with various departments within the University to produce its materials. It also runs a programme of training courses in various aspects of educational technology.

*Universidad Nacional de San Luis, Centro de Tecnologia Audiovisual, Avda Quintana 135, 5700 – San Luis (Contact: Jorge Omar Silva, Director)

The Centre is responsible for the design, production and supply of AV material to courses within the University; it assists in setting up AV centres in schools and institutions, organizes and produces educational broadcasts, and runs training courses in AV techniques at all levels.

Telescuela Tecnica (Technical Tele-School), San Juan 250, Buenos Aires

Part of the National Council of Technical Education (CONET); produces and transmits programmes in technical education in Buenos Aires and other cities of the Argentine Republic by different media (TV, radio, press, etc).

AUSTRALIA

Institutions of further and higher education

*Adelaide College of Advanced Education, 46 Kintore Avenue, Adelaide SA 5000 (Contact: Mr R Swain, Head, Research and Development Unit)

University of Adelaide, Advisory Centre for University Education, Adelaide, 5000 (Contact: R A Cannon, Director)

The Centre offers professional assistance to staff seeking help to improve the effectiveness of their teaching; research into higher education, audio visual production.

Australian National University, PO Box 4, Canberra, ACT 2600

*1. Instructional Resources Unit (Contacts: Mr C A Clark, Director; Mrs D E Rossiter, Head of Production Services)

The Instructional Resources Unit was established in July 1975 to provide a range of audiovisual services to the University. The Unit aims to support and supplement the teaching and research programmes of the University by offering educational and technical assistance in matters relating to planning and development, as well as implementation of curriculum and research materials. Full production facilities are available and audio, video and slide/tape programmes produced by IRU are available for purchase. Lists are available on request.

*2. Office for Research in Academic Methods (ORAM) (Contacts: Mr A H Miller, Director; Dr J A Slee, Lecturer)

Established in 1975 to assist in the evaluation and improvement of teaching and learning methods, the main objectives of the Office are: to encourage an interest by the academic staff of the University in increasing the effectiveness of teaching and learning; and to collect, maintain, organize and analyse information useful in the planning and decision-making processes of the University, particularly with respect to the allocation and effective use of resources. ORAM researches into matters such as teaching loads and costs, curriculum and syllabus construction, student admission qualifications, academic performance and related matters, are intended to contribute to the maintenance and improvement of standards within the University. Additionally, seminars, supported by a consultation service on matters such as course design and teaching methods and assessment, are arranged for academic staff. Audiovisual services in the University are provided by a separate group, the Instructional Resources Unit.

Bunbury Catholic College, Rodstead Street, Bunbury, Western Australia, 6230 (Contact: Br Bernard Halpin, Computing Co-Ordinator)

Bunbury Catholic College is a co-education secondary school (students aged 12-17 years). In 1978 funding was obtained to instal a DEC PDP 11/34 time-sharing system for Computer Assisted Learning. The system continues to support CAL and also now supports Computer Studies courses and some internal school administrative functions.

Canberra College of Advanced Education, Teachers as Evaluators Project, PO Box 1, Belconnen, ACT (Contact: Neil Russell, Project Director).

This is essentially a project which aims to provide teachers with the materials, skills and expertise to conduct their own evaluations and report these to parents, school boards and school authorities. The Project has now been operating for four years and has produced a considerable amount of material for teachers and in-service leaders.

*Canberra College of Advanced Education, Instructional Media Centre, PO Box 382, Canberra City, ACT 2601 (Contact: Mr F Morgan, Senior Lecturer, Instructional Media Centre)

Caulfield Institute of Technology, Educational Development Unit, 900 Dandenong Road, Caulfield East, Victoria 3145 (Contact: Charles Noble, Head of Educational Development Unit)

The Centre is responsible for staff development: seminars and workshops, assistance with course development, dissemination of information. Materials produced include teaching and subject evaluation questionnaires;

'How to Study' – multi-media package; multi camera colour video recordings; audio recording of conferences, seminars and lectures; sound-slide programmes.

*Cumberland College of Health Sciences, 9th Floor, 28-36 Forveaux Street, Surry Hills, NSW 2010 (Contact: Mr F Warren, Director, Educational Services Unit)

Deakin University, Centre for Educational Services, Gelong, Victoria 3216 (Contact: J E Gough, MA, DCP, MEdAdmin, Dean)

Deakin University is playing a major role in the development of tertiary off-campus studies in Victoria. In its first few years it has published over 150 volumes of teaching materials and has enrolled over 3000 off-campus students. The Centre for Educational Services is an academic service concerned with the development of teaching materials, providing student support services, and co-ordinating the interaction of the distance student with the University. In particular it is responsible for: advice to the University and to course teams on aspects of course design and development; professional and support services for the production of printed teaching materials; professional and support services for the production of audio and video teaching materials – monitoring developments in communication technology relevant to the design of self-instructional materials; institutional research, evaluation studies and assistance with the collection and dissemination of feedback data on course materials, support services and student progress; induction and in-service training of staff members concerned with writing self-instructional materials or teaching distance students; dealing with off-campus enquiries from students and prospective students, arranging the distribution of teaching materials and associated functions and providing support services necessary to optimize the teaching/learning experience for students; developing and supervising a regional network of study centres; ensuring that proper co-ordination is effected between course teams and the Library and between course teams and the bookshop and between these organizations and the Operations Unit; developing a full range of specialist student services, available to both on- and off-campus students and developing strategies for making these accessible to the distance student.

*Flinders University of South Australia, Bedford Park, SA 5042 (Contact: The Director, Educational Research and Resources Unit)

Footscray Institute of Technology, Educational Development Department, PO Box 64, Footscray, Victoria 3011 (Contact: Robert L Taylor)

The Department undertakes the preparation of instructional materials; maintenance of audiovisual hardware; curriculum advice; in-service education programmes; institutional research programmes.

Gippsland Institute of Advanced Education, Switchback Road, Churchill, Victoria 3842 (Contact: Mr K Smith, Head, Educational Services Division)

Griffith University, Centre for the Advancement of Learning and Teaching, Nathan, Queensland 4111 (Contact: Dr R A Ross, Director, CALT)

Academic: assistance and advice in course design, including teaching and assessment procedures; course evaluation; surveys and analyses; reports on specific internal issues. Audiovisual: supply, maintenance and operation (where necessary) of equipment; advice on the design of teaching materials;

production of audiovisual (single media or linked multi-media) materials for use within the University; design of publicity material and University publications.

*Institute of Advanced Education, Department of External and Continuing Education, Darling Downs, PO Darling Heights, Toowoomba, Queensland 4350

*1. Instructional Design Group (Contact: Alistair Inglis)

The Group's main activity is the development of packages for distance teaching. Materials produced include structured instructional texts, audio tapes, videotapes, illustrated practical study guides, experimental kits, assessment instruments. Advisory and development services are offered.

*2. Higher Educational Research, Evaluation, and In-Service Section (Contact: M P McFarlane)

The Section designs and conducts formative evaluation processes appropriate to the management of distance teaching; produces computer-based formative evaluation systems; and offers consultation, development of systems, conduct of seminars and workshops services.

Lincoln Institute of Health Sciences, Department of Educational Resources, Swanston Street, Carlton, Victoria 3053 (Contact: Dr Hugh Batten)

The Department of Educational Resources offers, and encourages the use of, a variety of resources by staff and students of the Institute and also by members of the relevant professions. The Department's resources are designed to meet the needs of individual staff and students, and include *Library Services,* print and non-print, which offer material in a variety of media to support teaching programmes, and also material of general interest. Equipment is also available; *Education Development Services* including in-service development offered to staff and students to monitor and improve the quality and effectiveness of teaching and learning; curriculum services where staff are assisted to formulate policy in relation to curriculum, planning of new courses, and review of existing courses; research services where encouragement and support are available to staff seeking to assess their teaching programme or to engage in research involving educational theory and practice; *Media Services* – technical, advisory and reprographic services; and *Computer Facilities:* computer services are available to support schools and departments in carrying out their educational and administrative functions and to support staff and students in their research programmes.

Macquarie University School of Education, Continuing Education Program (previously a unit of the Centre for the Advancement of Teaching), North Ryde, NSW 2113 (Contact: Dr Rex Meyer, Fellow in Continuing Education)

This Unit was established in August 1979 to cater for the rapid expansion of services in continuing education for the educational profession previously administered by the Macquarie University Centre for the Advancement of Teaching. Main services provided are general training in processes of teaching and learning; consultancy in educational technology; postgraduate programmes in continuing education. Publications include training manuals (in mimeographed, loose-leaf format) for all minicourses.

*Melbourne State College, 757 Swanston Street, Carlton, Victoria 3053

(Contact: The Director, Tertiary Education Research Unit)

University of Melbourne, Centre for the Study of Higher Education, Parkville, Victoria 3052 (Contacts: Professor David Beswick, Director; Mr John Julian, Co-ordinator, Audio-Visual Services)

The Centre for the Study of Higher Education is an academic department in the Faculty of Education. It provides a consultative service on problems of higher education within the University and undertakes research in the field generally. The Centre is organized in two sections: research and development (including staff development), and audiovisual services. Each section carries a consultative/teaching load and all academic staff undertake research into higher education, especially policy studies, and instructional design and evaluation. The Centre also supervises research students and undertakes teaching activities for the postgraduate diploma in education (tertiary method), Masters and Doctoral degrees. Staff development activities include courses in induction and in-service training seminars for the University teaching staff.

Monash University, Higher Education Advisory and Research Unit, Wellington Road, Clayton, Victoria 3168 (Contacts: Dr Terry Hore, Director; Ian D Thomas, Senior Lecturer in Charge, Educational Technology Section)

The Unit is organized into two sections: the Advisory and Research Section organizes and conducts in-service programmes for academic staff; provides advisory and consultation services for all matters related to teaching in a tertiary institution, eg evaluation, assessment, teaching methods, use of media; conducts research into aspects of higher education; conducts courses leading to the MEd degree. The Educational Technology Section provides a range of audiovisual and consulting services to support the teaching in all faculties, computer centres, libraries and teaching hospitals. Activities include equipment and personnel loan, assessment of AV requirements, installation of AV facilities, production of TV, film, audio and multi-media programmes, replay and dubbing of TV programmes, film screenings. A videotape catalogue of programmes available from the Educational Technology Section is available on request.

Murdoch University, Educational Services and Teaching Resources Unit (ESTR), Perth, Western Australia 6150 (Contact: Dr R J McDonald, Director)

The Educational Services and Teaching Resources Unit has been established to promote and assist teaching and learning throughout the University. Staff of the Unit collaborate with academic staff in the development of teaching and assessment methods, and the production of audiovisual materials; the Unit also organizes seminars and workshops on teaching and learning. ESTR conducts research to assist teaching, assessment, and policy decisions, and also operates a Learning Skills programme, in which students are given assistance in the context of their course work.

University of Newcastle, Division of Medical Education and Programme Evaluation, New South Wales 2308 (Contact: Associate Professor C E Engel, Chairman)

The DMEPE was established from the inception of the Faculty and has contributed to the planning of the Faculty's innovative undergraduate medical education programme which accepted its first students into the five-year course in March 1978. The Division is responsible to the Faculty Board of the Faculty and acts as a facilitator in the planning, design, implementation, assessment (of students' progress and achievement), and evaluation of the programme. The Division provides facilities for the design and production of learning materials and test instruments. The Division is organized in three sections: Academic, Technical, and Information. The Academic Section assists in the systems approach applied to the problem-solving, fully integrated, small group and individual-learning curriculum (no course of lectures). The Section assists in the selection and formulation of the problems used for problem solving and learning, in the specification of learning objectives, in the instructional design of learning experiences and learning materials, in tutor training, in designing test instruments, in the analysis of test results, and in the evaluation of the programme, as well as in the selection of candidates for admission to the Faculty. The Section is actively involved in educational research.

The Technical Section has become a separate unit, The Medical Communication Unit, under the Dean for administration, with Professor Engel as Academic Director. This unit now includes staff employed by the teaching hospital, a move towards providing a regional facility for all health professions. It provides facilities for the production of photographs, drawings, etc, audio-tapes, videotapes, exhibits and printed programmes. A number of materials in a variety of media have been produced for use on the course. The Information Section assists in the selection, appraisal and ordering of educational materials from outside the University, cataloguing and issuing of educational materials to groups of students.

University of Newcastle, Central Audio Visual Services Unit, Shortland, NSW 2308 (Contact: Bede G Jordan, Director)

*University of New England, Armidale, NSW 2351 (Contact: Dr D Watkins, Research Fellow, Educational Research Unit)

*New South Wales Institute of Technology, PO Box 123, Broadway, NSW 2007 (Contact: Mrs J Lublin, Educational Development Branch)

University of New South Wales, PO Box 1, Kensington, NSW 2033

1. Centre for Medical Education Research and Development (Contact: Professor K R Cox, Director)

Established in 1973 with the primary goal of assisting in raising standards of health care through the advancement of education for the health professions, the Centre trains teaching staff for the health professions, provides consultative services and conducts research. It operates at the faculty level within the University of New South Wales Medical School, at the national level in collaboration with various institutions within Australia, and at the regional level in collaboration with the World Health Organization as the WHO Teacher Training Centre for Health Personnel in the Western Pacific Region. The Centre offers courses leading to degrees of Doctor of Philosophy and Master of Health Personnel Education, and short courses on specific educational topics. Applied research and evaluation studies are carried on aimed at improving the quality of education for health personnel and its relevance to health care needs. The Centre provides consultative services to teaching institutions and professional associations seeking assistance with educational and

management problems; support to institutions and individuals with whom
the Centre has worked; and production of self-instructional materials on
educational technology for teachers of health workers in collaboration witl
the World Health Organization's Learning Materials Project. *Publications*
include a monthly newsletter; research and review monographs.

2. Tertiary Education Research Centre, (Contact: Dr J P Powell, Acting
Director)

The centre produces 16mm films about various aspecs of higher education,
especially 'trigger films' for use in staff development programmes; training
programmes for staff in the use of educational technology for teaching
purposes; advice on and supply of films for teaching purposes; research anc
development activities relating to the use of educational technology in
curriculum development and teaching experiments; use of videotaping to
provide feedback on teaching; services of document reading facility in
processing and providing feedback to staff and students on examination
results. Catalogues of films and publications are available free on request.

**Queensland Institute of Technology, Educational Research and
Development Unit,** GPO Box 2434, Brisbane, Queensland 4001 (Contacts:
Derick Unwin, Head of Unit; Don Litster, Educational Research Officer)

Activities include various aspects of educational research; production of
teaching materials; faculty development; microcomputer-based CAL. A full
range of technical services is available including video and audio recording
suites. Publications include an occasional newsletter, *Memo-ERDU,* reports
on research projects, etc.

*University of Queensland, Tertiary Education Institute, St Lucia,
Queensland 4067 (Contact: Professor Ernest Roe, Director)

The Institute acts as a clearing house for the exchange of information
among directors of research and development units in Australia and New
Zealand. Other areas of activity are research into the University of
Queensland's teaching and learning operations; a consultative service to
other academic departments and to individual staff on problems of teaching
and assessment; organization of seminars, courses, etc in the above areas;
information services (both material produced by the Institute and collected
from elsewhere for dissemination within the University); practice studio for
academic staff (AV equipment and materials).

Royal Melbourne Institute of Technology, Education Unit, 124 La Trobe
Street, Melbourne, Victoria 3000 (Contact: N Henry, Head of Unit)

The Unit conducts regular workshops for teaching staff on tertiary teaching
methods and occasional conferences on educational topics of interest. It
also offers workshops on particular instructional techniques such as
experiential group methods, contract learning, television studio methods
and the use of photography for the production of instructional materials.
Teaching staff are given assistance with instructional design and evaluation.
A major proportion of the Unit's activity is concerned with the production
of instructional programmes in various media.

**Salisbury College of Advanced Education, Educational Technology
Department,** Smith Road, Salisbury East, South Australia 5109 (Contact:
Dr Deane W Hutton)

The Educational Technology Department at Salisbury CAE offers a

Graduate Diploma in Educational Technology and provides elements in several other courses in the College including: Visual Communication; Educational Design; Communication Technologies – Past and Present; and Communication Technologies – Present and Future. The major research function of the Department was the recently completed national research and development project in visual education which was funded by the Australian Government's Curriculum Development Centre. The visual Education Curriculum Project developed a set of teacher resource materials which stress the potential of the visual in learning across the curriculum, in both primary and secondary schools. The resource materials (nine books and three videotapes) discuss the classroom use of photographs, drawings, diagrams, film, television, visual analogy and mental imagery – and have been published by the Curriculum Development Centre, Canberra.

South Australian College of Advanced Education, Educational Technology Department, City and Underdale Campuses (Contact: Mr D A Dent, Educational Technology Dept)

*South Australian Institute of Technology, North Terrace, Adelaide, SA 5000 (Contact: Mr D Thompson, Audio-Visual Services Officer, Educational Services Unit)

*Swinburne College of Technology, Education Unit, PO Box 218, Hawthorn, Victoria 3122 (Contact: Bernard Hawkins, Head of Unit)

The Education Unit was established to serve the staff of both the College of Advanced Education and the Technical College divisions of Swinburne College of Technology Ltd. The Unit plays a central role in the College's programmes of educational technology, curriculum development and innovation, educational research, staff development, and course evaluation. Main activities and services provided are: (a) Educational technology facilities: the educational technology services of the College are under the auspices of the Education Unit and a full range of services are available; (b) CAI research and development: the COALA CAI system has been developed under the guidance of the Education Unit, and a number of computer packages and simulations are being used by several departments in the College; (c) Consultation services for staff: members of the Education Unit provide consultation and advice for College staff on a wide range of topics related to educational skills and development; (d) Supervision of curriculum development projects: development projects funded by the College are supervised and monitored by the Education Unit; (e) Staff development: the Education Unit maintains a collection of reference materials which may be used by staff members and is also responsible for organizing staff seminars on a wide range of topics; (f) Course evaluation: assistance in course evaluation is provided by the Education Unit through consultation with staff concerning appropriate evaluation techniques and through the development and distribution of evaluation instruments; (g) Educational research: the Education Unit is active in a variety of both small- and large-scale research projects – the personnel of the Unit are available to assist staff engaged in research projects, particularly regarding matters of research design, statistical procedures, design and location of appropriate research instruments, and publication of results. Publications produced include *Feedback* (Newsletter of the Education Unit), a number of booklets and research reports, and *Students' Introduction to the COALA CAI System* (tape/slide programme).

*Tasmanian College of Advanced Education, Educational Practices Unit,
Box 1214, Launceston, 7250 (Contact: Paul H Northcott)

The Educational Practices Unit's function is to assist staff and students in improving the quality of teaching and learning. From 1 March 1979 the Unit was made administratively part of the External Studies Unit and based at the Newnham Campus, Launceston. The EPU advises staff, when invited, on design, development and evaluation of courses and procedures and practices used in student assessment. Students are helped with problems of a study skills nature. Consultancy work outside the College has been undertaken by a number of Australian and foreign institutions. Educational research has been undertaken in relation to the PSI (personalized systems of instruction) programmes developed in physics, chemistry, surveying, mathematics and pharmacy. Research has also been undertaken on laboratory skills and work experience. Important functions of the EPU are to initiate and support innovation in teaching practices and to encourage evaluation of courses at the design and development stages as well as at the conclusion of the teaching of the programmes. The Educational Practices Unit provides courses on communication, programmed learning and curriculum design, and Australian educational history. Occasional seminars are given. Nine resources packages have been compiled on major topics in the field of teaching and learning in higher education. Special interests have been developed in the following areas: (1) The design and development of courses. A feature of CAE courses is that rigorous course design is required for external accreditation and reaccreditation. Special assistance is given to groups when preparing courses for the new instructional milieu of a CAE; (2) The design and development of off-campus study programmes and the special needs of external students; (3) The design and development of integrated, multi-media approaches to teaching and learning. As the Audio Visual Services Department progressively adopts a research/advisory role (as distinct from its predominantly services and production functions) the EPU is better able to work more closely and productively with AV Services; (4) In reader education the EPU works in close co-operation with the Library in the important area of student study skills, including library use, note-taking, essay-writing and mastery of the literature. A useful array of approaches to the development of writing skills is being developed in an attempt to assist students to improve the quality of their writing. Some success has been recorded in alerting staff to consider more carefully the intellectual skills required in various writing tasks set.

The University of Tasmania, Higher Education Research and Advisory Centre, GPO 252-C, Hobart, Tasmania 7001 (Contact: Dr H E Stanton)

The Centre offers personal consultation on problems associated with teaching; attendance at lectures, tutorials and seminars in an advisory capacity (including videotaping, if required); conducting beginning-of-year exercises to facilitate student interaction; conducting courses and seminars within departments or faculties to meet specific needs, eg small group work for tutors of a particular department, assessment procedures that may be followed by a faculty, etc; advising faculties and departments on teaching methods, assessment procedures, use of audiovisual materials, course design, etc; conducting induction courses for new staff members, part-time staff, etc; conducting courses and seminars in which staff members from many different departments come together to discuss common problems; assisting individual staff members, departments and faculties to conduct research into their teaching methods; assisting staff to gain feedback from students on the effectiveness of their courses.

Torrens College of Advanced Education, Holbrooks Road, Underdale, SA 5032 (Contact: Mr A R Barton, Research Unit)

Now amalgamated with another college to form *South Australian College of Advanced Education.*

Warrnambool Institute of Advanced Education, Education Unit, PO Box 423, Warrnambool, Victoria 3280 (Contacts: F Bosch, Head, Education Unit and External Studies; J Parker, Media Officer)

Services offered include provision and maintenance of the Institute's audiovisual equipment; preparation of learning materials for internal and external students; advice to staff on techniques of teaching and assessment; assistance to students in the preparation of course work and assignments; loan of videotapes and video-cassettes to local educational institutions; and short courses on the use of audiovisual media.

Western Australian Institute of Technology, Kent Street, Bentley – WA 6102 (Contact: Mr D J G Holroyde, Director, Centre for Communication and The Arts)

***The University of Western Australia,** Nedlands, WA 6009 (Contact: Mr A W Anderson, Director, Research Unit in University Education)

Other organizations

***Australian Broadcasting Commission (ABC),** Box 487, NSW 2001

Conducts training programmes for educational radio writing, direction, production and evaluation.

Australian Capital Territory Schools Authority, Educational Media Services (Curriculum Branch), O'Connell Education Centre, Stuart Street, Griffith, Canberra, ACT 2603 (Contact: Peter Miles, Head, Educational Media Services)

Areas of activity include a technical advisory service to schools/administration; equipment support to staff development programmes; media training programmes for teachers/ancillary staff; production of curriculum materials in all media; media access for schools of high-cost, low-use equipment; general media consultancy to schools. Materials produced are tape/slide, tape/booklet, tape/slides/prints/OHPs/maps kits, videotapes and booklets covering most of the broader curriculum area. Services offered include high speed audio cassette dubbing service for pre-primary and secondary schools; library maintenance/slide copying/videodubbing/disc to tape/16mm to video.

The Australian Council for Educational Research Limited, Radford House, Frederick Street, Hawthorn, Victoria 3122 (Contact: Dr J P Keeves, Director)

ACER is an independent body concerned with research, development and service in education, with interests as wide as the definition of education. It is not limited geographically to what goes on in Australia, but is concerned with matters of importance to Australian educators. Tests, books, and kits are made available by ACER's Distribution Services Division to teachers, psychologists and other qualified users, and professional assistance in the selection of tests and materials to suit teachers' needs is available from Advisory Services. ACER publishes: *The ACER Newsleter,* with news of research findings and other matters of interest to teachers, *The ACER Educational Catalogue,* and *The ACER Annotated Catalogue of Tests and Materials.*

ASET – Australian Society of Educational Technology, PO Box 143, Kensington, NSW 2033

The Australian Society of Educational Technology is a national body with provision for state chapters. There are five chapters of the Society representing New South Wales, Victoria, Queensland, South Australia and Western Australia. The President and Secretary of each state chapter form the body of the National Council which elects from its members a Yearbook editor and a National Executive, consisting of President and Secretary/Treasurer. The present National Executive is: Mrs Robin Bishop, Educational Consultant, NSW (President), Ms Rosemary Moon, State Library of NSW (Secretary); Mrs L Osbourne, Swinburne College of Technology, Victoria, (Yearbook Editor). Within the constitution of the National Body, each state chapter of ASET is autonomous and represented by its own President, these being: South Australia – Mr C Dunnett, Educational Technology Centre, 81 Flinders Street, Adelaide, 5000; Victoria – Dr John Hedberg, Centre for Study of Higher Education, University of Melbourne (enquiries ASET Victorian Chapter, PO Box 372 Hawthorn, Vic, 3122); NSW – Mrs Robin Bishop, Educational Consultant (Enquiries – ASET NSW Chapter, PO Box 143, Kensington 2033); WA – Dr Irma Whitford, Murdoch University, (enquiries ASET, WA Chapter, Mt Lawley CAE, 2 Bradford Street, Mt Lawley, 6050); Queensland – Mr G Roberts, Brisbane College of Advanced Education, Mt Gravatt Campus, PO Box 82 Mt Gravatt, Queensland 4122.

The Society has grown rapidly. Although each state chapter reflects the needs and interests of the members within that state, the Society as a whole has a general concern for 'design, application, evaluation and development of systems, methods and materials to improve the process of human learning'. Members of the Society are drawn from a wide range of organizations and educational institutions. The range of interests of the Associations' members are expressed in many newsletters published by each state chapter, as well as in the annual Yearbook received by all members. Because of the widespread nature of the members of ASET National Council most meetings are held by national telephone conference hook-up. Meeting procedures for such hook-ups have been established and the success of this method of meeting forms the basis for the National Body.

*Department of Education (NSW) Division of Services, Teaching Resources Services, PO Box 439, North Sydney, NSW 2060 (Contacts: W W Robertson, Head; R A Neeson Deputy Head)

Teaching Resources acts to increase the availability and range, and to improve the quality of, resources suited to NSW school needs through the provision of professional assistance and services to schools, teachers and others involved with education. Evaluation and information programme: evaluation of audiovisual materials, equipment and educational technology developments; dissemination of information on resources and educational technology developments; appraisal information from Equipment Advisory committees, information sheets on new resources, equipment sheets, Dial-a-Resource Service for software and equipment. Development and innovation programme: *Equipment Advisory Committees* in various curriculum areas (infants, primary, secondary, special and child migrant) work with Teaching Resources development officers and curriculum officers, to produce 'master' materials. *Development officers and Teaching Resources support staff* supervise editing and trial of all learning kit components. Refinement and updating of existing resources. *Support for selected development projects* originated by Regional Resources Committees or recommended work from individual teachers. Reproduction and distribution of resources programme: quality control of bulk reproduction of resources, after trial and recommendation by Advisory Committees, bulk packaging and despatch of resource materials organized by Teaching Resources Distribution at Burwood and decentralized distribution of new resources, through the regional Professional Services Centres where new resources are on display.

*Department of Education (Northern Territory), Media Services, Department of Education, PMB 25, Winnellie, Northern Territory 5789 (Contacts: Gil Jennex, Supervisor, Media Services; Mike Forster, Education Adviser, Technical Services)

Media Services is responsible for AV hardware repair and maintenance; audio and videotape duplication; AV hardware display and standards; AV in-service workshops and courses; AV advisory service.

Department of Education (South Australia), Educational Technology Centre, 81 Flinders Street, Adelaide, South Australia 5000 (Contact: C W Dunnett, Principal)

The activities of this Centre can be divided into four broad categories: production of software; evaluation of hardware and software; consultation and training in all areas of educational technology; and research, application, and innovation with regard to the educational use of new technologies. Approximately 850 Government and non-Government schools in the urban and rural areas of South Australia are served through liaison with 10 Regional Education Offices. Advice and assistance in areas of technology are given to other Government departments.

In consultation and co-operation with Education Department curriculum committees, this Centre produces flexible component resources that are combined into five package styles: Pic-a-Paks, Pic-a-Prints, Audio Packs, Pic-a-Projects, and Multi-Packs. All are topic-based. These are sold to schools, with the proceeds being used to replace stock. Pic-a-Paks contain a card which indexes the contents with black-and-white illustrations. Currently, over 500 titles are available. Approximately 70 Pic-a-Prints have been produced. They contain sets of large colour prints (400mm × 280mm) and an index card, and sometimes are supported by printed material. Audio Packs contain at least 1 audio-tape and any combination of small colour prints, drawings, printed material, and resource information. Approximately 100 titles are available. Pic-a-Projects are intended to provide teachers with activities to support instructional periods for Primary students. Multi-Packs are composed of various combinations of the four packs described, all of which are based on the same topic. Catalogues are available for all packages produced.

The Centre's software services include courses for teachers on software production. Schools across the State also take advantage of the free duplication service of audio- and videotapes from the Tape Services section. Hardware is evaluated and the information published for guidance in purchases made by schools. Among the Centre's continually updated publications are *Which? photocopier* and *Which? audio visual equipment.* Equipment services include training on operation and maintenance.

In anticipation of the Australian domestic satellite, research was initiated and trials continue to be carried out from Adelaide to remote schools and homesteads with regard to terrestrial and extra-terrestrial communications for distance education. Concerning other research activities, the Centre has become a Prestel subscriber in order to further videotex research on behalf of the State. In-service information sessions on the new Copyright Act are conducted, and support material is designed and produced by this Centre. Research also continues in areas such as video disc systems and regional communication centres in schools.

Department of Education (Victoria)

1. Audio Visual Resources Branch, 234 Queensberry Street, Carlton, Melbourne 3053 (Contact: Mr T A King)

This Branch is part of the Special Services Division of the Education Department of Victoria. Its functions are to disseminate audiovisual methods and materials throughout the primary and post-primary schools of the Education Department and the private schools of Victoria.

*2. Support Services, Planning Services, 13th Level, Nauru House, 80 Collins Street, Melbourne 3000 (Contact: John Ward, Co-ordinator)

The Support Services Unit is responsible for providing the Planning Services of the Education Department with the support services in the field of library, audiovisual, printing and publishing, and it does this for the whole of the Education Department. It also provides these services for technical and further education (middle level vocational programmes) and colleges in the education system of Victoria and is responsible for curriculum development and the production of teaching and learning materials.

Department of Education (Western Australia), Audio Visual Education Branch, 296-304 Vincent Street, Leederville, Western Australia 6007 (Contact: The Superintendent, Audio Visual Education Branch)

The Branch is concerned with the provision and methodology of audiovisual education in schools. Services offered include a loan library of audiovisual materials including motion films, filmstrips, slide sets, audio and video tapes, study prints, gramophone records, overhead projector transparencies, all either from commercial sources or from the Branch's own productions; a purchase library of filmstrips, all produced by the Branch. The contents of both libraries range from the pre-school to tertiary. The Branch works with the Australian Broadcasting Commission in the production of schools broadcasts. Information on audiovisual materials and methods is disseminated through in-service courses, catalogues and journals.

*Modern Teaching Methods Association, 101 Wallan, Victoria 3654

The Association arranges lectures, discussions, courses, seminars and conferences, and conducts a National Conference in May each year. It publishes the journal *Modern Teaching* (about eight issues per year) and a newsletter *Coffee Talk* (as often as necessary) to communicate between members and the Volunteer Council which governs operations. The Association operates a cassette tape library and will facilitate contacts between members with similar interests or engaged on similar projects.

National Textile, Clothing and Footwear Industry Training Committee, c/o Chamber of Manufactures, 60 York Street, Sydney 2001 NSW (Contact: G R Engel, Manpower Development Executive)

The Committee is responsible for training and development on an industry-wide basis. It produces individualized learning packages, disseminates information about training and development matters, and offers analysis of training needs, organization of courses and seminars at all levels.

Ran School of Training Technology, HMAS Cerberus, Westernport, Victoria, 3920 (Contacts: The Officer in Charge; The Publications Officer)

The School is responsible for training in the areas of training management; job/task analysis; systematic course design; quality control of training; instructional techniques. It offers a consultancy service in all aspects of a systems approach to training throughout the Royal Australian Navy. It also documents and develops the Training System used by the Royal Australian Navy.

*Sydney Training Centre, Department of Employment and Youth Affairs, 4th Floor, Edgecliffe Centre, 203-233 New South Head Road, Edgecliffe 2027 (Contact: Dennis L Reed, Executive Officer)

The Training Centre was set up in 1972 for the purpose of training trainers at all levels in the Private Sector. All course members are nominated by their organization. Courses conducted cover instructor training, training trainers to use standard 'supervisor' packages (similar to those offered by the UK Department of Employment). There is also a three-tiered training officer programme, and some specialist courses, eg apprentice trainer, discussion techniques.

Tasmania Media Centre, 252 Argyle Street, Hobart, Tasmania (Contact: The Supervisor of Teaching Aids)

The Media Centre produces integrated learning materials for 400 schools and colleges and is responsible for the selection, acquisition and maintenance of $2,000,000-worth of electronic equipment in these schools; and centralized media library including audio and video duplication systems to serve 400 schools. It offers access to media for teachers to produce their own material; in-service help involving two programmed media-mobiles to teach school-based personnel; seminars and workshops on media management.

AUSTRIA

Bundesstaatliche Hauptstelle für Wissenschaftliche Kinematographie CBHWK), Schönbrunnerstraße 56, A-1050 Vienna (Contacts: Dr Erika Maletschek, Ing Peter Levenitschnig)

Non-commercial office attached to the Austrian Ministry of Science and Research. Federal Centre of Scientific Film (16mm only) for Austrian universities, museums, archives, medical clinics and other scientific institutions. Three kinds of film: for research, instruction and documentation. Main activities are the making of scientific films for and in co-operation with scientific institutions in Austria; lending archive of scientific films: over 3000 titles on several subjects: films from own production and films made by others including a full archive of the *Encyclopaedia Cinematographica*; giving technical advice and delivering seminars and lectures; publishing a catalogue and a journal; and fostering contacts to similar institutions abroad. Publications include the printed catalogue *Wissenschaftliche Filme, Katalog 1974* and several amendments (new ctalogue in preparation) and the journal *Wisenschaftlicher Film* (published about twice a year).

Institut für Algemeine Pädagogik an der Wirtschaftsuniversität Wien, Türkenschanzstrasse 18, 1180 Vienna

The Institute undertakes teacher training, research on instructional technology, and advises on course planning in higher education.

Institute of Educational Technology, Media Didactics and Engineering Education of the Austrian Universities (inter-university research institute), Universitätsstr 65-67, A-9010 Klagenfurt (Contact: Dr A Melezinek)

Research in the field of educational technology, media didactics and engineering education; documentation and assessment of equipment and systems used with field of educational technology; advice and help in the making of educational productions, and on planning and installing ET facilities at universities.

BANGLADESH

*****Audio-Visual Education Centre,** Dhanmandi, Dacca-5 (Contact: Audio-Visual Education Officer)

The Audio-Visual Education Centre's principle functions are: to train teachers in the use and care of AV equipment and the development of teaching techniques with AV aids, the provision of workshop facilities for them; to maintain and develop a library of AV materials, available textbooks on loan or free distribution; to maintain an information service on all matters relating to AV aids, including the production of bulletins and catalogues; exhibitions; to provide design expertise as appropriate. As a pilot project, the Centre is assisting in the development of 100 schools with respect to AV aids.

Bangladesh Education Extension and Research Institute, Dhanmandi, Dacca-5 (Contact: The Director)

The Institute was established in 1959 to provide short course in-service training to secondary teachers and to support the improvement of secondary education through a pilot school network. It has since expanded its operations to include the training of headmasters, teacher trainers for primary and secondary levels, and teacher training at the higher secondary level. It provides short courses for teachers in most school subjects, and workshops on specific topics related to curriculum development; the organization of conferences for principals and senior teachers of teacher training colleges; assistance to professional groups and educational institutions in planning and executing development plans undertaken by government; assistance to government in preparing developmental schemes. Curriculum development specialists at the Institute have been involved in preparation of the new national curriculum and in preparation of textbooks for the primary level. The Institute has produced a number of publications in English and Bengali.

UNICEF (United Nations Children's Fund), Bangladesh Office, UNICEF, PO Box 58, Dacca-5 (Contact: Keith Warren, Education Adviser)

In Education, the Dacca office offers assistance to schools, non-formal education, instruction in income-generating activities, training in community development, literacy for school drop-outs and for women, instruction and demonstration in domestic village technology and educational aid to handicapped children. The Education Section of the Dacca UNICEF office also includes social services and comprises six professional staff with an annual operating fund of about $4 million per year. Bangladesh is one of the largest UNICEF offices. Other UNICEF offices throughout the world usually include similar educational activities among their other assistance projects.

Village Education Resource Center, Anandapur, Savar, Dacca (Contacts: Shaikh A Halim, Project Director; M A Awal, Chief, Technology Unit)

The Village Education Resource Center is a project of Save the Children (USA) and funded by UNICEF. It was established in September 1977 to support different national and international organizations engaged in rural development with training in communication approaches, techniques and materials. It has also been working on appropriate technology based on local needs.

BELGIUM

AIMAV – Association Internationale pour la Recherche et la Diffusion des Méthodes Audio-Visuelles et Structuro-Globales, *see under International Centres of Activity*

Association Mondiale des Sciences de l'Education – AMSE (World Association for Educational Research – WAER), Henri Dunantlaan 1, B-9000 Gent (Contact: Mrs Professor Dr M-L van Herreweghe, President of the Association)

The Association was founded in 1953 to foster the development, on an international level, of research in the field of education. Its main activities include organization of international congresses every four years; publication of scientific works or promotion of such publications; exchange of information among its members or with third parties; establishing centres of liaison. The Association publishes its bulletin *Communicationes* twice a year, and the Proceedings of its world congress (every four years).

*Dienst didactische Films en Audiovisuele Media (Film and AV Media Education Service), Ministerie van Nationale Opvoeding en Nederlandse Cultuur, Handelskaai 7, 1000 Brussels (Contact: E Hambrouck)

The 'Dienst didactische Films en Audiovisuele Media' of the Ministry of National Education and Dutch Culture is the national library of educational films and the national centre for audio visual aids in Belgium. It aims to encourage a wider, more varied and efficient use of AV aids in any sphere where there is a teaching job to be done and attends to the totality of the educational AV infrastructure concerning software as well as hardware. It places at the disposal of teaching establishments films and AV materials; to do this the Centre maintains a library of 16mm and Super 8 films, available on loan to educational establishments throughout the country. Some of these films are produced at the Centre, others are acquired from commercial producers. Where appropriate, foreign materials are acquired and suitably adapted. A full catalogue is available. The Centre's technical department concentrates entirely on the problems of audiovisual aids equipment. It holds and supplies a wide range of apparatus and audio and video software for the National Audiovisual Centre and Pedagogical Media Centres in Colleges of Education throughout the country. The department makes equipment and expertise available to regional AV centres and to in-service teacher training courses.

Fondation Universitaire Luxembourgeoise, rue des Déportés 140, B-6700 Arlon (Contact: Jacques Mambour, Département Psychopédagogique)

The teaching activities of the Foundation are concerned (a) with psychology, teacher training, and educational technology, (b) 'éducation permanente' for adults, and (c) environmental sciences, medicine (geriatrics) and (e) neurolinguistic and special education. It produces film, programmes, syllabuses, educational TV broadcasts, and scientific publications.

University of Liege

1. Laboratoire DOCEO (SMATI, Sart-Tilman, Bât B19, B-4000 Liege 1) (Contact: M O Houziaux, Co-Director of the Project)

The Laboratory started the design of CAI-systems as early as 1962. Since 1971, the Computer-Assisted Anamnesis and Medical Teaching Project sponsored by the National Fund for Medical Research was conducted in co-operation with the Institute of Medicine. As a result of hardware and software studies, SIAM-DOCEO II, an audiovisual multilingual system, has been used since 1972 to perform two main functions: medical interviewing in many areas of pathology (with computer-aided diagnoses, therapeutics, follow up); teaching patients, nurses and physicians. The area of application is now extending to various fields, namely chemistry, psychological achievement testing, French grammar, understanding spoken English for French-speaking people, photography etc. A special author language (LPC) allows a high flexibility in programming conversational processes.

2. Laboratoire de Pedagogie expérimentale, Institut de Psychologie et des Sciences del'education, Department of Educational Research, Université de Liege au Sart Tilman, 4000 Liege 1 (Contact: Professor Gilbert L de Landsheere)

This Department has three functions: training future teachers of education in educational research methods and techniques; carrying out fundamental and sponsored applied research in the field of education; in-service training of teachers in evaluation and educational research methods. Main research and service fields are: pre-school education; teacher behaviour research (development of analysis system of verbal and non-verbal interactions in the classroom); readability and/or intelligibility of verbal and audiovisual messages; educational technology including CAI; development of evaluation instruments for the classroom; achievement surveys of school systems. Materials, review articles and books are published regularly.

Limburgs Centrum voor Moderne Leermiddelen (LCML), (Limburgs Centre for Modern Teaching Methods), Vereniging voor Wetenschappelijk Onderwijs Limburg – Postuniversitair Centrum, Universitaire Campus, B-3610 Diepenbeek (Contact: Paul Ameloot)

The LCML is a teachers' and resources centre. Its main object is to contribute to qualitative educational improvement through integration of educational teaching aids in the teaching process. The different activities and initiatives are announced through an information bulletin. The Centre produces slide-series, video programmes and transparencies.

Catholic University of Louvain, Departement de Communication Sociale, Petite Rue de la Lanterne Magique, 1348 – Louvain la Neuve (Contact: Professor A Gryspeerdt)

The Department is concerned with teaching and research in 'social communication'. It produces textbooks for the courses, audiovisual features, and research papers.

Metallurgie Hoboken-Overpelt, B-2710 Hoboken (Contact: R F J Noiroux)

Metallurgie Hoboken-Overpelt is one of the leaders in the field of non-ferrous metals metallurgy, employing nearly 7000 people. Materials produced include basic chemistry and physics PI courses. The Educational Department provides training for workers up to the rank of head foreman and supervises the training of the company's staff personnel.

Rijksuniversiteit, Seminarie en Laboratorium voor Didactiek, H Dunantlaan, 9000 Ghent (Contact: Professor Dr A De Block)

The organization undertakes research on programming and educational technology as a part of general educational research, and produces programmed materials.

*Service d'Etude des Méthodes et des Moyens d'Enseignement (SEMME), Faculté des Sciences Psycho-Pédagogiques, 21 place du Parc, 7000 Mons

The Faculty undertakes research on educational technology, educational objectives, systems analysis in education and experimental pedagogy, and has produced programmed courses.

BENIN (PEOPLE'S REPUBLIC OF)

*National Institute of Training and Research in Education, Boîte Postale 200, Porto Novo (Contact: Mme Renee Labrouche)

BOLIVIA

Accion Cultural Loyola (ACLO), Calle Loa No 602 – Casilla 538, Sucre (Contact: Padre Jorge Trias, SJ)

Christian-based non-formal education for small farmers.

*Consejo Nacional de Educación Superior (National Council for Higher Education), Casilla 4722, La Paz (Contact: Doctor Vidal Botelho Herera, Director de Ensenanza e Investigacion Cientifica, Consejo Nacional de Educacion Superior)

*Escuelas Radiofónicas de Bolivia (Radio Schools of Bolivia), Casilla 5946, La Paz

A private, Christian-oriented non-profit-making association, broadcasting programmes on literacy, culture and educational topics for a largely rural adult audience, the Escuelas Radiofónicas is an umbrella organization coordinating the work of regional radio stations in Bolivia.

*Radio 'Nuestro Senor de Burgos', Mizque, Cocha Bamba (Contact: Padre Mario Comina)

Offers programmes of literacy training for rural areas. A private, religious organization.

BRAZIL

Institutions of further and higher education

*Universidade Federale de Bahia (Federal University of Bahia), Nucleo de Tecnologia Educacional, Salvador, Bahia (Contact: Ruth Teixeira Viera)

The Centre is set up to cater for the needs of the various faculties of the University. In addition it performs some research and organizes occasional courses and seminars on aspects of educational technology.

*Instituto Metodista de Ensino Superior (IMES) (Methodist Institute of Higher Education), Faculdade de Communicação Social, Setor de Multimeios, Rua do Sacramento 230, São Bernardo do Campo, São Paulo (Contact: Professor Reinaldo Brose, Head, Setor de Multimeios)

Areas of activity include multi-media instruction at university level and research in various aspects of educational technology. The Faculty of Social Communication offers BA degree courses in journalism, publicity or public relations.

*Pontificia Universidade Católica do Rio de Janeiro (Catholic University of Rio de Janeiro), Faculty of Education, Rua Marquês de São Vicente 209, Gavea, Rio de Janeiro (Contact: Professor Vera Maria Candau, Co-ordinator, Postgraduate Course of the Centre of Technology)

Offers an educational technology option in the undergraduate degree course in pedagogy.

Universidade Federale do Rio de Janeiro (UFRG) *see* Nucleo de Tecnologia Educacional para a Saude *under Other organizations*

Universidade Federal do Rio Grande do Norte, Núcleo de Tecnologia Educacional, SITERN – Sistema de Teleducação do Rio Grande do Norte, Rua Princesa Isabel, 758, Cidade Alta, ZC 59.00 Natal, RN (Contact: Carlos Augusto Lyra Martins, General Manager)

Project 'SACI' was developed by the National Institute for Space Research (INPE). This was the 'satellite education' project. The developmental work on its software was performed during 1971/73 in the state of Rio Grande do Norte and SACI materials came to be an integral part of the primary educational system between 1973 and 1976. SITERN is the successor to SACI, marked by the transfer of production and management from INPE to the University in 1977, with the participation of the Educational Department of Rio Grande do Norte State. SITERN now accounts for about 40,000 elementary education pupils in the state and reaches outlying rural areas where there are no schools, no electrical energy and no good roads (all broadcast materials are for TV). Now, SITERN is also providing rural teachers with specialist training courses. The system has set up an independent transmission network, transmitting over 56 hours of educational broadcasts weekly and giving the same quality of reception as the commercial networks, in most cases to schools whose TV sets are supplied by rechargeable batteries.

Pontificia Universidade Catolica do Rio Grande do sol (PUC/RS), Laboratorio de Enseñanza de Postgraduación en Educación, Av Ipiranga 6681, Porto Alegre, RS (Contact: Dra Délcia Enricone)

Apart from various internal projects using educational technology, PUC-RC offers graduate courses in educational technology, training programmes for the professional development of teachers and also programmes for internship.

Universidade Federal de São Carlos (Federal University of São Carlos), Centro de Educação e Ciencias Humanas, Via Washington Luis, km 235, CP 384, 13560 São Carlos, SP

Service centre of the University, developing the theoretical principles of education and its technology through courses and specific researches.

Other organizations

Associação Brasileira de Technologia Educacional (ABT), Rua Jornalista Orlando Dantas, No 56, 22231 – Rio de Janeiro, RJ (Contact: Angela Parente Ribeiro Mazzi)

ABT is a private, non-profit-making organization concerned with scientific, technical and organizational aspects of educational technology. It was created in 1971 and now has about 2000 associates all over the country. Among its activities are included the publication of a technical review (*Tecnologia Educacional*), technical publications of studies and researches, the promotion of seminars, conferences and courses, and an Information Centre for its members and for the educational community. It also provides planning, assessment and evaluation services for specific projects, and publishes books and course materials.

*ABTD – Associação Brasileira de Treinamento e Desenvolvimento (Brazilian Association for Training and Development), Rua João Adolfo 118/11° Andar, São Paulo (Contact: Paulo Roberto de G Pizarro, President)

This is a private association of professionals concerned with industrial training and human resources management. It has close ties with the American Association for Training and Development (ASTD); it organizes many courses and seminars and occasional national conferences. It is active in promoting educational technology in industrial training.

Brazilian Literacy Movement Foundation – MOBRAL, Ladeira do Ascurra 114, Rio de Janeiro 22241 (Contact: Mrs Marilia Santos da Franca Vellozo, Special Assistant to the President)

MOBRAL was created in 1967. Due to its characteristics of community participation and its main objectives which centre around the eradication of illiteracy and the continuing education of adolescents and adults, MOBRAL can be considered as an instrument which not only aims at, but also allows for, the social promotion of its clientele – the less favoured classes – through its several programmes. The Functional Literacy Programme, the very first programme launched by MOBRAL, allows the adolescents and adults to put into practice the skills of reading, writing and calculation, acquired during the five months' duration of the programme, and therefore to search for better living conditions. In order to support the students in the educational process already started in the Functional Literacy Programme, MOBRAL has created several other programmes such as the Integrated Education Programme, equivalent to the first four years of primary school, the Cultural Activities Programme, the Professionalization Programme, the Community Action Programme, the Community Education for Health Programme, the Sports for All Campaign, the recently elaborated Technology of Scarcity Programme, and the Education of the Consumer Programme. Entering the field of new technologies applied to education, MOBRAL has launched the Community Health Education Programme by Radio, in special transmissions, and the Functional Literacy by TV Programme. After ten years of intense activity towards the reduction of adult illiteracy rates in the country, MOBRAL is now launching a national pre-school programme aimed at children under six years of age.

*Centro Audiovisual Mackenzie – CAVIM, Rua Matia Antonia, 403 – Vila Buarque, CAP 01222 São Paulo (Contact: Ivone Correa da Costa Parra)

The Mackenzie Audio Visual Centre was begun 12 years ago, to furnish audiovisual equipment, materials and services to all the departments of the Mackenzie Institute, which includes kindergarten level through to special postgraduate courses. The Centre evaluates, acquires, catalogues and circulates the audiovisual equipment and materials used by the professors and students; produces audiovisual materials; assists professors and students in the selection and use of resources; and trains the professors and students in the use of AV aids and materials. There are three general areas of activity: selection and circulation of materials and equipment; production – photographic, graphic arts, cinema; and instruction and training in the areas of orientation, courses and seminars, and publication of audiovisual methods and techniques. A catalogue of materials is available on request.

*Centro de Desenvolvimento de Recursos Organisacionais (CENDRO), Rua Marquês de Leão 455, Salvador, Bahia

The Centre has a team of educational technologists and develops special purpose training materials for industrial and government organizations. It also offers organization development services.

Centro de Ensino Tecnico de Brasilia – CETEB, Unidade da Fundação Brasileira de Educação – FUBRAE, Avenida W, 5, Quadra 910, Bloco D, No 32, SGAS, DF (Contact: Sergio Faria, Director)

CETEB is a private agency within the Brazilian system. It was established in 1965 by the Brazilian Foundation for Education (FUBRAE) as a unique organization charged with the responsibility of improving human resources for the education system of Brazil by promoting pedagogical innovations. The guiding principle of CETEB is experimentation with innovative ways of teaching, using an open, flexible approach in order to meet felt needs. In order to fulfil this function, CETEB has two specific purposes: (i) to provide courses of a specific, focused nature to meet immediate needs not met in other school systems, and (ii) to introduce innovations after pilot study and development.

*Centro de Treinamento para Professores de Ciencias Exatas e Naturais de São Paulo – CECISP (São Paulo Training Centre for Teachers in the Exact and Natural Sciences), Caixa Postal 11.234 (Pinheiros), 05421 – São Paulo (Contact: Norma Maria Cleffi, Executive Director)

The São Paulo Science Education Centre was established in 1965 by the Federal Ministry of Education, the State of São Paulo Ministry of Education, and the University of São Paulo. The main functions of the organization are production of curriculum projects for science teaching for primary and secondary level, training courses, and research on science education issues.

Departamento de Recursos Tecnológicos para a Educação (Department of Technological Resources for Education), Rua 13 de maio, 55 Boa Vista, Recife, Pernambuco (Contact: Veralúcia Rodrígues Lins)

The Department of Technological Resources for Education is an organ of the Secretariat of Education in the state of Pernambuco, responsible for the co-ordination, use and development of educational technology throughout the state. The Department plans and produces instructional material for various areas of the school curriculum and for human resources training. It maintains a lending service of audiovisual materials, such as film, records, slides, filmstrip, serial-albums, maps, cassettes, etc, and equipment such as retroprojectors, cassette recorders, film projectors (16mm and 8mm), slide projectors, play-recorders, episcopes, amplifiers, opticards, etc. Its main function is to co-ordinate the activities of the *Teaching-Learning System Material,* and its Broadcast Centre, *Laboratory of Didactic Aid,* established in schools to help teachers and students improve the quality of the teaching-learning process. The Department sends instructional and audiovisual material to elementary and secondary schools, reaching directly 400,000 students and 15,000 teachers. In addition, this Department is responsible for the propagation and co-ordination of courses by radio and television, for establishing and supervising the TV and radio reception centres, and giving technical orientation to the tele-teachers.

Enseñanza Supletoria (Supplementary Teaching), Ministerio de Educação e Cultura, Departamento de Ensina Supletivo, Brazil

The aim of the organization is to supplement the regular school system for those who have not completed the normal process of education. It provides programmes and materials which are followed up by classroom studies supported by the mass media channels.

Fundação Centro Brasileiro de Televisao Educativa – FCBTVE (formerly PRONTEL), Rua da Imprensa, 16-90 andar, Rio de Janeiro (Contact: Cláudio José da Silva Figueiredo, President)

Set up in 1972 by the Ministry of Education and Culture, named PRONTEL and reconstituted, in 1981, as a foundation supported by the same Ministry, this is the official federal government organ responsible for the nationwide co-ordination and execution of instructional and educational activities employing communication media or other technological resources. The new Foundation has four areas of activity: Television, Radio, Cinema and Informatics functioning as production, exhibition and research organs.

The FCBTVE also provides technical and financial aid to agencies – public or private – and supports projects of technological innovation and training.

Fundaçâo Centro Brasileiro de TV Educativa, Avenida Gomes Freire, no 474, Rio de Janeiro, RJ

The Foundation was created in 1967 by the Ministry of Education and Culture, with the aim of producing and distributing educational TV materials and programmes. It has good installations and modern equipment and employs about 920 people. In 1980 1650 programmes were produced totalling some 2600 hours. Actual transmissions included programmes of other Brazilian and foreign organizations, amounting to some 21,500 hours of open broadcast, and reached, by the microwaves system of EMBRATEL, over 40 per cent of the Brazilian Territory, through the National System of Teleducation, integrated by 9 Brazilian Educational TV Stations.

(Editor's note: two replies were received from FCBTVE, from different addresses. The first of these two entries – above – was the most recent but, in view of the uncertainty, both are given here.)

Fundaçâo Centro Educativo do Comunicacâo Social do Nordest (CECOSNE), Rua José Osorio 124, 5000 Recife, PE (Contacts: Armia Escobar Duarte, Eva Dormelas Camara and Janete Carvalho Pires)

CECOSNE is a registered charitable organization, juridically recognized. Its main purpose is to work out new technology to educate the underprivileged to help themselves in an evolving world. CECOSNE works under Christian inspiration. It was founded in 1968 as a Centre of Studies on Social Communication at the School of Philosophy of the Federal University of Pernambuco. It works as a laboratory, researching, experimenting and testing new technology. Its activities include educational research, courses and seminars; audiovisual production; and puppetry. It runs several courses (some residential), notably on creativity, communications and the mass media (language).

*Fundaçâo Centro Nacional de Aperfeicoamento de Pessoal para a Formaçâo Profissional – CENAFOR (Central National Foundation for the Training of Vocational Trainers), Rua Rodolfo Miranda 636, 01121 Sâo Paulo

The Foundation is concerned with questions and problems of vocational training (formaçâo profissional) on a national basis. It is attached to the Ministry of Education, housing a project of the United Nations Development Programme, through the International Labour Office. It undertakes professional training of teachers, technicians, instructors and specialized staff involved in vocational training, in formal and non-formal education in the primary, secondary and tertiary areas of the economy; production of and assistance in the use of teaching aids (audiovisual, printed, self-instructional, programmed instruction (Keller plan, etc); research analysis and evaluation of needs for vocational training in view of propositions; centralization, processing and dissemination of information on vocational training; administration of scholarship programmes at home and abroad for professionals involved in vocational training; technical assistance and exchange with similar institutions at home and abroad.

Fundaçâo Educacional Padre Landell de Moura – FEPLAM, Avenida Bastian 285, Porto Alegre, Rio Grande do Sul (Contact: Erika Coester

Kramer, Executive Director)

FEPLAM was created in 1967 with the aim of developing 'educational programmes which contribute to the development of man, as an individual and as a member of society'. Much of its work is based in the out-of-school community. Working originally mainly through the medium of radio, it now offers a variety of courses in a variety of media. With a permanent staff of over 120, its production has been extensive. It has over 2000 separate radio lessons on tape, covering such topics as education for work, 'second-chance' elementary and secondary curricula for adults, rural/agricultural training, mechanical/industrial training and pre-school education. All these lessons are also available on cassette tape, and in addition FEPLAM produces and distributes some TV courses and slide-tape and multi-media courses. All the courses are supported by teacher/monitor manuals, implementation/evaluation schemes and printed media (books, workbooks, posters, work-cards, study guides). Its production of paper has justified the installation of its own printing department. The courses are studied in one of three regimes – 'organized' (requiring regular attendance at study centres staffed by training monitors), 'controlled' (requiring regular contact with the course organizers by visits or correspondence although the radio programmes are studied at home), or 'individual' (independent study). About 329,000 adults (in 14 years) in Rio Grande do Sul and other states have formally taken courses since FEPLAM's inception (the current rate approaching US$85,000 annually). In addition, there is an unknown informal public who listen to the programmes without a formal registration and many of the courses have also been bought by other organizations in other states. The training of human resources for the application of educational technology (distance education) and the development of research projects (evaluation and new methodologies) are two other areas which are being promoted in the last years. Though mainly supported by state and Federal funds, FEPLAM also receives technical and financial assistance from the Konrad Adenauer Foundation, West Germany, Unesco and the International Development Research Centre – IRDC/Canada.

*Fundação Maranhense de TV Educativa (Educational TV of Maranhão), Rua Armando Vieira da Silva, Sao Luis, Maranhão (Contact: João Vicente de Abreu Neto, Director-General)

One of the pioneer instructional TV projects in Brazil, aiming at the secondary (11 to 15) age groups. In 1968, less than 5 per cent of this age group was in formal education. By 1970, as a result of the TV project, over 20 per cent participated and the proportion has climbed steadily. Thus the state of Maranhão has a lower-secondary education system based primarily on TV lessons and supporting activities organized by trained 'orientators' working with groups in outlying communities. These orientators are not trained as teachers. About 500 work with over 12,000 students per year. Weekly TV transmission time is 35 hours. A typical lesson has 15 minutes of transmission, supported by 45 minutes of pre-planned small group study, organized by the orientators.

*Fundação Padre Anchieta – TV Cultura, Av Gomes Freire 474, Rio de Janeiro (Contact: Antonio Soares Amora)

Production centre for educational radio and TV programmes. Operates the ETV channel of Rio de Janeiro.

*Fundação Pandia Calogeras, Belo Horizonte, Minas Gerais

The Foundation uses radio and TV broadcasts to support the work of schools and to prepare adolescents and adults for their role in the economic life of the country.

*Fundação TVE Amazonas (Educational TV of Amazonas) Rue Major Gabriel, Manaus, Amazonas (Contact: Professor Ernesto R de Freitas Pinto, Superintendent Director)

Transmits not only TV but also radio programmes for the very sparsely populated state of Amazonas. In many municipalities with small populations this is the only upper primary education available. Trains group leaders who organize local listening/viewing groups. About 70 new leaders are trained annually, 100 retrained, and 9000 students (age groups 10 to 12) participate annually in the project.

Instituto de Radiodifusão Educativa da Bahia – IRDEB, Salvador, Bahia

The Institute is responsible for educational services through the means of mass communication in the State of Bahia, it has a Center of Production (radio, correspondence, radiovision and self-instructive materials), an FM and Short Wave Broadcasting Station and co-ordinates the use of five hours a week for education in 30 commercial broadcasting stations of the State of Bahia.

Presently, it trains alphabetizing teachers, using radiovision; it brings teachers, supervisors and administrators up-to-date through the Program of Technical Assistance to the Human Resources of Primary Education; it cares for students and teachers of the rural area, preparing students' books, teacher's guide, radio broadcasting and broadcasting guides; it also cares for 5000 students lacking suppletive education in primary and high school levels through radio and correspondence; it gives assistance to regular students with a programme of attendance to learning disabilities in Communicating and Expressing (Reading and Writing Portuguese) during the last four grades of primary school; it also gives asistance to people through informative and cultural programmes.

As to technical co-operation, it participates in national and international agreements gaining technological know how (Canada and Holland) and/or propagating this to Portuguese-speaking countries (Training and Probation in Broadcasting Area for African Countries).

MOBRAL, *see Brazilian Literacy Movement Foundation*

Nucleo de Tecnologia Educacional para a Saude/Centro Latino-Americano de tecnologia Educacional para a Saude – NUTES/CLATES (The Centre for Educational Technology for Health/Latin-American Centre for Educational Technology for Health), Centro de Ciéncias Médicas, Bloco A, Sala 26, Universidade Federal do Rio de Janeiro (UFRJ), Ilha do Fundão, Rio de Janeiro (Contact: Dr Luis Carlos Lobo or Jorge Galperin, Directors)

The Centre (Nucleo) of Educational Technology for Health was formed in the Health Sciences Center of UFRJ in 1972. Shortly afterwards the Pan American Health Organization funded a Latin American Centre attached to the Nucleo. The Centre has been operating since then with the following aims: (i) to develop courses in the health sciences in the biomedical sciences and in health, based on clear objectives and incorporating the principles of educational technology; (ii) to promote individualized systems of instruction; (iii) to develop audiovisual courses and aids, videotapes, slides, etc; (iv) to prepare programmed instruction materials and self-study modules; (v) to develop the use of simulation techniques in clinical training, etc; (vi) to develop software for CAI systems in biomedical training; (vii) to perform research and developmental studies in educational technology; and (viii) to train personnel from the health sciences professions (throughout Latin America) in all the above techniques. Within the UFRJ are offered services of TV, CCTV, film, photography, learning resources centre, audiovisual library, computer, etc, and to a wider public, the Centre offers short and long training courses in topics such as modularized instruction, training systems design, teaching principles in higher education, educational simulation, evaluation, group dynamics, educational planning, CAI, audiovisual media, etc. The Centre has about 70 full-time staff (30 professionals) and often runs courses in conjunction with other organizations (eg management training/consultancy organizations), becoming increasingly involved with educational technology in general, as against only medical areas.

Núcleo de Televisão e Rádio Universitárias, Canal 11, Av Horte, s/n, Santo Amaro, Recife, Pernambuco

The programmes of the Educational TV and Radio Station of the Federal University of Pernambuco are aimed not so much at the university students as at the local adult population. The Centre works in co-operation with the SINTED (National System of Educative Television).

Programa Nacional de Teleducação (PRONTEL), *see* Fundação Centro Brasileiro de Televisão Educativa

*SEC/RJ – Secretaria de Educacao e Cultura de Rio de Janeiro (The Secretariat for Education and Culture of Rio de Janeiro), Centro de Tecnologia Educacional, Rua do Passeio 62/10° Andar, Cinelándia, Rio de Janeiro (Contact: Professor Wanda Aragão)

The state Secretariat has produced several courses for its own staff using programmed instruction, modularized systems and correspondence. These include the training of teachers in science teaching techniques and the training of supervisory and administrative staff for schools. The educational Technology Centre also plans and produces some educational radio and TV courses, as well as co-ordinating the distance education activities of other agencies in the state of Rio de Janeiro.

*SENAI – Servico Nacional de Aprendizagem Industrial (National Service for Industrial Apprenticeship), Departamento Nacional, Av Conselheiro Nebîas, Rio de Janeiro (Contacts: Cel Sady Boana Mussoi, Director; Maria Elena Clausen, Servico de Recunos Didaticos)

SENAI operates a network of technical colleges throughout Brazil. The national department in Rio is concerned with overall planning and control. The Service of Didactic Resources is concerned with the development of systems and media for technical and industrial training. There is also a Division of Educational Technology, concerned with research and development and teacher training.

TECHNE, Avenida Brigadeiro Faria Lima 1781, 13th Floor, Sao Paulo

The oldest-established programmed learning/training design firm in Brazil.

Originally named 'Matética' (mathetics) in 1964, it now offers general training design services.

Tecnologia da Educação S/C Ltd (EDUTEC), Rua Lopes de Oliveira 79, 01152 Sao Paulo

The organization specializes in large-scale training/performance modification projects. Its methodology is based on behavioural analysis.

BULGARIA

*Board of the Media of Educational Technology, Boulevard 9 Septemvri, 224 Sofia

Research at all school levels, including vocational.

*Studio of AV Materials, Loyan St 16, Film Centre, Sofia

BURUNDI

*Bureau d'Education Rural (Office of Rural Education), BP 2660 Bujumbura (Contact: Thaddée Butare)

CAMEROON, UNITED REPUBLIC OF

*Centre for Publishing and Production of Education and Research, Boîte Postale 808, Yaounde (Contact: M Jean-Paul Njoya)

Institut de Pedagogie Appliquée à Vocation Rurale (IPAR) BP 4135, Yaounde (Contact: M Joseph Mballa)

Founded in 1969, IPAR's objectives were to carry out a reform of elementary teaching; to produce the necessary teaching materials; and to train personnel to use them. The outcomes of its researches are now being applied in education generally, and particularly with regard to teaching methods and teaching materials. It also operates an important in-service retraining scheme for elementary school teachers, operated through various regional centres.

*Rural Vocational Education Centre of Beua, Boîte Postale 124, Beua (Contact: The Director)

CANADA

Institutions of further and higher education

The University of Alberta, Edmonton, Alberta T6G 2J9

1. Committee for the Improvement of Teaching and Learning (Contacts: Mr J Laing (Secretary), 2-1A University Hall; Ms W M Bryan (Research Liaison), 1-16 University Hall)

The functions of the Committee are to gather, analyse and assess information on various aspects of university teaching and learning in order to improve both, and to initiate research under its own auspices or in conjunction with other individuals, offices or organizations. It will publish its findings and make appropriate recommendations so that more members of the academic community will become aware of ways to improve teaching and learning.

2. Division of Educational Research Services, Faculty of Education
(Contact: Dr S Hunka)

The Division is a service organization to assist graduate students and
academic staff members of the Faculty with problems in research design,
statistics, and computer assisted instruction. Primary activities involve
consultation with users regarding research design problems and methods of
analysis as well as the development of computer programs. Current research
developments in computer-assisted instruction include the design of
software for microcomputers and a DEC VX 11/780 using intelligent
terminals and high resolution colour monitors.

3. Audiovisual Media Centre, Faculty of Education (Contact: Dr Kenneth
Bowers, Co-ordinator)

Founded about 1965 to furnish equipment services and acquisition and
production of audiovisual materials to support the teaching research and
public relations functions of the Faculty of Education. Includes production
of television, sound-slide, graphics, photographic and similar materials for
faculty use, administers an equipment operation training facility and carrel
area, both with auto-instructional materials for student or faculty use.
Produces about 30 educational TV programmes per year, besides numerous
slide sets, tape recordings and displays for instructional, research, and
public relations. Also adminsters a microcomputer laboratory for student
and faculty use.

**4. International Television Research and Information Centre
(Clearinghouse),** NB-125, Education Centre (Contact: Dr D J Engel,
Project Director, Nan MacLeod-Engel, Director of Collections)

ITRIC is an institution specializing in research and the collection,
processing, dissemination of research information on the effects of
television on society. A number of bibliographies have been prepared in
support of research projects both at the U of A and for other agencies.
These bibliographies may be purchased. Information about the in-house
collection is available upon request. Research papers, published and
unpublished, are actively sought for inclusion in the collection.

Athabasca University, 12352 – 149 Street, Edmonton, Alberta, T5V 1G9
(Contact: Dr R H Paul, Vice-President, Learning Services)

An open university serving Western Canada. Courses in programmes
leading to the BA and BAdmin are offered at a distance. Present student
body about 6000 (mostly working adults) and increasing rapidly. The
institution makes some use of courses developed at other open universities.
Main activities include: BA programme – 65 + courses in humanities,
science, social scinece; BAdmin programme – concentrations available in
accounting, general administration and public administration, and many
courses under development; student development – emphasis on teaching
students career and educational planning skills, time-management and study
skills at a distance; instructional design – group of eight responsible for
designing new courses and improving the instructional system;
research – major research project on the management and motivation of the
adult learner in distance education; tutorial services – implementation of a
tutor training programme; regional support centres in Calgary, Ft
McMurray, and plans for network throughout Alberta. Materials are
available (subject to copyright restrictions on sales) for 65 + self-study

course packages (university level). Details of published papers are available on request.

*Atlantic Institute of Education, 5244 South Street, Halifax (Contacts: Dr Richard F Lewis; Dr Charles P McFadden)

British Columbia Institute of Technology, 3700 Willingdon Avenue, Burnaby, BC V5G 3H2 (Contact: W D Robertson)

A two-year post-secondary technical institution specializing in career-oriented programmes in business, engineering and health technologies; student registration of 3500 full-time and 30,000 part-time; established in 1963; serves the entire province of British Columbia and a population of approximately 2,000,000; provides specialized instruction to business and industry; contains an active distance education arm with 3500 students; and is dedicated to the concept of open education.

*University of British Columbia, Department of Communications, Media and Technology, Faculty of Education, Vancouver (Contact: Dr Patricia Montgomery, Chairman)

Activities include teaching (undergraduate/graduate degrees), research, service, media production and the Department offers workshops, seminars, consultation, instructional design/development and field development programmes.

The University of Calgary, General Faculties Council Standing Committee on Instructional Methodology and Development, 2920-24th Avenue, NW, Calgary T2N 1N4 (Contact: The Chairman c/o Vice President)

The Committee aims to encourage inter-faculty research into learning, and to organize and assist in the funding of conferences, workshops and seminars on instructional methods.

*Carleton University, Committee on Instructional Development, Ottawa K1S 5B6 (Contact: Dr G R Love)

Concordia University (Sir George Williams Campus), Graduate Program in Educational Technology, Department of Education, 1455 Ouest Boul de Maisonneuve, Montreal (Contacts: Professor P David Mitchell, Director; Dr Gary M Boyd, Associate Professor, Educational Technology)

Activities include postgraduate preparation of educational technologists (one-year diploma, two-year Master of Educational Technology, PhD); research in learning and instructional design, human communication, media effectiveness, systems analysis and planning, philosophical aspects of educational technology, computer-based systems, print and media production, media, instructional research and development, computer-aided learning, tele-education.

Ceneca CAAT, Centre for Learning and Teaching, 1750 Finch Avenue E, Willowdale M2N 5T7 (Contact: Klaus Schwarzkopf)

The Centre provides a consulting service and a series of workshops for faculty members and groups. Research is carried out on microteaching.

Confederation College Resource Centre, College of Applied Arts and Technology, PO Box 398, Thunder Bay, Ontario P7C 4W1 (Contact: Miss G W Maki, Supervisor)

The Centre provides consultation and support services to academic divisions in the following areas: staff development, curriculum development, research design and analysis, print and audiovisual instructional support, distance learning system design.

*University of Guelph (Contact: Professor G A B Moore)

Areas of activity include instructional media and development, staff development and instructional development, materials and media production, consultation, production, facilities design, media evaluation, teaching workshops, course evaluation, development grants.

*Université Laval, Département de Technologie de l'Enseignement, Faculté des Sciences de l'Education, Quebec 10e (Contact: Philippe Marton)

The Department offers undergraduate and graduate teaching programmes. A list of publications is available on request.

McGill University

1. Centre for Teaching and Learning Services, 815 Sherbrooke Street West, Montreal, Quebec H3A 2K6 (Contact: George L Geis, Director)

Areas of activity include professional and technical consultation with individual faculty and groups or administrative units on the improvement of teaching and learning, evaluation of teaching courses and programmes; special projects, workshops, seminars and publications in support of such improvement; support of change activities by professors; research in instructional handbooks on university teaching; comprehensive guides to the evaluation of courses, teaching and programmes; manuals on specific topics such as evaluating student work. A publications list is available. A mailing list is maintained for occasional announcements.

2. Centre for Medical Education, Faculty of Medicine, 1110 Pine Avenue W, Montreal (Contact: Dr Hugh Scott)

Projects include a survey of audiovisual software and the publication of a newsletter; the Centre is also involved in the development of new courses, self-instructional modules and specialized teaching skills.

*McMaster University, Program for Educational Development, Faculty of Health Sciences, Hamilton (Contact: Dr V R Neufeld)

*Memorial University of Newfoundland, St John's, Newfoundland

*1. Extension Service (Contact: Susan Sherk, Publications and Information)

The Extension Service was created in 1959 to assist in the development of the isolated outport communities of Newfoundland, filling gaps in existing educational, administrative and cultural services. The internationally-known Fogo Process of Community Development was an early Extension Service success. The Service provides community education programmes, media services including film and videotapes, and film services.

*2. Institute for Research in Human Abilities (Contact: Dr Patricia A Jones, Director)

The Institute conducts basic research in the psychology of education and perception – cultural aspects of ability, innovation in instruction, socialization and exceptional children.

*3. West Coast Regional College, Corner Brook (Contact: Dr A M Sullivan, Principal)

Activities include innovation-evaluation of instruction and instructors, research in ETV, media and materials production.

*Université de Montréal, Service Pédagogique, 5858 Côte des Neiges, Suite 430, Montréal (Contact: Pierre Dalceggio)

The Service operates as an instructional development centre, offering workshops and seminars for the faculty, and curriculum development.

*North Island College, Fort Manor, 156 Manor Drive, Comox, BC (Contact: Co-ordinator of Research and Development)

North Island College is a small, relatively new community college serving northern Vancouver Island and the Central Coast region of British Columbia. North Island College is a new hybrid: it represents the marriage of the North American community college concept with the British-inspired but worldwide ideology of open learning systems. The College that resulted sees education as a community-based service and the role of the college as the delivery agent of those services. North Island College has not 'de-schooled' society, but has effectively 'unspaced' and 'untimed' learning and thus made educational opportunities available to people throughout the College region. By concentrating on delivery and using high quality courses developed elsewhere (Athabasca University, the British Open University, Coast Community College, etc), North Island College has increased the number of participants in open learning to an order greater than any early open learning system. In 1979/80 the College has a budget of $4 million and will serve some 2000 students (of which 1500 will be in university transfer programmes) and another 6000 in community education programmes. In its college programmes the institution offers some 94 distant study courses of which about half are university courses.

The Ontario Institute for Studies in Education, 252 Bloor Street West, Toronto, Ontario M5S 1V6 (Contact: for general information – Mary Stager, Office of Field Services and Research; for information concerning educational and instructional technology – Dr W P Olivier, Department of Measurement, Evaluation, and Computer Applications)

The Ontario Institute for Studies in Education was founded by statute in 1965 to pursue three major objectives in the field of education: graduate studies, research and development, and field development. The Institute includes ten academic departments; work concerned with educational and instructional technology is focused in the Department of Measurement, Evaluation, and Computer Applications. In the Department of MECA, the Individualization Project has since 1969/70 been engaged in extensive research and development work in the area of Computer-Assisted Instruction. This Project, which has developed hardware, software and curricula, has involved co-operation among a large number of agencies and individuals, particularly those instructors at Ontario's Colleges of Applied Arts and Technology whose students have been to date the principal users of the CAI system. At present, the Project has expanded considerably from its initial concentration on remedial mathematics to a number of other Colleges of Applied Arts and Technology subjects, to high school mathematics, and to institutions outside Ontario. Recently, work has begun on developing a system for producing interactive video discs for skill training.

Open Learning Institute, *see under Other organizations*

Université du Québec, à Montréal (UQAM)

*1. Service de Pédagogie (formerly Centre d'Application des Media Technologiques à L'Enseignement et à la Recherche – CAMTER), CP 8888, 3465 Durocher, Montréal H3L 3P8 (Contact: Jean Dumas, Director)

2. Télé-Université, 214 avenue Saint-Sacrement, Québec (Contact: Clement Marquis)

The Télé-Université is part of the University of Quebec; it was formed in 1972 and its mandate is to supply broadcast adult education to the population of Quebec. The Télé-Université has offered broadcast teaching services in three programmes: one intended for the general public, the other two aimed at supplementing the work of teachers. It has at its disposal a team of teachers and a team of specialists in educational technology. The Télé-Université has produced multi-media courses for each of its programmes, as follows: 15 courses in the programme 'Knowledge of Man and the Environment'; 20 courses in the teacher-improvement programme in Mathematics; 15 courses in the teacher-improvement programme in French. Most of these courses are based on printed material, but the Télé-Université has produced several audiovisual documents (television, diaporamas) and some educational games.

*Queen's University, Faculty of Education, Kingston, Ontario (Contacts: Dr Dale Burnett)

The Faculty undertakes pre- and in-service education, including MEd programmes in administration and curriculum. The use of small-stand-alone computers (SSACs) in the classroom has been developed. A set of four exercises that illustrate various factors involved in reading have been developed and are operational.

*St Lawrence CAAT, Learning Resources Centre, Portsmouth Avenue, Kingston K7L 5A6 (Contact: Sherwin Raichman)

The Centre's range of activities include the design, development and production of materials for use in meeting educational objectives and running workshops. A Testing Centre provides opportunities for programme-related testing, diagnostic (academic and personality) testing and remedial testing.

Saint Mary's University, Department of Chemistry, Halifax, Nova Scotia (Contact: Dr Keith Vaughan, Chairman)

The special educational technology interests of the Department are carried out in the context of its undergraduate teaching programme. They are the evaluation of chemical card games as learning aids, the teaching of university general chemistry by the Keller Plan (PSI), and the development of courses in non-traditional areas – eg environmental and marine chemistry.

University of Saskatchewan, Department of Educational Communications, Academic division of the College of Education, Saskatoon (Contact: Professor F B Brown)

Activities include teaching; faculty consultation; instructional development and material preparation; operation of (a) communications laboratory, (b) curriculum materials preparation laboratory.

University of Victoria, Department of Creative Writing, PO Box 1700, Victoria, BC V8W 2Y2 (Contact: W D Godfrey)

Currently conducting the NATAL/TELIDON project, involving implementing NATAL on an IBM 4341 sysem using various terminals for delivery, including TELIDON. Publications include *Gutenberg Two* and *The Telidon Book*.

*The University of Western Ontario, Office of Service and Research in Medical Education, Faculty of Medicine, London N6A 5C1 (Contact: Dr Bruce P Squires)

Services offered include consultation, production, instructional design, evaluation of curriculum, courses and student performance, self-instructional packages, faculty development.

York University, Instructional Aid Resources, Toronto (Contact: David A Homer, Director)

Total media services – television, audiovisual, photography, graphics, etc and their production and distribution to the University community.

Other organizations

Alberta Educational Communications Authority, Edward's Professional Centre, Suite 502, 10053 – 111 Street, Edmonton, Alberta T5K 2H8

1. The Authority

Administers the Alberta Educational Communications Corporation Act: relates government education department needs to ACCESS, a government corporation which produces, acquires and distributes educational materials; and designates all educational television channels and supervises educational programming in the province of Alberta.

2. Curriculum Branch-Learning Resource Unit, West Wing, Devonian Building, 11160 Jasper Avenue, Edmonton, Alberta T5K 0L2 (Contact: Martin Adamson, Associate Director of Curriculum for Media)

The Learning Resource Unit develops policies and procedures for learning resource evaluation and selection; trains teachers in the analysis of instructional materials; and co-ordinates the development of production proposals to meet the needs of the provincial curriculum. The unit also provides consultation and some co-ordinating service to the five Regional Film Centres in the province.

*Association for Media and Technology in Education in Canada (AMTEC), PO Box 174, Station W, Toronto, Ontario M6M 4Z2

The specific purposes and objectives of the organization are to promote applications of educational media and technology in improving education and the public welfare; to foster co-operation and interaction among institutions and organizations concerned with educational media and technology; to provide leadership and organizational support to develop interests of the Association; to strive to improve the qualifications of and conditions for effective performance of those using educational media and technology; to increase and diffuse knowledge about educational media and technology through meetings, professional contacts, reports, papers, discussions, publications and similar means; to promote research, demonstration, experimentation and improvement in the use of educational media and technology; and to identify and analyse critical issues and developments in educational media and technology and to seek to provide constructive solutions to them through the selection, organization and dissemination of valid and useful information.

Canada Employment and Immigration Commission, Training Directorate, Phase IV, Place du Portage, Hull, Quebec (Contact: W H Farrell, Director)

Training and development programmes are provided for employment counsellors, immigration officers, unemployment insurance agents, managers and support staff.

Canadian Communications Research Information Centre (CCRIC), PBP 1047, Ottawa, Ontario, K1P 5V8 (Contact: A K Prakash, Director)

Canadian Education Association, 252 Bloor Street West, Toronto, Ontario M5S 1V5

*Canadian Film Institute, 75 Albert Street, Suite 1105, Ottawa, Ontario K2P 5E7 (Contact: Executive Director)

Functions of the Institute are to encourage and promote the study, appreciation and use of films and television. Areas of activity include the National Film Theatre, the National Film Library, the Publications Department, the Ottawa International Animated Film Festival. Publications include *CFI Bulletin* and *Film Canadiana Yearbook of Canadian Cinema.*

Canadian Forces Training Development Centre, CFB Borden, Borden, Ontario, L0M 1C0

Responsible for the training of senior personnel in training development, instructional techniques, instructional supervisor, programming, training design, and audiovisual techniques. Also responsible for providing training consulting services as well as R and D in training technology for the Canadian forces.

Canadian Forces Training System, Canadian Forces Base Trenton, Astra, Ontario, K0K 1B0

The training system's role is to provide individual Training for officers, men and women to meet the requirements of the Canadian Armed Forces. Projects currently under way include: implementing self-pacing as a delivery medium for instruction in formal course and in on-job training situations: developing and implementing five technical courses at the CF transport training squadron; study of the Individual Training System; improving the readability of training manuals; training development – concepts and organizations. Recent publications include: *Catching Up,* a look at the why and how of training development; *Tech-Train '99,* a conceptual view of how the Canadian Armed Forces will train technicians in 1999; *Current Applications of Computer Assisted Learning in the Canadian Forces.*

*Canadian Information Processing Society, 243 College Street West, Fifth Floor, Toronto M5T 1Y1, Ontario

*The Canadian Library Association, 151 Sparks Street, Ottawa K1P 5E3, Ontario

The Canadian Library Association places emphasis on publications of direct and immediate value to librarians in the carrying out of their responsibilities. The association regularly publishes the *Canadian Periodical Index,* the *Canadian Library Journal,* a professional journal devoted to the examination of issues in librarianship, and *Canadian Materials,* which reviews print and non-print materials produced for use in Canadian schools.

Canadian Society for the Study of Education (including several subsocieties, eg Education Research), College of Education, University of Saskatchewan, Saskatchewan S7N 0W0

*Collins Bay Institution, Acheron College, PO Box 190, Kingston, Ontario (Contacts: Helmut Bauer, Instructor, Technical Training; D L Hornbeek, Supervisor, Technical Training)

The Institution provides theoretical and practical training according to the standards of the Ontario Ministry of Colleges and Universities in a specially equipped multi-media instruction and learning centre through individualized programmes.

Department of Manpower and Immigration, *see* Canada Employment and Immigration Commission

International Communications Institute, PO Box 8268, Station F, Edmonton, Alberta (Contacts: A C Lynn Zelmer; Amy M Zelmer)

ICI is a non-governmental agency, a partnership registerd in Alberta since 1968. The active partners have backgrounds in Media Production and Use; Non-Formal (Adult) Education; Health Services and Educational Administration. ICI engages other consultants, technicians, etc as required. The main activity of the Institute is the development of educational programmes and materials on a consultant basis with a major emphasis on the appropriate use of technology. ICI has carried out programmes in Canada, India, Sri Lanka, Ethiopia and other developing countries for governments, NGOs and UN Agencies.

National Film Board of Canada (NFBC), PO Box 6100, Montreal, Quebec H3C 3H5

The Institution's functions are to produce films, other audiovisual materials and still photographs that 'interpret Canada to Canadians and to other nations'. NFBC's productions are used in education, by community groups, and are shown commercially in theatres and on television in Canada and around the world. The Film Board produces some 100 films each year in English and French. The NFBC maintains offices and film libraries in 27 cities across Canada and has distribution offices in London, New York, Paris, Tokyo and Sydney.

National Research Council of Canada, Information Science Section, Building M-50, Montreal Road, Ottawa, Ontario K1A 0R8 (Contact: J W Brahan, Section Head)

The National Research Council carries out research and development of technology for Computer Assisted Learning. Activities include development of the NATAL language and CAL system and integration of Videotex and CAL. Particular emphasis is placed on industrial training applications of CAL.

Nova Scotia Department of Education, Education Resource Services/Education Media Service, 5250 Spring Garden Road, Halifax,

Nova Scotia B3J 1E8 (Contact: Bernard Hart, Assistant Director, Education Resource Services)

Education Media Services is responsible for procuring or producing and distributing all media materials to the schools of the Province of Nova Scotia which they are not able to supply on their own. The role of Media Services is to work with curriculum planners to determine which media materials would be useful in meeting curriculum objectives. Staff are then responsible for procuring or producing and distributing the materials. Staff also work closely with other agencies such as the Canadian Broadcasting Corporation and the National Film Board. In the case of the CBC, Media Services uses one hour of television transmission time per day to reach schools with educational television materials. Staff have also been experimenting with the use of cable television as a more flexible transmission system. Full media services are available, and productions include a range of films, videotapes, filmstrips, and transparency sets, ETV guides and catalogue. Further details are available on request.

*The Ontario Educational Communications Authority (OECA), PO Box 200, 2180 Younge Street, Station Q, Toronto, Ontario M4T 2T1 (Contact: P Annesly, Director, Information Services)

The OECA is an autonomous provincial crown corporation administering educational broadcasting in Ontario. Currently the OECA operates an educational television network, TVOntario, with nine outlets. Other northern areas are reached via microwave cable link. The broadcast day extends for 16 hours with programmes aimed at pre-school, in-school, teachers and adult (open sector) learners. The Authority also operates the Provincial Broadcast Service for two to three hours, using the facilities of the CBC, its affiliates and private stations across Ontario; provides a cable package for viewers in communities not reached by the TVOntario network; and provides videotapes and audiotapes through its VIPS distribution systems.

*Ontario Society for Training and Development, PO Box 537, Postal Station K, Toronto, Ontario M4P 2G9

Open Learning Institute, 7671 Alderbridge Way, Richmond, British Columbia V6X 1Z9 (Contact: Dr J Bottomley, Planning, Research, and Analysis Officer)

The Institute offers distance education programmes in adult basic education, career, technical and vocational subjects and in academic disciplines leading to a first degree. No conventional face-to-face courses are offered. Programmes are open to all students over the age of 18. Students are supplied on a paced basis with learning packages, each comprised of a number of audio, print, visual and other materials. On the basis of the supplied materials, students submit assignments by mail to tutors for grading and comment. The student also has telephone access to the tutor. Each student has access to an adviser who can provide study support, programme planning advice, etc. Some courses are supported with video materials while others are primarily video-based. These are broadcast through the provincial educational television network through the Cable system. Plans include the development of basic numeracy and literacy courses, degree courses in eight subjects, and a variety of career, technical and vocational courses.

*Saint-Jean-Sur-Richelieu (CEGEP), Services Pédagogiques, 30 Boul du Séminaire, CP 310 Saint-Jean, J3B 5J4 (Contact: Regis Dubuisson)

Research investigations on the audio-tutorial approach to biology (in conjunction with the Media Resources Centre).

Special Resource Committee on Instructional Media, c/o Association of Medical Colleges, 151 Slater Street, Ottawa, Ontario

The Committee represents Biomedical Communications Directors across Canada and addresses national issues such as standardized medical media catalogues, and exchange of media information.

Teaching and Instructional Support Division, Department of Education, PO Box 2000, Charlottetown, PEI (Contact: Tom Rich, Media Co-ordinator)

The Media Section of Teaching and Instructional Support exists to provide Department staff and schools assistance in selecting and using media materials and equipment, and provides consultation and technical support for the production of media learning materials. Close liaison is maintained between the Section and the five regional administrative units in the Province. Production facilities and assistance are obtained through the Audio Visual Services Centre. Main activities include: workshops at the school level in media use; consultation services on equipment purchase; co-ordination of department media production activities; production of monographs and media materials on educational technology and media use; evaluations of the use of media materials and delivery systems. As well as various AV presentations, a number of reports and studies have been published.

*University Film Association (UFA), University of Windsor, Windsor, Ontario N9B 3P4 (Contact: Dr Peter Dart, Department of Radio-TV-Film, 217 Flint Hall, University of Kansas, Lawrence, KS 66045)

The University Film Association is a professional association of people with the following common purposes: (i) furthering and developing the potentialities of the motion picture medium for purposes of instruction and communication throughout the world; (ii) encouraging the production of motion pictures in the various educational institutions; (iii) engaging in the teaching of the art and science of motion picture production techniques film history, criticism and/or related subjects; (iv) serving as a central source of information on film instruction and film production by educational institutions, and (v) providing means for the sharing of ideas on the various activities involved in teaching film courses, in producing and distributing motion pictures and allied materials. The Association holds an Annual Conference and members include film teachers and students, producers, business firms and educational institutions. Publications include the quarterly *Journal of the University Film Association*. The Vice-President's Newsletter *Digest* is published several times a year. The Association also publishes its *UFA Membership Directory*.

CENTRAL AFRICAN REPUBLIC

*Institut Pédagogique National, BP 872, Bangui

Produces prototype educational materials and is responsible for the country's Educational Broadcasting Service (Service de la Radio-Télévision Scolaire).

CHILE

Universities

*Centro de Perfeccionamiento, Experimentación e Investigaciones Pedagógicas (CPEIP), Casilla 16162, Correo 9 Providencia, Santiago (Contact: Juan Cox Huyneeus)

CPEIP is a high level unit of the Ministry of Education and Culture, with the overall responsibility of raising the quality of education as it develops in the state system. Its main functions include: research; improving teacher performance; curriculum development; development of innovatory techniques; technical assistance and support; publications.

*Universidad Austral de Chile, Box 567, Valdivia (Contacts: Francisco Marin Herrada, Faculty of Medicine; Juan Luis Iglesias Diaz, Faculty of Education; Maria Angelica Rodrigues, Faculty of Education)

Personalized instruction courses in biostatistics, for medical students; research into multi-media courses at the university level; application of systems analysis to the design of university courses.

Universidad de Chile, Servicio de Desarrollo Docente (Teaching support service of the University of Chile), Dirección General Académica y Estudiantil, Diagonal Paraguay 265, Torre 15, Piso 15, Santiago

The Service co-ordinates some educational technology activities in the faculties and campuses of the University. Activities are extensive and embrace a wide range of media, techniques and teacher training.

Pontifica Universidad Catolica de Chile (Pontifical Catholic University of Chile), Bdo O'Higgins 340, Santiago

1. Teaching Methods Program – Programa de Pedagogía Universitaria (Contact: M Angélica Olivares, Director)

The aim of this Programme is to improve the quality of teaching and learning. It develops and provides the support systems necessary to promote, initiate and evaluate teaching innovations. Regular workshops, seminars and courses on various aspects of educational technology are also provided for the academic community.

2. Educational Technology Department, Diagonal Oriente 3.300, Santiago (Contact: Mariana Martelli U)

Teaching at undergraduate and postgraduate level; research in the areas of instructional systems: design, development and evaluation; teacher training in the areas of foundation, development and evaluation of instructional strategies; consultancy in instructional systems design and evaluation and development of instructional materials.

3. Media Support System – Programa de Medios Audiovisuales (Contact: Carmen Vergara, Director)

The Media Support System designs and produces audiovisual material for the different faculties of UC. It also provides photography and sound services. The programme includes diapofilms and educational videos upon the request of the different faculties, as well as counselling in technical aspects of audiovisual materials and their uses.

4. Telecourse of Division Continuing Studies – TELEDUC, Dirección de

Educación Universitaria a Distancia (Contact: Teresa Matte, Director)

Academic programme consisting of a group of courses aiming to satisfy the educational requirements of vast sectors of the community, through television distance videos. Methods used include books developing the course contents, weekly television programmes, and evaluations every six months. The University awards a certificate to those finishing the course who attain the standards required.

5. Departamento de Curriculum y Evaluación (Curriculum and Evaluation Department), Diagonal Oriente 3.300, Santiago (Contact: Iván Meza or Enrique Pascual)

Research in the areas of production, validity of autoinstruction materials and of individualized teaching designs. Learning packages to teach development and planning of curriculum at undergraduate and postgraduate level, as well as in the area of evaluation.

6. Co-ordinadora Departamento (Contact: Vilna Papié V)

A university department with a teaching and research function, the School offers courses in educational technology, programmed learning, educational television, etc. It also provides an audiovisual service including course evaluations.

*Universidad de Concepción, School of Education, Concepción (Contacts: Gladys Riquelme del Solar; Isabel Millan Arrate; Lila Silva Labarca)

*Universidad del Norte, Antofagasta (Contact: Professor Roberto Char Jure, Department of Education)

*Universidad Catolica de Valparaiso, School of Education, Valparaiso (Contacts: Professor Isaias Aguayo Escobar; Luis Bertoglia; Amilcar Morales; Pedro Ahamada Acevedo)

Other organizations

*Fundación Radio Escuela para el Desarrolio Rural – FREDER (Radio Foundation for Rural Development), Los Carrera 951, Casilia 5-0, Osorno

FREDER is a private, non-political organization supported by the Catholic church. It aims to use radio to support the religious, cultural and social development of rural Chile, and develop the productive capacity of rural families. Radio lessons are followed up by tutored classroom work supported by slides and print materials.

*Instituto Nacional de Capacitación Profesional – INACAP (National Institute of Professional Training), Santiago (Contacts: Sergio Elliot; Guillermo Rodriguez Santa Cruz; Sergio Ponce)

INACAP is the national technical training organization, producing and distributing audiovisual aids, media and distance education courses to training schools. Use of daily newspapers as a medium for a mathematics course for adults (the daily page supplemented by correspondence tuition). Production of programmed instruction materials and radio/TV programmes, administered as a distance education system for adults. Courses include industrial communications and relations, engineering mathematics, quality control, etc.

OREALC, *see Regional Centres of Activity – South America*

COLOMBIA

Accion Cultural Popular (ACPO), Apartado Aerero 7170, Bogotá (Contact: Department of Planning and Evaluation)

ACPO is a private organization aiming to bring education to rural Colombia and concentrating, though not exclusively, on informal education of adult farm workers. ACPO uses radio to broadcast its different courses, and local tutors are trained to assist their less educated companions in using the linked radio and printed sources.

Asociación Latinoamericana de Teleducación (ALTE), *see Regional Centres of Activity – South America*

*Inravision (Contact: Fernando Alford Cortazar, Director)

Inravision is the national institute of radio and television with two separate organizations:

*1. Fondo de Capacitacion Popular – Inravision, Avenida Caracas No 63-09, Apartado Aereo 52999, Bogotá, DE

The objective of this organization is to improve the education of adult workers through TV, radio and written material. Its main functions are to plan, produce and send out programmes of basic education for adult, primary and intermediate education up to the 9th grade, including basic literacy material; to train guides or monitors who advise adult students at reception centres; to broadcast programmes for cultural extension – science, folklore, sports, music – and for community service (communal action, co-operation, health, nutrition, handcrafts, etc); and to improve programmes for teacher training. Programmes are broadcast through 'Canal 11', through the national broadcasting station and through some private radio stations. Printed materials can be bought at the agricultural stores of the 'Caja de Credito Agrario' (an official bank).

*2. Television Educativa Escolar – Inravision, Via El Dorado, Can, Bogotá, DE

Objectives are to enrich the learning activities of children; to make use of human, technical and material resources for help and support to teachers; and to help the direct teaching and learning process. Teacher guides are published for all subjects at all grades, and programmes are broadcast throughout the country.

Ministerio de Educacion Nacional, División de Documentación e Información Educativa, Apartado 80359, Bogotá (Contact: Silvia Castrillon de Miranda, Jefe División)

The Division was created in November 1976 with the following functions: (1) to organize school libraries and educational documentation centres; (2) to advise Centros Experimentales Pilotos in its bibliographical and documental tasks; and (3) to provide documentation services to the offices and bureaux of the Ministry. Main services provided are: (1) teacher training courses for school librarians; (2) advisory services to: educational institutions at a national level, Centros Experimentales Pilotos, and educational institutions with similar interests.

CONGO

*Institut National de Recherche et d'Action Pédagogiques – INRAP (National Institute for Educational Research and Implementation), BP 2128, Brazzaville (Contacts: Jean-Francois Obembe, INRAP; M Mouanza, Chef du Service du Matériel Pédagogique)

COSTA RICA

*Cinemateca Nacional (National Film Archives), Ministry of Culture, Youth and Sports, Apartado 10.081, San Jose (Contact: Antonio Yglesias)

Stimulates and organizes film festivals to help the Costa Rican youth know international cine.

Instituto Centroamericano de Extension de la Cultura, Apartado 2948, 1.000 San Jose

Founded in 1963 to provide cultural and educational opportunities for those who cannot attend a centre of learning, particularly those in rural areas of Central America; broadcasts half-hour programme six days a week through 45 stations. Its almanac has 600,000 copies.

*Instituto Costarricense de Ensenanza Radiofonica (Costa Rican Institute of Radio Teaching), Apartado 132, San Pedro Montes de Oca, San Jose (Contact: Franz Tattenbach, Director)

Produces adult education programmes for primary school curriculum in close co-ordination with the Ministry of Education.

CUBA

*Radiotelevisión Educativa del Ministerio de Educación (Educational Broadcasting of the Ministry of Education), Ministerio de Educación, Havana

A formal state organization to help the economic and political development of Cuba, using the mass media. Formal and informal systems are used to support programmes aimed to reach all sections of the population; subjects include basic literacy, cultural and political material, school subjects at all levels, and higher education and professional training.

CYPRUS

Educational Broadcasting Service, Ministry of Education, Nicosia (Contact: Stelios G Sycallides)

The Service was instituted in 1966 to take charge of activities connected with educational television. Since then, it has developed into a service responsible for all activities falling within the domain of educational technology. The Service is responsible for the following major activities: educational radio, educational television, AV aids, and publications. The Service also undertakes in-service training of teachers in subjects that are related to its activities and responsibilities, and provides the schools with (i) radio and television programmes, both for pupils and teachers; (ii) supplementary material in the form of teachers' and pupils' notes, sets of pictures and/or slides; (iii) catalogues containing approved AV aids; the Service also runs a film, slide-tape and record library.

Pedagogical Institute, PO Box 5365, Nicosia (Contact: Dr J G Koutsakos, Director)

The Institute is incorporated within the Ministry of Education. It has a number of functions, all concerned with teaching and learning from pre-primary to post-secondary level. These are in-service teacher training; curriculum development; preparation of learning materials for teachers and pupils; educational research; and documentation, translation and dissemination of educational information. The main activities are directed to in-service training of teachers, especially of those teachers who have recently become secondary school teachers and who are regarded as being on probation. For these, the Institute prepares booklets, slides and tape recordings, usually within subject-centred departments, eg science, mathematics. Many members of the Institute are currently involved in curriculum renewal at primary and secondary level, in co-operation with inspectors, teachers and teachers' organizations.

CZECHOSLOVAKIA

Komenium, Prague 1, Staromestskenam 25

Undertakes research, production and domestic distribution of materials.

Učebné Pomöcky, 975 35 Banská Bystrica, Ul Janka Krafa 3

Research, production and domestic distribution of materials.

DENMARK

*Association for the Study of Programmed Instruction, Egernvaenget 310, DK-2980 Kokkedal

The Danish Institute for Educational Research, 28 Hermodsgade, DK-2200 Copenhagen N (Contact: Jasper Florunder, Director)

The objects of the Institute are as follows: (a) to carry out scientific research and studies of importance to educational activities; (b) to assist in developmental projects for which scientific support is required and to offer advisory service, planning, collection and analysis of educational material; (c) to provide students of psychology and education with trainee facilities at the Institute; (d) to publish reports of its activities and provide information in general, relating to matters of interest in the field of education; (e) to construct and distribute tests and similar material which by their nature cannot be made freely available.

Danmarks Radio, Educational Broadcasting Department, Planning Section, Islands Brygge 81, DK-2300, Copenhagen S (Contact: H Engberg-Pedersen)

The Educational Broadcasting Department has a full-time staff of approximately 50 people and is responsible to the Danish National Institute of Educational Media for schools and adult education broadcasting. The planning section has the following functions: (i) the long-term planning of educational broadcasting in Denmark and associated research in the form of national surveys of needs (adult education) 'mapping' of resources and constraints; (ii) formative evaluation: developmental testing of new series, investigations into the feasibility of adapting educational TV materials from abroad for use in Denmark; (iii) summative evaluation: large-scale projects are usually investigated in co-operation with external agencies or institutions;

(iv) identification and development of appropriate channels for informing potential 'consumers' (adult education) of course materials and channelling feedback on their merits; and (v) documentation, a limited amount of research and development work of general relevance to the production of educational broadcasting and texts for schools and adult education. The Planning Section prepares evaluation and research projects for internal and external use. Projects of general or international interest are reported to the Nordic Council's Documentation Project on Research and Development in Adult Education. The Section plans to expand the publication of its research findings in English and German journals. Services offered are: *internally:* documentation, research and development facilities for schools and adult education broadcasting sections, and publications section; *externally:* evaluation and planning facilities for the Ministry of Education (the National Institute for Educational Media, the Department's policy boards). Co-ordination of planning and evaluation work with that of Scandinavian colleagues, especially in the field of modern languages for adults. Monitoring research and development projects reported by the Nordic Council Documentation Project in the field of identification and analysis of language needs for the CCC, Council of Europe project concerning 'a European unit/ credit system for modern language learning by adults'. Recent publications include the evaluation and survey reports made available nationally and within Scandinavia to interested parties (Danish – abstracts in English/ German are to be prepared on an *ad hoc* basis).

*National Institute for Educational Media, Gl Kongevej 164,4, DK-1850, Copenhagen V (Contact: Knud-E Hauberg-Tychsen, Managing Director)

The National Institute for Educational Media is an independent Government institution under the Ministry of Education. In accordance with the Act which founded the Institute in 1974, its functions are to register and catalogue educational media; to provide information about the production and supply of educational media; to act as co-ordinator between producers and users of educational media; to negotiate with Radio Denmark, the Danish Government Film Office or other producers on acquisition of materials for educational purposes and, in certain cases, to undertake or support the acquisition of other educational media; against payment to ensure that educational media are processed; to distribute films, audio-tapes, etc to schools and other educational institutions; and to distribute materials to the regional centre collections.

National School of Education, Rigensgade 13, 1316 Copenhagen K (Contact: W Marckmann, Rector)

Statens Filmcentral, Vestergadt 27, DK-1456, Copenhagen K (Contact: The Director)

The Danish Film Law describes the purpose of Statens Filmcentral: 'The function of Statens Filmcentral shall be to produce and purchase short films for educational and information purposes, as well as short films of predominantly artistic content, and to distribute such films to the extent that distribution is not handled by other bodies'. The distribution from Statens Filmcentral consists of 1300 different films in 13,000 prints. The principal user of Statens Filmcentral's distribution is the non-commercial sector of the film public. Schools and other educational institutions, libraries, local clubs, trade unions, film clubs, etc are among the many borrowers of films from

Statens Filmcentral. In 1977-78 there were 240,000 bookings, while 80,000 inquiries had to be refused because of shortage of prints. All productions are carried out by private Danish film companies on the basis of suggestions from the Committee or from film directors, or in principle from anybody who wishes to make short films. Productions are also initiated by the Programme Committee exclusively. About 20 Danish short films annually are produced through Statens Filmcentral.

DOMINICAN REPUBLIC

Radio Santa Maria, HIDV, Apartado de Correos 55, La Vega (Contact: Antonio Cabezas Esteban, Director)

This is an educational radio station producing primary and secondary material, mainly of a cultural rather than an instructional nature. Some students study in organized groups, but many receive the programmes at home without any special organization. The programmes are also used by many existing schools.

ECUADOR

Centro Internacional de Estudios Superiores de Comunicacion para America Latina (CIESPAL), Ave Almagro y Andrade Marin, Apartado No 584, Quito (Contacts: Dr Luis E Proano, General Director; Lodo Marco Encalada, Technical Director; Mr José Steinsleger, Publisher Assessor at CIESPAL)

CIESPAL (International Centre of High Studies of Communication for Latin America) was founded in 1959 by an agreement between the Ecuadorian Government, Unesco and the Central University of Ecuador. It was created to promote co-operation, to bring specialized courses to the Social Communication Schools of Latin America, and to give courses at postgraduate levels in all aspects of communication. It has been supported by the contributions of the Friedrich Ebert Foundation, Unesco and many governments and universities of the region. Its main activities lie in such areas as: *Professional training* – specialized courses and study programmes in the investigation of communication, educational and scientific journalism and communication for development; *Documentation:* the Documentation Center of CIESPAL is part of the worldwide net of document centres organized by Unesco to collect, process and spread information about documents and problems on social communication; *Research* and development of research techniques into communication in Latin America, with specific investigations into methodologies of social communication. The Publishing Department produces the Centre's journal *CHASQUI.*

*Escuelas Radiofónicas Populares del Ecuadore – ERPE (Popular Radio Schools), Apartado 47-55, Riobamba (Contact: P Rubén Veloz, Director)

ERPE is a private, non-profit-making Christian organization, with the primary aim of setting up literacy and other basic education programmes using radio and other AV media. It aims to provide lifelong education for rural workers, using radio transmissions, backed by private materials and the help of a local tutor to lead study groups.

EGYPT

Ain-Shams University College for Women, The Audiovisual Laboratory (Department of Curricula and Methods of Teaching), Asma Fahmy St, Heliopalis, Cairo (Contact: Dr Mahassen M R Ahmad)

The Laboratory was established in 1969 as a training laboratory in the Department of Curricula and Methods of Teaching. It functions as a training laboratory for student teachers on AV preparation and use, and as an AV centre for the College.

*The American University in Cairo, Division of Public Service, 113 Kasr el Aini Street, Cairo

The University is fully equipped with language laboratories, video tape, CCTV, microteaching. Slides, filmstrips, 16mm and 8mm silent films, video lessons, language laboratory programmes, and multi-media kits are produced. Services include maintenance, repair and distribution of AV equipment, designing and producing VTR programmes, language laboratory materials, AV courses, training of graduate students on designing and using AV-oriented courses.

EIRE

Institutions of further and higher education

University College Cork – Teaching Development Unit, University College, Cork (Contact: Susan Sayer, Director)

The post of Director of Teaching Development is new as of 1981, both for University College Cork and for Ireland. A Unit is being formed which will develop a programme to encourage and contribute to the professional development of academic staff. The existing Audiovisual Service has become responsible to the new Director.

University of Dublin, Centre for Language and Communication Studies, Trinity College, Dublin 2 (Contact: Mr D G Little, Director)

The Centre has a research and development function in language and communication studies, particularly in relation to the technical services that it provides. It also has special responsibility for the development of television in third-level education in Ireland. The Centre has four academic staff, including a television producer, and six technicians. It is equipped with two language laboratories, a phonetics laboratory, a sound recording studio, two television studios, and a photographic unit.

The Centre provides service courses in phonetics and general linguistics, and the academic staff participate in the teaching programmes of various departments. The chief research and development interests are self-instructional language learning, phonetics, and television production.

The Centre accommodates the language laboratory teaching of modern language departments, the microteaching activities of the School of Education, and all television productions undertaken in the Arts faculties. It also provides a photographic service for Arts departments.

*University College Dublin, Audio Visual Centre, Department of Education, Dublin 4 (Contact: Dr Seán Ó Éigeartaigh)

Mater Dei Institute of Education, Clonliffe Road, Dublin 3 (Contacts:
Sr Bernadette MacMahon, Teaching Strategies Programme; Mr Andrew G
McGrady, Lecturer of Educational Technology; Mrs B O'Hara, Resource
Centre)

The Institute offers a four-year course to prepare students to teach religious
education and a secular subject at post-primary level. Microteaching has been
an integral part of the education course since 1972. A Teaching Strategies
Programme has been devised based on the work of Gagné, Peel, Taba and
Fowler. Further research and development of these is being undertaken. The
production of audiovisual material to meet specific instructional objectives
and a consideration of media education, form part of the required
coursework for all students. The Institute also offers a one-year foundation
course in theology. Audiovisual feedback techniques are used to facilitate
practical work in preaching and reading the Scriptures. The Institute is
equipped with an 80 sq m black and white production CCTV studio, two
video teaching laboratories and a single camera colour EFP unit. Assemble
editing is also available. A resource centre specializing in material for
teaching religious education has been established in recent years. Staff and
students have combined to produce the 'Gift of God Series', a set of multi-
media resource kits for teaching slow learners.

Other organizations

AnCO – The Industrial Training Authority, PO Box 456, Baggot Court,
27-33 Upper Baggot Street, Dublin 4 (Contact: Ms Una Maguire, Research
Officer)

AnCO's functions are to provide and to promote the training of the Irish
workforce at all levels in commerce and industry. It provides training for
first-year apprentices and for unemployed adults in 14 training centres and
leases training from other training institutions and from companies; and it
promotes training in Irish industry through an advisory service and through a
grants scheme. These two main functions are supported by the services of a
Research and Planning Division, a Curriculum Development Section and by
Instructor Training and Staff Development Units.

Each Training Centre and the Head Office is equipped with a wide range of
audiovisual and reprographical equipment; library facilities include access to
relevant software. In development are: the making and adaptation of
software programmes, structures for the co-ordination of training technology
activities and research into the application of computer-assisted learning and
computer-assisted management to training.

The Communications Centre, Booterstown Avenue, Co Dublin (Contact:
Mr Tom O'Hare, Director)

The Communications Centre began media training in 1967 and since then has
helped to train people from all over the world, who believe that the mass
media have made it necessary to rethink our approach to the means of
communication. Clients include educationalists, industrialists, clergy, public
administrators, government officials, politicians, businessmen, professional
organizations, the defence forces, people from developing countries and the
general public, all of whom take one or more of the numerous Training and
Media Production courses. The main course is a three-month Broadcasting
Course which is offered each autumn. This is a modular course treating most

aspects of media production. Facilities include a full broadcast specification radio production studio and a colour television production studio. The Communications Centre also offers consultancy services in such areas as: needs assessment, job/task analysis, educational system planning, course design, materials development, media production and evaluation, communications audit, distance education, educational technology in developing countries.

Computer Education Society of Ireland (Chairman: Mr Brendan Mackey, Vocational School, Wexford; Secretary: Miss M A Sheehan, Mount Anville Secondary School, Goatstown, Dublin 14)

The Society endeavours to provide a forum in which the various aspects of computer education may be examined and discussed, courses arranged, seminars and guest lectures organized, policies formulated, recommendations made, and discussions held with other bodies. The Society holds courses for teachers, usually during summer holidays. It issues a newsletter four or five times a year. There are at present five branches in the following areas: Cork, Dublin, Limerick, Kilkenny, Waterford. Branch activities include meetings/courses/lectures/demonstrations.

Drumcondra Teachers' Centre, Dublin 9 (Contacts: Patrick B Diggins, Director; Dee Coogan, Secretary)

The Teachers' Centre was established to provide a meeting place for the dissemination of knowledge and information to all teachers, especially by the organization of seminars, conferences, lectures, debates and symposia, and in-service courses and by all other means subject to the approval of the Committee; to promote and encourage research and experimental projects in the field of Irish education; and to act as a resource centre which would enable teachers to prepare and construct equipment and materials for use in their own schools and in addition to facilitate the display of teachers' and pupils' work and materials and to provide for a display of textbooks, materials and equipment.

Higher Education Authority, Committee on Audiovisual Aids, 21 Fitzwilliam Square, Dublin 2 (Contact: Mr M Hallinan, Assistant Secretary)

General monitoring role in relation to audiovisual matters in the various institutions of higher education in Ireland.

Irish Association for Curriculum Development, 1 Bellevue Road, Glenageary, Co Dublin (Contact: Mrs Kathleen Quigley, Hon Secretary)

The Association's main aims are (1) to co-ordinate and encourage curriculum development in schools; (2) to act as an advice, reference and information centre for curriculum development; and (3) to organize conferences, seminars and lectures on matters of educational interest. It holds five or six conferences each year on some aspect of curriculum development. Publications include a twice-yearly journal *Compass; A Survey of Attitudes of Post Primary Teachers and Pupils* by John Raven *et al* in three volumes; and a periodic Newsletter.

Limerick Teachers' Centre, Summerville Avenue, Limerick (Contact: Mr Liam O'Broin, Director)

The Centre offers an elective programme of in-service professional development courses for teachers at all levels – generally geared to expressed needs of serving teachers in the Centre's catchment area.

Ancillary services include a range of audiovisual reprographic equipment for use by teachers, including photocopying; a teachers' reference library; slides; filmstrips; records and tapes; a list of available substitute teachers, sent to all schools at regular intervals. School requisites may be purchased inexpensively at the Centre.

National Film Institute of Ireland, 65 Harcourt Street, Dublin 2 (Contacts: Malachy O'Higgins, BL, MA, Director; Martin McLoone, Film Education and Media Studies Officer; Elizabeth Hall, Film Librarian)

The Institute is mainly an educational and industrial film lending library with about 4000 titles currently in its library. It also holds courses in film and media education for schools, etc and with the Health Education Bureau operates two mobile film units which travel around the country showing films on health education to schools. The Institute holds an annual amateur cine competition.

Radio Telefis Eireann, Educational Programmes Department, Donnybrook, Dublin 4 (Contact: Head of Educational Programmes)

RTE is the national broadcasting authority for Ireland. The Educational Programmes Department is responsible for the provision on radio and television of educational projects, radio and television, at all levels: it funds adult educational programmes out of its own resources; it receives funds from the exchequer, when it is required to provide services for schools.

EL SALVADOR

Dirección General de Comunicación y Tecnología Educativa, Final 13 Avenida Sur, Nueva San Salvador, El Salvador CA (Contact: Carlos Antonio Burgos, Director)

Created as the Dirección de TV Educativa in 1967 during a complete overhaul of the national educational system, early in 1981, with the addition of other curricular activities, it became the Dirección General. It serves an open audience of 50 per cent of the population and has 200,000 students.

ETHIOPIA

Ministry of Education

*1. Basic Education Section, Department of Adult Education, PO Box 4921, Addis Ababa

*2. Material Preparation and Production Division, Department of Adult Education, PO Box 4921, Addis Ababa

*3. Science Curriculum Development Centre, PO Box 3671, Addis Ababa

FINLAND

University of Jyväskylä, Institute for Educational Research, 40100 Jyväskylä 10

Educational R and D, educational information and documentation.

*Finnish Audio-Visual Association, PL 842, Helsinki 10

*The Finnish Institute of Leadership Training, Pohjoiskaari 34, 00200 Helsinki 20 (Contact: K Eloranta, Principal)

A training institute specializing in management, industrial engineering, personnel management, organization research and development.

Valtior AV-Keskus (State AV Centre), Hakaniemenkatu 2, 00530 Helsinki 53 (Contacts: Miss Aino Toivonen, Director; Georg Korkman, Acquisitions)

The Centre is concerned with the promotion of instructional technology, the provision of information (periodical *OPPIMA*, eight issues per year), the distribution of films, tapes and slides, etc and the testing of equipment.

FRANCE

*AFCET, 156 boulevard Péreire, BP 571, 75826 Paris, Cedex 17

The aim of AFCET, a scientific association, is to identify, extend and unify scientific knowledge in connection with 'operations research, computer science and systems analysis and control'. AFCET publishes seven journals: *RAIRO – Recherche Operationelle/Operations Research; RAIRO – Informatique/Computer Science; RAIRO – Automatique/Systems Analysis and Control; RAIRO – Analyse Numérique/Numerical Analysis; RAIRO – Informatique Théoretique/Theoretical; Informatique et Gestion; Automisme;* and sponsors meetings, conferences and working groups

*AVCD, 71 boulevard Richard-Lenoir, 75011 Paris (Contact: Monique Caze, Executive Director)

AVCD undertakes market studies, needs studies, conference organization. Services include documentation on devices, software and services. Publications: *AVCD* (weekly); *AVCD* (monthly); *AV Directory* (1 – Hard, 2 – Soft); French AV software producers.

Agence de Co-operation Culturelle et Technique, *see* Centre d'Information et d'Echanges – Télévision

*Centre Audiovisuel – Ecole Normale Supérieure, 2 avenue du Palais, 92210 Saint-Cloud (Contact: R Lefranc, Director)

The Centre Audio-Visuel was created in 1947 as a research laboratory near the Higher School of Education in Saint-Cloud, and as an advisory service in the audiovisual field of the Higher Education branch of the Ministry of Education. Main activities include *Research:* mainly on expression and communication, distance teaching, teacher training, use of media in higher education; *Production:* of four kinds – experimental production for research, prototype production for universities, production for teacher training in educational technology, and/or distance education in arts, law, economics and medicine; *Training:* given in a one-year intensive course and short courses. Services offered by the Centre include research and evaluation for universities and private organizations; materials production on request; training not only for teachers but for 'éducation permanente' for various organizations; and national and international expertise (for example for Council of Europe, for Unesco, etc). The Centre publishes many research reports and studies (available on request) and contributes to many books and reviews. Films are distributed by SFRS (Service du Film de Recherche Scientifique, 95 Boulevard Raspail, 75006 Paris). Language methods are sold by private companies. TV programmes are broadcast by the national organization.

Centre d'Information et d'Echanges-Télévision, Agence de Co-opération

Culturelle et Technique, 19 Avenue de Messine, 75008 Paris (Contact: Jean-Claude Crepeau)

CIE-TV is concerned with innovations in educational systems (and thereby problems), especially in the field of broadcasting. The Information Centre on Instructional Technology maintains a documents collection in the field (books, periodicals and audiovisual documents). It publishes (monthly) *Direct* (studies and bibliographic information), and *Teledocumentation* (a bibliographical bulletin on various subjects with six issues per year). Services include information searches, viewing of audiovisual documents and specialized bibliographies.

*CIRAL – Centre d'Informations et de Recherches Appliquées en Langues (Centre for Information and Applied Research in Languages), Université de Toulon, Faculté de Droit, 83130 La Garde (Contact: David Crookall)

Applied research into foreign language learning/teaching with emphasis on the communicative use of language.

*CNDP (National Centre for Teaching Documentation), 29 rue d'Ulm, 75230 Paris, Cedex 05

CNDP is responsible for elaborating and distributing teaching documentation, eg documentation on the content of courses, using all written and audiovisual sources principally intended for teacher training and follow-up training; giving help for the training of teachers of all levels.

Centre Régional de Documentation Pédagogique – CRDP (Regional Centre for Educational Documentation), 75 cours d'Alsace et Lorraine, 33075 Bordeaux Cedex (Contact: René de la Borderie, Director)

The Bordeaux CRDP was set up in 1955. There is a CRDP in each *Académie* (educational district): these are public establishments charged with helping teachers to develop their attitudes, aimed at encouraging the introduction of modern teaching methods especially through the use of audiovisual aids. The Bordeaux CRDP has the extra distinction of being the only one to have a research service (by contact with the *Institut National de Recherche Pédagogique*). Specializing in audiovisual communication research, the Bordeaux CRDP has worked out a theory and established an experimental base under the heading of ICAV (Initiation to Audio-Visual Communication). This theory treats pupils as active individuals confronted with an audiovisual message. The component educational practices are centred on communication as an object of study.

Ecole Nationale Louis Lumière, 8 rue Rollin, 75005 Paris (Contact: Adrien Touboul, Director)

The School provides formal training in cinematography and related techniques. It operates from four separate buildings in Paris covering all aspects of colour and monochrome photography and cinematography including optics, film laboratories, studio facilities and sound equipment. The School has an important collection of old cinema equipment. The School trains students in photographic processing, photography, cinema and sound. The latter three categories are trained for a State diploma, the *Brevet de technicien supérieur*, in their chosen field. Entry is by competitive examination and courses last two years. The Training Centre for Audio-Visual Arts and Techniques offers various courses – still very cinema-centred – in wider audiovisual disciplines including use of video and videotape recorders. The Centre offers flexibility in its courses and hopes to co-operate with industry and professional bodies and commercial companies in adapting its efforts to existing and future needs.

*Education 2000, Institut Supérieure de Pédagogie, 3 rue de l'Abbaye, 75006 Paris (Contacts: Jean-Michel di Falco; Gilles Delavaud)

Services offered include conferences, training courses, audiovisual courses, audiovisual and video productions, and Super 8 film.

*IDA (Institut de l'Audiovisual), 30 rue Henri Barbusse, 75005 Paris (Contact: Madame Jadoul)

Teaching of photography, video, short film making (16mm and Super 8mm), and the making of slide shows with synchronized sound.

Institut National de Recherche Pédagogique – INRP (National Institute of Educational Research), 29 rue d'Ulm, 75005 Paris

1. Groupe de recherche sur les applications éducatives de la télématique et des télécommunications, INRP, 91 rue Gabriel Péri, 92120 Montrouge (Contact: Robert Quinot, Docteur en Sciences de l'Education)

The aim of this research department of the INRP is to study the educational applications of telematics and telecommunications. The activities of the research team are being developed within four sections: (1) videotex (ie both interactive videotex, Teletel type, using the telephone connected network, and broadcast Teletext, Antiope type, using the TV networks of distribution); (2) distance communication, requiring no special software and using the following equipment: speakerphone, teleconferencing system (audiophony, telewriting, picturephone), facsimile transmission of documents; (3) videodisc, domestic type, 'institutional', semi-adaptive or computer-interfaced player; (4) communication satellites (live broadcast satellites, telematics-oriented satellites or satellites with mixed loads). Each section's programme includes experimental productions, experiments carried out in state schools (upper and lower secondary schools, primary schools), the continuous updating of scientific information, permanent contacts, and even prearranged actions, with foreign organizations working in the same fields.

The research activities have been developed in consultation with French experts in these areas, such as: Centre National d'Etude des Télécommunications (CNET), Direction Générale des Télécommunications (DGT), Centre Commun d'Etudes de Télévision et de Télécommunications (CCETT), Centre National d'Etudes Spatiales (CNES), etc. In the field of the educational applications of the new techniques, four leading trends are being studied: (1) access to documentary data banks (bibliographical, textual, audiovisual data), so as to back up teachers' actions and students' autonomous activities; (2) distance teaching for pupils or students who either are disadvantaged by their geographical situation and various handicaps or cannot, out of vocational reasons, perform traditional school activities; (3) support of individualized learning processes within the framework of formal education; (4) specific features and combined utilization of new communication techniques.

*2. Division Informatique et Enseignement (Contact: Christian Lafond)

The Division is responsible for the study of computer-assisted instruction and the applications of micro-data processing to teaching.

*IREM, Université de Nancy 1, Case officielle 140, 54037 Nancy, Cedex

Research into the teaching of mathematics, and education of mathematics teachers. Materials produced include research reports, programmed courses, films.

*Laboratoire de Psychologie de Travail, 41 rue Gay Lussac, Paris 5e (Contact: J Leplat)

Research into aspects of adult training including work analysis, cognitive processes.

GERMANY, FEDERAL REPUBLIC OF

Institutes of further and higher education

Akademie für Lehrerfortbildung, Kardinal-von-Waldburg-Strasse 6, 8880 Dillingen/Donau (Contact: Ludwig Häring, Direktor der Akademie)

The Akademie für Lehrerfortbildung is the central institution for the in-service training of teachers from all types of schools below university level in Bavaria. It was established by the Bavarian Ministry of Education in 1971. The Akademie organizes in-service training courses relating to methodology and educational innovation, developments in technology, science and arts. Reports about courses of general and wider interest are published in the series *Akademieberichte*. Detailed information is available on request.

*Universität Dusseldorf, Abteilung für Bildungsforschung und pädagogische Beratung, Erziehungswissenschaftliches Institut, Universitatsstrasse 1, D-400 Dusseldorf (Contact: AOR Dr Lutz F Hornke)

The Department is concerned with training of students in education (diploma candidates and secondary school teachers). Some emphasis is placed on educational diagnostics, test construction, and computerized as well as non-computerized adaptive testing. With computerized adaptive tests small calculators and small microprocessors are used. Development and empirical research in the field of testing and adaptive testing in particular; research in diagnostic processes and decision making at the school level.

Fernuniversität, ZIFF – Zentrales Institut für Fernstudienforschung (The Central Institute for Research into Distance Study), D-5800 Hagen (Contact: Professor Börje Holmberg, Director)

ZIFF was organized when the Fernuniversität was founded. Its tasks are to carry out basic and applied research on distance study. ZIFF has two university chairs of its own, and shares three chairs with faculties (marked *). Each of these is in charge of one area of work although some overlapping occurs. *Adult education in general** (Head: Professor Otto Peters – the present Vice Chancellor of the University and thus at present on leave from ZIFF); *The development of distance study* (Head: Professor Börje Holmberg – at present director of ZIFF); *Organization and administration of distance study* (Head: Professor Kurt Graff); *Psychology** (Head: Professor Helmuth E Lück); *Empirical social research** (Head: Professor Gunther Büschges). ZIFF makes its research results available through publications, correspondence, lectures and seminars. It also scrutinizes Fernuniversität courses and offers an internal consultative service. ZIFF is not otherwise engaged in the operational activities of the University. It publishes two series of occasional papers, *ZIFF – Papiere* and *ZIFF – Hinweise*. Apart from these a number of reports have been published by the work units of the ZIFF chairs. With few exceptions these publications are in German.

Universität Frankfurt, Institut für Didaktik der Physik, Graefstrasse 39, D-6000 Frankfurt am Main (Contact: Professor Dr Klaus Weltner)

Development of physics curricula, master programmes and adjunct programmes to textbooks; application of information theory and graph theory to educational problems.

Informationszentrum für Fremsprachenforschung der Philipps-Universität, Lahnberge, D-3550 Marburg/Lahn

Universität Kiel, see Institut für die Pädagogik der Naturwissenschaften

***Pädagogische Hochschule,** Ahornstrasse 55, D-5100 Aachen (Contact: Professor Dr Ralf Schwarzer)

Instructional research, curriculum evaluation, aptitude-treatment interaction, mastery learning.

Pädagogische Hochschule Reutlingen, AV-Zentrum, Postfach 680, D-741 Reutlingen (Contact: Professor Dr Martin Rauch, Leiter des AV-Zentrums, Fach Schulpädagogik)

Studios for video-productions (Unterrichtsdokumentationen).

University of Tübingen, Centre for New Learning Methods, Institute of Education 11, Muenzgasse 11, D-7400 Tübingen 1 (Contact: Professor Dr Walther Zifreund)

The Centre for New Learning Methods is a department of the Institute of Education 11 of the University of Tübingen. The Centre offers courses and training programmes, mainly for university students but also for teachers, in the following fields: computer-assisted instruction, simulation and model learning; interaction analysis; interactional improvisation method and interactional gaming research; research in foreign language teaching and language laboratory techniques; and microteaching. These specializations are organized in research groups. The Centre has a research library of some 5000 volumes, and since 1978 has produced a series of books entitled *Neue Lernfahren* (New Learning Methods); it also co-edits the quarterly *Unterrichtswissenschaft* (Instructional Science), and has produced a wide range of books, articles, videotapes and computer diskettes.

Other organizations

***Bayerischer Rundfunk,** Telekolleg, Postfach, D-8000 Munchen 2 (Contact: Dr Walter Flemmer)

A broadcasting institution responsible for school and college TV programmes which also produces multi-media programmes.

***BTZ (Bildungstechnologisches Zentrum GmbH),** Bodenstedtstr 7, D-62 Wiesbaden

CDC: Carl Duisberg Centren, gemeinnützige Gesellschaft mbH, Hansaring 49-51, D-5000 Cologne 1

Catholic Media Council (Publizistische Medienplanung für entwicklungslander EV), Bendelstrasse 7, PO Box 1912, D-5100 Aachen (Contacts: Dr Franz Josef Eilers; Dr Marcel Vanhengel)

Evaluation and advice on communications projects submitted, or to be submitted, by applicants from Asia, Africa, Latin America and Oceania, to Church (mainly RC) Funding Agencies. Materials produced include an information bulletin (twice a year), and service papers (occasionally).

Deutsches Institut für Internationale Pädagogische Forschung (German Institute for International Educational Research), Schloss-Strasse 29, D-6000 Frankfurt-Main 90 (Contact: Professor Dr Wolfgang Mitter, Director of Research Board)

The German Institute for International Educational Research has existed since 1951 as an independent foundation under public law. Research work is entrusted to research departments and research teams as follows: *Department of General and Comparative Education* – comparative investigations about school systems in industrialized countries in the view of the interrelationship between the educational and employment systems; inquiries into topical issues in the Federal Republic; research into computer-assisted instruction. *Department of Psychology* – research into decision theory, investigations and construction of tests (achievement, personality). *Department of Sociology* – research into the interrelationship between school and society in developing countries (above all, Africa and South-east Asia); investigation about parents' participation in the school system in the Federal Republic. *Department of Economics of Education* – research into school management and into issues concerning the regionalization of the school system in the Federal Republic and abroad (micro-analyses). *Department of Law and Administration of Education* – research into topical constitutional, legislative and administrative issues of the educational systems in the Federal Republic and the European Community. *Department of Educational and Psychological Statistics, Research and Methods* – fundamental methodological investigations and data processing. *Department of Vocational Education* (now being set up) – research into career guidance and choice. The Institute maintains a library with more than 110,000 volumes and about 600 periodicals including much foreign literature.

*Deutscher Lehrmuttel Verband eV, Eppsteiner Strasse 36, 6000 Frankfurt-am-Main 1 (Contact: Helmut Jünger, President; Roger von Naso, Geschäftsführer)

*Deutscher Volkschochschulverband – Pädagogische Arbeitsstelle, Holzhausenstrasse 21, D-6000 Frankfurt/Main (Contact: Herbert Bohn)

General activities: scientific services and supply, publications for institutes of public adult education (Volkhochschulen). *Special activities:* information about educational technology in the field of courses for adult education. Publications: *Unterrichtsmedien-Dienst.*

*FEoLL-Institut für Bildungsinformatik, D-479 Paderborn 1, Pohlweg 55 (Contact: Professor Dr Milos Lánsky)

GPI: Gesellschaft für Pädagogik und Information, Pohlweg 52, D-479 Paderborn

*Helmholtz-Institut für BMT an der TH Aachen, D-51 Aachen, Foethestrasse 27-29 (Contact: Miss K Meyer-Hartwig)

Production of course materials in the field of biomedical engineering.

Hermann Schroedel Verlag KG, Foreign Department, Hildesheimer Str 202-206, D-3000 Hanover 81

*Institut für Dokumentation und Information über Sozialmedizin und offentliches Gesundheitswesen – IDIS (Institute for Documentation and Information about Social Medicine and Public Health), PO Box 54-08, Westfelderstrasse 17, 4800 Bielefeld 1 (Contact: Dr G Murza)

The Institute produces documents for the information of all those interested in the field of medicine in the widest sense. Beyond this, the Institute is responsible for the organization of health education for its local region – 'Land Nordrhein-Westfalen'. A wide range of information media is used, including audiovisual teaching techniques.

Institut für Erziehungswissenschaft (Contact: Professor Dr Johannes Zielinski, Director, der Rheinisch Westfalischen Technischen Hochschule, Eilfschornsteinstr 7, D-51 Aachan

Institut für Film und Bild in Wissenschaft und Unterricht (FWU), Bavaria-Film-Platz 3, 8022 Grünwald (Contact: Professor Dr Walter Cappel, Director)

Production of audiovisual materials (including printed materials such as descriptive notes and teacher guides) for all areas of education, from pre-school to primary and secondary education, vocational training, teacher training and adult education; promotion of educational technology; sale of the materials to audiovisual centres, schools, educational TV and others; a data base is run for a complex information system about audiovisual teaching aids; testing of hardware. Materials produced include 16mm film, videotapes, audiotapes, 8mm single concept films, 8mm sound films, tape-slide series, slide series, overhead transparencies. Besides providing audiovisual materials as described above, FWU offers an advisory service for the integration of audiovisual techniques in education and teaching; seminars and conferences are organized; selected information is supplied to educational institutions, research institutes, educational authorities, AV experts and teachers. It also offers an advisory service concerning technical equipment; test reports on hardware are issued.

Recent publications include catalogues of audiovisual materials, a bibliography of audiovisual literature, *AV Pädagogik* and *AV Unterricht*, publications dealing with the use of AV media in teaching and education, *AV Technik*, a series concerned with the technical equipment used in education, and *AV Forschung*, a publication on media research. A publications list is available on request.

Institut für die Pädagogik der Naturwissenschaften (IPN) an der Universität Kiel (Institute for Science Education (IPN) at the University of Kiel), Olshausenstr 40-60, D-2300 Kiel 1 (Contact: Professor Dr Karl Frey, Managing Director; Dr Thorsten Kapune, Head of Administration Department)

The Institute for Science Education (IPN) at the University of Kiel was founded in 1966 as a supraregional research institute. Approximately 40 scientists and 40 technical staff members work at the institute. The IPN is comprised of the following departments: Biology Education, Chemistry Education, Physics Education, Educational Science, Educational and Psychological Methodology, and Administration and General Services. An interdisciplinary approach is used when dealing with the field of science and technology teaching. The Institute's main activities include: basic research in science teaching; development of curricula for the teaching of science in schools; development of processes for the testing and evaluation of curricula/syllabi; information and documentation in the field of science education; and promotion of international co-operation in science teaching research. The IPN publishes several books and reports on its work in various fields.

Institut für den Wissenschaftlichen Film, Nonnenstieg 12, 3400 Göttingen

The Institut für den Wissenschaftlichen Film (IWF) is the central institution in West Germany dealing with the production, publication and distribution of scientific films, of three main types: research films in co-operation with scientists; films for higher education in collaboration with university teachers; and films for documentation.

Internationales Zentralinstitut für das Jugend- und Bildungsfernsehen, Rundfunkplatz 1, D-8000 Munich 2

*Intertip AG Zürich, Munich Branch, Josephspitalstr 15, D-8 Munich

Typing and spelling courses have been published for 4 to 8 and 8 to 12-year-olds (by Correll, called 'Tipsi' and 'Colortip' respectively), using a teaching typewriter with key-locking device, colour code and other features to facilitate learning and reduce errors.

*Pädagogisches Zentrum, 1 Berlin 31, Uhlandstrasse 96-97 (Contact: Mrs H B Bassen, Librarian)

Literature for all kinds of programmed instruction and CAI; German language teaching programmes. Materials produced include *Deutschsprachige Lehrprogramme* (1975), 7th edition. Services offered: teacher counselling on programmed instruction and CAI.

Professor Dr Schmid, D-2390 Flensburg, Am Burgfried 10

Cybernetics analysis of language; information psychological analysis of learning and language; simulation of learning phases.

Unesco Institute for Education, Feldbrunnenstrasse 58, D-2000 Hamburg 13 (Contact: The Director)
See International Centres of Activity

Zentralstelle für Programmierten Unterricht und Computer im Unterricht (The Central Organization for Programmed Learning and the Computer in Education), Schertlinstrasse 7, 8900 Augsburg (Contact: Dr Karl-August Keil)

The Central Organization was founded in 1968. It is a Government Institute and is under the control of the Bavarian Ministry of Education and Culture. Its main task is the dissemination of programmed learning and the support of the use of the computer in schools. Regional activities are co-ordinated and the use of programmed education is evaluated. In the main the supporters of the project are working teachers, particularly teachers of mathematics and physics. An important project for the support of computer use in schools was undertaken in the period from 1971 to 1977. The main activities of the Centre are: the support of evaluation processes in the development of programmed learning school books; the collection of information about programmed learning and the use of the computer in education and the dissemination of information through conferences and the publications programme; the promotion of interaction between scientific and educational praxis; the support of government agencies through co-operation with various government committees in a consulting capacity; the development of programmes; research in the field of education of lesser importance is undertaken. Support for teacher training is given in both fields and the Centre also gives advice to designers of programmes and to schools on the acquisition and use of computers. It runs a programme exchange system. The Centre publishes lists of accepted PL textbooks and computer programs, bibliographies, and working documents on the introduction and use of the computer, and prints programmed learning materials. It also publishes a journal called *BIIS* for teachers.

GHANA

University of Cape Coast, Institute for Educational Planning and Administration, Cape Coast (Contact: The Acting Director)

The Institute was established in August 1975 as a semi-autonomous Unit within the Faculty of Education, University of Cape Coast, on the basis of a joint agreement between the Government of Ghana and Unesco/UNDP for two-and-a-half years. It was part of the agreement that after that period full responsibility for the project would be transferred to the University of Cape Coast. By February 1978 Unesco support for IEPA project had come to an end, and the Institute is now supported by the Ghana Government. The objectives of the Institute include: the development of in-service training programmes for educational planners, administrators, curriculum planners and evaluators, guidance counsellors, inspectors of schools, and financial administrators; the carrying out of research in education and administration; the continuous evaluation of in-service training activities, and the establishment and maintenance of effective communication with the Training Division of the Ghana Education Service. The Institute also runs a Master's degree programme in Educational Administration on behalf of the Faculty of Education.

*Curriculum Research and Development Division, Ghana Education Service, PO Box 2739, Accra (Contact: The Director)

The Curriculum Research and Development Division (CRDD) is one of the Divisions within the Ghana Education Service. It is concerned with reviewing and revising curricular offerings at all levels of pre-university education. It develops and implements new syllabuses and participates in providing in-service training for teachers. The CRDD operates by subject areas whereby language, mathematics, science, environmental (social) studies and cultural studies materials are developed by subject panels at workshops and meetings. Other sections within the Division are concerned with guidance and counselling, measurement and evaluation and audiovisual aids.

Ghana National Audio-Visual Aids Centre, Information Services Department, PO Box 745, Accra (Contact: Mr R E Nyatepe-Coo, Chief Technical Officer, Audio Visual Aids)

The Ghana National Audio-Visual Aids Centre is charged with the production of projected and non-projected aids for various ministries, departments, institutions and other organizations. The Centre produces mainly slides, filmstrips, posters, charts, handbills, book-covers, flip-charts and illustrations. It also runs courses in AV aids techniques and the handling of equipment.

GUATEMALA

*Federation Guatemalteca de Escuelas Radiofoñicas – FGER (Guatemalan Federation of Radio Schools), 8a Calle 11-13, Zona 1, Oficina 303

The aim of FGER is to develop basic education, community development and primary level education in rural and poor urban areas, using radio programmes supported by trained local tutors.

*Program de Educación Basica Rural (Programme of Basic Rural Education), 1a Av No 8-53, Zona 1, Guatemala City (Contact: Mario Dardóu, Director)

Special Adult Literacy Programme is directed toward 'campesinos' to assist them in improving their systems of agricultural production and educate them to solve their basic everyday problems, using innovative, low-cost educational technology.

*Programa de Educación de Adultos por Correspondencia PEAC, 3a Ave No 1-28, Zona 1, 5° piso, Guatemala, CA (Contact: Professor Napoleon Orozco Franco, Jefe Tecnico y Administrativo)

Produces correspondence courses for adults who have not had the chance to study the normal school curriculum at the appropriate time. The materials are almost entirely printed and consist of pamphlets, self-study texts, evaluation and self-evaluation tests and control documents which the student sends back to the organization.

*Radio MAM TGMN, Cabrican, Quezaltenango, CA (Contact: Herminio Perez Lopez)

Broadcasts educational radio to teach rural development. These broadcasts are supported by group meetings with trained organizers in 'radio clubs'. Other programmes aim at cultural and vocational training of rural workers.

HAITI

*Projecto de Radio Escolar y Educativa, Damien, Port-au-Prince (Contact: J Philippe)

Broadcasts educational radio, for use both in school and by out-of-school groups, which reaches 80 per cent of the country. Programmes include citizenship, vocational programmes, elementary school curriculum and foreign languages.

HONG KONG

The Chinese University of Hong Kong, Senate Committee on Instructional Development, Shatin, NT (Contact: Dr R F Turner-Smith, Instructional Development Officer)

The Committee is responsible for promoting the improvement of teaching and learning within the University and overseeing the operation of the University Instructional Media Services (UIMS). Teaching and learning are promoted through an Office of Instructional Development. UIMS is established to provide all AV hardware and software services on campus. Services offered include consultation; small grants for staff projects in instructional areas; organization of seminars and workshops on instructional topics; provision of resource materials on topics in higher education; provision and maintenance of all AV hardware; software production facilities including photography, graphics and television.

Hong Kong Polytechnic, Education Technology Unit, Hung Hom (Contact: B D Hutchinson, Co-ordinator, Education Technology)

The Unit has a general brief 'to improve the effectiveness of the teaching/learning process in the Polytechnic' and to this end it concentrates on the following four functions: *Teaching/learning methodology:* in-service training courses in teaching methodology are available for full- and part-time members of the Polytechnic staff. Seminars and workshops on specific topics are held to inform staff of relevant new developments and techniques. The Unit also offers courses and workshops to organizations outside the Polytechnic. It operates a Study Skills course for students. *Provision of audiovisual equipment and software in the Polytechnic:* the Unit is responsible for providing hardware and software to all courses within the Polytechnic. *Instructional development services:* the Unit provides the advice and assistance with the selection, production and use of instructional media and equipment. *Programme development:* the Unit's Programme Development Officers are associated with the Polytechnic's Divisions, Institutes and Departments with the role to actively stimulate and assist in the production of teaching/learning packages and PSI systems.

HUNGARY

*****Attila Jozsef University,** 6701 Szeged, Dugonics tor 13, PO Box 393

BME Tanárképzo és Pédagógiai Intézet (Technical University of Budapest, Institute for Teacher Training and Education), H-1111, Budapest, Egri Ju 1/Eép III em (Contacts: Professor Dr J Fekete, Dr E Biszterszky, Dr F F Gyaraki)

The Institute consists of two departments (Psychology and Education) and the Research Group for Engineer Education. The main task of the Institute is teacher training for technical, secondary and apprentice schools. In addition to this the Institute takes part in psychological and educational research. The main research projects in which the Institute is interested are: special problems of ergonomics, and curricular and methodological problems of technical education at secondary, college, and university levels. Concerning the latter it also deals with investigations into educational and instructional technological problems.

*****Eötvös Loránd Tudomanyegyetem, Department of Education,** Pesti Bu 1, Budapest (Head: Professor Sándor Nagy) (Contact: Ivan Falus)

The Department consists of 13 lecturers; two professors, five senior lecturers, four lecturers and two assistants, and a special research unit in the field of programmed learning, teaching process and teacher training. The research activity covers: programmed learning, individualized instruction, theory of teaching, microteaching. The Department provides a diploma in education and special courses in educational technology, theory of instruction, research methods in education, etc. On average, six applicants per year receive their PhD in the field of educational technology at the Department. The Department is the co-ordinating body of research on teaching, covering the whole area of educational technology in Hungary.

*****Felsöoktatási Pedágogiai Kutatokózpönt (Research Centre for Pedagogy of Higher Education),** 1431 Budapest, Rigó utca 16

The Centre is directly supervised by the Ministry of Education. Organizational division: Department of Theory of Higher Educational Institutes' Organization, Department of Psychology and Sociology, Department of Pedagogy, Department of Information and Organization, Finance Office. Scientific research work is carried on, organized and co-ordinated in the field of higher education, and the results are issued by the Centre. Volumes of studies and monographs, accounts on research work, conference proceedings, informational issues, and bibliographies are produced. Publications include the publication of results attained in the field of research, methodological counselling, organization, documentation, reference for experts of the Centre and for institutes in Hungary and abroad, associated with or related to the Centre, and for institutes of higher education.

*International Computer Education and Information Centre, H-1502, Budapest 112 POB 146 (Contact: Dr Gregorits Ferenc, Head of Section)

The International Computer Education and Information Centre (SZAMOK) provides education, application and information services. Professional qualification courses and refresher seminars are run for Hungarian and foreign participants. The Centre provides for practical training by granting access to up-to-date computing facilities. The development of software packages supporting the education and the application of computers as well as the publication of technical books and the editing of journals are also important activities of SZAMOK. The Institution maintains a computerized library information and retrieval system, covering several thousands of books and periodicals in the field of computing.

*MüM Szakoktatási és Továbbképzési Intézet (Centre Supplying Vocational Institutes with Training Aids), 1087 Budapest VIII, Berszenyi u 6 (Contact: Létási István, Director)

Preparing subject-matter instruction for the training and development of skilled workers; preparing audiovisual aids and testing applications of such aids and technologies in the training and development process; carrying on research work on pedagogical problems; carrying on research work in the field of adult education; cyclical development of directors and instructors of vocational training schools.

*National Centre for Educational Technology (OOK), Veszprém, Schönherz Z u 2-4, 8200, and **Department for International Relations,** 1502 Budapest, Pf 260 (Contact: F Genzwein, General Director)

OOK has teams of specialists in educational systems design, programmed instruction, media development, microteaching, etc. Its main areas of concentration at present are the reform of elementary and secondary education being introduced in Hungary and the development of pre-service and in-service teacher training in educational technology. To these purposes the Centre is developing multi-media and self-instructional packages including AV media. The Centre works in conjunction with a network of regional centres throughout the country helping in this way locally based pre- and in-service training. There is also a programme of research in various aspects of educational technology and a regular programme of courses, both long- and short-term, for basic and specialist training alike. The establishment of the National Centre for Educational Technology has been aided by a Unesco/UNDP project of technical co-operation. Several of the

Centre's staff have been on fellowships and study tours abroad, and several international experts have spent periods of time at the Centre assisting with the development of its various projects.

Országos Pedagógiai Intézet (National Institute for Education), 1071 Budapest Gorkij fasor 17-21 (Contacts: Dr A Arato; Dr Z Báthory)

The National Institute for Education (OPI) works in close co-operation with the OOK. Both are governmental organizations directed by the same ministry. Responsibility is divided so that the OPI is more responsible for basic research in curriculum development and the foundation of educational technology in curricula, whilst the OOK is more concerned with the development and implementation of educational technology.

*Pedagogical Institute for Vocational Training, Budapest IX, Könyves K48-52

SZAMOK, *see* International Computer Education and Information Center (above)

Tömegkommunikációs Kutatóközpont (Mass Communication Research Centre), Akadémia u 17, 1054 Budapest (Contacts: Dr Tamás Szecskö, Director; Krisztina Hernádi, Secretary)

The Centre is the main Hungarian workshop on communication research. Its main activities include sociological and psychological research on communication; planning and prognosticating the results of mass communications; public opinion research; publication of a professional quarterly, and various other publications on mass communication; and maintaining a documentation and research library on mass communication. Publications which are circulated outside the Centre include *Membrán*, (monograph series), books by Hungarian and foreign authors, occasionally in foreign languages (English, Russian); *Jel-Kép*, a professional quarterly on mass communication (occasionally with a special number in English); and *Tanulmányok, Beszámolók, Jelentések* (Studies, Accounts, Reports) – the publication of the results of research work carried out in the Institute.

INDIA

Institutions of further and higher education

Himachal Pradesh University, School of Education, Simla 171005 (Contacts: Dr S P Ruhela, Head; Dr Anand Bhushan)

The School conducts Bachelor, Master and Post-master courses in education. In collaboration with the Correspondence Wing of this University, instructional material is being prepared for the use of regular and correspondence students. The School also offers guidance services to teachers, and to administrators and researchers in education.

Central Institute of English and Foreign Languages, Hyderabad 500 007 (Contact: Head, Department of Materials Production)

The Central Institute of English and Foreign Languages (CIEFL) is a deemed university committed to the study of English and foreign languages, the organization of research, the training of teachers, and the production of teaching materials. The Institute runs a number of post-MA courses which include research degrees. Educational technology forms an important part of its activities and is used for various purposes. The Institute's Department of Materials Production prepares teaching materials for schools, colleges and other needs, organizes courses and guides scholars in materials including programmed materials production, in the design of curricula for various purposes and conducts short courses/seminars from time to time. The Institute has been rendering consultancy services to various educational institutions and other bodies on the production of materials, the design of syllabuses and the use of educational technology for various purposes in the country.

Maharaja Sayajirao University of Baroda, Centre of Advanced Study in Education, Faculty of Education and Psychology, Lokmanya Tilak Road, Baroda 2 (Contact: M S Yadav, Professor)

Open School, *see under Other organizations*

South Gujarat University, Department of Education, University Campus, Surat-395 007 (Contacts: Dr G B Shah, Professor and Head of Department; Dr Motilal Sharma)

As one of the teaching departments of the University, the Department has been functioning for the last ten years. Major areas of concentration include educational technology; non-formal education, adult education and continuing education. The Department provides specialization in educational technology at MEd level. Research is conducted both at MEd and PhD level, and specialization in educational technology is provided at both levels. Institutional projects are undertaken from time to time, eg *Microteaching Project*, in collaboration with Lancaster University (UK) (Director of the Project – Dr G B Shah); and *Microteaching Without Hardware*, undertaken with financial support from Unesco (Director of the Project – Dr G B Shah). The following two projects are being conducted at present: *Radiovision Project*, financially supported by the Indian Space Research Organization (Principal Investigator – Dr Motilal Sharma); and *Systems Approach to Non-formal Education*, with financial support from NCERT, New Delhi (Principal Investigator – Dr Motilal Sharma). The Department has a Resource Unit of Programmed Learning Materials and Psychological Tests which is referred to by scholars from different institutions. An Educational Technology Resources Centre is being developed, to provide consultancy to different institutions in the design and implementation of training programmes and the use of instructional materials. Research consultancy is provided at individual and group level through seminars and personal contacts.

Dr G B Shah is now the President of the Indian Association for Educational Technology.

Other organizations

*The Association for Theological Extension Education, 13 Hutchins Road, Cooke Town, Bangalore 560 005 (Contact: The Director)

The Association gives training in theology and practical Christian subjects using programmed texts supported by tutorials in 30 centres.

Central Board of Secondary Education, *see* Open School (below)

Central Institute of English and Foreign Languages, *see under Institutions of further and higher education*

*Centre for Development of Instructional Technology (CENDIT), CLL

Safdarjung Development Area Community Centre, New Delhi 110016

Offers training in the production and use of film and video materials for education/training.

Directorate of Adult Education, Ministry of Education and Social Welfare, 34 Community Centre, Basant Lok, Vasant Vihar, New Delhi 110057 (Contact: The Director)

The Directorate serves as a National Resource Centre for India in matters relating to adult education. It assists in the conceptualization, formulation, co-ordination and evaluation of the National Adult Education Programme initiated by the Government of India. The main functions of the Directorate are: training and orientation of key personnel in adult education at various levels; evolving new approaches and methodologies of curriculum formulation for different categories of learner; production of illustrative learning/teaching materials; data collection and evaluation of adult education programme; initiating experiments and innovative efforts; conducting and stimulating research, surveys and studies; promoting adult education through dissemination of information, documentation and clearinghouse services; bringing out a variety of publications for use of planners, administration, research workers, organizers, teachers and learners (details of publications available on request) and to act as a forum for pooling of experiences and exchange of ideas. The activities are carried out through the following Units set up in the Directorate: Literacy Materials and Methods; Innovative and Promotional Materials, Publications and Dissemination; Training of Personnel and Population Education; Development Activities; Urban Adult Education Programmes; Liaison with Media and Public Relations; Follow-up Programmes, Prize Competition, Case Studies and Departmental Reports, Monitoring, Data Processing and EValuation Studies; Planning Co-ordination, Administration and Common Technical Facilities.

There are 14 State Resource Centres for Adult Education, as follows:

State Resource Centre for Adult Education
Teachers Training College
Gujarat Widyapeeth
Ashram Road, Ahmedabad (Gujarat)
(Contact: Shri Purshotam Bhai A Patel, Principal)

State Resource Centre for Adult Education
Department of Adult Continuing Education
Osmania University, Hyderabad (Andhra Pradesh)
(Contact: Shri Iswara Reddy, Director)

State Resource Centre for Adult Education
DEEPAYATEN
138-D, New Shrikrishanpuri
Patna-800001 (Bihar)
(Contact: Shri M P Srivastava, Director)

State Resource Centre for Adult Education
c/o Post-Graduate Department of Education
Kashmir University, 48 Naseem Bagh Campus
Hazratbal, Srinagar-190006 (Jammu & Kashmir)
(Contact: Dr Salamatullah, Honorary Director)

State Resource Centre
c/o Kerala Adult Non-formal Education for Development (KANFED)
Sakshartha Bhavan, Trivandrum-69014 (Kerala)
(Contact: Shri P N Panicker, Honorary Director)

State Resource Centre for Non-formal Education
Education Department
c/o Office of DPI (Haryana)
Ferozi Building, Sector 17
Chandigarh (Haryana)
(Contact: Dr (Miss) Swaran Agtish, HESI, Director)

State Resource Centre for Adult Education
Indian Institute of Education
128/2 Karve Road, Kothrud
Pune-411029 (Maharashtra)
(Contact: Dr (Mrs) Chitra Naik)

State Resource Centre
Karnataka State Adult Education Council
PO Box No 2 Krishnamurthypuram
Mysore-570004 (Karnataka)
(Contact: Shri M B Prakash, Director)

State Resource Centre for Adult Education
Utkal Navjeevan Mandal
PO Angul, Dhenkanal (Orissa)
(Contact: Shri B B Mohanty, Director)

Regional Resource Centre for Adult Education
c/o Centre for Adult and Continuing Education
Punjab University
Chandigarh (Punjab)
(Contact: Shri K L Zakir, Co-ordinator)

State Resource Centre for Adult Education
38 Jobner Bagh
Jaipur-6 (Rajasthan)
(Contact: Shri Ramesh Thanvi, Director)

State Resource Centre for Non-formal Education
TN Board of Continuing Education
18 Adams Road, Chepauk
ASI Building, Madras-600005 (Tamil Nadu)
(Contact: Dr R Gomez, Director)

State Resource Centre for Adult Education
Literacy House
PO Alambagh Kanpur Road
Lucknow (Uttar Pradesh)
(Contact: Shri B S Singh, Director)

State Resource Centre for Adult Education
c/o Bengal Social Service League
1/6 Raja Dinendra Street
Calcutta-700009 (West Bengal)
(Contact: Shri S N Maitra, Honorary Director)

ICA (International Co-operative Alliance for Asia), Regional Office, New Delhi, *see* CEMAS *under International Centres of Activity*

ISOD – International Society for Organization Development, 12K Dubash Marg, Fort Bombay, *see under International Centres of Activity*

Indian Association for Educational Technology, *see* South Gujarat University, c/o Dr G B Shah

*Indian Association for Programmed Learning and Educational Innovations, c/o National Council of Educational Research and Training, Sri Aurobindo, Marg, New Delhi 110016

The Language Development Project (LDP), Education Department, Municipal Corporation of Greater Bombay, Gilder Tank Building, Dr Bhadkamkar Marg, Grant Road, Bombay 400 007 (Contact: Mrs Shalini Shantikumar Rele, Superintendent, Language Development Project)

The language situation in Bombay is very complex as almost all the principal languages in the country are spoken there. The Municipal Corporation of Bombay therefore gives instruction in ten languages in its schools from grade I to grade VII. Moreover, children attending Corporation schools come from the lower strata of society and they already suffer from linguistic handicap; the language development programme is therefore very necessary for them. The Language Development Project came into existence with the financial assistance of the Ford Foundation in its initial five years, and it is now funded by the Municipal Corporation of Greater Bombay.

The Project aims at improving and developing the standard of language teaching and learning in municipal schools. Its functions are: (1) organization of in-service teacher training programmes; (2) preparation of instructional materials for teachers and pupils (including correspondence materials); (3) research and evaluation in the field of language teaching and learning; (4) development of curriculum resources centre for teachers. These functions are carried out in five major language areas – English, Marathi, Hindi, Gujarati and Urdu. Material produced and published can be broadly categorized as: (i) diagnostic tests for teachers of English (published); (ii) handbooks for teachers; (iii) workbooks for pupils; (iv) collections of short stories, nursery rhymes, dramas, poems (graded); (v) glossaries of words; (vi) radio broadcast lessons (relayed); (vii) booklets on various aspects of language eg grammar, spelling, clusters, etc.

National Council of Educational Research and Training (NCERT), Sri Aurobindo Marg, New Delhi 110016 (Contact: Dr S K Mitra, Director)

1. Department of Educational Psychology and Foundations of Education (NLERT)

The Department is engaged in research, development and training in programmed learning and educational technology. It organizes short training courses in programmed learning and educational technology every year. It also organizes workshops aimed at developing learning materials for correspondence instruction, multi-media packages, scripts for instructional television programmes, as well as lessons for educational broadcasts. It is also engaged in developing multi-media packages for primary and secondary education and also for non-formal education in rural areas.

2. Centre for Educational Technology (Contact: Professor Mrs Vijaya Mulay, Principal)

The Government of India set up the Centre for Educational Technology (CET) in 1973 as a constituent unit of the National Council of Educational

Research and Training (NCERT) to promote the use of educational technology for improving the quality and reach of education. UNDP and Unesco have also assisted in the growth and development of the Centre. It has an Academic Wing and a Technical Wing. The former has five units: Systems Design and Innovation, Production, Training, Evaluation and Co-ordination. The Technical Wing manages the technical areas and provides engineering services. At present the major activities of the Centre are *Systems design and innovations:* designing effective alternative systems for maximizing educational gains and reducing costs and wastage in education; *Production:* prototypes of audiovisual and print materials for use in formal and non-formal systems of education; multi-media packages using mass-media for dissemination of information at less unit cost and teaching a large audience; *Training:* for developing competence in the design and management of new systems using educational technology, of scriptwriters for educational television and radio, of writers of self-instructional materials, and of teacher educators in educational technology; *Research and evaluation:* studies of systems, innovations, methods and materials developed by CET or by other agencies; *Resource Centre:* setting up software and hardware banks and making materials/facilities available to outside agencies for preparing instructional materials; *Consultancy and extension:* consultancy to State Educational Technology Cells, Universities, Training Colleges in matters of educational technology (co-ordination of activities of the State ET Cells), exchange of materials and personnel, documentation, and serving as a clearinghouse of information. Other services provided include orientation and training programmes in educational technology; studio facilities to individuals and institutions for preparing educational films (editing, sound recording and animation); consultancy in setting up studios and the purchase of suitable equipment, production of materials, in evaluation and research designs, etc. The Centre has produced a large number of materials and training manuals, and has published reports and case studies relating to its various activities.

Open School (Central Board of Secondary Education), H-24, Green Park Extension, New Delhi 110016 (Contact: Dr O S Dewal, Director)

The Central Board of Secondary Education set up the Open School in 1979 in New Delhi to cater to the educational needs of housewives, employed adults, drop-outs and out-of-school learners specially of the disadvantaged sections of the society. The Open School designs its own syllabi, prepares its own instructional material, most of it in print but some of it on audiocassettes. It offers a very flexible scheme of examination. A student can take all the subjects in one year or over a period of five years and the examinations are held twice a year. The Open School also prepares project or preparatory material for weak students.

The school offers secondary and senior certificate courses, and in the second phase the school will offer technical, vocational and life enrichment courses. The school has a Central Unit, Educational Technology and Graphic Unit, and Course Production and Course Writing units. Products already include preparatory or bridge instructional material in Hindi, English, social sciences, science and mathematics, instructional material for the secondary level course in subjects taught in Open School, and a criterion-referenced test.

The Open School has also published a book *Writing for Distance Teaching* and a *Manual for Editors.*

INDONESIA

*Centre for Communication Technology for Education and Culture, Ministry of Education and Culture, J1 Cenderawasih, Ciputat, Iromolpos 7/KBYCP, Jakarta Selatan (Contact: Yusufhadi Miarso)

The Office of Educational and Cultural Research and Development is responsible for the initiation and development of a project to find ways of using media for delivery of instruction; in particular modules and radio for open junior high school, radio for in-service training for primary school teachers and radio and cassettes for non-formal education.

*Centre for Curriculum and Educational and Cultural Facilities Development, Jalan Jenderal Sudirman, PO Box 297 Kebayoran, Jakarta (Contact: Dr Soedijarto, MA)

This Centre is one of the four centres of the Office of Educational and Cultural Research and Development (known as the BP3K), a unit of the Ministry of Education and Culture. Its main functions are: to develop a model of a comprehensive curriculum system for primary-secondary schools through a series of research and development activities conducted at pilot schools; to standardize the national curricula for primary school, junior and senior secondary schools (both general and vocational), and teacher training school for primary school teachers (1974-77); to develop prototype science kits; to develop models of formative and summative evaluation using criterion-referenced tests; to conduct experiments on mastery learning strategy; to develop guidance and counselling programmes to support the implementation of curriculum innovation; and to develop skill education programmes as a part of general education. The main services provided by this Centre are as follows: giving consultancy, especially to other units of the Ministry, concerning the development, implementation and evaluation of the curricula; giving assistance to the other units of the Ministry of Education and Culture in monitoring the implementation of the curriculum; conducting in-service training to promote the professional competence of personnel from other units of the Ministry in implementing the curriculum; conducting seminars and workshops, in the framework of disseminating innovative concepts in education; and conducting pre-investment studies/ research as an input for the other units of the Ministry for the planning of their programmes or projects. Publications include a number of self-instructional materials and science kits for schools, and a set of teachers' packages on counselling and on remedial and enrichment programmes; sets of guidelines on educational technology techniques.

*Institute of Teacher Training and Education of Ujung Pandang, Kampus IKIP Gunungsari Baru, Ujung Pandang (Contact: Dr Abdul Karim, Rector, IKIP Ujung Pandang)

IKIP Ujung Pandang was founded in 1965. It is particularly concerned with higher education preparing educational experts and producing high school teachers. IKIP is a centre for social research and social service. It also functions as a flexible learning resource centre and a place where theories and practical activities can be related.

*Project IMPACT (PAMONG), Solo, Central Java.

Project IMPACT arose out of a search for an economical and effective delivery system for mass primary education. IMPACT is an acronym for Instructional Management by Parents, Community and Teachers. The

Project was designed and initiated by the Regional Centre for Educational Innovation and Technology (INNOTECH), one of the educational centres of the Southeast Asian Ministers of Education Organization (SEAMEO) composed of eight Southeast Asian countries. The main characteristics of the project are: (1) the teacher acts as 'instructional supervisor', providing direction and organization in the use of a variety of learning resources; (2) community members with particular skills are enlisted to provide specialist instruction, and older students help in conducting specific courses, tutorials and remedial instruction; (3) teacher aides assist in the administration of the Community Learning Centre; (4) education is modular, on the basis of one module per (average) two weeks' learning time. Each module has been systematically designed. Some modules are tied to group work, instructional radio programmes etc.

*Staya Wacana Christian University, The Center for the Advancement of Teaching (CAT), JI Diponegoro 54-58, Salatiga, Jawa Tengah (Contact: Dr Willi Toisuta, Director)

CAT was set up at Satya Wacana early in 1976 with the simple goal, 'to improve the quality of the teaching-learning process'. The Centre undertakes the following functions: regular discussions, seminars, workshops and lectures on instructional methods including microteaching demonstrations; informal and formal consultations about teaching methods and the use of AV aids to both students and lecturers; periodic demonstrations of special teaching methods (eg role play, simulation, team teaching, slides and films or other effective means of communication) and of educational hardware. Also demonstrations of the application of instructional technology by using the overhead projector, CCTV, slide-tapes, etc; the preparation of a programme for the Diploma of Higher Education, which aims to improve professional competence in the system of instruction for lecturing staff; regular research activities among Satya Wacana students and lecturers on teaching and teaching-learning processes. The Centre is a place for teachers to meet as professionals (Teachers' Centre) in an effort to achieve co-operation between Satya Wacana and the Board of the Indonesian Teachers' Union, and is also a source of materials for the University's distance learning system programme. The Centre gives supporting facilities in the form of assistance or production of audiovisual aids for teaching, such as graphics, photographs, slides, and audio tutorial programmes for commercial use; some instructional kits are also produced. The Centre also has an information service, and conducts research into teaching and learning.

IRAN

No communications have been received from contacts in Iran since the 1978/79 edition.

IRAQ

The Arab Centre for Audience Research (ACAR), PO Box 27007, Mansour, Baghdad (Contact: Dr Nawaf Adwar, Director General)

ACAR was established in 1979 within the Arab States Broadcasting Union (ASBU). Its functions are to carry out studies and research concerning the Arab radio and television audience. It also aims at developing these fields so as to arrive at a specific scientific method in accordance with the needs of

Arab radio and TV services; the Centre undertakes the training of staff to carry out such studies and research for the purpose of improving and developing radio and TV programmes.

ISRAEL

Centre for Educational Technology, 16 Klausner Street, Tel Aviv (Contact: Dr Yona Peless, Director General)

The Centre for Educational Technology is a non-profit organization founded by the Rothschild Foundation in 1971. The Centre is active in a number of fields in the domain of education and instruction in Israel. The main areas are the introduction of the computer as an effective tool in the improvement of the teaching process, individualized instruction in the primary grades, fostering awareness of the use of media in the educational system and the development of vocational courses according to the needs of Israel's economy and armed forces. Its main activities include: TOAM System – Computer Assisted Drill and Practice; Teaching Computer Science in High Schools; Individualized Instruction in the Primary Grades; Environmental Safety Programme for Elementary Schools; Media Now – Introducing Media (Television, Radio, Press, Photography) into the Teaching-Learning Process; Multi-Media Vocational Courses (Electronics, Electricity, Accounting, Technical Drawing, etc); Production of Music Programmes and Instructional Programmes (Audio, Video and Film); and work for the Technological Institute for the Blind. The Centre also produces textbooks and AV materials.

*Department of Education in Technology and Science, Technion, Israel Institute of Technology, Haifa (Contact: Professor Arye Perlberg)

*1. The Laboratory for Research and Development in Teaching and Learning

The Laboratory undertakes research and development projects in teaching, training and learning, with special emphasis on pre- and in-service teacher education. Special attention is paid to innovative methods in teacher training. The Laboratory is also associated with research projects in other institutes and undertakes a range of evaluatory studies in various aspects of teacher training.

*2. Research and Development Center for Education in Technology and Science and for Vocational Training

Its activities include the development and evaluation of curricula for students of a range of technical subjects.

Haifa University, *see* Institute of Science Education (below)

Institute for Teaching Aids, 43 Brodetsky Street, PO Box 17168, Tel Aviv

Design of teaching aids in technological education; production of hardware and software, books.

The Institute of Science Education and the Improvement of Teaching, Haifa University, School of Education of the Kibbutz Movement, Oranim, PO Kiryat Tivon (Contacts: Dr Chaim Hadomi, Director; Dr Eliezer Manneberg, Programme Chairman)

The general aid of the Educational Media and Technology Programme is to bring the substance of instructional media and technology to bear meaningfully on issues of educational practice. The activities of the programme range from the conceptualization and clarification of instructional problems to the creation of methods and frameworks for their solution. Particular emphasis is given in the programme to the developing relationship between the humanistic approach in open education and the instructional application of findings from the behavioural science disciplines and technology. The programme is organized on the basis of task analysis of the roles and functions being carried out by educational practitioners. Using this as a basis, courses and instructional modules have been developed through a clarification of the skills, knowledge, and attitudes essential to success as school media specialists, instructional developers and elementary and high school teachers. The programme contains a core of media experiences in the form of formal courses and open workshops that are shared by all the specialist programmes.

*Instructional Television Center, 14 Klausner Street, Ramat Aviv, Tel-Aviv (Contact: Yaacov Lorberbaum, General Manager)

The Centre produces and broadcasts educational and instructional programmes to the formal and non-formal education system as from the lower pre-school age group up to university level.

Israel Association for Instructional Technology, 12 Zamenhoff Street, Tel Aviv (Contact: Z Tirosh)

Professional association of persons interested in educational technology and its applications (research, production, distribution, implementation). Membership: educationists, researchers, planners, producers, distributors of instructional media (1980: 120 members). It offers: publications (newsletter, semi-annual bulletin, directories); conferences and workshops; competition of teaching and training films (yearly); and information services.

*The Israel Institute of Productivity, 4 Henrietta Szold Street, Tel Aviv (Contact: Dr Chaim Levy, Academic Adviser to the Training Centre)

The Institute's general objective is to 'initiate activities leading to increased productivity and better resource utilization' at all levels, and it provides a large range of courses in all aspects of industrial training.

Ministry of Education and Culture, The Pedagogic Centers, 19 Jaffa Road, Jerusalem 91911 (Contact: Shimon Sharoni, Director)

The Pedagogic Centres comprise a network of 38 regional centres, co-ordinated by the National Centre. The Pedagogic Centres provide media, software and consultancy services to local educational establishments at all levels. An important and developing aspect of their work is the provision of Regional Teachers' Centres, and the development of resource centres within the schools which will take over the servicing of media needs from the Regional Centres.

Government agencies

Ministry of Education and Culture, Pedagogic Centers, 19 Jaffa Road, Jerusalem

Ministry of Education, The Educational Television Center, 14 Klausner Street, Ramat Aviv

Israel Broadcasting Authority, School Broadcasting Department, Helene Hamalka Street, Jerusalem

Ministry of Labour, Institute for Teaching Aids, 43 Brodetsky Street, Ramat Aviv

Public and semi-public institutions

Center for Educational Technology, 16 Klausner Street, Ramat Aviv

University departments

Department for Audiovisual and Communications Media in Education (DACME), Hebrew University, Mount Scopus, Jerusalem

Tel-Aviv University, Ramat Aviv, Tel-Aviv

*1. MATAL – The Israeli Science Teaching Center for Kindergarten and Elementary Schools, The School of Education (Contact: Professor David Chen)

The Centre is engaged in research and development of curricular materials for grades 5 to 13. It is affiliated with the School of Education, Tel Aviv University and has operated since 1970. The Centre is authorized by the Ministry of Education and is engaged in dissemination of the programmes in the system. Activities include (1) development of curricular materials for science teaching grades X to VI (teachers' guides, students' materials, television programmes, teaching aids); (2) teacher training (in-service) – planning, learning materials, implementation; (3) evaluation: formative and summative evaluation, item back and diagnostic tests; and (4) research: cognitive research, curriculum research, and classroom studies.

*2. NILI – The Individualized Instruction Project, School of Education (Contact: Professor David Chen)

Established in 1972, the Project is a joint venture of Tel-Aviv University, the Ministry of Education, the Educational Technology Center, and the Municipality of Yavne. The Project is based on a systems approach and is aimed at optimization of the learning system at the classroom level. The empirical experiment consists of six experimental and 200 affiliated schools.

ITALY

ANCIFAP (National Association of the IRI Centres for Vocational Training and Specialization), Piazza della Repubblica 59, 00185 Rome

ANCIFAP designs, implements and evaluates vocational training programmes for organizations and companies in Italy and abroad. Training activities are carried out in the following fields: electrical, electronic, telephone, mechanical, motorcar, steel, shipyards, aeronautics, textiles, mining services. There are four main areas of specialization: qualification courses for workmen, training activities for workmen already in employment, supervisory and technician training, and instructor training. The Association works through large inter-company centres, using more local arrangements for smaller programmes. It co-operates in projects and the development of programmes with study and research agencies, and also carries out studies, researches and assistance activities in the field of training needs and supplying of software, also in situations of socioeconomic or industrial development.

ANCIFAP receives subsidies from central and local government funds.

Professor E Arcalni, Via Madesimo 22, I 00135 Rome

Language teaching in universities and by radio; production of audio courses; research in software.

Biblioteca di Documentazione Pedagogica (formerly **Centro Didattico Nazionale di Studi e Documentazione (National Centre for Educational Research and Documentation),** Palazzo Gerini, Via Buonarroti 10, Florence

The former Centre offered bibliographies and documentation services, and was connected with documentation centres in Geneva, Strasbourg, Paris and Brussels. Special attention was given to sections on schoolbooks, pedagogical museums, children's and juvenile literature. It had an IBM system for automatic documentation. The organization is now being restructured, however, and there may well be changes.

*Centro Europeo Dell' Educazione di Villa Falconieri (European Centre for Education at Villa Falconieri), Frascati, nr Rome (Contact: Professor Mario Fierli, Via Vascello 25, Rome)

Situated in a magnificent Renaissance villa in a large park on the hills near Rome, the Centre has good educational technology equipment and offers residential facilities for in-service courses, seminars, etc for up to 40 people including foreigners. For official arrangements write to: Ufficio Studi e Programmazione, Ministero PI, Via Carcani 61, Rome.

*Centro Nazionale Italiano Tecnologie Educative – CNITE (The Italian National Centre for Educational Technology) (Contact: Professor Mauro Laeng)

The Centre promotes studies and research, organizes courses and seminars, produces prototypes of multi-media courses (of Italian, maths, economics, finance and other subjects) on a non-profit basis. It is linked with Unesco, the Council of Europe (Eudised Project), and IEA Association for the Evaluation of Educational Achievement.

*Centro Studi e Applicazioni di Tecnologie Avanzate (The Centre for Study and Application of Advanced Technology), c/o Instituto di Fisica, Universita di Bari (Contact: Professor Aldo Romano)

The Centre promotes studies about educational engineering, computer-assisted and computer-managed instruction, with contributions from an IBM team.

Consiglio Nazionale Delle Ricerche (National Research Council), Istituto per le Tecnologie Didattiche, Via All' Opera Pia 11, 16145, Genoa (Contact: Professor Rinaldo Sanna)

The Institute carries out basic and applied research on educational technology. Results are published in *Internal Reports* and in magazines regarding this field. The aim is to adapt existing methodologies or original ones to actual educational needs in public organizations, such as the Regione Liguria (Health education programme); RAI/TV/Department of School and Education; Adult Education Structure; Project Geodynamics, CNR and others. Educational systems subject to research are CAI; combined TV/book programmes; interactive use of video disc.

*Istituto dell Enciclopedia Italiana, Via Paganica 4, Rome (Contact: Professor Francesco Schino)

Founded by Count Treccani degli Alfieri in the 20s, the Institute is the major editing institute, officially supported by public funds, for the national encyclopaedia and other major books. It has set up an audiovisual section, which produces slides, films and tapes for training programmes and adult education.

*Istituto di Pedagogia, Sezione Audiovisivi (Institute of Education, Audiovisual Section), Via S Francesco 33, Padua (Contacts: Dr L Galliani; Dr M Bernardinis)

The AV Section started operation in a small way in 1968. Since then it has been equipped with a CCTV and a mobile TV unit. It is used both in research on AV language and communication, and in didactic activity with students of AV methodology and didactics. The AV chair is part of the Pedagogic Institute of the University of Padua. Its main activities are didactics and research. *Didactics:* the Institute holds an optional annual course in AV methodology and didactics in which students become acquainted with AV instruments and their pedagogic use. At the end of the course they are able to produce an AV message intended for teaching or for pedagogic debate. *Research:* deals with the image-word relation, examined from different viewpoints. Other researches relate to the possibilities of TV as a medium when applied to vocational teaching, to folk theatre, and to architecture. The Institute produces an annual review, *Studi cinematografici e televisivi.*

*IRI – Istituto per la Ricostruzione Industriale (Institute for Industrial Reconstruction), UCTI – Ufficio per le Co-operazione Tecnica Internazionale (The Office for International Technical Co-operation), Via Torino 98, 00184 Rome (Contacts: Dr Ferdinando Orlandini; Dr Luciano Fanfani)

UCTI operates within the External Relations Department of IRI, as the unit responsible for the Institute's international technical co-operation activities. It was founded in 1962 with the purpose of carrying out training courses in Italy for technical and management staff coming from industrializing countries. Its activities include IRI courses for middle and middle-high managers coming from industrializing countries and courses commissioned and financed by outside agencies. In addition to its courses UCTI provides co-operation in the design, implementation and development of training projects for workers, technicians and management staff in industrializing countries, and assistance to United Nations or other government bodies fellowship holders in organizing individual in-plant training programmes. It has produced a number of materials for use on courses.

ISTUD – Istituto Studi Direzionali, Spa Cso Umberto I, 67, 28049 Stresa (No) (Contact: Dr ssa Fiorella Nahum)

ISTUD is a private post-experience management school, located in Stresa, which has been operating since 1971 at the inter-company level. In structure it is a joint stock company, with 104 members consisting of Italian and multi-national concerns, and industrial associations, including Assolombarda (one of the most active) and Confindustria (the National Federation of Italian Industry) which joined in 1977. It carries out teaching and research in the field of management, and its main services include teaching and research. All ISTUD courses are residential and are held with active teaching methods (case history, business game, role playing, etc). All courses are inter-company. No additional services are provided for participants. It holds a stock of some 200 case studies on industrial company problems, and publishes research reports.

*RAI – Dipartimento delle Transmissioni Scolastiche ed Educative per Adulti, Viale Mazzini 14, Rome (Contact: F Schino)

Università di Roma, P le A Moro, 00185, Rome (Contacts: Enrico Mandolesi, Cesare M Ottavi, Aldo Visalberghi, Graziella Ballanti, Luciana Fontana, Clotilde Pontecorvo, Renzo Titone, Enrico Arcaini)

The largest university in Europe (more than 130,000 students enrolled), it has a centre for AVM and TV named CATTID (Centro per le applicazioni della televisione e delle tecniche d'insegnamento a distanza – The Centre for the application of television and techniques of distance learning).
Experimentations on distance teaching and AVM utilization are carried on by A Visalberghi (Seminar of Educational Sciences, Faculty of Letters and Philosophy), G Ballanti, L Fontana and C Pontecorvo (Chairs of Istituzioni di pedagogia, Faculty of Magistero), E Mandolesi (Institute of Architecture, Faculty of Engineering), and E Arcaini (Chair of English, Faculty of Magistero), Professor Cesare M Ottavi is the Director of CATTID, the Chairman of which is Professor Mandolesi.

*Professor Dr R Titone, Via Ugo Bartolemi 23, I 00136 Rome

Language teaching; teacher training.

IVORY COAST

INADES, Documentation NFE, 08 Boîte Postale 8, Abidjan 08 (Contacts: Philippe Dubin, Training; Nicole Vial, Documentation)

Concerned with research and documentation on educational activities and services pertinent to Africa and the Ivory Coast (economic development, agriculture), and thereby with adult education – including correspondence courses for training and development. Various publications.

JAMAICA

Adult Education Organization of Jamaica, *see* JAMAL Foundation (below)

Educational Broadcasting Service (EBS), Ministry of Education, Multi-Media Centre, 1-3 Caenwood Road, Kingston 5, Jamaica (Contact: Mr C R Smith, Officer-in-Charge)

EBS is responsible for the production of radio and TV programmes in support of curriculum developments and general national objectives, and for the maintenance and operation of studio equipment. It also organizes seminars for teachers on the use of radio/TV and AV aids. Programmes are broadcast via the Jamaica Broadcasting Corporation to schools and other institutions. Materials produced include *Teachers Guides* to programmes; videotapes and audio tapes of programmes; some workbooks and charts.

JAMAL Foundation, 47b South Camp Road, Kingston 4, Jamaica (Contact: Mr Eric Brown, Acting Director)

The JAMAL Foundation was set up in 1974 to tackle the problem of illiteracy amongst an estimated 500,000 persons 15 years and over. Its functions are: to eradicate illiteracy in Jamaica within the shortest period; to improve literacy skills of the adult population of Jamaica; and to develop human resources and enable citizens to participate meaningfully in national development. It runs a series of field operations to recruit teachers and students, and arranges for buildings and mobile units. It is also very involved in teacher training, production of instructional materials, and supervising the adult education programme, as well as conducting evaluation and research. It publishes a monthly newspaper, as well as guides, student readers, etc. The JAMAL Foundation relies heavily on radio transmissions to supplement face-to-face teaching.

JAPAN

University centres

*Aichi University of Education, Centre for Educational Technology, 1 Hirosawa, Igaya-cho, Kariya City, Aichi Prefecture, 448

Activities include research on computer-assisted instruction, educational information retrieval, analysis of teaching behaviour, use of knowledge in education. Publications include *Research Report* Nos 1-26; *Monograph* No 1.

*Akita University, Centre for Educational Technology, Faculty of Education, 1-1 Tegatagakuencho, Akita City, 010

Activities include research on CAI using a microcomputer; analysis of the instruction at the University and the experimental schools by use of CCTV; research on individualized and/or grouped learning by use of teaching machines; research and development of AV materials. Publications include *Center News* and *Research Report on Educational Technology* (annually).

*Chiba University, Centre for Educational Technology, Faculty of Education, 1-33 Yayoi-cho, Chiba-shi

Activities include orientation of student teaching through the use of CCTV; instructional analysis, study of educational materials in TV programmes; and audiovisual education. Services and technical information related to educational technology are available for the staff and students of the Faculty of Education.

*Fukui University, Research and Guidance Centre of Teaching Practice, Faculty of Education, 9-1, 3-chome, Bunkyo, Fukui-shi

Activities include study of instructional processes, development of learning programmes and teaching materials, development of methods of educational evaluation, development of systems for behaviour analysis, educational clinics, teaching practice and in-service training, and collection and arrangement of educational and research materials. *The Research of Educational Technology* Nos 1-3 (1977-79) is also published.

*Fukuoka University of Education, Centre for Educational Technology, 279 Akama, Munakata-machi, Munakata-gun, Fukuoka Prefecture, 811-41

Activities include study of learning theories (information theory approach), systems approach for the processing of learning and instruction, audiovisual education, making of a teaching machine, study of simulation at pre-education level of student-teachers, and the study of instructions analysis. Publications include *Letters of the Centre for Educational Technology of Fukuoka University of Education*, Nos 1-11. Workshops are offered on 16mm movies, educational technology, and electronic data processing.

*Gifu University, Curriculum Research and Development Centre, Faculty of Education, Nagara, Gifu City, 502

Curriculum research includes research concerning objective test structures; analysis of psychological processes in learning and the evaluation of learning; development of teaching-learning materials on physics, general science and mathematics; open field science learning activities; and development of English teaching-learning packages. Educational technology activities include instructional design and analysis by the use of the CBE system, CBE systems computer program development, management of an item library, and production of a range of teaching materials including some for computer-based or computer-assisted instruction.

*Hokkaido University of Education, Centre for Educational Technology, Nishi 13 Minami 22, Chuo-ku, Sapporo City, Hokkaido, 064

Activities include development of a scientific programme for elementary school by the visual method; developmental study on the uses of CAI in teacher training; computer programs for data processing; and instructional analysis by use of CMI system. The Centre offers the following services: instructional analysis by use of CCTV; analysis and management of educational data.

*Iwate University, Centre for Educational Technology, Faculty of Education, 18, 3-chome, Ueda, Morioka City, 020

Activities include curriculum development, study of classroom analysis, and studies for the improvement of teacher-training methods. Publications include *Center News and Bulletin of the Center* (name undecided, annual). Services include provision of CCTV facilities, hire of AV materials, and instruction of students in educational technology.

*Kagawa University, Centre for Educational Technology, Faculty of Education, 1-1 Saiwai-cho, Takamatsui City, Kagawa Prefecture, 760

Activities include: basic studies in CAI, CMI and EDPS; research and development of pre-service and in-service teacher education programmes; research in curriculum development and instructional materials production. Publications include annual report, research report, *KACET News.* The Centre also offers technical advice to faculty members for their research and development activities; training for computer programming and instructional materials production techniques; publication services, such as the annual report, research report and *KACET News.*

*Kamazawa University, The Educational Technology Centre, Faculty of Education, 1-1 Marunouchi, Kanazawa City, 920

Activities include co-operative research with elementary school teachers in designing and analysing instruction materials; psychological study of children's reactions to TV programmes; monthly meetings for the observation of instruction in public schools; lending services for AV materials and instruments; training courses for teachers in the use of media. Publications include *Kyoikukogaku Kenkyu* – Studies in Educational Technology.

Kobe University, The Educational Technology Centre, Faculty of Education, 3-11 Tsurukabuto, Nada-ku, Kobe City, 657

Research and instruction in educational technology by means of a computer system; audiovisual facilities and measuring equipment; analysis of school work; research and development of school curriculum; research and development of teaching materials and teaching instruments; orientation of teaching practice; analysis of laboratory experiment data; and instruction in educational technology for students. Publications include *The Report of the Educational Technology Centre* (annual); *Educational Technology Centre News* (quarterly).

Kyoto University of Education, Centre for Educational Research and Training, 1 Fujinomori, Fukakusa, Fushimi-ku, Kyoto City, 612

Research activities include designing and analysing techniques of instructional material production, new teaching methods for pre-service and in-service teacher training, development of CAI and CMI systems for the teacher's self-training; other services include educational data processing for researchers and teachers, training courses and workshops on educational technology to in-service teachers and students, and technical advice and support for instructional material production. Publications: training packages (including gaming and simulation models) for teacher education; computer programs called *Analysing Program Packages for Educational Research (APPER)*, and their operation language coupler, and *Technical Reports*.

*Mie University, The Educational Technology Centre, Faculty of Education, 1515 Kamihamacho, Tsu City, 514

Activities include research on instructional processes, production of the New English Aptitude Test and research on its practical application, the making of the Teacher's Attention Map in classroom and research on its practical application, and the effects of audiovisual information on teaching programmes.

*Miyagi College of Education, Teachers' Centre, 641 Kamisugi, Sendai City, Miyagi Prefecture, 980

Activities include creation of 'skilful and effective' teaching, production of new instructional materials and segments, inquiries into the methods for analysing teaching and instructional aids, research in the teaching-learning process, filing the records of teaching situations through VTR and other ways, and liaison with local and foreign teachers and researchers. Publications include *Bulletin of Teachers' Centres* (in Japanese), and an extra bulletin of teachers' centres, usually three times a year (in Japanese).

*Nagasaki University, Centre for Educational Technology, Faculty of Education, 1-14 Bunkyo-cho, Nagasaki City, 852

Work is centred around research on a prefectural-wide CMI (Computer-Managed Instruction) system, called the NIGHT System (each letter represents the initial letter of the remote islands of Iki, Goto, Hirado and Tsushima, plus Nagasaki); the implementation of a MMTS (Multi-media Teaching System) in the teacher training programmes; and the teaching process of instructional learning and its monitoring system by TSS. The Centre for Educational Technology is maintained for service, as well as for educational research. The Centre processes data from pupils' and students' records through a variety of steps, as required, and assists instructional programmes by providing material and VTR equipment, if necessary, for classroom use. It also produces and duplicates VTR tapes at the request of faculty, teachers and researchers. Publications include *Teaching Material* (programmed instruction) for classroom instruction; Annual Reports on the Centre for Educational Technology (1974, 1975, 1976, 1977); *Studies in Teaching-Learning Programmes* Vol 1 (Oct 1975), Vol 2 (March 1976), Vol 3 (Sept 1976); *Seasonal Report:* Journal of Educational Technology (1977-78).

Nara University of Education, Educational Technology Centre, Takabatake-cho, Nara City, 630

Activities include the investigation of new ways of teaching, the accumulation of records of teaching, data processing by the use of SORT/ Merge, instructional analysis with CCTV, consultation with research fellows, and co-operation with teachers of attached schools and lending of educational instruments. Publications include a manual for users of CCTV (in Japanese), an annual report of researchers, and an outline of instrumentation at the Centre.

Niigata University, Centre for Research and Instruction in Educational Practices, Faculty of Education, 8050 Igarashi-Ninocho, Niigata City, 950-21 (Contact: Hisao Sakadida)

Founded in April 1980, the Centre's main function is research and instruction in educational practices through audiovisual facilities and educational technology. Its main activities include: the development of effective teaching-learning systems and educational materials through educational technology; research and instruction in educational practices; giving assistance to the Student-Teacher Committee concerning planning, implementing, and improving the student-teacher programme; and putting the facilities, machines, VTRs, and other data of the Centre to the use of the teaching staff and students. The Centre plans and implements the University Extension Sessions, and produces AV materials for elementary and secondary schools. It publishes a *Bulletin* and *Center News*.

*Okayama University, The Educational Technology Centre, School of Education, 1-1 Naka, 3-chome, Tsushima, Okayama City, 700

The Centre offers service and technical support for the following activities, not only to staff members but also to students: research, audiovisual education (CCTV and language laboratories), training students in the development of educational media and other practice activities; a CCTV system connecting the Centre with attached schools. The Centre has developed a Response Analyzer System with a minicomputer and an electronic device for correcting pronunciation in foreign languages. Publications include magazines on educational technology.

*Tokyo Gakugei University, The Centre for Engineering Science in Education, 1-1 Nukuikita-machi, 4-chome, Koganei-shi, Tokyo, 184

Research into innovations in education, including elementary school and university levels; teaching practice and in-service training using the Classroom Simulation System; information science. Centre staff advise those who want to use its facilities, namely a computer system including CAI terminals, a combined CCTV system (CCTV system including a video studio, a multi-aid guided instruction system, and a classroom simulation system). These systems are open to the University faculty and students for research on educational technology, classroom work, and other purposes. The Centre publishes *Newsletter* (in Japanese).

Tokyo Institute of Technology, The Centre for Research and Development of Educational Technology (CRADLE), 2-12-1 Oh-okayama, Meguro-ku, Tokyo, 152

Research activities include research into and development of the principles and methods of educational technology, and its use in the improvement of educational systems; development of new systems for higher education. The Centre also offers annual courses in educational technology. Materials developed include educational video materials (about 70 reels so far), training programmes and equipment for special education, three new systems by optical fibre for transmitting lectures to remote campuses, programmes for computerized evaluation systems giving comments to students. The Centre has also developed a variety of teaching machines.

*Shinshu University, The Educational Technology Centre, Faculty of Education, 6 Nishinagano-machi, Nagano City, 380

Activities include studies of instructional processes, the production of teaching materials, and guidance methods. The Centre undertakes teacher training in instructional technology, computer training, and curriculum development. Publications include the *Report of the Educational Technology Center* Nos 1-6 (1975-78) and *Center News* Nos 1-8 (1974-79).

*Utsunomiya University, The Centre of Educational Technology (attached to the Educational Department), 350 Mine-machi, Utsunomiya City, Tochigi Prefecture, 320

Activities include the development of instructional equipment; the filing of educational information; assistance to students with their instructional practice and skills; and computer services, including scientific calculations, and programme development. Data processing services are offered. Training is given in the use of computers. The Centre also rents out instructional aids, and it publishes *Bulletin of the Centre of Educational Technology* Nos 1-2.

*Yokohama National University, Centre for Educational Technology, Faculty of Education, 156 Tokiwadai, Hodogaya-ku, Yokohama City, 320

Activities include studies for the improvement of teacher training, pre-service teacher training and studies in teacher training, studies concerning the teaching-learning process, and studies on images and their recognition. The Centre holds an AV library and rents out hardware for educational research. It publishes *Educational Practice Research* Nos 1-2.

Other organizations

*Council of National University Centres for Educational Technology, c/o Educational Technology Centre, Tokyo Gakugei University, Mukui-Kitamachi, Koganei, Tokyo, 184 (Contact: Professor Masami Koganei, President)

*Educational Technology Journal Association of Japan, c/o Educational Technology Centre, Tokyo Gakugei University, Nukui-Kitamachi, Koganei, Tokyo, 184

*Japan Audio-Visual Education Association, 1-17-1 Toranomon, Minato-ku, Tokyo, 105 (Contact: Tasuo Moriwaki, Director)

The Association is a public non-profit-making organization aiming at the promotion and development of the effective use of audiovisual aids in education. Through the Japan Audio-Visual Information Centre for International Service, it communicates with some 80 countries, collecting and disseminating information on audiovisual education. With the Japan Association of Manufacturers and Distributors of Educational Materials and The Electric Industries Association of Japan it sponsors the annual Japan Exhibition of Educational Materials (JEMEX), participates in international film festivals and organizes national exhibitions and competitions. It has also published a series of handbooks and catalogues.

*Japan Council of Educational Technology Centres, c/o Unesco and International Affairs Bureau, Ministry of Education, Science & Culture, Kasumigaseki, Tokyo, 100

*Matsushita Audio/Visual Education Foundation, Shuwa-Onarimon Building, 6-1-1 Shinbashi, Minato-ku, Tokyo, 105

The Foundation co-operates with other educational facilities throughout Japan and receives aid and guidance from them in planning research and in the use of equipment and techniques. The AV Research Association set up by the Foundation is developing techniques for software production and use of equipment. The Foundation also runs a programme to encourage the planning of research. Its AV Education Centre and Language Laboratory School offer educators the opportunity to use fully equipped facilities to try out software formats.

*LL School (Osaka School), 2F Osaka-Ekimae-Daiichi Building, 4-20 Sonezaki-ue, Kita-ku, Osake, 530

JORDAN

*University of Jordan, Instructional Media Centre, College of Education, Amman (Contact: Dr Hani Saleh, Dean)

The Centre was established in 1975 as part of the College of Education to aid in the instructional process. It currently functions as a training and production centre. All kinds of equipment are available for the use of both instructors and students. The Centre also boasts a film library.

*Educational Radio and Television Section, Curriculum and Teaching Materials Directorate, PO Box 1930, Amman (Contact: Hashem El-Hassan, Head of ETV and Radio Section)

The Ministry of Education, with the co-operation of Jordan Television, started transmitting ETV programmes as direct teaching to secondary schools in 1968 and with the co-operation of Radio Amman started transmitting educational radio programmes as direct teaching for elementary and junior high schools in 1971. Programmes cover language, religion, science and arts. The Section is also responsible for providing schools with equipment and maintenance, and the issue of taped programmes, and it also runs training courses for teachers in the field of the use of broadcasts.

Ministry of Education, Directorate of Curricula and Teaching Aids, PO Box 1979, Amman (Contact: Dr Ali Abdul Raziq, Director)

The Directorate is responsible for furthering the use and understanding of teaching aids in education and training; planning and production of educational materials; TV and radio programmes for education; running

courses in educational technology, and providing the following services: film
library, maintenance workshop, printing unit, art unit, supply unit.

KENYA

Co-operative College of Kenya, PO Box 24814, Nairobi (Contacts: Mr J M
Nzioka, Principal; Mr G A Okeyo, Director of Studies)

Co-operative College of Kenya is a national institution with the objectives of
training Co-operative Personnel in both the Co-operative Movement and
from the Government Ministry of Co-operative Development. Basic
Intermediate and Advanced Courses are offered to the personnel of both
organizations. Amongst the various college departments, there is the
Education Media Services Department, whose functions include
correspondence courses, radio programmes and publicity and production of
educational materials relating to co-operative development for both the
Movement and the Government of Kenya. Materials produced are related to
the Co-operative Movement and Co-operative Development in Kenya.

Environment Liaison Centre, PO Box 72461, Nairobi (Contact: Delmar
Blasco, Executive Officer)

The ELC has three major functions: (1) to liaise among environmental non-
governmental organizations (NGOs) and between them and the UN
Environment Programme; (2) to support the development of environmental
NGOs in the Third World; and (3) to take advocacy positions on important
international environmental issues. The ELC maintains a library of relevant
periodicals and subject-matter files and publishes a quarterly journal,
Ecoforum. Environmental education and development communications are
two topics of interest.

Kenyatta University College, Faculty of Education, Department of
Educational Communication and Technology, PO Box 43844, Nairobi
(Contact: Dr Henry Okello Ayot, Chairman of the Department)

The Department of Educational Communication and Technology conducts
courses for BEd degrees in the University of Nairobi. All BEd students are
required to complete prescribed courses in educational communication and
technology in general and subject methods. Courses are designed to provide
prospective teachers with necessary criteria and skills for selecting and using
appropriate teaching media to enable them to communicate effectively in the
classroom. Courses aim to make students resourceful in the production of
teaching aids from local resources and aware of the necessity for
management of resources in the school environment.

Kenya Institute of Education, Educational Media Service, PO Box 30231,
Nairobi (Contact: R H J Thompson)

The Educational Media Service is a division of the Kenya Institute of
Education, which is responsible for developing curricula for pre-university
education both in school and out of school. The Educational Media Service
specialists work with curriculum specialists in the development and
production of curriculum materials. It is staffed and equipped to produce
radio and audio-taped programmes, tape/slide, video and TV programmes,
16mm films and pictorial and print materials. The main output of the
Educational Media Service at present consists of radio programmes for
primary and secondary schools and for teachers. Motivational films, tape/

slides and videotapes for educational materials are linked to courses developed in the Kenya Institute of Education and are supported by teachers' notes, charts and pupils' pamphlets. The Educational Media Service has four sections: Audio, Visual, Resources and Technical Services. The Resources section is responsible for producing pictorial and print materials and other teaching aids and for dissemination of materials and ideas to users. The Technical Services section provides operational services. Educational Media Service specialists work with the Research section of the Kenya Institute of Education in the evaluation of the materials produced.

University of Nairobi

*1. Department of Educational Communications and Technology, Faculty of Education, PO Box 43844, Nairobi (Contacts: Dr G S Eshiwani, Chairman of Department; Mrs A Nabwera, Microteaching and Educational Technology; Mrs B Njogah, Educational Resources Centre)

Educational and instructional technology, both science and arts for secondary education in East Africa; educational and instructional technology for primary teacher education in Kenya; microteaching and interaction analysis – cognitive skill training for all students in the Faculty; audiovisual resources development, maintenance and retrieval research for secondary and teacher education. The Department produces a full range of AV media productions, also programmes for national radio and TV.

2. Institute of Adult Studies, University of Nairobi, PO Box 30197, Nairobi (Contact: The Director)

The Institute is made up of three departments: Extra-Mural Department, Residential Courses Department, and Correspondence Courses Department (see next entry). The main functions of the Institute are to: provide professional adult education for adult educators and extension workers; provide leadership and management training for policy-makers; provide distance education through combinations of media; produce and disseminate materials and information in adult education for use by trainers and others; provide professional consultancy and advisory services to government and non-government organizations which are engaged in training programmes; provide research and evaluation skills and techniques for people engaged in diagnosing and solving organizational or group problems; establish contact and understanding between the University and the general public through the Extra-Mural Department's activities all over the country; and co-operate with other national and international institutions and organizations in organizing professional training workshops, seminars, courses and conferences.

3. Correspondence Course Unit (CCU), PO Box 92, Kikuyu (Contact: Ben Gitau, Assistant Director, Institute of Adult Studies, in charge of Correspondence Course Unit)

The Unit is a constituent part of the Institute for Adult Studies. Courses include upgrading courses for teachers, as well as courses for government and private organizations and private persons. The CCU produces learning materials and provides consultancy services on the production of such materials. The Unit also produces training handbooks for health trainers, extension workers, managers and many others. Other services include consultancy on correspondence course design to other institutions such as the Co-operative College of Kenya, Kenya Institute of Education, and Kenya Institute of Administration.

Unesco Office of the Regional Communication Adviser, Nairobi, *see Regional Centres of Activity – Africa*

*URTNA Programme Exchange Centre, PO Box 50518, Nairobi (Contact: Mr Kassaye Demena, Director)

URTNA Programme Exchange Centre is one of the organs of the Union of National Radio and Television Organizations of Africa (URTNA), whose headquarters are in Dakar, Senegal. The Union has 34 active members (from the African Continent) and 12 Associate members (from outside Africa). The functions of the organization include providing a mechanism for radio and television programme exchange and bringing together radio and/or television programme makers for the purpose of exchanging programming and programme use experiences. The Centre also maintains a programme archive. It organizes workshops and seminars for radio and television personnel.

KOREA

*Korean Educational Development Institute (KEDI), 20-21 Woomyon-dong, Kang Nam, Seoul

KEDI is responsible for developing distance learning, in particular a 'High School in the Air'. The main objective of this project is to provide high school education, through modern educational technology, for workers, school drop-outs and other out-of-school youths and adults who wish to continue their education. The main role of KEDI with regard to these high schools is fourfold: (i) it provides the instructional plan; (ii) it produces instructional materials in the form of special textbooks, which are designed for self-study; (iii) it plans and produces radio lessons; and (iv) it evaluates, through a universal test given each semester, the performance of students. This project operates with the co-operation of regular high school teachers. Instruction covers 15 subjects of the normal curriculum of a regular high school. The students study through semi-programmed textbooks, attend schools (attached to regular high schools) every other Sunday to get face-to-face instruction from teachers, and listen to radio broadcasts for one hour every day in the morning and evening.

KUWAIT

Arab States Educational Technology Centre, *see Regional Centres of Activity – Middle East*

Institute of Teachers Education, Edailiya, Kuwait, PO Box 34055 (Contacts: Dr Mohamed A Farghali, Dean; Dr Marzoug Y Al-Gounaim, Associate Dean for Academic Affairs; Dr Mahmoud A R Shafshak, Chairman of Department of Education, Psychology and Educational Technology; Mr Sayed H Hannora, Educational Technology Consultant – special address: Salmiya, PO Box 1025, Kuwait)

The Institute of Education was established in 1972 and is the only teachers' training institute for men in Kuwait (there is another one for women). The Institute is maintained and financed by the Ministry of Education. Although it is not a simple task to change traditional patterns of teaching and learning, the Institute is trying to make future teachers enthusiastic and more interested in the new technology of education. Microteaching is strongly featured in its training, and it also has language laboratories. Publications cover all aspects of its work.

Ministry of Education

1. Curriculum and Text Books Department, Ministry of Education, Kuwait (Contacts: Mr Ibrahim M O Abalkhail, Director; Mr Faisal Abdul-Jader, Curriculum Supervisor)

The Curriculum Department was first introduced in the Ministry of Education in 1976. The tasks of the department are: designing and developing curricula; preparing and printing textbooks; liaising between the supreme committee for planning and curricula and the committees working in developing teaching of the various subjects. It produces reports on its work.

2. English Language Teaching Inspectorate (ELT), PO Box 7, Safat (Contact: Dr Ali H S Hajjaj, ELT Inspector-General)

The Inspectorate is responsible for supervising, taking part in, planning for and developing English language teaching all over the country.

3. The Media Department, Ministry of Education, Kuwait (Contact: Mr Sulmon Al-Dukhail Al-Humaidan, Director)

The department produces AV aids for different school subjects; meeting the needs of schools and institutions; and maintaining and evaluating such teaching materials. It is therefore involved in production, distribution and evaluation activities. Its products include cassette tapes for language teaching; video and films; slides; OHP transparencies. It also publishes some books and evaluation reports.

LIBERIA

*ELWA, Box 1 92, Monrovia (Contact: Public Information Office)

ELWA is the radio ministry in West Africa for the Sudan Interior Mission, an independent interdenominational, evangelical faith mission founded in 1893. It provides a variety of services through broadcasting and extensions, ie providing films, cassette-lending library and other material on religious educational topics. Main services provided include broadcasting, medical, educational and extension (church growth) services.

LUXEMBOURG

Office du Film Scolaire, Centre Audiovisuel, BP 2, Walferdange (Contact: Ed Kohl)

Services are available to schools and pre-school and vocational educational organizations. The services are an audiovisual library (free of charge), a technical department (maintenance and advice), production of audiovisual materials including slides, tapes, transparencies and 16mm films, and teacher training.

MALAGASY REPUBLIC

*National Centre for the Production of Teaching Materials (INSREP), BP 3109, Tananarive

Production and development service for teaching materials for the Ministry of Secondary and Basic Education.

MALAWI

*Ministry of Agriculture and Natural Resources, Extension Aids Branch, PO Box 594, Lilongwe (Contact: M M A Mphepo, Principal Extension Aids Officer)

Extension Aids Branch aims at assisting the whole of the Ministry of Agriculture and Natural Resources in communicating through media. Thus it provides teaching material for the Ministry staff engaged in extension activities, and aims to create an interest in rural people in modern farming methods. It is much concerned with the health and proper nutrition of rural people and works hand in hand with other extension services. It provides mass coverage through radio, circulates visual materials, offers maintenance and mobile cinema service, media evaluation services and printing services for written media.

MALAYSIA

Ministry of Education

1. Curriculum Development Centre, Ministry of Education Malaysia, Pesiaran Duta, Kuala Lumpur 11-04 (Contact: Ms Asiah Bte Abu Samah, Director)

Activities are planned and executed within five curriculum programme areas: (i) development of language curriculum; (ii) development of primary school curriculum; (iii) development of secondary school curriculum; (iv) curriculum research and evaluation; and (v) training and dissemination of curriculum. *Materials produced:* (i) syllabuses for primary and secondary schools; (ii) multi-media curriculum materials for teachers and pupils; (iii) project working papers and professional papers; and (iv) reports of research and evaluation studies. *Services offered:* (i) orientation and training of selected personnel at the national level who are responsible for conducting training of in-service teachers at the state/district level as part of the dissemination process; and (ii) dissemination of curriculum materials to schools and other educational agencies.

2. Educational Media Service, Jalan Ampang, Kuala Lumpur 04-05 (Contact: The Director, Educational Media Service)

The Service is responsible for planning and production of programmes for broadcast to schools through radio and television; planning, production and distribution of AVA materials to schools; training of teachers in media use and evaluation; loan of AV materials, eg charts, filmstrips, 16mm films, audio-cassettes (radio programmes) to schools from the National AV Centre, Kuala Lumpur. Recent publications include *Educational Media Service Journal*, December 1978.

3. Lembaga Peperiksaan Malaysia (Malaysia Examinations Syndicate), Jalan Duta, Kuala Lumpur 11-04 (Contact: Mr Omar Bin Mohd Hashim, Director of Examinations)

The Syndicate is a Division of the Ministry of Education and as a fully-fledged government body, its development as well as operational costs are fully funded by the Government. Main services provided are: full conduct of the Syndicate's own examination, the bulk of which includes the various levels of the country's national school level examinations; the administration of over 30 degree and professional examinations in collaboration with local and external agencies; development of General Aptitude Tests for the Ministry of Labour and Manpower and the Ministry of Youth, Sports and Culture for the selection of candidates into special vocational and industrial institutions; development of series of aptitude tests for registrants seeking employment at Labour Offices; development of Diagnostic Test for Standard 3 in Bahasa Malaysia, English, Chinese and Tamil Languages and Mathematics; development of achievement tests (essay and objective) for various levels of national examinations for school; conducting measurement research; conducting courses in Test Construction, Educational Measurement and Evaluation, Aptitude Test Administration and training courses in marking on regular basis; providing professional advice on examinations standards with particular reference to school level examination; processing, analysing and issuing results and certificates of national examinations besides servicing computers needs of other divisions within and outside the Ministry of Education.

University Sains Malaysia (Science University of Malaysia), The Teaching-Learning Advisory Unit, Chancellory, Universiti Sains Malaysia, Penang (Contact: The Co-ordinator)

As a fast growing institution, USM rapidly came to realize the importance of improving the quality of teaching-learning, and has set up many initiatives in the form of staff development programmes and workshops. It is particularly concerned with *distance learning* techniques and materials (many of its students are off-campus). The Teaching-Learning Advisory Unit is concerned, therefore, with: improving teaching methods and effectiveness; offering consultancy and advice to teaching staff; promoting new teaching methods; study skills for students; research into teaching-learning. The Unit is now beginning to overcome the initial teaching staff resistance and is beginning to be influential. The Teaching-Learning Advisory Unit is not a staff development unit *per se*; in USM, academic staff recruitment comes by dribs and drabs and this section of the university population does not form a reliable and durable ally to teaching-learning activities. On the other hand, the student population is a vast continuum of teaching-learning resources to be tapped, and it is indeed the students who form the backbone of the Teaching-Learning Advisory Unit's success. Activities conducted include study workshops, tips on time management and research into learning problems. Facilities made use of by students include typewriting, photocopying, duplicating, book wrapping, graphic services etc.

Technical Teachers' Training College, 4½ Mile, Cheras Road, Kuala Lumpur (Contact: The Principal)

The College conducts pre-service and in-service courses for training teachers for academic and vocational secondary schools in trades, industrial arts and commercial studies. All courses are conducted in the national language (Malay) with English as a strong second language. Leadership and expertise in curriculum development and innovation are also provided in the above specialized areas. International collaboration can be arranged through the Ministry of Education, Kuala Lumpur.

MALI

*Centre de Formation Professionelle (Professional Training Centre), Bamako

Institut National Pédagogique

*1. Division de l'Information et de la Documentation Pédagogique (Division of Information and Educational Documentation), Ministère de l'Education National, Boîte Postale 119, Bamako

*2. Section Sciences Naturelles (Natural Sciences Section), Boîte Postale 71, Bamako

*3. Télévision Scolaire du Mali (Mali Educational Television), Centre for Research and Audiovisual Production, Boîte Postale 71, Bamako

URTNA Technical Centre, *see Regional Centres of Activity – Africa*

MALTA

*Resource Centre, Faculty of Education, New University, Msida (Contact: Professor Charles Farrugia)

The Centre's objectives are to promote and facilitate the adoption of advanced pedagogical techniques based on the concept of educational technology. This concept combines the use of validated instructional methods with the planned use of the communication media. The Centre serves local educational needs particularly in the provision of hardware and software and the training of teachers in educational technology and the use of equipment.

MAURITANIA

*Institut Pédagogique National, Service de la Radio Educative, Boîte Postale 616, Nouakchott

MAURITIUS

The Audio Visual Centre, 6 Thomy Pitot Street, Rose Hill (Contact: The Principal Education Officer)

The Centre provides educational back-up for primary and secondary schools through the media of radio and TV. It was inaugurated in 1969, and has since provided daily TV and radio programmes. Programmes on teaching methodology also appear on TV; teachers' notes and other back-up materials are produced. The Centre has launched a cine-club project since 1980 for students of all primary and secondary schools and the Mauritian Government is presently proposing to nationalize the Centre by providing formal and non-formal education through radio, TV, and correspondence courses on agriculture, health, co-operatives and other sectors of the socioeconomic system.

Mauritius College of the Air, District Courthouse, Moka (Contact: The Director)

Set up by the International Extension College, Cambridge, UK, the Mauritius College of the Air undertakes multi-media educational activities in formal and non-formal education.

MEXICO

*Agricultural University at Chapingo (Contact: Ing Edilberto Nino Velazquez, Presidente de la Rama de Divulgación Agricola, Colegio de Post-Graduados,

Kilometro 39 de la Carretera Mexico-Taxco, Estado de Mexico)
The University has made interesting use of radio for rural development.

*CEMPAE (Centro para el Estudio de Medios y Procedimientos Avanzados para la Educación) (Centre for Advanced Methods and Procedures in Education), Insurgentes Sur No 1480, 15° piso, Mexico 12, DF

A decentralized federal body working in the public interest by producing projects and programmes. CEMPAE aims to produce educational materials for open learning systems, using semi-programmed and group methods.

Centro Nacional de Tecnologia Educativa (National Centre for Educational Technology), Avenida Acueducto S/N, Ampliacion Tepepan Xochimilco, Mexico 23 DF

The Ministry of Public Education (SEP), through the General Direction of Industrial and Technological Education (DGETI), subordinated to the Under-ministry of Technical Education and Research (SEIT), founded the National Centre of Educational Technology (CeNalTE), to fulfil the aims of the Mexican Government. Its objectives are the improvement of technical education in the medium high level to raise the quality of technological education. To fulfil this aim CeNalTE, works in educative investigation, designs and produces material resources to aid technical instruction, and trains teachers about the use and handling of the principles of technical instruction. These objectives are important to fulfil the actual and long-term occupational needs of the country. CeNalTE is organized in the following manner: general direction, planning department, production department, administrative department and psycho-pedagogy department. To improve its work, CeNalTE also has the direction of the Centre of Technological Studies No 49, an educative institution dedicated to prepare professional technicians in communication, graphic design and audiovisual resources.

*Consejo Nacional Tecnico de la Educacion (SEP), Luis Gonzalez Obregon 21, Mexico 1, DF

A planning body for technical education which emphasizes the evaluation of courses by means of precisely stated objectives.

*Dirección General de Educación Audiovisual, Calz Circunvalacion Esq, Tabiqueros, Col Morelos, Mexico 2, DF (Contact: Ing Ariel Tellez de la Parra, Sub-director Tecnico de los Medios de Comunicacion)

Concerned with tele-education (distance education) and educational technology, the organization produces a range of materials including radio programmes for basic secondary education. Services offered include transmission of programmes for the 'Telesecundaria'; transmission of programmes for the 'Radioprimaria'; printing and publishing (in offset) various educational materials; preparing graphic artwork – originals for slides, films, transparencies, etc; photography – preparing, processing and copying still and 16mm movie film, litho plates, etc.

ILCE – Instituto Latinoamericano de la Comunicación Educativa, *see Regional Centres of Activity – South America*

*The National Polytechnic, Channel 11 (Contact: Lic Juan Saldana, Director Canal 11, Prolongación de Carpio 475, Colonia Santo Tomas, Mexico 17, DF)

Preparatoria Abierta (Open Study pre-university level), Instituto Tecnológico y de Estudios superiores de Monterrey, Nuevo León (Contact: Lic Alfonso Rubio y Rubio, Vice-Rector de Ensenanza Media).

This centre founded in 1973, operates very much like the British Open University, offering general education courses at the highest level. It was set up jointly by the technical institute of Monterrey and the Centre for the Study of Media and New Teaching Methods (CEMPAE). This open system is made up of seven elements: a methodology for reading and learning; textbooks, workbooks, anthologies, study guides and laboratory manuals written in a different format from those used in traditional Mexican education (the book is divided into 16 units and each unit represents at least eight hours of study); a minimum library of three books per course that support the content of the textbooks; 16 30-minute TV programmes for each course which provide additional information but primarily motivate the student to learn a particular field; a tutorial service for the 36 different courses; an evaluation subsystem and the communications network.

*Servicio Nacional do Adrestratinento Rapido de la Mano do Obra en la Industria (National Service of Rapid Training of Manual Workers in Industry), Calzada Azcapotzalco, La Villa 209, Mexico 16, DF

*Sistema de Ensenanza Abierta del Colegio de Bachilleres (Open Learning System of the Colegio de Bachilleres), Luisiana 59, Col Napoles, Mexico 18, DF (Contact: Lic Ma Teresa Romero Nogueron, Subdirectora Tecnica)

Aims to supply secondary education to the inhabitants of rural areas where secondary schools have not existed. Uses a lot of self-instructional texts, teaching aids and job aids, together with a few modules of TV and radio programmes, somewhat like the British Open University, though of course aiming at a lower-level clientele. Students gather in study centres which are equipped with CCTV and video recording facilities providing a high level of flexibility of learning rate and time. The study centres are staffed by trained group leaders who take part on a semi-teacher basis, answering questions and solving students' problems.

*Telesecundaria, Dirección General de Educación Audiovisual, Calzada de Circumvalación y Tabiqueros, Mexico 2, DF (Contact: Lic Eduardo Lizalde, Director)

An educational television system intended to give secondary school education to children in rural areas. It uses a combination of TV lessons, direct teaching and self-study from texts. Typically each lesson has a presentation on TV of about 20 minutes' duration and the rest of the hour is used by the semi-trained teacher following a pre-prepared lesson plan. The self-study takes place in between group meetings and includes practical exercises and activities to be performed in the field as well as book learning. Information is also available about Radioprimaria, a pilot system based at San Luis Potosi.

UNAM (Universidad Nacional Autonomo de Mexico)

*1. Televisa (Contact: Octavio Menduet, Productor Ejecutivo, AV Chapultepec 18, Mexico 7, DF)

The commercial television system, Televisa, makes and transmits programmes – 'Introduccion a la Universidad' – for the National Autonomous University, UNAM. UNAM itself at the last count had 19 CCTV systems.

*2. Radio Universidad. Details are available from Dr Abelardo Villegas,

Director, Radio Universidad, Adolfo Prieto 133, Col del Valle, Mexico 12, DF

*3. Consero de Metodologia y Apoyo Educativos de la Universidad Nacional Autonomo de Mexico (Council of Methodology and Educational Aids of the National Autonomous University of Mexico), Mexico, DF

Training in educational systems, methodology, design of courses, evaluation of student achievement, programmed instruction – for the staff of the University.

NEPAL

*Centre for Educational Research, Innovation and Development, Maharajganj, Kathmandu (Contact: Dr Prem Kumar Kasaju, Executive Director)

With the introduction of a new national education system in 1971, the education sector in Nepal has been carefully planned to make it consistent with national development efforts. In this context the Centre was established in early 1976 for the purpose of testing the effectiveness of various educational programmes in operation, identifying problems in their implementation and consolidation, and working out suggestions and new strategies. The Centre's activities are mainly concerned with undertaking applied and policy research in education, including effectiveness of vocational education, cost benefit in school education, children's perceptive development at the primary school level, etc; operating action research and innovative projects such as integrated non-formal education, education for rural development, etc; organizing seminars and workshops; and publishing educational journals (one journal in English and one in Nepali have been published each year; seminar and project reports are published in English and/or Nepali).

NETHERLANDS

Institutions of further and higher education

University of Amsterdam, Prinsengracht 227, Amsterdam

1. Teacher Training Department (Contact: Mia Lezer, Senior Lecturer)

Dynamics of group behaviour, groups in schools; analysis of individual behaviour, microteaching and other mirroring techniques.

2. Dr E M Buter

Areas of interest: applied educational science and educational technology; courses in applied educational science with necessary software; course guide on applied educational science; handbook on same; publications are forthcoming on research for training parody for specialists in meso-level functions, co-editing of *Handbook of Educational Practice*; training in microteaching; varied courses on applied educational science; training in the use of media.

3. Dr J P Boorsma

Areas of interest: university courses in educational technology.

4. Audio Visual Centre, Pedagogy and Applied Educational Technology Section (Contact: W N Koorn)

5. Centre for Educational Research of the University of Amsterdam, Singel 138, PO 3753, 1001 AN, Amsterdam (Contact: Dr A H van den Berg, Director)

On 1 January 1981 the new Centre for Educational Research of the University of Amsterdam started its activities. In this new research institute, founded by the University of Amsterdam, the activities of two former institutes will be continued: the Kohnstamm Institute (founded in 1970 on the initiative of Professor Dr Ph I Idenburg) and the Foundation Research Institute for Applied Psychology (founded in 1961 by Professor Dr A D de Groot). The Centre for Educational Research has as its objects to make scientific insights subservient, through research, to the improvement of education. The main research activities take place in the field of art education, evaluation of educational innovation, motivation, language education, comprehensive school, social education, adult education, off-school supervision services. Practically all research projects carried out in the centre are policy research projects. This means that research is carried out on assignment from policy-making institutions, such as ministries, provincial authorities, municipalities and international organizations. For information, apply to the management or general secretariat at the above address. The Library and Documentation Department is at Keizersgracht 119, Amsterdam

6. The Centre for Research into Higher Education at the University of Amsterdam, (Centrum voor Onderzoek van het Wetenschappelijk Onderwijs, COWO), Oude Turfmarkt 149, 1012 GC Amsterdam (Contact: Henk J M van Berkel)

Like every Dutch university, the University of Amsterdam has an educational research centre, viz the Centre for Research into Higher Education (COWO). COWO is a research centre as well as a central service unit. It currently consists of approximately 14 educational researchers and is headed by a co-ordinating 'triad' that is periodically elected from COWO staff. This currently consists of Dr Bert Camstra, Dr Tim A M van Dijk and Dr Henk J M van Berkel. The aims of the COWO may be listed as follows: to undertake both fundamental and applied research and development into problems of higher education, and to promote the application of the results thereof in the University's department; to provide instruction and advice to teachers, students, departments and the central University administration, on educational and instructional matters; to provide assistance in the (re-)structuring of course and curricula; and to undertake teacher development, by means of the COWO University Teacher Courses.

*Catholic University, Nijmegen, Institute of Educational Sciences, Erasmuslaan 40, Nijmegen (Contact: A Jaspers)

Theory and history of education, comparative education, curriculum theory, educational technology, reading, teacher education, educational research, education and training of educational professionals (researchers, teachers in education, counselling and guidance).

Delft University of Technology

1. CAI Project, Julianalaan 132, 2628 BL Delft (Contact: Charles van der Mast)

The CAI project is a research project in the Computer Science Department of the University. The objective of the project is research concerning the implementation of CAI, using the most recent technological developments. A concept in the practical realization and organization of CAI has been formulated termed 'Modular CAI'. An experimental system was designed following this concept to evaluate advantages against disadvantages. The presentation of courseware takes place on mini- and microcomputers whilst the development and evaluation is supported by larger systems. The project is continued on aspects of changeability and flexibility of this modular concept, especially on the role of microcomputer and video discs. Most experiments and designs concern hardware and software but some educational research is done in co-operation with representatives of other disciplines.

2. Department of Electrical Engineering, PO Box 5031, 2600 GA, Delft (Contact: F Koornheef)

3. Department of Philosophy and Social Sciences, Kanaalweg 2b, Delft (Contact: Dr J Vastenhouw)

Curriculum development.

Eindhoven University of Technology, Department of Educational Psychology, PO Box 513, HG 9.25, 5600 MB Eindhoven (Contacts: M Groen; J C Rodenburg-Smit)

The Department provides courses for student teachers and for some graduate students of technology. Research interests include: (a) counselling of beginning teachers; (b) use of PDP 11 in observation systems; (c) learning of practical skills.

Erasmus University, Department of Educational Research and Development, PO Box 1738, 3000 DR Rotterdam

The Department specializes in research and development of all aspects of university education.

Additionally, the Interfaculty Working Group for Educational Research seeks to co-ordinate activities aimed at improving teaching throughout the university. This involves conducting research, and maintaining an awareness of research results and activity elsewhere. The IWG also carries out developmental and evaluative projects in the University, and offers teacher training courses; it is also interested in study skills and study methods.

Leiden University

1. Department of Educational Development, Faculty of Medicine, Wassenaarseweg 62, 2333 AL Leiden (Contact: Dr W van Hilten)

Curriculum development at faculty management level: the development of general clerkship; the design of new courses, evaluation of the entire teaching programme. Teacher training courses on basic elements of education, teaching methods, AO instruction, examinations and evaluation. Advice is given on the formulation of multiple-choice questions and to individual teachers and committees on different topics. A course is given to students in order to improve their study methods.

2. Educational Research Centre, Boerhaavelaan 2, 2334 EN Leiden (Contact: Dr D N M de Gruijter)

Research and evaluation of areas such as factors related to study success; test theory and examinations. Advice to staff.

3. LICOR (Leids Interdisciplinair Centrum voor Onderwijs Research), Leiden University, Stationsplein 12, 2312 AK Leiden (Contacts: D de Jong, M Beishuizen)

Research organization; fundamental and applied research in education: motivation, independent learning, teacher education, educational technology (CMI, TV research). Financing: foundation for educational research. Research is programmed along five lines of development: (1) self-responsible learning; (2) differentiation and didactics; (3) teacher education; (4) educational technology – computer use in education (CAI, CMI), educational TV for 4- to 16-year-old children, media as a means to individualization; (5) other topics eg education for cultural minorities. Research is reported in Dutch.

4. Futures Research Unit, *see under Other organizations*

Lerarenopleiding (Teacher Training Institute) Ubbo Emmius, *see under Other organizations*

University of Nijmegen – CAI group KUN, Institute for Research and Development in Higher Education (IOWO), Verlengde Groenestraat 75, 6525 Ej Nijmegen (Contact: Dr F H D Gastkemper)

The CAI group KUN was formally established at the University of Nijmegen in 1979 and placed under the administration of the University's Institute for Research and Development in Higher Education. The main objectives in creating a specialized central agency were to stimulate appropriate usage of the computer as an educational medium and to give one group the responsibility of overseeing general intra-university CAI activities. For the group itself, these objectives imply activities in the areas of information and demonstration, analysis of demand and design, and implementation and evaluation of programmes.

Since its inception, the group has been co-operating closely with various departments in developing new applications of CAI and implementing suitable ones from elsewhere. For this purpose various types of soft- and hardware have been used. Documentation and evaluation reports (mostly in Dutch) on programmes, procedures and provisions are available on request from the above address.

Twente University of Technology, The Educational Centre, Postbus 217, 7500 AE Enschede

The Educational Centre consists of the Centre for Educational Research and Development (Contact: Jan M Donders) and the Audiovisual Centre (Contact: Jan A Kobus). Both Centres work closely together as Central Service Units to the University. Services of the CERD are focused on course development, teacher training and consultancy.

The Audiovisual Centre develops AV programmes and multi-media learning aids using the media video (colour), 16mm film, tape-slide and printed material.

University of Utrecht, Afdeling Ouderzoek en Ontwikkeling van Onderwijs (Department of Research and Development in Higher Education), Maliebaan 5, Utrecht (Contacts: Dr G W Ackers; Dr C A Hawkins)

The Department of Research and Development in Higher Education offers professional assistance to all those concerned with education within the University of Utrecht – teachers and students alike – in those situations where teaching and learning actually take place – within course teams or project groups, in seminars and short courses, in university departments, institutes and laboratories.

Other organizations

Central Bureau for Research into University Education (CBOWO), Postbus 590/Pr Beatrixlaan 428, Voorburg

This Centre supports and co-ordinates the activities and the research done at tertiary level by the different university centres for research into university education.

*Commando Logistiek en Opleidingen, tav Hoofd Bureau Onderwijskunde, PO Box 460, 3700 AL Zeist

European Bureau of Adult Education, Nieuweweg 4, PO Box 367, 3800 AJ Amersfoort (Contact: W Bax, Director)

The Bureau is a non-governmental organization established in 1953 to encourage mutual awareness and to develop contacts among those promoting adult education in the various European countries. The Bureau sponsors general conferences and meetings for those with common work problems. It publishes conference reports, a *Directory of Adult Education Organizations in Europe,* and a twice-yearly *Newsletter* devoted to specific topics. A full publications list is available on request.

Futures Research Unit (FRU), Department of Social and Organizational Psychology, State University of Leiden, PO Box 9509, 2300 RA Leiden (Contacts: P P van der Hijden; J H G Klabbers)

FRU is concerned with the study and analysis of social systems, and to this end makes great use of interactive computer simulation and gaming. It has developed a mathematical model for the Netherlands education system which is used for planning exercises, and has other games and simulations relevant to research, planning and educational training.

Instituut voor Cognitie Onderzoek (ICO), 8 Weesperplein, Amsterdam

Fundamental research on cognitive learning, thinking and memory.

Interchurch Co-ordination Committee for Development Projects, Bultenpepersdreef 224, 5231 HL Den Bosch (Contact: Tom Draisma, Secretary for Southern Africa)

Main activities include *Research*: systems approach to educational policy-making in Southern Africa with a centre-periphery frame of reference (Zambia, Mozambique, South Africa); and *Consultancy*: for development projects in Southern Africa, through the Interchurch Co-ordinating Committee for Development Projects. Details of Mr Draisma's publications are available on request.

The Kohnstamm Institute for Educational Research, *see* University of Amsterdam, Centre for Educational Research

Lerarenopleiding (Teacher Training Institute) Ubbo Emmius, PO Box 1018, Leeuwarden (Contact: Dr Klaas Bruin)

The 'Lerarenopleiding Ubbo Emmius' is one of several new teacher training institutes established in the Netherlands since 1970. It has a special interest in simulation and gaming and in the last six years has developed a range of simulations and games on social subjects (geography, social studies, history, economics, health education) for use within the Institute and in secondary education. At present work is in progress on the construction of theories of problem-oriented education, to make a more stable base for the introduction of educational innovations such as projects and simulation/games. In August 1979, the Institute organized the 10th conference of ISAGA, the International Simulation and Gaming Association. The Institute organizes workshops on simulation/gaming for interested people from the new teacher-training institutes and for teachers in secondary education. A bibliography of simulation and gaming literature and material, available at cost price, is published annually.

Nederlandse Bioscoopbond, 2 Jan Luykenstraat, 1071 CM Amsterdam (Contact: L Claassen, Film Production Department)

Nederlandse Bioscoopbond is a trade organization of companies dealing with film and AV production, distribution and cinema exhibition.

Nederlands Instituut voor Audio-visuele Media (NIAM), Sweelinckplein 33, Postbus 63426, 2502 JK The Hague (Contact: H J L Jongbloed, Director)

Production and distribution of audiovisual programmes on behalf of primary and secondary education; educational/technological information.

Netherlands Universities' Joint Social Research Centre (SISWO), OZ Achterburgwal 128, 1012 DT Amsterdam, PO Box 19079, 1000 GB Amsterdam (Contacts: Dr J Dronkers; Dr H Kleyer)

SISWO has a strong interest in the sociological aspects of education, and seeks to stimulate and co-ordinate research in this area (a staff of three).

Philips Research Laboratories, Project Centre, 5664 AN Feldrop (Contact: Dr D J Kroon, Cld WO)

In a research laboratory for the electronic industry, this group is engaged in research on the applications of new and existing electronic media for self-instruction. Special attention is given to combinations of personal computers, video-discs, video-cassette recorders, programmable audio-recorders, viewdata etc. Possibilities and limitations are studied from technical as well as from educational viewpoints. The group co-operates with educational research groups at universities, publishers, etc working in similar fields.

*Projektenbank, Wustenlaan 80, Santpoort

A 'bank' for reports and evaluations, and other documentation on school projects which lends out proven materials on request.

Research Instituut voor het Onderwijs in het Noorden (RION) (Educational Research Institute in the North of the Netherlands), Nieuwe Stationsweg 5-9, 9751 SZ Haren (Contact: Professor Dr B P M Creemers)

RION is funded by the Foundation of Educational Research and by the Department of Education, with the objective of advancing research on education on a non-profit basis. It is particularly concerned with: primary education; secondary education; curriculum research; educational administration; and participative education. For the future it is becoming involved with evaluation of educational innovations; internal school organization; evaluation and decision-making; schooling of teachers; special education; teacher planning; and practical learning.

*Royal Netherlands Air Force, c/o Prins Clauslaan 8, The Hague (Contact: Lt Col G J Cramer)

*Professor J Schouten, c/o Vrije Universiteit, De Boelelaan 1105, Kamer 15A-18, 1007 MC, Amsterdam

Stichting Bio-Wetenschappen en Maatschappij, Wassenaarseweg 56, 2333 AL, Leiden; Postbus 617, 2300 AP, Leiden (Contact: Mrs E Joyce Birfelder)

An organization concerned with promoting knowledge and awareness of the life sciences and society, mostly to secondary school pupils and students, but also to others.

Stichting Film en Wetenschap (Foundation for Film and Science), Hengeveldstraat 29, Utrecht (Contact: Dr J J D Konijn)

The use of audiovisual media in Dutch higher education; production, acquisition and distribution of audiovisual programmes; educational technology; information and advice. The Foundation undertakes production of programmes by order of Dutch universities and other institutions in higher education; previews and acquisition of programmes from other countries; distribution of such programmes to universities and schools, including audio-tapes with recordings from the historical sound archive; information and educational technology advice about audiovisual programmes; technical advice; lending of literature about audiovisual media in higher education; production of materials. Publications include the SFW quarterly *Registratie* (in Dutch); articles about audiovisual media in higher education, educational technology and audiovisual media, information about new programmes and literature, etc.

*Stichting Nederlandse Onderwijs Televisie, Postbus 80500, 2508 GM 's Gravenhage (Contact: A H M van Zon)

School TV in the Netherlands is realized in co-operation between Stichting NOT and NOS (broadcasting). The overall objective of School TV is to offer, on the basis of the average pedagogic/didactic situation in the schools, projects of an innovative character in terms of content and/or methodology. NOT is responsible for the content of the programmes, the accompanying materials as well as for promotion and research for all the series; NOS is responsible for the production, direction and transmission of the programmes.

Stichting Teleac, PO Box 2414, 3500 GK, Utrecht (Contact: Dr H C van Schalkwijk)

The Teleac Foundation is an organization covering the field of adult education for broadcasting and multi-media in the Netherlands, producing 12 to 14 multi-media courses every semester. These courses contain radio and television programmes, textbooks, correspondence courses, documentary material, audio-tapes and audio records, slides, experimental kits, etc, depending on the educational aims of the course. The courses vary every semester as far as the subject is concerned. Every year, 232 hours of television air-time is used and 260 hours of radio air-time. One or two language courses each year are usually given and the subjects of the other courses are chosen for professional as well as for leisure time activities. The level of the courses depends on the target group between primary education, viz Open School and post-academic. Forthcoming course programmes are offered in art, history, French, Latin, photography, the Ancient World, English, Spanish, communication, economy, sport (fishing), astronomy, the history of music, medical courses, gardening, etc.

Technical Film Centre of the Netherlands (TFC), 17 Arnhemsestraatweg, 6881 NB Velp (near Arnhem)

TFC was founded in 1954 as an independent, non-subsidized institute. Its objective is the promotion of the use of audiovisual aids in industry and education. TFC employs 45 people and disposes of various facilities for demonstration and showing audiovisual media (hardware and software). Its main activities include distribution of audiovisual media by means of sales and rentals; distribution of sponsored films on free loan; production of slides and tape/slide presentations; production of various language versions; sales and rentals of audiovisual equipment (projectors, video, sound); and the servicing and repair of audiovisual equipment. The Centre produces a number of film catalogues, categorized according to subject.

Vereniging Van Leveranciers Van Audio-Visuele Media (Association of Manufacturers and Importers of Audio Visual Aids), PO Box 90617, Nassau Zuilensteinstraat 9, 2596 CA Den Haag (Contacts: Dr Ir A P Kole; J Kortenhorst)

The Association aims to provide the use of audiovisual aids in professions, companies and institutions. It organizes the audiovisual fair 'Mediavisie' (once every two years) in co-operation with the Association of Tape/Slide Producers, the Association of Film Producers, and the Association of Video Dealers provides information on innovations and existing products; information on courses as regards audiovisual training; market research; contact and co-operation with other institutions; and participation in commissions of government.

Voorlichtingsdienst van Ministerie van Onderwijs en Wetenschappen (Information Service of the Ministry of Education and Science), Nieuwe Uitleg 1, 2500 EN-'s Gravenhage

NEW ZEALAND

Institutes of further and higher education

University of Auckland, Audio-Visual Centre, Private Bag, Auckland (Contact: Robert Boyd-Bell, Head of the Audio-Visual Centre)

The Centre was established to provide all Departments of the University with professional audiovisual programme production and equipment services. It has a three-camera colour television studio (PAL/Umatic and Time Base Correction) with mobile capacity and a single camera colour studio in the School of Medicine; a sound recording studio, the University photographic services, central language laboratories, equipment loan and maintenance services. The Centre is also involved in the design of teaching spaces and ancillary equipment and provides technical services to the Theatre Arts complex. Some instruction is provided in television production techniques and teaching skills associated with audiovisual aids.

*Massey University, Faculty of Education, Palmerston North (Contact: Dr Graham J F Hunt)

Postgraduate Diploma in Instructional Systems (DipIS), sponsored jointly by the Faculties of Education and Business, research in the interaction of learner characteristics with instructional strategies, research, development and evaluation of learning packages (programmes, tape/slide and videotape), particularly for use in pre- and in-service vocational tertiary education. A range of materials is available. Training, research, consultancy and materials development in educational technology are undertaken. These activities are particularly directed to vocational and tertiary settings. Workshops for industry and government are organized by the Human Resources Development Programme of the Managed Education Development Centre, Massey University.

University of Otago, Higher Education Development Centre, PO Box 56, Dunedin (Contacts: Dr David Teather, Director; Dr Terry Crooks, Research and Advisory Section; Mr Robert van der Wyver, AV Production Section; Mrs Shirley Ascroft, AV Study Section)

The brief of the Centre is to facilitate the improvement, by research and practical means, of the quality and effectiveness of teaching and learning in the University by, *inter alia*, gathering and disseminating information about teaching and learning at tertiary level; providing confidential, consultative services relating to teaching and learning; assisting staff who have been awarded 'Teaching Development Grants'; conducting research into aspects of teaching and learning for staff and for students; providing courses for credit on aspects of tertiary education and the supervision of research students in this area; participating, as appropriate, in the work of policy-making boards and committees of the University; providing a full range of audiovisual production and audiovisual library services. The AV Production Section includes recently re-equipped colour TV and sound studios; the AV Study Section includes teaching spaces for individual and group use of media and a library of some 3000 AV programmes.

New Zealand Technical Correspondence Institute, *see under Other organizations*

Victoria University of Wellington, University Teaching and Research Centre, Private Bag, Wellington (Contact: Professor J L Clift)

Areas of activity include provision of study programmes; teaching appraisal; course evaluation; support for teaching innovations; advising on the production of audiovisual aids; research into higher education; teaching of higher education. The Centre is a source of help and advice to departments and members of staff who wish to consult with it on aspects of course planning, organization, teaching programmes, lecture preparation and presentation, the conduct of seminars, tutorials, laboratories and other teaching and learning situations, the working out of examination objectives and techniques and, in general, a comprehensive range of teaching methods including the use of teaching aids. The Centre will also provide assistance to any official University Group wishing to undertake a survey to obtain information needed for decision-making on educational matters.

Teachers' colleges

Auckland Teachers' College, Private Bag, Symonds Street, Auckland 3 (Contact: O Carleton, Principal Lecturer in Media, Department of Learning Resources)

Christchurch Teachers' College, PO Box 31-065, Christchurch (Contact: J T Dykes, Principal Lecturer, AV Department)

Dunedin Teachers' College, Union Street, Dunedin (Contact: M Cowell, Senior Lecturer in AV Education)

Hamilton Teachers' College, Private Bag, Hamilton (Contact: E Crotty, Senior Lecturer in AV Education)

North Shore Teachers' College, PO Box 36036, Northcote, Auckland 9 (Contact: C T Goodall, Senior Lecturer in AV Education)

Palmerston North Teachers' College, Private Bag, Palmerston North (Contact: A Thomas, Head, AV Department)

Secondary Teachers' College: Auckland, Private Bag, Symonds Street, Auckland 3 (Contact: E Beavis, Senior Lecturer in AV Education, Director of Teaching Resources Centre)

Wellington Teachers' College, Private Bag, Karori, Wellington 5 (Contact: D Mundell, Senior Lecturer in AV Education)

Other organizations

Department of Education, Resources Development Division, Wellington (Contact: Assistant Director, Resources Development)

Producing, commissioning, lending and purchasing resources for learning for schools. Developing effective systems for the use and management of these resources.

*National Film Library of New Zealand, PO Box 9583, 6th Floor, Cubewell House, Kent Terrace, Wellington (Contact: G Peart, Manager)

*New Zealand Correspondence School, Private Bag, Wellington (Contacts: O Tate, Principal; Mrs G Boraman, Public Relations Officer)

The Government Correspondence School has four major sections: (a) pre-school; (b) primary. Basic education is offered to New Zealand children unable to attend local schools, due to geographic isolation or a physical handicap, also to New Zealand children overseas for limited time. A sub-section provides a resource centre for parents of intellectually handicapped children and education for the child himself. Enrichment programmes provided for gifted children in small towns and rural areas; (c) secondary basic education for children as above. Also courses for pregnant schoolgirls and the socially maladjusted child. Adults eligible to enrol to improve academic qualifications. Specialized courses for English as a second language, prisoners and adults with literacy problems; (d) tertiary in-service teachers who aim to improve qualifications and pre-service training to become teachers. Courses are printed booklets. Languages also have pre-recorded cassettes by native language speakers. Science and woodwork students have prepared boxes of apparatus. Services include daily broadcasts. Weekend seminars run throughout the year. School camps ranging from one month downwards are run to provide social contact for isolated children. Five resident teachers are situated throughout the country to assist with liaison. Courses are provided to secondary school students throughout the country should circumstances warrant it. Papers on various aspects of the school are available from the PRO on request.

New Zealand Council for Educational Research (NZCER), PO Box 3237, Wellington (Contacts: Mr N A Reid, Chief Research Officer, Test Development; Mr G A Wagner, Senior Research Officer, Adult Learning)

A statutory body, set up to carry out educational research and provide information and advisory services, its main activities are research programmes in early childhood education, Maori schooling, and adult learning; test development programme; information and advisory services; and a publication programme. Its publications include: *SHEIK (Study Habits Evaluation and Instruction Kit)*; Progressive Achievement Tests; Study Skills tests; *Going To School* (slide-tape instructional/discussion package).

New Zealand Technical Correspondence Institute, ICI Materials and Resource Unit, Wyndrum Avenue, Private Bag, Lower Hutt (Contact: A E Kinsella, Principal)

The Unit is responsible for in-service training of tutors, development of teaching material for tutors, production of videotape and audiotape material, research into effectiveness of teaching programmes, organization of remedial teaching and preparation of audio material for dyslexic handicapped students.

*Royal New Zealand Air Force, No 2 Technical Training School, RNZAF Base, Wigram, Christchurch

Systems approach to trade training and the use of programmed materials.

*Royal New Zealand Navy, Naval Training Group, HMNZ Naval Base, Devonport, Auckland (Contact: Captain D H O'Donoghue, OBE, RNZN)

The Naval Training Group of the Royal New Zealand Navy was formed in 1975 in order to control and co-ordinate the increasing range and complexity of the training of individuals including both formal training and on-the-job training at sea. In particular, the Naval Training Group was given the following tasks: (a) the establishment of channels of communication with training agencies in New Zealand and overseas; (b) the examination of current training patterns to: (i) eliminate any low-priority content or duplication of effort, (ii) determine the degree of leadership and management training appropriate to the RNZN, (iii) review and update training publications; (c) examination and analysis of the training requirements to achieve the most effective use of resources allocated to training; (d) examining and making recommendations on the application of objective training techniques to the RNZN. Since its inception the Naval Training Group has: (a) promoted the adoption of systems training and progressively all training within the RNZN will be objectivized; (b) formed a Management School: eventually, all RNZN personnel will receive training in the school as they progress to supervisor or higher management levels; (c) obtained recognition and membership from the New Zealand Institute of Management; (d) set up centralized control and co-ordination of both resources and training implementation. Being a young organization, the Royal New Zealand Navy's Naval Training Group is still evolving in scope and organization adopting the experience of similar organizations both within New Zealand (such as the Army Training Group) and overseas (such as the Royal Australian Navy School of Training Technology) to local needs and resources.

NIGER

*Institut National de Documentation, de Recherche et d'Animation Pédagogique, Ministère de l'Education National, Niamey (Contact: M Saadon Galadima)

Television Scolaire du Niger, Boîte Postale 309, Niamey

NIGERIA

Institutes of further and higher education

Ahmadu Bello University, Educational Technology Centre, Zaria (Contact: The Director)

College of Education, Abraka, Bendel State

1. Educational Resource Centre, (Contact: C Noah Musa, Director)

Established in 1976 with Unesco assistance to provide ancillary support services for the institution's teacher education programme, the Educational Resource Centre is a unit of the Education Department. Its main activities are: provision of lectures to NCE teachers in instructional media; provision of instructional materials services to teachers, students and college community; running of in-service seminars for microteaching; providing audio-equipment for lectures, equipments for film projection, etc; and providing space for small group seminars, lectures, etc.

*2. Science Curriculum Development Centre, Science Equipment Workshop

National Technical Teachers' College (Federal Ministry of Education), Akoka, PO Box 269, Yaba (Contact: Mrs S O Ogun, Head of Educational Technology Section)

This Section of the National Technical Teachers' College (NTTC) combines teaching and service by offering lectures and workshops to students on a regular basis as part of education courses leading to the award of the National Certificate of Education (NCE Technical) and the one-year Technical Teacher's Certificate in different disciplines. The primary functions of this Section are: to give instruction on audiovisual methods; to encourage the use of both locally and commercially produced material for teaching and learning effectiveness; to run courses in the production of audiovisual materials; and to render production service to lecturers for effective teaching techniques. There is a CCTV studio heavily used by the College community.

*University of Ibadan, Department of Teacher Education, Ibadan (Contacts: Professor P O Okunrotifa; Dr T A Balogun)

Courses are taught in media and instructional technology to non-degree, undergraduate and postgraduate students of education. Other activities include systems applications to the educational process, curriculum design, analysis and evaluation, and instructional product research; task analysis of African Primary Science Programme (APSP) units; production of AV aids of all sorts, using local materials as well as programmed texts in several fields of the curriculum including the teaching of the Yoruba language; co-operative participation in local, national and international courses and programmes in media use and instructional technology, and consulting services.

*University of Ife, Department of Educational Technology, Ile-Ife (Contacts: Dean, Faculty of Education; Head, Department of Educational Technology)

The Department of Educational Technology was established in 1976 following the reorganization of the Audiovisual Centre. It is one of seven departments in the Faculty of Education involved in teacher training. The Department is both a teaching and a service unit. Its primary function is academic. Courses are offered for the Master's and Doctor's degrees in Educational Communications and Technology where students may develop expertise in the administration of educational technology, instructional development, and production of resources. Undergraduate courses are offered towards the BA, BSc and BEd degrees in Education, providing potential teachers with skills in the design and preparation of instructional resources. Audiovisual services are provided to the University campus including consultation, design, production and maintenance. The facilities include a CCTV system, audio production unit, photographic unit and a 16mm film production unit. A comprehensive brochure is available upon request covering the department and its functions. In addition a newsletter is published quarterly and circulated to interested persons.

University of Ilorin, Educational Resources Unit, Faculty of Health Sciences, University of Ilorin, PMB 1515, Ilorin

The Unit was established to service the innovative training programme of the Faculty of Health Sciences, of the University of Ilorin. Its activities include the preparation and presentation of teaching materials for medical students involved in an integrated course, with a strong emphasis on community work and service, and based, as far as possible around the solution of problems rather than the rote learning of facts.

University of Jos, Instructional Technology Unit, Faculty of Medical Sciences, Jos (Contact: A J Brooks)

The Unit was established in January 1978, to advise on economical and efficient learning techniques, and to design self-instructional materials. The Unit, at present based at the University Teaching Hospital, is now serving the whole University. The Unit's brief at present includes production of videotapes, tape/slide programmes, structured learning materials; design of learning spaces; consultation on teaching/learning methods and curriculum design. Its facilities include a television studio and associated control room fully equipped with colour cameras, and video editing facilities; a photographic section, graphics section, audiovisual library and library of educational information, and information sources. The Unit organizes occasional workshops in educational technology, audiovisual techniques, and television production.

Unit produced materials are being used throughout the University, in educational broadcasting and in some other Nigerian universities.

Future development will include increased liaison with other Nigerian universities, for the exchange of materials, on a nationwide basis, and upgrading of television post production facilities.

University of Lagos, Centre for Educational Technology, Faculty of Education, Yaba (Contact: Mr A Aroloye)

The Centre for Educational Technology now serves the whole university. Its primary aim is the improvement of instruction through more efficient communication between the teacher and the learner. It also serves as a resource centre for teaching devices, materials and ideas for improving education. It has sections concerned with: graphics; photography; resources; and electronics (language laboratories, CCTV, and maintenance/repairs). It has produced some CCTV programmes and publishes a *Film Catalogue* and occasional *Newsletters*.

*University of Nigeria Teaching Hospital, Medical Illustration Unit (Audio-Visual Services), Faculty of Medicine, Enugu (Contact: Mr M O Nwamoh)

Main functions include production and maintenance of instructional materials in the Medical School and Teaching Hospital of the University of Nigeria, as well as offering audiovisual services to other educational institutions. The Unit is equipped to provide video, photographic and graphic services.

Other organizations

ECWA Productions Ltd, Kano Road, PMB 2010, Jos, Plateau State

ECWA Productions Ltd is a church-owned organization with the sole aim of enhancing the spiritual growth of the church in Nigeria. EPL seeks to accomplish this objective through the use of both the electronic and print media, etc. Its main activities include: distribution of: Christian and educational literature, home and office stationery items through its chain of bookshops throughout the country (Challenge Bookshops); counselling and Bible correspondence courses through our Challenge enquiry centre; production of audiovisuals, records and cassettes; production of programmes which are broadcast over Radio ECWA, Monrovia, Liberia to millions of Nigerian listeners and others in West and Central Africa; and a film hire service.

Federal Ministry of Education

1. National Educational Technology Centre, PMB 2027, Kaduna (Contact: Mr Francis Z Gana, Director)

The Centre (NETC) was established with the following functions: the development and production of instructional aids; the training of educational broadcasters and audiovisual aids specialists; the conducting of seminars and workshops on the application of AV technology of classroom teaching; the development of visual aids materials and equipment through the use of local resources and talents based on the country's educational system; and the provision of advisory services to the State Governments on audiovisual matters.

2. Teacher Resource Centre, Ministry of Education, Plateau State, Jos (Contact: Head of Unit)

Activities: teacher training, curriculum development, graphic and reprographic materials, library. *Services:* consultancy, reprographic.

3. Modern Aids to Education Centre, Ministry of Education, Enugu (Contact: The Assistant Chief Inspector of Education)

*Science Equipment Centre, 1A Birrel Avenue, Yaba, Lagos

NORTHERN IRELAND

See Centres of Activity in the UK

NORWAY

International School of Technology, Prof Kohts V 108, Box 10, 1321 Stabekk, Oslo

ISOT A/S is an educational centre providing services linked to transfer of technology. Providing technical and educational assistance ISOT utilizes resources of its member enterprises, backed by a broad combination of know-how and experience available through industrial organizations, institutions and research centres in Norway. ISOT offers basic vocational training in various technical fields and has specialized in the maritime sector – from basic to advanced level within offshore petroleum technology and fishery. ISOT offers assistance at all steps necessary to facilitate the conditions for formal training and experimental learning: feasibility studies; analyses of training needs; design of complete training programmes; preparing curricula in all languages; development and production of material and training aids; planning, construction and operation of training centres; delivery and maintenance of equipment; providing of training of staff and instructors; and project evaluation and follow up. ISOT A/S is registered with UN agencies and the international development banks as educational consulting company.

The National Council for Innovation in Education, Erich Mogensøns vei 38, Oslo 5, Norway (Contact: Øystein Engeland)

Educational innovation in all types of schools: administration, financial support, advice and information concerning educational innovations. Reports on projects, annual reports on innovation in education, and one periodical, *Forsoksnytt.*

The NKI Foundation, *see* International School of Technology (above)

Norsk Korrespondanseskole, Industrigt 41, Oslo 3 (Contact: Aaleiv Nedberg, Managing Director)

Self-owned, non-profit, private correspondence school, controlled by the Law of Correspondence Schools and government regulations for accreditation of correspondence schools as well as individual courses. Correspondence students receive financial support from the Norwegian government. Additional activities include the publishing of educational books, development and production of educational material to customer order, and services to other educational institutions in allowing them to use available computer systems for administrative as well as educational purposes.

*Norwegian State Broadcasting System, NRK/Skolefjernsynet, Majorstua, Oslo 3

*University of Oslo, Institute for Educational Research, Box 1092, Blindern, Oslo 3 (Contact: The Director)

The Institute's fields of research are: history and theory of education, comparative education, educational psychology, sociology of education, and didactics (including R and D work resulting in educational programmes).

*Universitetsforlaget, Department for Educational Planning, Avdeling for Undervisningsplanlegging, PO Box 2670, St H, Oslo 1

PAKISTAN

*Allama Iqbal Open University, Institute of Educational Technology, Sector H-8, Islamabad (Contacts: Dr S M Zaman, Vice-Chancellor; Mrs Muzaffari Quraishi, Registrar)

The University was established in 1974 at Islamabad. The University exists to make opportunities available for lifelong education, particularly to those who must continue earning their livelihood while they study. Principal beneficiaries of the programme of the University are the masses, particularly those in the rural areas. The University also endeavours to remedy the intellectual isolation of teachers and others working for the promotion of rural improvement and community development. The University runs courses in 11 different academic Departments, using correspondence texts backed up by radio and TV programmes and tutorial contact at study centres.

Ministry of Education

1. Instructional Technology Section (Curriculum Wing), Ministry of Education, Sector H-9, Islamabad (Contacts: Mr Mohammad Rawal Veryamani, Joint Educational Adviser; Mr Gauhar Rahman Abbasi, Deputy Educational Adviser; S Habib-ur-Rehman, Specialist (IT))

Originally, the Instructional Technology Section was set up under the Central Bureau of Education. Later on, the Ministry of Education was expanded and the Section was merged in the Ministry of Education so as to enable it to extend its services to a wider range of educational institutions. The Section is equipped with the latest pieces of equipment and staffed by highly skilled personnel. The major function of the Section is to provide training facilities to master educators from teacher training institutions of all levels in Pakistan. The Instructional Technology Section has also been provided with a mobile unit which extends 'on-the-job training facilities' to all levels of institutions. Every year various courses are conducted to expose teachers to the latest pedagogical theories, techniques and skills. The Section's main activities are to: conduct seminars and workshops in the field of instructional technology; develop project schemes for the enhancement of the philosophy of educational technology; develop low-cost teaching aids for junior schools with the help of locally available materials; give professional inputs to 15 micro-teaching clinics established in the colleges of education; and extend services to those agencies who may require services of the Section to meet their educational objectives. Other services are: *Concept Development Cell*: the Cell is the part of the Instructional Technology Section which urges visitors and teachers to write down what they have in their minds to be materialized for production of teaching aids. The Cell is not only challenging for visitors, but also for those who are responsible for giving shape to words and ideas.

2. National Bureau of Curricula and Textbooks, Ministry of Education, Islamabad

Curriculum development in Pakistan is a joint responsibility of the Federal and Provincial Governments. The curriculum development groups in the provinces and those under the Federal Government form a network and work jointly, assisting each other in carrying out curriculum reforms. Staff from schools, universities, teacher training institutions, research institutions and other governmental agencies work throughout the year on a part-time basis, designing and testing curricula, training teachers and producing various kinds of instructional materials and teaching aids.

*Science Education Centre, Institute of Education and Research, Punjab University, New Campus, Lahore (Contact: Professor M Zafar Iqbal)

Under the Science Education Project a model science education centre has been set up as a pioneer resource centre with modern laboratory facilities. The Centre acts as a nucleus for disseminating information and developing and evaluating curricula and materials.

PAPUA NEW GUINEA

*College of External Studies, PO Box 179, Port Moresby

The College offers a range of correspondence courses at secondary level. Innovatory curriculum materials are being devised and a library on correspondence education is being established.

Department of the Prime Minister, The Office of Information, PO Box 2312, Konedobu (Contact: The Director, Office of Information)

Full media services including the following (some of these to PNG overseas Embassies and Commissions only): (a) press release service (Government news only); (2) wire service; (3) publications – newspaper, magazine, periodicals, general information policy and educational etc; (4) film unit – produces educational, cultural, historical and training films in three languages (English, Melanesian Pidgin and Mota); (5) videotape unit – production as above; (6) photographic unit – as above; (7) film and video library (PNG distribution only, although borrowing can be arranged through some overseas diplomatic offices on a restricted list on occasions); (8) field communications: a network of field officers staffed with extension workers in all the 20 provinces active in 'face-to-face' contact with the community; (9) display and exhibitions – one major overseas exhibition planned each year. Internal displays as required.

*University of Papua New Guinea, Teaching Methods and Materials Centre, PO Box 4820 University Post Office, Papua New Guinea

The Centre is responsible for teacher education; acquisition of learning and teaching (curriculum) materials; provision of information to schools and other educational institutions on sources of materials and lending service for direct usage in teaching or for preview purposes; research into problems of education in Papua New Guinea associated with curriculum development. It produces a bi-monthly bulletin related to new ideas and methods on education and containing information of sources of latest materials produced elsewhere; tape/slide programmes; research reports. Services to schools and training institutions include: instruction in the use of teaching machines and the production of audiovisual aids; advice on methods of teaching and the use of audiovisual aids in teaching; lending of TMMC materials for teaching and for preview purposes; recording of video programmes and tapes; the use of TMMC resources for research and reference; copying of pre-recorded audiovisual materials.

PARAGUAY

*Centro de Teleducación del Ministerio de Educación (Centre of Tele-education – Ministry of Education), Iturbe 372, Asunción (Contact: Mabel Palarios, Director)

General assistance to the educational system (ETC and educational radio).

Universidad Nacional de Trujillo, Asunción
1. Department of Educational Sciences (Contacts: Professor Eduardo

Gallardo; Professor Atilio Leon)

2. Department of Second Language and Linguistics (Contacts: Professor Aramis Angulo; Professor Ernesto Zierer)

Research into systems approach to curriculum design, algorithmic procedures in teaching and learning; application of informational psychology and quantitative procedures in teaching, learning and evaluation; use of video equipment in second language teacher training. Publications include *Revista de Pedagogia Cibernetica e Instruccion Programada* (ed A Leon), *Didattica Cibernetica e Insegnemento delle Lingue*, E Zierer (1975) Felice le Monnier, Florence, Italy, occasional search papers and reports.

PERU

*Ministry of Education, Lima 1 (Contact: Dra Rosa Maria Saco de Gueto, Instituto Nacional de Investigaciones y Desarollo Educativo (INIDE) (National Institute for Education and Research Development))

National Institute of Teleducation, Ministero de Educación Publica, Parque Universitaria, Lima (Contact: Mercedes Apraiz de Barrenechea)

The Institute is concerned with all aspects of AV education. It provides an educational service at all levels including 'éducation permanente', to the whole nation.

*Pontificia Universidad Catolica del Peru (Catholic University of Peru), Campo Universitario, Final Av Bolivar, Pueblo Libre, Lima 21 (Contacts: Raul Palacios, Agustin Campos, Jose Domingues, Adriana Flores de Saco, Rosa Maria Saco de Ceuto (CETUC), Centro de Investigación de Tecnologia Educativa Aplicada (CITEA) (Centre for Study of Applied Educational Technology))

CETUC trains specialist personnel in all aspects of the use of media for educational and cultural development purposes, produces programmes and audiovisual materials (16mm and Super 8 film, TV, audio recordings, slides, etc), performs research into the use of media for education and development and offers a media service to the University. It also has a library and organizes an annual 'festival of tele-education'. CITEA has primarily a research and teaching function. Research reports; general articles, bibliographies and reading lists; information bulletins are also published.

Proyecto Latinoamericano de Teleducación de la Fundación Konrad Adenauer, *see under Regional Centres of Activity – South America*

PHILIPPINES

University of the Philippines

*1. Science Education Center, Vidal Tan Hall, Diliman, Quezon City (Contact: Dr Dolores F Hernandez, Director)

The University of the Philippines Science Education Center (UPSEC) started in 1964 as a Ford Foundation project. In 1969 it was established as a permanent unit of the University and, in 1975, as a result of an IBRD project, it became the National Curriculum Development Center for science and mathematics. Its functions are to develop curriculum materials in science and mathematics for both elementary and high school levels, formal and informal; to offer teacher-training programmes for degree or non-degree courses, formal or *ad hoc*, long-term or short-term; to conduct research in science education, basic as well as applied. The academic activities revolve around at least six programmes: curriculum development, training, community and extension, curriculum evaluation, research, and teaching aids and equipment. Curriculum development work is mainly in connection with the National Textbook Project of the Ministry of Education and Culture. Other curriculum activities are smaller in scale, although equally important, among them being non-formal materials exemplifying the application of technology to education. Needless to say, curriculum evaluation activities go hand in hand with curriculum development. UPSEC activities in teacher training are largely related to the nationwide Science Education Project of the Philippines, an integrated approach to science and mathematics teacher training. Under this scheme UPSEC is responsible for the training of teacher trainers for selected schools from different parts of the country. UPSEC also offers short-term courses on specific school subjects, running from 18 to 50 hours.

*2. Regional Center for Educational Innovation and Technology (INNOTECH), 3rd Floor, College of Education Building (Contact: Dr Liceria Brillantes Soriano, Director of INNOTECH)

INNOTECH is one of seven centres/projects of SEAMEO (Southeast Asian Ministers of Education Organization). It is the major educational research and training arm of SEAMEO. It provides the institutional capability for assisting member countries to identify their educational problems and to help them seek solutions to those problems. The Centre has a range of facilities and professional resources for developing and testing low-cost educational delivery systems for mass primary education without sacrifice of quality. It also provides training for key personnel to become effective change agents in the SEAMEO member countries; a range of courses is available. The following research projects are also under way: *Project IMPACT* (Instructional Management by Parents, Community and Teachers) aims to develop an effective and economical delivery system for mass primary education. *Project RIT* (Reduced Instructional Time) aims to reduce teachers' instructional time without resulting in a lower level of students' accomplishment. *Project CB-BLP* (Community-Based Basic Learning Package) aims to provide out-of-school youths and adults with relevant basic learning in primary education in a relatively short time. *Project NTR* (Non-traditional Roles of Teachers) aims to help improve teacher education and is designed to develop a variety of teacher preparation/improvement packages (TPPs/TIPs) for training or retraining personnel in major types of non-traditional educational programmes used or likely to be used in the Region. Regular publications: *INNOTECH Newsletter* (bi-monthly); *INNOTECH Journal* (semi-annual).

Population Center Foundation (PCF), South Superhighway (off Nicholls Interchange), Makati, Metro Manila; PO Box 2065 MCC, Makati, Metro Manila

PCF is a private foundation set up in 1972 to tackle the population problem in the Philippines. It is therefore concerned (in part) with the production of teaching packages and AV kits designed to put across the family planning message in rural areas. It is also involved in the training of outreach workers for the programme.

Southeast Asia Interdisciplinary Development Institute (SAIDI), PO Box 3400, Manila; 470 Arzobispo Street, Intramuros, Manila (Contacts: Dr Jacqueline E Blondin, President-Founder; Matricio Getigan, Executive Vice-President; Bernard Calilao, Administrative Officer; Dr Perla Rizalina M Tayko, Academic Dean)

The Institute saw its beginnings in 1965 when it launched a specialized programme in educational media and technology for educators all over the Philippines. This programme was affiliated with three Graduate Schools, namely: Ateneo de Manila University, University of Santo Tomas, and Philippine Christian University. SAIDI offered then the major field of educational media and technology to students pursuing either masters or doctoral studies in these institutions. Since 1972 the Institute has also moved into the field of executive training, and offers courses to students from all over SE Asia; the main thrust of its activities lies in the area of formation, training and development of individuals, groups, organizations and communities in SE Asia.

The Institute provides three major areas of services, namely: consultancy to individuals, groups, organizations and communities; professional and technical assistance in training and development for specific identified needs and problems of individuals, groups, organizations and communities; and educational services for graduate and postgraduate studies. Its products include: materials (instructional and curricular in nature) for institutions' use in training and development; *SAIDI Journal* for the publication of the researches of students and faculty at the Institute.

*Technological University of the Philippines, Educational Technology Department, Ayala Boulevard, Manila (Contact: Mr Cristeto P Bonilla)

The conversion of the former Philippine College of Arts and Trades into the Technological University of the Philippines (TUP) in June 1978, gave rise to the establishment of several departments and centres in TUP. The Educational Technology Department is one of the departments established in January 1979 under the Research and Development Centre (R & D). The ETD promotes and encourages the use of modular instruction in industrial training through holding of seminar-workshops for the dissemination of information and provides advice and assistance on the use of modules in their training programmes. It provides assistance to other vocational/ technical institutions in modular instruction, development of learning resources and audiovisual learning. It conducts seminar-workshops on educational technology in technician education and training for the heads of technical/technician institutions who have training-management responsibilities for manpower development.

National curriculum development centres in the Philippines

*UP Science Education Center, Vidal Tan Hall, University of the Philippines Campus, Diliman, Quezon City (Contact: Dr Dolores Hernandez, Director)

*Language Study Center, Philippine Normal College, Taft Avenue, Manila (Contact: Dr Fe Otanes, Director)

*National Research and Development Center for Teacher Education, Ministry of Education and Culture, Arroceros, Manila (Contact: Dr Lourdes E Sumagaysay, Acting Assistant Director and Officer in Charge)

*Social Studies Center, Ministry of Education and Culture, Vidal Tan Hall, Room 305, UP Campus, Quezon City (Contacts: Dr Leticia Salazar-Constantino, Chief and Project Director; Ms Fe A Hidalgo, Acting Assistant and Project Co-ordinator – Elementary)

POLAND

Adam Mickiewicz University

*1. Department of Didactic, ul Szamarzewskiego 89, 60-568 Poznán (Contacts: Dr Kazimierz Denek, Head of Department of Didactic, Professor of Education; Dr Tadeusz Krajewski, Professor of Education)

*2. Institute of Educational Technology, ul Slowackiego 20, 60-823 Poznán (Contacts: Professor Dr Leon Leja, Head of the Institute; Docent Dr Waclaw Strykowski, Vice-Director of the Institute and Professor of Educational Technology)

The Institute of Educational Technology of Adam Mickiewicz University in Poznán was founded by Professor Leja in 1965 as one of the first academic institutions in Poland working on the problems of educational technology at university level.

*University of Gdánsk, Institute of Pedagogy, Gdánsk-Oliwa, ul Krzywoustego 19 (Contact: Professor Dr Hab Klemens Trzebiatowski)

The Institute of Pedagogy belongs to the Department of Humanities, University of Gdánsk. Its two major functions are: supplying higher-level education for future teachers and tutors – day, extra-mural and postgraduate studies – and directing research work in the field of education. The Institute includes administratively permanent research and lecturing teams dealing with: educational theory; general didactics; didactics for mentally retarded children, children with difficulties and the like; history of educational systems and curricula.

The Pedagogical University, Centre for Didactic Machines, ul Podchoráżych 2, 30-084 Kraków (Contact: Dr Eustachy Berazowski, Professor of Education, Head of the Centre)

Poznán Technical University, Centre for Educational Technology, ul Strzelecka 11, 61-845 Poznán

1. Dr Ryszard Piasek, Assistant Professor of Educational Technology, Head of Postgraduate Teachers Training Centre in Educational Technology

Fields of interests: development in theory and practice of educational technology, application of AV media, teacher training and staff development, higher education policy.

2. Dr Waldemar Prussak, Assistant Professor of Educational Technology

Fields of interests: educational film, new methods of physics teaching, computers in education.

Research Institute for Science Policy and Higher Education, ul Nowy Swiat 69, 00-045 Warsaw (Contact: Dr Michat Bron Jr)

Teaching adults with media, adult educators and adult educationists training.

University of Warsaw

1. Department of Didactics, Institute of Pedagogy, ul Szturmowa 1, 02-678

Warsaw (Contact: Professor Dr Wincenty Okoń. Professor Dr Okoń is also chairman of the Pedagogical Sciences Committee in the Polish Academy of Science)

2. Adult Education Chair, Institute of Education, ul Szturmowa 1, 02-678 Warsaw (Contact: Mrs Agnieszka Bron-Wojciechowska)

Adult learning, distance education.

*University of Wroclaw, Co-operative Team for Prognosing and Creating Models of Education, Institute of Pedagogy, ul Dawida 1, 50-527 Wroclaw (Contact: Dr dr hab Ryszard Lukaszewicz)

PORTUGAL

*Instituto de Tecnologia Educativa – ITE (Institute of Educational Technology), Rua Florbela Espanca – 1799 Lisboa Codex (Contact: Dr Alfredo Betamio de Almeida, President)

ITE is a central department of the Portuguese Ministry of Education which provides assistance to schools, mainly with audiovisual materials including audio and video materials. It also provides training courses in AV media. Services are provided through the government departments dealing with higher and basic education and through schools (basic, secondary and high schools) and other cultural institutions. ITE produces all necessary materials for educational television and other general ways of teaching.

Instituto Portugués de Ensino a Distância – IPED, Av Elias Garcia, 137, 1093 Lisboa (Contacts: Professor A Rocha Trindade, President; Professor Maria Emilia Ricardo Marques, Head of Educational Technology Department; Mrs Manuela Oliveira, Secretary of the Scientific Board)

The IPED is a higher education institution, teaching at a distance. The target population of students are adults, geographically scattered and professionally active. The Institute is a forerunner of the Portuguese Open University (Universida de Aberta Portuguesa) which will be launched in two years' time. Courses now in production are mainly formal, aiming to provide opportunities to teaching staff to complete their academic qualifications while in service. Informal courses on subjects such as Portuguese culture, language and history are also planned. The IPED has four departments: Educational Technology Department; Pedagogy Department; Didactical Material Production Department (Text, Audio, Video); Documentation Centre. Co-ordination and policy-making are carried out by a Scientific Board whose members are university professors and researchers on educational problems; the higher authority with respect to IPED is the Ministry of Education.

RUMANIA

CEPES – Centre Européen pour l'Enseignement Supérieur, *see under Regional Centres of Activity – Europe*

*Centre for Educational Media, Neferilor 12, Bucarest

The Institute for Pedagogical and Psychological Research (Institutul de Cercetari Pedagogice si Psihologice), 70634 Bucarest 5, str Sfintii Apostoli nr 14

The Institute undertakes teaching and psychology research into content, teaching technology and multi-media methods of pre-school, primary and secondary teaching as well as teaching handicapped children. To similar ends, research is being carried out on the integration of higher education with research and production. Another area of research is the education of schoolchildren, character training, their ideological, political, moral and civic education, preparing them technically and practically, developing their creativeness and scientific thinking, as well as their educational and professional orientation. Teaching management is another concern. Some of this work will result in treatises on the history of pedagogic thought in Rumania, and works on teaching and psychology in general. Publications include manuals and programmes, multi-media educational materials, educational TV, evaluation tools, school programmes, materials for independent study, education research projects.

SENEGAL

*Direction de la Recherche et de la Planification, Ministère de l'Education Nationale (Contact: Georges M'Bodj)

*Ecole Normale d'Enseignement Technique Masculin, Route Ouakam, BP 5004, Dakar

*Lycée Technique Maurice Delafosse, Canal IV, Dakar

*Radio Educative Rurale du Sénégal, Orts BP 1765, Dakar (Contact: Baba Counta)

*Television Scolaire du Sénégal, BP 10148, Dakar-Liberté (Contact: Saliou Maugane).

SINGAPORE

AMIC – Asian Mass Communication Research and Information Centre, *see under Regional Centres of Activity – Asia*

Curriculum Development Institute of Singapore, Bukit Timah Campus, Cluny Road, Singapore 1025 (Contact: The Director)

Institute of Education, Department of Instructional Technology, Bukit Timah Campus, Cluny Road, Singapore 1025 (Contact: The Director, Institute of Education)

Areas of activities: training student teachers in the theories and practice of educational communications; designing and implementing courses in instructional technology, microteaching and the evaluation of instructional skills via video-recording and playback. *Materials produced:* audiovisual materials for instructional purposes, including videotapes on basic teaching skills. *Services offered:* offering courses to pre-service and in-service teachers in educational communications, and in the preparation and production of audiovisual materials; providing media support services to the students and teaching staff of the Institute; and advising schools in the setting up of media resource centres. *Recent publications:* the Institute publishes the following materials regularly: *Singapore Journal of Education; Teaching and Learning* (a publication for teachers); *Institute of Education Newsletter; Institute of Education Prospectus;* and *Institute of Education Annual Report.*

Language Project Centre, Portsdown Road, Singapore 0513 (Contact: The Director)

***Regional Institute of Higher Education and Development (RIHED),** CSSDI (Civil Service Staff Development Institute) Building, Heng Mui Keng Terrace, Singapore 5 (Contact: Dr Banphot Virasai, Deputy Director)

RIHED is an autonomous institution supported by the governments of Indonesia, Malaysia, Singapore and Thailand. The express purpose of the Institute is twofold, namely 'to stimulate and facilitate co-operation among the universities and the governments of the countries in South East Asia, and to enhance the contributions of higher education to the social and economic development of the countries of the region and of the region as a whole'. RIHED has performed several tasks including the setting up of a reference library, the conduct and publication of research projects centred in institutes of higher learning and relating to development within the region, sponsorship or co-sponsorship of seminars and conferences, and the encouragement and facilitation of inter-university and inter-country co-operation. All the activities are principally focused on the contributions or bearing of higher education on the social and economic development of the countries of the region and of the region as a whole. To make known its programmes and to give current information and discussions relating to higher education and development, RIHED publishes the *RIHED News* once every four months. In book form the Institute has published essays, research reports, and results of national and international seminars and conferences.

***Singapore Educational Media Service,** 29 Harding Road, Singapore 1024 (Contact: Peter Seow, Deputy Director Media)

The Singapore Educational Media Service (SEMS) was established in April 1973 as a branch of the Ministry of Education with the integration of the then Singapore Educational Television Service (ETV) and the Audio Visual Section of the Ministry of Education. The objectives of SEMS are to contribute towards the improvement of education in general and to support the school in areas where educational media can best serve; to introduce innovative approaches to education; to encourage teachers to utilize new developments in educational technology in order to enhance classroom teaching; to provide schools with consultancy as well as developmental services pertaining to media materials. The ETV Section of SEMS produces programmes for primary and secondary schools and junior colleges. It concentrates on language, arts, science and mathematics. The Media Section of SEMS serves all schools and junior colleges, and its main functions are developing media materials for schools; providing advice and consultation on media development; and training teachers in the use of educational media. SEMS also operates an Instructional Materials Library (IML), which offers member schools multi-media kits, films, filmstrips, pre-recorded audio-tapes, video-cassettes and other media materials. It publishes teachers' notes for TV programmes and a quarterly magazine, *SEMS*.

SOUTH AFRICA

***University of Cape Town, Teaching Methods Unit,** Rondebosch 7700 (Contact: Professor J H F Meyer, Director)

The Unit was established in 1977 to improve the quality of teaching and learning at the University of Cape Town. It provides, within the university, the infrastructure for teaching improvement activities to take place. It also provides the necessary knowledge, expertise and facilities for these activities. Main activities include the design, implementation and evaluation of university courses; the identification and illumination of teaching and learning problems; the design of learning materials and learning spaces; conducting regular in-house courses on all facets of teaching improvement; the prosecution of research in the areas of course evaluation, media, and student learning problems; the use of sophisticated colour television and sound studios; maintenance of audiovisual equipment; photographic colour processing, slide duplication and artwork reproduction; and consultancy on teaching and learning problems. Publications include *Methomix*, a quarterly newsletter containing practical information on the improvement of teaching, and occasional research reports.

*Institute for Educational Research, PO Box X41, Pretoria (Contact: Mr J B Haasbroek, Director)

The Human Sciences Research Council (HSRC) was instituted as a statutory organization in 1969, with the function to 'undertake, promote and co-ordinate research in the human sciences, advise the Government and other bodies on the use of research findings, and disseminate information on the human sciences'. The Institute for Educational Research is one of 11 institutes of HSRC, and undertakes research directed towards producing guidelines for a sound educational system in South Africa. Research is done in the fields of psychopedagogics (educational psychology), sociopedagogics, didactic pedagogics, orthopedagogics, comparative education, school guidance, educational technology and pre-school, formative and formal education. The research in the above fields is co-ordinated where possible and there is also liaison with the other institutes of the HSRC. The Institute consists of four sections, Psycho- and Sociopedagogical Research, Pre-primary and Primary Educational Research, Special (for the mentally retarded, autistic, highly-gifted, *et al*), and Comparative Educational Research and Curriculum Research. Research on educational technology (eg computer-assisted learning and instruction, the use of television in instruction) and educational statistics forms a sub-section of the Section for Curriculum Research. Relevant publications (available through the Human Sciences Research Council, Pretoria); Hattingh, D L, *Programmed Instruction*; Haasbroek, J B, 1975, *Aids in the School Context*; Liebenberg, C R, 1978, *The Incorporation of Television in Teacher Training in the RSA*; Fourie, W N, 1978, *Reading Assistance: Various Methods of Approach*; Serfontein, C P, *Computer Assisted Instruction: Remedial Mathematics Instruction in Absolute Values* (to be published); Hattingh, D L, *Manual for the Writing of Computer Assisted Instruction Programmes* (to be published).

University of the Orange Free State, PO Box 339, Bloemfontein 9300

*1. Bureau for University Education (Contact: Professor A H Strydom, Director)

The aim of the Bureau for University Education (BUE) is to promote planning, improvement, innovation and preservation of education as laid down by the educational policy of the University of the Orange Free State. At present the BUE consists of three Sections: (a) the Section for Education Development, whose functions are to present courses, seminars, symposia and workshops for lecturers to improve teaching, planning, etc, and to provide lecturers with scientific literature, advice and information concerning educational matters; (b) the Section for Educational Research, whose functions are to initiate, plan and implement experimental educational research projects on the campus, to compile, computerize and disseminate information, documents and literature, and to establish contact with similar research units; (c) the Section for Educational Technology, which provides the on-campus audiovisual services including the management of equipment and the production of materials.

*2. Research Unit for Education System Planning (Contact: Professor D Vermaak)

The Research Unit for Education System Planning (RUEP) was established towards the end of 1974 as part of the Department of Comparative Education at the Faculty of Education of the University of the Orange Free State. RUEP assists education departments of developing countries in Southern Africa to identify educational objectives in the light of their general targets for development and to restructure existing educational systems and to alleviate problem areas. Research is carried out on educational systems in the following areas: analysis of systems, external factors influencing the system, education in Africa, and planning methods and approaches.

University of South Africa, The Department of Educational Technology, PO Box 392, Pretoria (Contact: John M Smith, Director)

The University of South Africa (UNISA) is a non-residential university presenting approximately 600 courses in 50 departments and six faculties to 55,000 undergraduate and postgraduate students mainly in Southern Africa and throughout the world. The Department of Educational Technology at UNISA is a service unit mainly training, advising and assisting teaching staff in the production and use of multi-media study material. Its functions are to monitor the needs of *all* departments in order to budget for and purchase hardware and software; to evaluate constantly newly available materials and equipment; to maintain a loan service of equipment to staff; to train teaching staff in media selection, scripting, planning for and the preparation of multi-media programmes; to assist in the production of multi-media study material; to maintain and repair all audiovisual equipment; to research the possibilities and effectiveness of multi-media in teletuition.

*University of the Witwatersrand, Johannesburg

1. Central Graphics Service (Contacts: Mr B Darlington, Acting Head; Mrs C Cardosa)

Main activities: the Service provides a continuous service for the Television Service of the University, produces a number of teaching aids for various academic departments, assists students, research workers and academics in the production of projects, dissertations and theses, as well as the regular production of the student newspaper.

2. Central Television Service (Contacts: Mrs K Turkington, Director; Mr F Cluley; Mr C Grove)

The studio complex of the Central Television Service is one of the most sophisticated in Southern Africa and comprises 13,000 sq metres and includes a colour television studio, a black and white television studio and two audio-studios.

SPAIN

*Ensenanza Programada e Ingeniería de Sistemas Educativos (EPISE), Muntaner 430, Barcelona 6 (Contact: Dr J M Ventosa)

Areas of activity: design and development of programmed learning courses/ distance education and training with programmed learning courses (since 1973) including: management training, clerical training and bank employee training at a distance.

*Escuela Municipal de Medios Audio-Visuales, C/Panadés n 12, Barcelona (Contact: D José Serra Estruch)

*Institutos de Ciencias de la Educación (ICEs) – Institutes of Educational Sciences.

There are 25 of these Institutes, at the following Universities: Universidad Autónoma de Barcelona; Universidad Autónoma de Barcelona a Lleida; Universidad Autónoma de Barcelona a Girona; Universidad Central de Barcelona; Universidad Politécnica, Barcelona; Universidad de Bilbao; Universidad de Córdoba; Universidad de Extremadura, Badajoz; Universidad de Granada; Universidad de La Laguna, Islas Canarias; Universidad Complutense, Madrid; Universidad Autónoma, Madrid, Universidad Politécnica, Madrid; Universidad de Málaga; Universidad de Oviedo; Universidad de Salamanca; Universidad de Santander; Universidad de Santiago, Santiago de Compostela; Universidad de Sevilla; Universidad Literaria, Valencia; Universidad Politécnica, Valencia; Universidad de Valladolid; Universidad de Zaragoza; Universidad de Deusto, Navarra; Universidad de Navarra, Pamplona; Universidad Pontificia de Salamanca.

*Instituto de Ciencias de la Educación, Universidad Complutense, Campus de Somosaguas, Madrid 23 (Contact: Dr Arturo de la Orden, Director Adjunto)

The Institute is organized into four departments: Teacher Training, Educational Research, Counselling and Guidance, and Instructional Technology. Each Department is headed by a specialist, and each is responsible to the Director and Co-Director of the Institute.

*Instituto Nacional de Ciencias de la Educación (INCIE), Ciudad Universitaria s/n, Madrid 3 (Contact: D Fernando Gómez Herrera, Director del Programa de Tecnología Educativa)

*Instituto Nacional de Empleo, C/Condesa de Venadito 9, Madrid-27

*Instituto Official de Radiodifusión y Televisión, Carretera Dehesa de la Villa Kml, Madrid-35

*Instituto de Técnicas Educativas (ITE) de Universidades Laborales, Alcalá de Henares, Madrid

*Servicio de Publicaciones del Ministerio de Educación, Ciudad Universitaria s/n Madrid 3

SRI LANKA

*Department of Examinations, Malay Street, Colombo 2 (Contact: D Percy Nanayakkara, Assistant Commission of Examinations, Data Processing Manager)

Sole examining body for the Government of Sri Lanka, conducting over 150 examinations and examining nearly one million candidates annually. Produces tests for administration centrally, statistical data and resource materials.

*Sri Lanka Broadcasting Corporation, PO Box 574, Independence Square, Colombo 7 (Contact: Mrs Indranee Herat Gunaratne, Controller, Education Service)

The Education Service of the Sri Lanka Broadcasting Corporation broadcasts programmes in Sinhala, Tamil and English to schools throughout the island at primary and secondary levels. Broadcasts are repeated in the evenings for the benefit of teachers, parents, and students at home. The subject areas to be broadcast are determined by a Joint Committee of Educational Broadcasting, whose membership comprises officials of the Ministry of Education and the Sri Lanka Broadcasting Corporation. The Ministry of Education also pays for half the transmission costs. Educational publications are also handled by the Service, and it also broadcasts programmes to university undergraduates (internal and external students) in collaboration with the University of Sri Lanka. At present the Service is engaged in planning educational programmes in science, English and population education to coincide with the country's new developmental project at a regional level.

SUDAN

*Educational Documentation Centre, PO Box 2490, Khartoum (Contact: I M S Shatir)

The Centre was established in 1967 to collect documents on education from Sudan and abroad. Its main services include bibliography services, library and photocopying. Publications include a quarterly bulletin in Arabic and English, *At Tawtheq Attarbawi (Educational Documentation)*, and the national report on education presented to IBE at Geneva.

SWEDEN

Esselte Studium, S-171 76 Solna

Publishers of school books and producers of school equipment and teaching aids for all levels.

*Forsvarets Brevskola (The Correspondence School of the Swedish Armed Forces), Fack, S-10045, Stockholm 90 (Contact: Bjorn Hall, Head of R&D)

In the autumn of 1942 when the Correspondence School of the Swedish Armed Forces (FBrevS) started, it was purely a correspondence school. Like its civilian equivalents the School has followed developments within the educational field, and today it can be considered more as a centre of educational technology within the armed forces. This development means that FBrevS today conducts a wide range of activities concerning most of the educational areas of application; from teacher training to production of study material supplementing the teachers, from education of conscript to training in leadership. This wide range can be taken as a result of the last few years' development towards integration of different study materials and experiences with a view to continuously improving the entire educational contribution.

University of Gothenburg, Department of Educational Research, PO Box 1010, S-431 26 Mölndal (Contact: Dr H Dahlgren)

*Ingemar Ternbo, Liber Laromedel, Slottsgatan 24, 205 10 Malmö

Publishing: educational textbooks, aids and systems, books on education and management.

Liber Hermods, Fack, S-205 10 Malmö (Contact: Erna Prior, Managing Director)

Hermods is the oldest and largest correspondence school in Sweden, and though a private organization is officially recognized as an educational institution by the school authorities. Courses in a wide range of subjects are offered both to individuals and to groups of students. In addition to single subject courses, Hermods also provides occupational course combinations in business, commerce and technology, and complete courses for secondary school qualifications and also a number of courses at university level. In co-operation with the Swedish Board of Education, Hermods runs some 40 overseas schools around the world, where correspondence education is combined with oral tuition. Traditional correspondence education is by no means Hermods' only way of teaching. For instance, audio cassettes are used in language courses and are at present being planned for guidance in other subject courses as well. The telephone is another new distance teaching medium which Hermods has started to use. Integrated multi-media courses with radio and TV programmes combined with correspondence teaching have been produced by Hermods and the Swedish Broadcasting Corporation since the 60s. Hermods also offers intensive courses in languages and international marketing, and consulting services for specially devised training for companies, authorities and organizations.

Hermods pays great attention to research and development activities in the field of distance education, particularly concerning the two-way communication between student and school or tutor. On its own, Hermods has developed CADE, a system for computer-assisted distance education which has been most favourably received by the students and, in addition, has aroused a keen interest among distance educators around the world.

*Linköping University, Department of Education, Fack, S-581 83 Linköping (Contact: Professor I Werdelin)

Educational research (adult education, teaching training, concept formation and learning, international education); the study of education, teacher training.

School of Education, Malmö, Department of Educational and Psychological Research, PO Box 23501, S-24500 Malmö (Contact: Professor A Bjerstedt)

The Swedish Educational Broadcasting Company, Utbildningsradion, Fack, S-11580 Stockholm

Sveriges Utbildningsradio AB (Swedish Educational Broadcasting Company) is a new radio and television company. Like Lokalradio AB (the company handling local radio services) it is a subsidiary of Sveriges Radio. The Company enjoys a free and independent status *vis-à-vis* public authorities, organizations and pressure groups. Utbildningsradion (UR) is to produce and broadcast programmes for the entire educational sector, ie pre-schools, schools, adult education, and university education. Certain guidelines have been drawn up by the Government. These particularly emphasize that UR should give priority to productions for disadvantaged groups such as those with only a short-term schooling behind them, and the physically and mentally handicapped. The importance of productions for immigrants, and of increased regional activities, is similarly emphasized. The Publishing Division will produce printed matter, series of colour slides, etc for use in direct connection with individual programmes or series. UR also collaborates with other publishing houses. UR has a staff of over 300, and its operations are financed by tax revenues from the National Budget.

SWITZERLAND

Abteilung für Unterrichts-Medien (AUM) (Division of Instructional Media), Medical Faculty, University of Berne, Inselspital 14, CH-3010 Berne (Contact: Jürg F Steiger, MD)

Functions of AUM include counselling, service, development and research in the field of instructional media for health professions (medical students, physician's continuing education, allied health personnel, patient instruction). There are ten full-time staff members: two MD, one secretary, three graphic artists, two photographers, and two technicians. Its goal is the diversification of traditional learning methods and resources in order to promote the concept of self education. Its services include the production of AV self-instructional programmes; running pedagogical seminars for physicians (topics: learning objectives, microteaching, instructional media, simulation techniques); and carrying out tests on AV hardware. It has now produced 470 self-instructional programmes (tape-slide; video; multi-media), and has published numerous papers in several languages on AV self-instruction in medicine.

*Association for Teaching and Learning Methods (GLM), PO Box 853, 4502 Solothurn (Contact: Dr Stephan Portmann)

GLM was founded on the initiative of the Institute of Occupational Psychology in October 1971 and is a non-profit-making Association under Swiss law. GLM supports the development and use of teaching and learning methods, particularly by promoting information and co-ordination, and the interchange of experience, and further development. As such, the Institute is one of many private and public bodies, who have devoted themselves to the same tasks which they perform in various ways. But again and again there has been, during the last few years, a lack of communication and co-ordination between the various types of institutions: public and private schools; organizations for public and private education and training; scientists and producers. The gap is closed by GLM, which sees itself as a forum of scientists and practitioners who, independently of interest politics, exchange experience and research results and offer this information to a wide circle. The immediate aim of GLM is to create practical and well-researched guidelines in this field, which is so confusing through its wealth of genuine and apparent innovations, and to publicize and stimulate new ideas. To this end GLM organizes regular professional events, seminars, conventions, information functions, and visits. It is concerned to further contact between its members and tries to assert and find recognition in the educational political field for its findings and experience. The membership rules of the Association provide for individual and group membership, which carries various privileges including free receipt of the Association's Bulletin.

CENCAV – Centre d'enseignement médical et de communication audio-visuelle, CHUV, CH-1011 Lausanne (Contacts: Dr P-H Gygax, MD, Director of Centre; Dr M F Ostini, PhD, Head, Instructional Design)

An audiovisual media centre created in 1974, CEMCAV has a staff of 18, of whom two are academics, and has administrative links with CHUV Medical Centre (approximately 4000 employees) and the Medical School of Lusanne University (approximately 1000 students and 120 faculty members). Its . activities include: planning of acquisition, distribution and use of media hardware and software for teaching, learning, and research in the health sciences; management of teaching and learning facilities which, within the compounds of the Medical Centre, are suitable for being used with all kinds of educational technology approaches; production of audiovisual materials and programmes geared towards more effective and efficient teaching and learning processes; creation of appropriate systems mechanisms for introducing instructional innovations in pre- and postgraduate, continuing and in-service medical training. Services include: medical photography, graphics, and medical illustration services for use in medical training, patient care, and health sciences research; audiovisual classroom and conference services for lecturers, paper sessions and poster sessions; production of slide-tapes, videograms, 16mm film sequences, and multi-media programmes primarily for in-house use and storage in the media centre; instructional design services for faculty, staff, and students requesting assistance in developing and managing instruction; and training of French speaking WHO fellows in the administration, selection, production, and use of audiovisual and educational technology in the health sciences. Materials produced include four 16mm films, 30 posters, 2316 transparencies, and 40,000 slides and photos. Publications in English: *Educational Technology and Instructional Development: Exemplifying Institutional Change*, Proceedings 6th International Conference on Improving University Teaching, Lausanne (Switzerland), July 9-12 1980.

*Centre de Psychologie, avenue de Clos-Brochet 32, CH-2000 Neuchâtel (Contact: Andreé Gonthier)

Educational technology and programmed instruction. Materials produced include instructional programmes and modular instruction and techniques to produce these pedagogical devices and the pedagogical design/planning.

*Centre de Recherches Psychopédagogiques, Cycle d'Orientation, avenue Joli-Mont 15A, 1211 Geneva 28 (Contact: M Metraux)

Guidance evaluation, research reports, automated system for test analysis, simulation/games, research, counselling and information.

Centre for Teaching and Research (Zentrum für Lehre und Forschung), Kantonsspital, Hebelstrasse 20, CH-4031 Basel (Contacts: Professor A Pletscher, Department of Research; Professor H P Rohr, Teaching; Dr R von Brunn, Medical Library)

The Centre for Teaching and Research consists of facilities for teaching, the medical library and the Department of Research of the University Clinics and Institutes of the Kantonsspital Basel. Although primarily a research and teaching centre, it uses and produces audiovisual materials.

Chaire de Pedagogie et Didactique, *see* Lausanne Ecole Polytechnique

*Fédération Suisse pour l'Education des Adultes (Swiss Federation for Adult

Education), Oerlikonerstr 38, Postfach, 8057 Zurich (Contact: Dr H Amberg)

Liaison with public authorities; training and techniques for adult education; publications include: quarterly journal *Education Permanente*, leaflets for teachers, guides on professional training for adult educators; enquiry service; exchange of information and documents.

GLM Gesellschaft für Lehr-und Lernmethoden, *see* Association for Teaching and Learning Methods (GLM)

*Institut Central Ort, CH-1247 Anières

Information institution which arranged the first demonstration of programmed learning in Europe.

Institut für Ausbildungs-und Examensforschung (IAE) der Medizenischen Fakultät der Universität Bern (Institute for Research in Education and Evaluation, Faculty of Medicine, University of Bern), Inselspital 14c, CH-3010 Bern (Contact: H G Pauli, MD, Professor and Director)

Educational institution established in 1971 through the co-operative financing of the Swiss Federal Government and Canton Bern. The Institute is an administrative part of the Faculty of Medicine of the University of Bern and is located in its medical centre. Its main activities are: health services research; educational development and research; and evaluation in medical education.

Institut Romand de Recherches et de Documentation Pédagogiques (Romand Institute of Educational Research and Documentation), 43 Faubourg de l'Hopital, CH-2000 Neuchâtel (Contact: Jacques-André Tschoumy, Director)

The Institute was created in 1969 to help in promoting and co-ordinating the efforts of the French-speaking Swiss cantons in the field of education up to and including secondary level. The Institute has three departments: *Research* – its task is to study the introduction of new curricula and to advise the school authorities of any corrective action that might seem necessary; *Teaching aids* – prepares handbooks, exercises, etc used in teacher training and in classrooms; *Documentation* – collects information needed by school authorities, teachers, students and the Institute itself. The Institute has been working for several years on the curricula of mathematics, French, German, music and environment. It produces teaching materials, research reports and a periodical, *Co-ordination*.

*I Vasek, Habsburgerstr 34, 6000 Lucerne

Advice on how to rationalize the teaching and learning process in general by the principles of algorithms; and working out a course for learning and teaching through TV. An English course for German-speaking people, and a German course for English-speaking people have been produced.

Lausanne – Ecole Polytechnique Federale, Chaire de Pedagogie et Didactique, Centre Est, CH-1015 Lausanne

The Chaire is concerned with teaching and learning processes, methods and problems. It has an interest in such matters as teaching innovations; the evaluation of learning; and it has an audiovisual centre which both teaches and produces AV materials.

*Service de la Recherche Pedagogique (Educational Research Service), 11 rue Sillem, 1207 Geneva (Contact: Dr Raymond Hutin, Director)

The main activity of the Service is studying the introduction of innovations in the teaching, apprenticeship and teaching aids fields. It is attached to the Department of Public Instruction (equivalent to the Ministry of Education) of the Canton of Geneva, serving the needs of a population of 350,000

Service des moyens audio-visuels du département de l'instruction publique, Cité Vieusseux 9, case postale 222, 1211 Geneva 28 (Contact: Maurice Wenger, Director)

The Service provides hardware and software equipment for schools, technical repair and maintenance service for AV equipment including TV, teacher instruction in the use of AV equipment, documentation. The Service also organizes conferences.

Swiss Federal Institute of Technology, Department of Behavioural Sciences, Turnerstrasse 1, 8006 Zurich

Co-ordinated science teaching with the help of the computer; evaluation (university and secondary school level); teaching methodology based on the concept of functions and analogy.

SYRIA

Damascus University, Faculty of Education, Damascus (Contact: Dr Fakhridin Kalla)

Training in educational technology for student teachers; designing training packages and self-instructional materials used for student and in-service teachers.

TANZANIA

Audio-Visual Institute of Dar-es-Salaam, PO Box 9310, Dar-es-Salaam (Contact: Joseph P Mahiga, Director)

The Audio-Visual Institute, established as a state organization by an Act of Parliament in 1974, aims chiefly to train Tanzanians in the art of film production; to produce educational/documentary films and other visual aids for national development; to distribute these films to all national institutions; to maintain all audiovisual equipment belonging to schools, colleges and all government ministries and state organizations throughout the country; and to carry out thorough research on the effective use of all these resources. The Institute has a complete sound studio, facilities for developing and editing 16mm film, and a maintenance department; it also serves as the National Film Library for the acquisition and distribution of 16mm films.

University of Dar-es-Salaam, Education Department, PO Box 35048, Dar-es-Salaam

Institute of Education, PO Box 35094, Dar-es-Salaam (Contact: The Director)

The Institute is a state organization established in 1975. Its functions are: to develop curricula for all levels of education except university; to initiate innovation and experimentation leading to development of new curricula, forms of organization and practice; and to collect and make available to the government and other public institutions, information on teaching, content of courses of study and current technological development in education. Its main activities cover: educational research and evaluation; innovation, reform and revision of curricula; school equipment development and book production; and publication and documentation of educational materials. Its main services include: the provision of information on teaching, content of courses of study and current technological development in education; maintenance and service of audiovisual equipment and materials; consultancy on textbook and supplementary book writing; and maintenance of standards of equipment and materials. It produces prototypes of school equipment; textbooks and teachers' guides; studies in curriculum development; and the *Tanzanian Education Journal.*

*Radio Tanzania, PO Box 9191, Dar-es-Salaam (Contact: Paul Andrea Sozigura)

THAILAND

APEID – Asian Programme of Educational Innovation for Development, *see under Regional Centres of Activity – Asia*

*Institute for Promotion of Teaching Science and Technology (IPST), 924 Sukumvit Road, Bangkok 11 (Contact: Dr Sukhum Sritanyaratana, Director)

IPST was established to develop modern science and mathematics curricula for elementary and secondary as well as vocational schools, and to promote teaching and learning methodology for both subjects.

Ministry of Education

*1. Centre for Educational Technology, Bangkok (Contact: Ms N Bhongbhibhat, Director)

The Centre is situated in the Ministry of Education in Bangkok. The main work of the Centre's staff of 102 is centred around five sections which between them cover the following activities: schools broadcasting covers social studies, Thai language and literature, music and song, and English. All broadcasts are supported by audiovisual materials, which are produced in the Centre's own AV workshops. General broadcasting and television programmes are put out in the evening for teachers and the general public; the main topics being religion, social studies and aspects of vocational education. As part of its administration and public relations programme, the Centre publishes two bi-monthly journals and a monthly educational radio and TV schedule booklet. In addition, an educational technology bulletin is issued occasionally, approximately two issues a year.

*2. Radio Correspondence Non-Formal Education Project, Bangkok

The Project is part of the government's effort to provide out-of-school education for the rural population and the urban poor, who will have continuous and increasing access to educational programmes. The Project is administered by the Radio Correspondence Committee, with members from the Departments of Non-Formal Education, Educational Techniques and Public Relations. This Committee is responsible for overall planning and for research, curriculum development, preparing model materials, training and evaluation. Regional inputs are provided by the four regional Research and Development Centres which also co-ordinate with Provincial Continuing Education Centres to carry out the day-to-day administration of the Project. The learning process in the Project is structured as follows: *Self-study:* each manual contains factual information relating to the study course. *Radio listening:* programmes are related to the regional environment and also comprise information additional to the manuals. The programmes focus on the learners' problems and help them find their own solutions. *Group meeting:* the learners discuss the work done during the week, exchange ideas and solve problems. They also discuss the issues which are related to the daily life conditions raised in the manuals and together decide on possible solutions and actions. Evaluation of the Project will be carried out, to determine attitudes of the learners, their actual knowledge of programme content, and how they have applied the information in their daily lives, and the figures for enrolment registrations.

The National Institute for Skill Development, Department of Labour, Din Daeng Road, Bangkok (Contact: Nitasna Theeravit)

The Institute, which is under the control of the Department of Labour (an integral part of the Ministry of the Interior) was started in May 1969 as a first-phase joint Thai/UNDP/ILO project. The Institute is playing a major role in skill promotion activities for industry. The policies governing the Department of Labour's training activities essentially aim at providing 'out-of-school' youth with the practical skills, knowledge and safe working attitudes necessary for employment. The duration of pre-employment courses varies from three to 11 months, the majority lasting six months. The training activities also provide for older workers and the redundant, by offering them opportunities to re-enter the training system and learn new skills or up-grade their level of competence. Regarding the other training activities, the Institute provides foreman training courses and instructor training courses for industries. Training Officers course is also provided with the aim to enable the industries to organize the in-plant training schemes. With its successful implementation, a second phase with continued UNDP/ILO support started from February 1974 continued to December 1979, to establish three other regional institutes for skill development in the West, East and North at Ratchaburi, Cholburi, and Lampang. An integral part of the overall Thai/UNDP/ILO project was a Thai/Israeli project of 3½ years' duration, from March 1974-1978, to establish a Training Aids Centre and Curriculum Development Unit. Owing to the success of the institutes, the Japanese Government has assisted in establishing an Institute in the North-east at Khonkaen which was fully operational in 1980, and the German Government has assisted in establishing another Institute in the South at Songkhla. A further Institute is planned for the Lower North at Nakornsawan by 1981 – making a total of seven institutes with a training capacity of approximately 8500 people per year.

Sukhothai Thammathirat Open University, Office of University Affairs, 328 Sri Ayudhya Road, Bangkok 4 (Contact: Professor Wichit Srisa-an, Rector)

Sukhothai Thammathirat Open University (STOU) is Thailand's Open University. It admitted its first batch of 82,139 students in 1980 for a range of degree and non-degree courses in Educational Studies and Management Science, while having a School of Liberal Arts providing foundation courses. Other courses to be offered in 1982 include those on Health Sciences, Law, Economics, Home Economics, Political Science and Agricultural Extension and Co-operatives. STOU sends printed course materials directly to its students and supplements them with audio-tapes and radio and TV broadcasts through national broadcasting networks. Other media will be available in the future. The University has co-operated with other national academic institutions for the provision of local study centres and their assistance in preparing materials and providing travelling lecturers.

*Thai-German Technical Teachers' College, King Mongkut's Institute of Technology, Faculty of Technical Education and Science, North Bangkok Campus, Bangkok

The Faculty is probably the most advanced institute in Thailand, in the adoption and use of educational technology techniques. It has its own resources centre, where a wide range of audiovisual aids is freely available to staff and students. Bachelor and master-degree students are well trained in educational technology techniques and, as a matter of course, use objectives, programmed instruction methods, visual aids, systems thinking, information mapping and problem-solving techniques. Teaching practice assessment, devised by a team of experts, is probably the most sophisticated in the East.

Unesco Regional Office for Education in Asia and the Pacific, *see under Regional Centres of Activity – Asia*

TONGA ISLANDS

The Audio Visual Centre, Audio Visual Aids Department, PO Box 113, Nuku-alofa (Contact: Mr Mateaki Ma'asi)

The Audio Visual Centre is a separate department under the Prime Minister's office. Its function is to help government departments, as well as other organizations and the public, in the production of teaching aids requiring graphics and reprographic work. It also supplies technical assistance with projected media. The Audio Visual Aids Department is involved in the production of teaching aids at different school levels in the form of charts, models, pictures and booklets. It produces posters, signboards and models for the Departments of Health and Agriculture. Its services are also available to members of the public needing any assistance in the production of graphic material, etc.

TRINIDAD AND TOBAGO

Caribbean Regional Council for Adult Education (CARCAE), c/o External Studies Unit, University of the West Indies, St Augustine, Trinidad and Tobago, West Indies (Contact: Esmond D Ramesar, Executive Secretary)

CARCAE was founded in 1978 and is associated with the worldwide work of the International Council for Adult Education (ICAE), for which it is one of many regional organizations. Its work is directed towards the non-Spanish speaking territories of the Caribbean, and is concerned: to promote adult education in all forms; to encourage the formation of national associations; to advise regional governmental organizations; to develop adult education as an academic discipline; and to hold seminars on adult education.

It offers non-graduate and postgraduate courses for teachers of adults (at UWI); it maintains a research library and documentation centre; it operates a clearinghouse on Adult Education; and it has put forward a proposal for formal adult education in the Caribbean.

TUNISIA

*Institut National des Sciences de l'Education (INSE) (National Institute of Educational Sciences), Ministry of Education, 17 rue d'Irak, Tunis

The Institute undertakes study activities and pluridisciplinary researches, elaboration and experimentation of psychopedagogical methods, training, documentation, publications. It liaises with its four Regional Centres of Pedagogical Documentation at Tunis, Bejà, Sousse and Sfax. Publications: *Revue Tunisienne des Sciences de l'Education* (research reports) and monographs on specific subjects.

UPPER VOLTA

Institut Nationale d'Education, BP 7043 Ouagadougou (Contact: Ignace Sanwidi, Director)

Educational research and the development of curricula at all levels; production of materials; training of educational personnel.

URTNA/CIERRO, *see under Regional Centres of Activity – Africa*

URUGUAY

*CINTERFOR – Centro Interamericano de Investigación y Documentación sobre Formación Professional (Inter-American Centre for Research and Documentation on Vocational Training), Casilla de correo 1761, Montevideo (Contact: Joáo Carlos Alexim, Director)

CINTERFOR was created by the International Labour Organization (ILO) at the request of the countries of the Americas, and was installed at Montevideo in 1964 in accordance with an agreement concluded with the Government of Uruguay. A very special system of international co-operation was thereby started, mainly based on mutual help among the countries of the Americas. The main functions of the Centre include: the promotion of permanent and active co-operation among vocational training institutions in the region; carrying out research studies, seminars and technical meetings on methods for planning, organizing, managing and evaluating the different modes of vocational training; co-operation in the appropriate training of personnel taking part in the vocational training process; and gathering, classifying and disseminating documentation on vocational training that may be of interest to countries in the region.

USSR

*Work in the field of educational technology is carried out in many educational, training and research institutions in the Soviet Union, particularly in Moscow, Leningrad and Kiev. Rather than giving an exhaustive list, the reader is advised to contact one of the following:

Professor N F Talyzina,
Department of Psychology,
Moscow State University,
18 Block 5,
Prospekt Marxa,
Moscow.

Professor A Ya Saveliev,
Institute for the Problems of Higher Schools,
3rd Kabelnaya St 1,
Moscow.

In some instances, it may be more convenient for readers to obtain information from United Kingdom sources. General information about education in the Soviet Union is available from:

The Centre for Russian and East European Studies (CREES),
University of Birmingham,
PO Box 363,
Birmingham 15.

The CEDAR Project at Imperial College has a particular interest in
computer-based learning (and in educational technology generally) in the
Soviet Union. Contact:

N J Rushby,
CEDAR Project,
Imperial College Computer Centre,
Exhibition Road,
London SW7 2BX

*The Institute of General and Educational Psychology, Academy of
Pedagogical Sciences of the USSR, The Laboratory of Learning and Mental
Development, Marx Prospekt 20, Moscow K9 (Contact: Professor N A
Menchinskaia, Director)

Theoretical research in programmed learning and educational technology,
designing of instructional programmes. Publications include books on theory
and experiments in PL instructional programmes, techniques of
psychological diagnosis for the construction of adaptive diagnostical
programmes, and preparation of instructional programmes with non-rigid
structuring, taking into consideration the ability of schoolchildren to regulate
their own progress.

VENEZUELA

*División de Tecnología Educativa (Educational Technology Division), Cuno
a Caja de Agua No 18, Caracas 101 (Contact: Freddy Sanabria)

Production of educational television programmes; production of educational
radio programmes; evaluation of textbooks and educational toys; production
of slides and educational filmstrips.

*INCE (Instituto Nacional de Co-operación Educative), Edificio Inca,
Avenida Nueva Granada, Caracas.

The national craft and technical training organization, operating a network
of technical colleges. Also produces distance education courses.

*Instituto Universitario de Tecnología, Apartado 40347, Caracas 104
(Contact: Federico Rivero Palacio, Director)

A higher technological institute, offering courses in engineering, etc up to
PhD level. Both individual courses and the overall structure of the Institute
incorporate many of the principles of educational technology. Much of the
teaching is by individualized, enquiry methods, personalized instruction and
simulation. A very carefully controlled reward/reinforcement system is built
into the institution, to encourage students to proceed to higher qualifications
and to choose appropriate options.

***Programa de Instrucción por Correspondencia (Programme for
Correspondence Instruction),** Avenida Nueva Granada, Caracas 104

This is a project for setting up correspondence education or technical training needs, which was set up by the National Institute of Educational Co-operation (INCE), Department of New Methods. The project produces the materials and implements the course, assigning each student to an instructor who accompanies him throughout the length of his studies. The amount of personal assistance given by instructors to students in this system is much greater than usual correspondence education, turning the course into a sort of part-time personalized instruction course.

Universidad Simón Bolivar

1. Unidad de Medios Audiovisuales (UMAV), Apartado Postal 80659, Caracas (Contacts: Professor Freddy Rojas and Professor Manuel Benavides)

The Simón Bolivar University is an experimental institution of higher education located in Caracas, Venezuela. The programmes offered by this institution deal specially with engineering and science. The majority of the teaching activity is supported by the Audio-Visual Aids Center which is well equipped with television studios, drawing rooms and photograph studios. The main function of this Center is to produce audiovisual material to be used individually or collectively by teachers and students.

2. Núcleo Universitario del Litoral (NUL) (Contacts: Professor Alfredo R Santaella and Professor Guillermo Alvarez)

The Littoral Campus, which was established by the Simón Bolivar University in 1976, is sited in the central coast of the country. A new system of learning, made up by the interaction of the different components that take place in any learning-teaching process, has been adopted by this new campus, based on the principle of 'learning by doing'. Puts emphasis on the individual capacity of each student, and provides higher education by using methods and techniques provided by the educational technology.

Centro de Television Educativa, Universidad del Zulia, Apartado 526, Maracaibo (Contact: Iraida Bermudez, Director)

Production of TV programmes and supporting media for use in university courses in educational technology. An information gathering/dissemination service. Publishes an information bulletin *Senales*.

VIETNAM

***Institute of Educational Science,** 101 Tran Hung Dao Street, Hanoi (Contact: Dr Nguyen Duc Minh, Acting Director)

The Institute of Educational Science was set up in 1961, as a result of the merger of some research units under the Ministry of Education. Its aims are to promote the study of Vietnamese educational science, solve scientifically the problems of educational reform, build up basic scientific theories for solving problems of general education, help improve the quality of all-round education, and contribute to the postgraduate training of teachers and educationists. There are ten research units: Education Section, Psychology Section, Section for Content and Method of General Education, Section for Politico-Ethical Education, Section for Physical Education and Physiology of Age Levels, Section for Ethnic Minorities Education, Defectology Section, Laboratory for Child Pschology Tests and Pedagogy, Section for Studying Problems of Education in South Vietnamese Provinces, and Section for Technical and Manual Education. There are four units to serve scientific

research, of which the most important is the Department for Scientific
Research Management (responsible for the postgraduate training of
educationists, information on educational science, scientific co-operation
with other countries, the management of research work on educational
science).

WEST INDIES
See Trinidad and Tobago

ZAIRE

***Centre Interdisciplinaire pour le Developpement et l'Education
Permanente – CIDEP (Interdisciplinary Centre for Development and
Continuous Education),** PO Box 2307, Kinshasa (Contact: Wembi-Kakese,
Director-General)

The Institution is part of the National University of Zaire. Its main function
is to improve the education of employed persons, to enable them to make a
positive contribution to the country's development. Activities are carried out
under the supervision of the Head of Academic Services. Main activities are
refresher and advanced courses for employees of companies and public
services; 'Development Background' courses, for agents working in
development projects; basic teaching – evening school training for employed
persons unable to attend university courses; research, documentation and
publication. The Centre runs a bookshop and publishes the trimestrial review
Etudes Zaireoises.

*Radio Télévision Scolaire, BP 32, Kinshasa/gombe (Contact: Dr Mpiutu
Mbodi)

***Régie Nationale des Actualités et des Productions Educatives et Culturelles
(RENAPEC),** BP 1698 Kinshasa 1 (Contact: Tala Ngal-I-Kambiaunia)

ZAMBIA

*Curriculum Development Centre, PO Box RW 92, Lusaka

*Educational Broadcasting Services, PO Box RW 231, Lusaka (Contacts:
W S C Bota, Controller, Box RW 231, Lusaka; P M Mulombe, Head,
ETVS, Box 1106, Kitwe; M Wakunguma, Head, ERS, Box RW 231, Lusaka;
M S Phiri, Head, AVALS, Box RW 295, Lusaka)

The Educational Broadcasting Services (EBS) is a Department of the
Ministry of Education and Culture. (The Ministry of Information and
Broadcasting provides transmission facilities only.) The specific objective is
to improve the quality of learning and teaching for every Zambian, to help
learner and teacher to go through a rich educational process so as to increase
enjoyment of learning; to enrich classroom teaching in schools; to bridge the
educational gap between schools throughout the country; and to promote
curriculum development. There are three main services: the Educational
Television Service which produces programmes based on the school syllabus:
these are transmitted to all schools within the television circuit; the
Educational Radio Service which also produces programmes based on the
school syllabus: these are broadcast to over 2700 primary and secondary
schools and 12 teacher training colleges; and the Audio-Visual Aids Service,

which works in close co-operation with its sister sections. It distributes and maintains school radio and television sets, film projectors, cassette players, etc and is responsible for lending to schools educational films and dubbed radio programmes, and for the production of teaching wall charts.

*Educational Television Service, PO Box 1106, Kitwe (Contact: P M Mulombe, Head)

The Service was established some 15 years ago in order to assist teachers in primary and secondary schools as well as teachers' colleges, by presenting to the students aspects of the school syllabus which teachers would normally find difficult to teach because of shortages of appropriate teaching aids; and for enrichment programming in order to widen students' experience and horizons. The Service is responsible for the production and transmission of both live and pre-recorded or taped programmes in Primary School Science, Art, Creative Activities and Social Studies (secondary programmes temporarily suspended), as well as film programmes in Careers, Primary English and Religious Education. As well as transmitting the programmes listed above, the production staff travel to the schools which have TV receivers to assist teachers in the use of TV lessons through workshops and seminars. The *teachers' notes* which accompany the programmes are published annually and are sent out to schools with the timetables and with forms to show how many pupils view programmes, as well as evaluation cards which are prepared and distributed to schools regularly.

University of Zambia

The University of Zambia was established in 1965 to provide the country's higher educational needs and to stimulate co-ordinated research activities into a wide variety of national and regional problems.

The present educational technology facilities were set up in 1970/73 chiefly to serve the needs of the University's largest school, the School of Education. The project, which was initially staffed and funded by Unesco, established a Centre which consisted of a large AV workshop, an off-set press, a recording studio and a small CCTV capability largely used to service and provide practical workshop facilities for students involved in BAEd and BScEd degree courses. Recently the Centre has been 'rationalized' and more closely integrated into the teaching and course structures of a number of departments housed in the School of Education. The educational technology and AV services function both as a teaching resource and as a service for staff and students wishing to learn and use the skills and techniques of educational technology.

*1. School of Education, PO Box 2379, Lusaka

Teacher education: microteaching, training in librarianship, consultancy in training systems. Consultancy in development of guided and/or programmed training systems. Consultancy in development of systematized instruction in already established programmes.

*2. Teaching Hospital, Lusaka (Contact: M Ausary, Chief Technician)

*3. David Livingstone College, Primary Teacher Training, Teaching Aids Unit, PO Box 1, Livingstone (Contact: William Gibbs, Director)

*4. Educational Technology and AV Services, School of Education, Box 2379, Lusaka

*5. Department of Adult and In-Service Training, School of Education (Contacts: Frank Dall, Co-ordinator AV Services, Lecturer in Educational Technology, Department of Education; Dr Tracy Harrington, Lecturer and Professor in Educational Technology, Department of Adult Education, School of Education)

*Zambia Railways, PO Box 929, Kabwe (Contact: L K Mwandu, Principal)

Vocational and management development training.

Section 5: Producers and Distributors of Programmes and Audiovisual Software

Introduction

This section now consists of three elements:

1. Producers and distributors of programmes and audiovisual software in the UK;
2. Producers and distributors of programmes and audiovisual software in North America;
3. Some useful catalogues.

The expansion of the Section title to include 'distributors' is in recognition of the difficulty in some instances of distinguishing between producers and distributors, especially when some of the former also act in the latter capacity for smaller producers.

Details entered in the listings are *as supplied by the publishers and producers of the material.* Also, in accordance with the procedure operating elsewhere in this edition, where a publisher has not responded to the request for an update on his entry, this is *indicated by the symbol* * before his name. (These entries will not appear in future editions unless updated information becomes available.)

It is regrettable that this Section does not yet include producers other than those in the UK and USA – this is not policy, but reflects simply the lack of information on such producers. The Editor will be very pleased to receive information from overseas producers, *particularly those producing materials in languages other than English.*

Similarly, *computer software* is very much a developing field and one which can confidently be expected to be of major importance by the 1984/85 edition. Some brief coverage is given in the UK and USA elements but the Editor will be pleased to receive additional information on developments in *any* country for inclusion in the next edition of the Yearbook.

Producers and Distributors of Programmes and Audiovisual Software in North America

This Section maintains the revised format established in the last edition of the Yearbook, namely a two-part list comprising:

Part 1: Index of publishers by subjects – a list of major subject headings, under each of which are given the names of producers who supply materials covering that subject;

Part 2: Publishers' and producers' names and addresses – major publishers and producers, and types of materials produced and subjects covered.

Details entered are those supplied by the publishers and producers of the material; where publishers have not supplied details on their subject coverage they are listed only in Part 2.

It is hoped that the format will prove a helpful starting point to readers looking for software materials; full details about individual items are available in the British Library's *British Catalogue of Audio Visual Materials.* It is also worth consulting the *Audio Visual Handbook,* edited on behalf of the Scottish Council for Educational Technology by John Henderson and Fay Humphries, and published by Kogan Page.

Computer-based Software

As outlined in the general *Introduction* to this Section, computer-based material is still very much a developing field, and accordingly details of computer-based software are not featured strongly in the listing. It is noteworthy, however, that several publishers of traditional materials (Longman, Macmillan, Thomas Nelson and Sons, John Wiley, etc) are already entering into this market. For the interim, the following organizations, which are listed in the Directory of Centres of Activity, are engaged in the exchange of computer programmes:

Advisory Unit for Computer Based Education, Director Dr W Tagg, Endymion Road, Hatfield, Herts *(Secondary, primary school programs)*

Basic Mathematics at University Level (project name), Director Professor J Hunter, Mathematics Department, University of Glasgow, Glasgow G12 8QW

Bristol Polytechnic Department of Computer Studies and Mathematics provides a small number of programs suitable for schools, for the RM380Z. For further information, contact: R J Margetts, Bristol Polytechnic,

Coldharbour Lane, Bristol BS16 1QY. Tel: 0272 656261 Ext 320

CALCHEM: Computer Assisted Learning in Chemistry (Leeds University)

The CAL Package Index, compiled by the CEDAR project, includes nearly 500 packages developed in the UK. Many of these are aimed more at the undergraduate level, but the index includes some software for schools. For further information, contact: Judith Morris, Cedar Project, Imperial College Computer Centre, Exhibition Road, London SW7 2BX. Tel: 01-589 5111 Ext 1160

CPE – The Central Program Exchange (formerly) the Physical Sciences Program Exchange) is based at Wolverhampton Polytechnic and has programs on chemistry, biology, physics, mathematics, geography and language. For further information, contact: Mrs Judith Brown, CPE, Department of Computing and Mathematics, Polytechnic of Wolverhampton, Wulfruna Street, Wolverhampton WV1 1L.
Tel: 0902 27371

CHESS – The Association of Computer Units in colleges of higher education, produces a short list of programs, primarily suitable for higher education, but with some programs suitable for sixth form work. The topics covered are accountancy, economics, and business studies. Contact via Hatfield Polytechnic, PO Box 109, Hatfield, Herts A10 9AB

Computer Assisted Learning – A University Service (project name), Director T F Goodwin, Computing Unit, University of Surrey, Guildford, Surrey

Computer Based Learning Project, Director J R Hartley, Leeds University, Leeds LS2 9JT

Computers in the Curriculum (Schools Council Project) – see Chelsea College. This project was founded in 1973, and has developed programs in biology, physics, chemistry, economics and geography, mostly for fourth and sixth form work. The materials have been developed by teachers, and thoroughly tested in the classroom. The programs are in BASIC and should run on most computer systems.

CUSC: Computers in the Undergraduate Science Curriculum (Chelsea College).

Engineering Sciences Program Exchange, Director Dr P Smith, Queen Mary College, Mile End Road, London E1 4NS

GAPE – The Geographical Association Package Exchange publishes a catalogue of geography packages. For further information contact: David Walker, Department of Geography, University of Technology, Loughborough LE11 3TU.
Tel: 0509 215751 Ext 22

MICE – This consists of a group of teachers working on software development. The group has only been in existence for a short time, but it is building up a library of programs, basically concerned with teaching computer appreciation and computer studies. For further information contact: Dr Morfydd Edwards, Polytechnic of the South Bank, Borough Road, London SE1.
Tel: 01-928 8989 Ext 2205/2050

MUSE Software Exchange Scheme is for MUSE (Mini and Microcomputer Users in Secondary Education) members only. The catalogue consists of programs developed by MUSE members – frequently practising teachers – with a clear indication of the age level at which the program would be useful. The subjects covered are mainly maths, statistics, and some chemistry and computer applications. For further information, contact: Charles Sweeten, MUSE, Freepost, Bromsgrove, Worcs B61 7BR

A useful listing of individual programs has also started to appear in the journal *Educational Computing*. Beginning in the June 1980 issue this directory of software has so far included packages on administration, business studies, computer science, computer studies (June), languages, mathematics (July/Aug), science, statistics (September). Many of the packages are drawn from the sources listed above. There are a considerable number, however, produced by individuals and commercial sources which have never appeared before in any listing.

Part 1: Index of Producers/ Distributors by Subjects

Subject headings
1. General crafts, hobbies, driving etc
2. Accountancy
3. Office practice
4. Management and supervision
5. Salesmanship and marketing
6. English language
7. English literature

8. English as a foreign language (EFL)
9-13. Languages
14. Librarianship
15. Logic
16. Mathematics
17. Health: first aid, sex information, nutrition, dentistry, veterinary surgery
18. Nursing and medicine
19. Physiology
20. Music
21. Drama
22. Dance
23. Art and architecture
24. Physical education
25. Teaching and learning: programmed instruction, training, analysis
26. Religion
27. History
28. Economics and politics
29. Social studies
30. Geography and geology
31. Psychology
32. General science
33. Biology
34. Chemistry
35. Physics
36. Electricity and electronics
37. Computers and computing
38. Engineering
39. Industrial safety
40. Industrial processes
41. Reading
42. Environmental studies
43. Teaching and teacher training

1. General crafts, hobbies, driving etc
BP Educational Service
Ivan Berg Associates
CTVC
Cement & Concrete Association
Consort Films
Creative Film Makers Ltd
Joan Davies
Dundee College of Education
ESL Bristol Ltd
ETV Films Ltd
Educational Media International
Educational Productions Ltd
Focal Point AV Ltd
Guild Sound & Vision Ltd
Nicholas Hunter Ltd
Lincolnshire Educational Television
Macdonald & Co (Publishers) Ltd
National Audio Visual Aids Library
Pitman Correspondence College Ltd
Service Training Ltd
Shell Film Library
The Slide Centre

The Technical Press Ltd
Tetradon Publications Ltd
Town & Country Productions Ltd
Viscom Ltd
John Wiley & Sons Ltd
Diana Wyllie Ltd

2. Accountancy
CST Training Resources Ltd
Cassell Ltd
The Certified Accountants Educational Trust
Dundee College of Education
ESL Bristol Ltd
Guild Sound & Vision Ltd
Hodder & Stoughton Educational
The Institute of Chartered Accountants in England & Wales
Institute of Chartered Accountants of Scotland
Lutterworth Press
Management Games Ltd
Melrose Films
Mobile Training
Multimedia Publishing Ltd
Olymp Training Ltd
Pitman Correspondence College Ltd
Road Transport ITB
Service Training Ltd
The Slide Centre
Transaid
Video Arts Ltd
Viscom Ltd
Waterlow Publishing Ltd

3. Office practice
Edward Arnold (Publishers) Ltd
BSIP ARS Magna Ltd
British Productivity Council
British Telecom
CST Training Resources Ltd
Cassell Ltd
Cassette Teaching Services (shorthand/ speed dictation)
Chiltern Consortium
Ron Clements Associates
Cybernetic Teaching Systems Ltd
Fergus Davidson
ESL Bristol Ltd
Educational Media International
Educational Productions Ltd
Engineering Industry Training Board
GP Systems Co Ltd
Guardian Business Services
Guild Sound & Vision Ltd
Helikon Imports
Holdsworth AV
ILEA Learning Materials Service
The Industrial Society

International Tutor Machines Ltd
LAMSAC
Longman Group Ltd
McGraw-Hill Book Co (UK) Ltd
Management Games Ltd
Melrose Films
Middlesex Film Productions Ltd
Multimedia Publishing Ltd
Olymp Training Ltd
Pictorial Charts Educational Trust
Pitman Correspondence College
Reach-a-Teacha Ltd
Road Transport ITB
SAGSET
Scientific Era Publications
Scottish & Newcastle Breweries Ltd
Service Training Ltd
The Slide Centre
Video Arts Ltd
Vistech
Waterlow Publishers Ltd

4. Management and supervision

Allyn & Bacon
Edward Arnold (Publishers) Ltd
BNA Communications Europe
BP Educational Service
BSIP ARS Magna Ltd
British Productivity Council
CST Training Resources Ltd
Cassell Ltd
Chemical & Allied Products Industry
    Training Board
Ron Clements Associates
Construction Industry Training Board
Cybernetic Teaching Systems Ltd
Distributive Industry Training Board
Diversey AV Ltd
Dundee College of Education
Du Pont (UK) Ltd
ESL Bristol Ltd
Educational Media International
Employment Relations Ltd
Guardian Business Services
Guild Sound & Vision Ltd
Helikon Imports
Hodder & Stoughton Educational
Holdsworth AV
Hotel & Catering ITB
The Industrial Society
Inst. of Supervisory Management
Instructa
International Tutor Machines Ltd
Knitting Lace & Net Industry Training
    Board
Larman Associates Ltd
Legal & General Assurance Society
University of London AV Centre
Local Government Training Board

McGraw-Hill Book Co (UK) Ltd
Management Games Ltd
Melrose Films
Merchant Navy Training Board
Middlesex Film Productions Ltd
Millbank Films Ltd
Multimedia Publishing Ltd
National Audio Visual Aids Library
National Coal Board
Olymp Training Ltd
Edward Patterson Associates Ltd
Pitman Correspondence College
Rank Audio Visual Ltd
Reach-a-Teacha Ltd
SAGSET
Scottish & Newcastle Breweries Ltd
Service Training Ltd
Selsdon Pack Management Centre
Sheffield City Polytechnic
Supervisory Management Training Ltd
Training Films International Ltd
Video Arts Ltd
Waterlow Publishers Ltd

5. Salesmanship and marketing

BNA Communications Europe
BP Educational Service
BSIP ARS Magna Ltd
British Productivity Council
CST Training Resources Ltd
Cassell Ltd
Chemical & Allied Products Industry
    Training Board
Ron Clements Associates
Fergus Davidson
Distributive Industry Training Board
Diversey AV Ltd
ESL Bristol Ltd
Guardian Business Services
Guild Sound & Vision Ltd
Hodder & Stoughton Educational
Hotel & Catering ITB
Institute of Grocery Distribution
Institute of Tape Learning
Instructa
International Tutor Machines Ltd
McGraw-Hill Book Co (UK) Ltd
Management Games Ltd
Melrose Films
Middlesex Film Productions Ltd
Multimedia Publishing Ltd
Olymp Training Ltd
Pitman Correspondence College
Rank Audio Visual Ltd
Road Transport ITB
Scottish & Newcastle Breweries Ltd
Selsdon Park Management Centre
Service Training Ltd
Training Films International Ltd

Video Arts Ltd
Viscom Ltd

6. English language
Edward Arnold (Publishers) Ltd
Audio Visual Productions
County of Avon Resources for Learnir
    Development Unit
BBC English by Radio/TV
Bell & Howell
Ivan Berg Associates
Boulton-Hawker Films Ltd
Cassell Ltd
Fergus Davidson
Drake Educational Associates
Dundee College of Education
Educational Media International
Educational Productions Ltd
Mary Glasgow
Guardian Business Services
Hertfordshire County Council
    Programmed Learning Centre
The Institute of Tape Learning
Instructa
Jordanhill College
Lincolnshire Educational Television
Longman Group Ltd
Multimedia Publishing Ltd
National Audio Visual Aids Library
Oliver & Boyd
Packman Research
Edward Patterson Associates
Pictorial Charts Educational Trust
Pitman Correspondence College
Reading University Reading Centre
Seminar Cassettes Ltd
Sound Education
Viscom Ltd

7. English literature
Audio Learning Ltd
Audio Visual Productions
County of Avon Resources for Learnir
    Development Unit
Ivan Berg Associates
Fergus Davidson
Drake Educational Associates
EAV Ltd c/o Mary Glasgow
    Publications Ltd
Educational Media International
Educational Productions Ltd
Mary Glasgow
University of London AV Centre
Longman Group Ltd
Macdonald & Co (Publishers) Ltd
National Audio Visual Aids Library
Oliver & Boyd
Open University Educational Enter-
    prises Ltd

Edward Patterson Associates Ltd
Rank Audio Visual Ltd
Seminar Cassettes Ltd
Sound Education
Teakfield Publishing Co Ltd
Visual Productions

8. English as a foreign language (EFL)
Edward Arnold (Publishers) Ltd
Audio Visual Productions
BBC English by Radio/TV
Bell & Howell AV Ltd
Boulton Hawker Films
Cambridge University Press
Cassell Ltd
Chiltern Consortium
Drake Educational Associates
English by Listening
Focal Point AV Ltd
Mary Glasgow
Harcourt Brace Jovanovich
Hodder & Stoughton Educational
The Institute of Tape Learning
Jordanhill College
Linguaphone Institute Ltd
Longman Group Ltd
McMillan-LTR
Macdonald & Co (Publishers) Ltd
Management Games Ltd
National Audio Visual Aids Library
Thomas Nelson & Sons Ltd
Pitman Correspondence College
Seminar Cassettes Ltd
Visual Productions
World of Learning Ltd

9 – 13. Languages
Allyn & Bacon
Edward Arnold (Publishers) Ltd
Audio Visual Productions
County of Avon Resources for
    Learning Development Unit
Hugh Baddeley Productions
Bell & Howell (Welsh)
Ivan Berg Associates
Boulton Hawker Films Ltd
Cassell Ltd
Fergus Davidson Associates Ltd
    (13 languages)
Dundee College of Education
EAV Ltd, c/o Mary Glasgow
ETV Films Ltd
Educational Productions Ltd
Euro-Lang Tapes
Exeter Tapes
Fordigraph
Mary Glasgow
HLL Publications
Harrap Didier

Harcourt Brace Jovanovich Ltd
Hodder & Stoughton Educational
ILEA Learning Materials Service
Institute of Tape Learning
Jordanhill College
Linguaphone Institute Ltd
University of London AV Centre
Longman Group Ltd
McMillan-LTR
National Audio Visual Aids Library
Thomas Nelson & Sons Ltd
Oliver & Boyd
Edward Patterson Associates Ltd
The Slide Centre
The University of Southampton
   Department of Teaching Media
Stillitron Ltd
World of Learning Ltd

14. Librarianship
Clive Bingley Ltd
Careers & Occupations Information
   Centre
Drake Educational Associates
Dundee College of Education
Educational Media International
Jordanhill College
The University of Southampton
   Department of Teaching Media

15. Logic
BSIP ARS Magna Ltd
ESL Bristol Ltd
Bell & Howell AV Ltd
Feedback Instruments Ltd
St David's University College
Service Training Ltd

16. Mathematics
Edward Arnold (Publishers) Ltd
Audio Learning Ltd
Audio Visual Productions
County of Avon Resources for Learning
   Development Unit
Bell & Howell AV Ltd
Ivan Berg Associates
Boulton-Hawker Films Ltd
Cassell Ltd
W & R Chambers Ltd
Chapman & Hall
Fergus Davidson
Drake Educational Associates
Dundee College of Education
Du Pont (UK) Ltd
ESL Bristol Ltd
Educational Media International
Eothen Films Ltd
Fordigraph
W H Green & Co Ltd

Guild Sound & Vision Ltd
Hertfordshire County Council
   Programmed Learning Centre
Hodder & Stoughton Educational
ILEA Learning Materials Service
ITL Vufoils Ltd
Institute of Tape Learning
Lincolnshire Educational Television
University of London AV Centre
Longman Group Ltd
Lutterworth Press
McGraw-Hill Book Co (UK) Ltd
Mathematical Pie
Oliver & Boyd
Open University Educational
   Enterprises Ltd
Edward Patterson Associates Ltd
Pictorial Charts Educational Trust
Rank Audio Visual Ltd
SAGSET
Service Training Ltd
The Slide Centre
Studio Two Educational AV
Technical Press Ltd
Tetradon Publications Ltd
Transaid
Transart Visual Productions Ltd
Viewtech AV Media Ltd
Visual Productions
Ward Lock Educational

17. Health: first aid, sex information,
   nutrition, dentistry, veterinary
   surgery
Audio Visual Productions
BLAT Centre for Health and Medical
   Education
Boulton-Hawker Films Ltd
Cassell Ltd
Fergus Davidson
Diversey AV Ltd (hygiene)
Dundee College of Education
ETV Films Ltd
Educational Media International
Educational Productions Ltd
Eothen Films Ltd
Focal Point AV Ltd
Foundation for Teaching Aids at
   Low Cost
General Dental Council
Guild Sound & Vision Ltd
Philip Harris Biological
Health Education Audio Visual
Helikon Imports
Hertfordshire County Council
   Programmed Learning Centre
G Hubert-White
ILEA Learning Materials Service
University of London AV Centre

Longman Group Ltd
Macdonald & Co (Publishers) Ltd
Middlesex Film Productions Ltd
Millbank Films Ltd
National Audio Visual Aids Library
Thomas Nelson & Sons Ltd
Oxford Educational Resources Ltd
Edward Patterson Associates Ltd
Pattison & Co
Pictorial Charts Educational Trust
Prentice-Hall International
Rank Audio Visual Ltd
SAGSET
Service Training Ltd
The Slide Centre
Sound Education
The University of Southampton
    Department of Teaching Media
Stewart Film Distributors Ltd
Studio Two Educational AV
Town & Country Productions Ltd
Viewtech AV Media Ltd
Viscom Ltd

18. Nursing and medicine
Edward Arnold (Publishers) Ltd
BLAT Centre for Health and Medical
    Education
Boulton-Hawker Films Ltd
Cassell Ltd
Chapman & Hall
Fergus Davidson Associates Ltd
ESL Bristol Ltd
Educational Media International
Educational Productions Ltd
Eothen Films Ltd
Fordigraph
Graves Medical Audio-Visual Library
Guild Sound & Vision Ltd
Philip Harris Biological
Helikon Imports
Hertfordshire County Council
    Programmed Learning Centre
Hodder & Stoughton Educational
University of London AV Centre
Longman Group Ltd
McGraw-Hill Book Co (UK) Ltd
Management Games Ltd
National Audio. Visual Aids Library
National Centre for Developments in
    Nurse Education
Oxford Educational Resources Ltd
Edward Patterson Associates Ltd
Pennant AV Systems
Prentice-Hall International
Rank Audio Visual Ltd
Seminar Cassettes Ltd
Service Training Ltd
Sheffield City Polytechnic

Sound Education
The University of Southampton
    Department of Teaching Media
Stewart Film Distributors Ltd
Town & Country Productions Ltd
Viewtech AV Media Ltd
Viscom Ltd
John Wiley & Sons Ltd

19. Physiology
Audio Visual Productions
BLAT Centre for Health and Medical
    Education
BSIP ARS Magna Ltd
Boulton-Hawker Films Ltd
Cassell Ltd
Fergus Davidson Associates Ltd
Dundee College of Education
Educational Media International
Educational Productions Ltd
Eothen Films Ltd
University of London AV Centre
National AV Aids Library
Open University Educational
    Enterprises Ltd
Oxford Educational Resources Ltd
Edward Patterson Associates Ltd
Marian Ray
Seminar Cassettes Ltd
Service Training Ltd
The Slide Centre
The University of Southampton
    Department of Teaching Media
Viewtech AV Media Ltd
Viscom Ltd

20. Music
Allyn & Bacon
Ivan Berg Associates
Fergus Davidson Associates Ltd
Dundee College of Education
EAV Ltd, c/o Mary Glasgow
ETV Films Ltd
Educational Media International
Educational Productions Ltd
Guild Sound & Vision Ltd
ILEA Learning Materials Service
Jordanhill College
Longman Group Ltd
Macdonald & Co (Publishers) Ltd
National Audio Visual Aids Library
Thomas Nelson & Sons Ltd
Open University Educational
    Enterprises Ltd
Pictorial Charts Educational Trust
Marian Ray
The Slide Centre
Sound Education
Teakfield Publishing Co Ltd
Viscom Ltd

21. Drama

Ivan Berg Associates
Fergus Davidson Associates Ltd
Dundee College of Education
EAV Ltd, c/o Mary Glasgow
ETV Films Ltd
Educational Media International
Educational Productions Ltd
ILEA Learning Materials Service
Jordanhill College
Lincolnshire Educational Television
University of London AV Centre
National Audio Visual Aids Library
Thomas Nelson & Sons Ltd
Open University Educational
    Enterprises Ltd
Rank Audio Visual Ltd
Sound Education
Teakfield Publishing Co Ltd
Visual Productions
Ward Lock Educational
Woodmansterne Ltd

22. Dance

Chiltern Consortium
Fergus Davidson Associates Ltd
Dundee College of Education
EAV Ltd
ETV Films Ltd
Educational Media International
Jordanhill College
Macdonald & Co (Publishers) Ltd
National Audio Visual Aids Library
Woodmansterne Ltd

23. Arts and architecture

Arts Council
Audio Learning Ltd
Audio Visual Productions
The Bodleian Library
Boulton-Hawker Films Ltd
Cement & Concrete Association
Commonwealth Association of
    Architects
Fergus Davidson Associates Ltd
Dundee College of Education
EAV Ltd
ETV Films Ltd
Educational Media International
Educational Productions Ltd
Eothen Films Ltd
Focal Point AV Ltd
Fordigraph
Guild Sound & Vision Ltd
Nicholas Hunter Ltd
Longman Group Ltd
Looking & Seeing Filmstrips
Macdonald & Co (Publishers) Ltd
National Audio Visual Aids Library

Open University Educational
    Enterprises Ltd
Edward Patterson Associates Ltd
Ann & Bury Peerless
Pictorial Charts Educational Trust
Resources for Learning Ltd
Service Training Ltd
The Slide Centre
Studio Two Educational AV
Timber Research & Development
    Association
Town & Country Productions Ltd
Viscom Ltd
Visual Publications
Woodmansterne Ltd
Diana Wyllie Ltd

24. Physical education and sport

Boulton-Hawker Films Ltd
BSIP ARS Magna Ltd
Chiltern Consortium
Creative Film Makers Ltd
Fergus Davidson Associates Ltd
Drake Educational Associates
Dundee College of Education
ETV Films Ltd
Educational Media International
Educational Productions Ltd
Guild Sound & Vision Ltd
Helikon Imports
G Hubert-White
ILEA Learning Materials Service
International Tutor Machines Ltd
Jordanhill College
Lincolnshire Educational Television
Macdonald & Co (Publishers) Ltd
National Audio Visual Aids Library
Edward Patterson Associates Ltd
The Slide Centre
Town & Country Productions Ltd

25. Teaching and learning: programmed instruction, training, analysis

County of Avon Resources for Learning
    Development Unit
BP Educational Service
Chemical & Allied Products Industry
    Training Board
Chiltern Consortium
Construction Industry Training Board
Council for Educational Technology
Cybernetic Teaching Systems Ltd
Fergus Davidson Associates Ltd
Drake Educational Associates
Dundee College of Education
Educational Productions Ltd
ESL Bristol
Engineering Industry Training Board
Guardian Business Services

Guild Sound & Vision Ltd
Helikon Imports
Hertfordshire County Council
    Programmed Learning Centre
Hotel & Catering ITB
G Hubert-White
ICI Film Library
Institute of Tape Learning
Instructa
International Tutor Machines Ltd
Jordanhill College of Education
Larman Associates Ltd
Legal & General Assurance Society
Lincolnshire Educational Television
University of London AV Centre
Local Government Training Board
Macdonald & Co (Publishers) Ltd
McGraw-Hill Book Co (UK) Ltd
Management Games Ltd
National Centre for Developments in
    Nurse Education
National Computing Centre
University of Newcastle Computing
    Laboratory
Oliver & Boyd
Open University Educational
    Enterprises Ltd
Edward Patterson Associates Ltd
Pitman Correspondence College Ltd
Reach-a-Teacha Ltd
Resources for Learning Ltd
Road Transport ITB
Scottish & Newcastle Breweries Ltd
Selsdon Park Management Centre
Service Training Ltd
Sheffield City Polytechnic
The University of Southampton
    Department of Teaching Media
Stewart Film Distributors Ltd
Tetradon Publications Ltd
Transart Visual Productions Ltd
Waterlow Publishers Ltd
John Wiley & Sons Ltd

26. Religion
Edward Arnold
County of Avon Resources for
    Learning Development Unit
Hugh Baddeley Productions
Boulton-Hawker Films Ltd
CTVC
Cassell Ltd
Chiltern Consortium
Christian Aid
Church Army AV Resources
Church Missionary Society
Fergus Davidson Associates Ltd
Dundee College of Education
EAV Ltd

ETV Films Ltd
Educational Media International
Educational Productions Ltd
Fordigraph
Mary Glasgow
ILEA Learning Materials Service
Jordanhill College
Longman Group Ltd
National Audio Visual Aids Library
Edward Patterson Associates Ltd
Ann & Bury Peerless
Rank Audio Visual Ltd
Scripture Union
Seminar Cassettes Ltd
The Slide Centre
Studio Two Educational AV
Transaid
Viscom Ltd
Visual Publications
Woodmansterne Ltd

27. History
Allyn & Bacon
Edward Arnold
Audio Learning Ltd
Audio Visual Productions
County of Avon Resources for
    Learning Development Unit
Hugh Baddeley Productions
Ivan Berg Associates
The Bodleian Library
Boulton-Hawker Films Ltd
Cassell Ltd
Chiltern Consortium
Colour Centre Slides Ltd
Community Service Volunteers
Dundee College of Education
EAV Ltd
Educational Media International
Educational Productions Ltd
Fergus Davidson Associates Lt '
Focal Point AV Ltd
Fordigraph
Guild Sound & Vision Ltd
Nicholas Hunter Ltd
ILEA Learning Materials Service
ITL Vufoils Ltd
Jordanhill College
University of London AV Centre
Longman Group Ltd
Macdonald & Co (Publishers) Ltd
National Audio Visual Aids Library
Oliver & Boyd
Open University Educational
    Enterprises Ltd
Edward Patterson Associates Ltd
Ann & Bury Peerless
Pergamon Press Ltd
Pictorial Charts Educational Trust

Rank Audio Visual Ltd
Shell Film Library
The Slide Centre
Sound Education
Studio Two Educational AV
Transart Visual Productions Ltd
Viewtech AV Media Ltd
Viscom Ltd
Visual Publications
Woodmansterne Ltd
Diana Wyllie Ltd

28. Economics and politics

Edward Arnold
Audio Learning Ltd
Boulton & Hawker Films
British Insurance Association
Centre for World Development
    Education
Fergus Davidson Associates Ltd
Dundee College of Education
EAV Ltd
Educational Media International
Educational Productions Ltd
Guild Sound & Vision Ltd
ICI Film Library
ILEA Learning Materials Service
Institute of Grocery Distribution
Institute of Tape Learning
Jordanhill College
Legal & General Assurance Society
Longman Group Ltd
Management Games Ltd
National Audio Visual Aids Library
Open University Educational
    Enterprises Ltd
Rank Audio Visual Ltd
Resources for Learning Ltd
SAGSET
Seminar Cassettes Ltd
Service Training Ltd
The Slide Centre
Sound Education
Studio Two Educational AV
Viscom Ltd

29. Social studies

Allyn & Bacon
Edward Arnold
Audio Learning Ltd
Audio Visual Productions
County of Avon Resources for
    Learning Development Unit
Hugh Baddeley Productions
Boulton-Hawker Films Ltd
Brunel University AV Centre
Cassell Ltd
Chiltern Consortium
Christian Aid

Community Service Volunteers
Fergus Davidson Associates Ltd
Dundee College of Education
EAV Ltd
ETV Films Ltd
Educational Media International
Educational Productions Ltd
Focal Point AV Ltd
Fordigraph
Mary Glasgow
Guild Sound & Vision Ltd
Health Education Audio Visual
ILEA Learning Materials Service
Jordanhill College
University of London AV Centre
Longman Group Ltd
Management Games Ltd
National Audio Visual Aids Library
Oliver & Boyd
Open University Educational
    Enterprises Ltd
Edward Patterson Associates Ltd
Ann & Bury Peerless
Pictorial Charts Educational Trust
Rank Audio Visual Ltd
Scripture Union
Seminar Cassettes Ltd
Sheffield City Polytechnic
The Slide Centre
Sound Education
Studio Two Educational AV
Viewtech AV Media Ltd
Viscom Ltd
Visual Publications
Diana Wyllie Ltd

30. Geography and geology

Aerofilms Ltd
Edward Arnold
Audio Learning Ltd
Audio Visual Productions
County of Avon Resources for
    Learning Development Unit
BP Educational Service
Hugh Baddeley Productions
Boulton-Hawker Films Ltd
Cassell Ltd
Centre for World Development
    Education
Christian Aid
Dundee College of Education
EAV Ltd
ETV Films Ltd
Educational Media International
Educational Productions Ltd
Fergus Davidson Associates Ltd
Focal Point AV Ltd
Fordigraph
W H Freeman & Co Ltd

Mary Glasgow
Guild Sound & Vision Ltd
Philip Harris Biological
Helikon Imports
ITL Vufoils Ltd
Institute of Tape Learning
Jordanhill College
University of London AV Centre
Longman Group Ltd
Macdonald & Co (Publishers) Ltd
National Audio Visual Aids Library
Thomas Nelson & Sons Ltd
Oliver & Boyd
Open University Educational
    Enterprises Ltd
Oxford University (Department of
    Geology & Mineralogy)
Edward Patterson Associates Ltd
Ann & Bury Peerless
Pergamon Press Ltd
Pictorial Charts Educational Trust
Rank Audio Visual Ltd
Marian Ray
Service Training Ltd
Sheffield City Polytechnic
Shell Education Service
Shell Film Library
The Slide Centre
Sound Education
The University of Southampton
    Department of Teaching Media
Space Frontiers Ltd
Studio Two Educational AV
Visual Publications
Transaid
Transart Visual Productions Ltd
Viewtech AV Media Ltd
Viscom Ltd
Woodmansterne Ltd
Diana Wyllie Ltd

31. Psychology
Audio Learning Ltd
BSIP ARS Magna Ltd
Brunel University AV Centre
Dundee College of Education
Educational Media International
Harcourt Brace Jovanovich
Holdsworth AV
Institute of Tape Learning
Jordanhill College
Lincolnshire Educational Television
University of London AV Centre
Open University Educational
    Enterprises Ltd
Edward Patterson Associates Ltd
Prentice-Hall International
Seminar Cassettes Ltd

Service Training Ltd
Sound Education

32. General science
Edward Arnold
Audio Visual Productions
County of Avon Resources for
    Learning Development Unit
BP Educational Services
BSIP ARS Magna
Ivan Berg Associates
Boulton-Hawker Films Ltd
Cassell Ltd
Chiltern Consortium
Fergus Davidson Associates Ltd
Drake Educational Associates
Dundee College of Education
ETV Films Ltd
Educational Media International
Educational Productions Ltd
Eothen Films Ltd
Focal Point AV Ltd
Fordigraph
Guild Sound & Vision Ltd
Helikon Imports
Hertfordshire County Council
    Programmed Learning Centre
ICI Film Library
ILEA Learning Materials Service
ITL Vufoils Ltd
Longman Group Ltd
McGraw-Hill Book Co (UK) Ltd
National Audio Visual Aids Library
Oliver & Boyd
Oxford University (Department of
    Geology and Mineralogy)
Pattison & Co
Pictorial Charts Educational Trust
Rank Audio Visual Ltd
Marian Ray
Royal Society for the Protection
    of Birds
Seminar Cassettes Ltd
Service Training Ltd
Shell Education Service
Shell Film Library
The Slide Centre
Space Frontiers Ltd
Studio Two Educational AV
Viewtech AV Media Ltd
Viscom Ltd
Visual Publications
Diana Wyllie Ltd

33. Biology
Edward Arnold
Audio Learning Ltd
Audio Visual Productions

BP Educational Service
BSIP ARS Magna Ltd
Hugh Baddeley Productions
Ivan Berg Associates
Boulton-Hawker Films Ltd
Brunel University AV Centre
Cassell Ltd
Chapman & Hall
Fergus Davidson Associates Ltd
Dundee College of Education
ESL Bristol
Educational Media International
Educational Productions Ltd
Eothen Films Ltd
Focal Point AV Ltd
Fordigraph
W H Freeman & Co Ltd
Guild Sound & Vision Ltd
Philip Harris Biological
Health Education Audio Visual
Helikon Imports
Hertfordshire County Council
    Programmed Learning Centre
Nicholas Hunter Ltd
ITL Vufoils Ltd
Institute of Tape Learning
Jordanhill College
University of London AV Centre
Longman Group Ltd
Macdonald & Co (Publishers) Ltd
McGraw-Hill Book Co (UK) Ltd
National Audio Visual Aids Library
National Centre for Developments in
    Nurse Education
Thomas Nelson & Sons Ltd
Oliver & Boyd
Open University Educational
    Enterprises Ltd
Pictorial Charts Educational Trust
Edward Patterson Associates Ltd
Pattison & Co
Pitman Publishing Ltd
Rank Audio Visual Ltd
Marian Ray
Royal Society for the Protection
    of Birds
Seminar Cassettes Ltd
Service Training Ltd
Shell Education Service
Shell Film Library
The Slide Centre
Studio Two Educational AV
Transaid
Viewtech AV Media Ltd
Viscom Ltd
Visual Publications
John Wiley & Sons Ltd
Diana Wyllie Ltd

34. Chemistry

Alcan Film Library
Edward Arnold
Audio Learning Ltd
Audio Visual Productions
BP Educational Service
Ivan Berg Associates
Brunel University AV Centre
Cassell Ltd
Chapman & Hall
The Chemical Society: Educational
    Techniques Subject Group
Fergus Davidson Associates Ltd
Dundee College of Education
Du Pont (UK) Ltd
Educational Media International
Educational Productions Ltd
ESL Bristol
Eothen Films Ltd
Fordigraph
W H Freeman & Co Ltd
Guild Sound & Vision Ltd
Helikon Imports
Hertfordshire County Council
    Programmed Learning Centre
Heyden & Son Ltd
Hodder & Stoughton Educational
Nicholas Hunter Ltd
ICI Film Library
ITL Vufoils Ltd
Institute of Tape Learning
Jordanhill College
University of London AV Centre
Longman Group Ltd
Macdonald & Co (Publishers) Ltd
McGraw-Hill Book Co (UK) Ltd
National Audio Visual Aids Library
Oliver & Boyd
Open University Educational
    Enterprises Ltd
Edward Patterson Associates Ltd
Pattison & Co
Pergamon Press Ltd
Pictorial Charts Educational Trust
Marian Ray/Shell Education Service
SAGSET
Service Training Ltd
Shell Film Library
The Slide Centre
Studio Two Educational AV
Technical Press Ltd
Tetradon Publications Ltd
Viewtech AV Media Ltd
Viscom Ltd

35. Physics

Edward Arnold
Audio Learning Ltd

Audio Visual Productions
BP Educational Service
Hugh Baddeley Productions
Ivan Berg Associates
Boulton-Hawker Films Ltd
Brunel University AV Centre
Cassell Ltd
Chapman & Hall
Fergus Davidson Associates Ltd
Dundee College of Education
EAV Ltd
ESL Bristol
Educational Media International
Educational Productions Ltd
Eothen Films Ltd
Fordigraph
Guild Sound & Vision Ltd
Helikon Imports
Hertfordshire County Council
    Programmed Learning Centre
Nicholas Hunter Ltd
ICI Film Library
ITL Vufoils Ltd
ILEA Learning Materials Service
Institute of Tape Learning
Jordanhill College
University of London AV Centre
Longman Group Ltd
Macdonald & Co (Publishers) Ltd
McGraw-Hill Book Co (UK) Ltd
National Audio Visual Aids Library
Oliver & Boyd
Open University Educational
    Enterprises Ltd
Edward Patterson Associates Ltd
Pattison & Co
Pennant AV Systems
Pictorial Charts Educational Trust
Pitman Publishing Ltd
Rank Audio Visual Ltd
Marian Ray
Scientific Era Publications
Service Training Ltd
Shell Film Library
The Slide Centre
Studio Two Educational AV
Tetradon Publications Ltd
Viewtech AV Media Ltd
Visual Publications

36. Electricity and electronics
Alcan Film Library
Edward Arnold
Audio Visual Productions
BP Educational Services
Brunel University AV Centre
CST Training Resources Ltd
Cassell Ltd
Chapman & Hall

Fergus Davidson Associates Ltd
Dundee College of Education
ESL Bristol
Educational Media International
Educational Productions Ltd
Eothen Films Ltd
Engineering Industry Training Board
Feedback Instruments Ltd
Fordigraph
Guild Sound & Vision Ltd
Helikon Imports
Heyden & Son Ltd
ITL Vufoils Ltd
University of London AV Centre
McGraw-Hill Book Co (UK) Ltd
National Audio Visual Aids Library
Oliver & Boyd
Open University Educational
    Enterprises Ltd
Pattison & Co
Pennant AV Systems
Pictorial Charts Educational Trust
Pitman Publishing Ltd
Rank Audio Visual Ltd
Scientific Era Publications
Service Training Ltd
Sheffield City Polytechnic
The Slide Centre
The University of Southampton
    Department of Teaching Media
Stewart Film Distributors Ltd
Studio Two Educational AV
The Technical Press Ltd
Viscom Ltd

37. Computers and computing
Applied Data Education Services Ltd
Edward Arnold
BP Educational Services
BSIP ARS Magna Ltd
Brunel University AV Centre
Cassell Ltd
Chapman & Hall
Chiltern Consortium
Cybernetic Teaching Systems Ltd
Fergus Davidson Associates Ltd
ESL Bristol
Educational Media International
Eductronics
Eothen Films Ltd
Feedback Instruments Ltd
Guild Sound & Vision Ltd
Heyden & Son Ltd
IBM: *see* Random Film Library
ICI Film Library
ICL-CES
Jordanhill College
LAMSAC
University of London AV Centre

Macdonald & Co (Publishers) Ltd
McGraw-Hill Book Co (UK) Ltd
Management Games Ltd
Melrose Films
The National Computing Centre
University of Newcastle Computing
    Laboratory
Oliver & Boyd
Open University Educational
    Enterprises Ltd
Oxford Educational Resources Ltd
Pattison & Co
Pennant AV Systems
Pictorial Charts Educational Trust
Pitman Publishing Ltd
Random Film Library
Seminar Cassettes Ltd
Service Training Ltd
The Slide Centre
Studio Two Educational AV
The Technical Press Ltd
Video Arts Ltd
John Wiley & Sons Ltd
Diana Wyllie Ltd

38. Engineering
Alcan Film Library
Edward Arnold
BP Educational Service
Hugh Baddeley Productions
British Productivity Council
Brunel University AV Centre
CST Training Resources Ltd
Carborundum Company Ltd
Cassell Ltd
Cement & Concrete Association
Chapman & Hall
Fergus Davidson Associates Ltd
Dundee College of Education
Du Pont (UK) Ltd
ESL Bristol
Educational Media International
Educational Productions Ltd
Edu-Tex
Engineering Industry Training Board
Eothen Films Ltd
Feedback Instruments Ltd
Guild Sound & Vision Ltd
Helikon Imports
ICI Film Library
University of London AV Centre
Looking & Seeing Filmstrips
Loughborough University CES
Macdonald & Jane's Publishing Group
McGraw-Hill Book Co (UK) Ltd
Management Games Ltd
Open University Educational
    Enterprises Ltd
Oxford Educational Resources Ltd

Pennant AV Systems
Pitman Publishing Ltd
Reach-a-Teacha Ltd
Service Training Ltd
Shell Film Library
The Slide Centre
The University of Southampton
    Department for Teaching Media
The Technical Press Ltd
Timber Research & Development
    Association
Viscom Ltd

39. Industrial safety
Edward Arnold
County of Avon Resources for
    Learning Development Unit
BNA Communication Europe
CST Training Resources Ltd
Cassell Ltd
Chapman & Hall
Chemical and Allied Products Industry
    Training Board
Consort Films
Construction Industry Training Board
Fergus Davidson Associates Ltd
Distributive Industry Training Board
Diversey AV Ltd (hospitals)
Du Pont (UK) Ltd
ESL Bristol
Educational Media International
Fire Protection Association
Food Drink and Tobacco Industry
    Training Board
GRD Productions
Guardian Business Services
Hotel and Catering Industry Training
    Board
Larman Associates Ltd
Legal & General Assurance Society
University of London AV Centre
Looking & Seeing Filmstrips (design)
Management Games Ltd
Merchant Navy Training Board
Middlesex Film Productions Ltd
Millbank Films
Open University Educational
    Enterprises Ltd
Oxford Educational Resources Ltd
Edward Patterson Associates Ltd
Pattison & Co
Rank Audio Visual Ltd
Reach-a-Teacha Ltd
Scottish & Newcastle Breweries Ltd
Service Training Ltd
Sheffield City Polytechnic
The University of Southampton
    Department of Teaching Media
Stewart Film Distributors Ltd

Training Films International Ltd
Video Arts Ltd
Waterlow Publishers Ltd

40. Industrial processes
Alcan Film Library
Edward Arnold
BP Educational Service
Cassell Ltd
Chapman & Hall
Fergus Davidson Associates Ltd
Dundee College of Education
Du Pont (UK) Ltd
Educational Media International
Feedback Instruments Ltd
Guardian Business Services
Guild Sound & Vision Ltd
Helikon Imports
ITL Vufoils Ltd
Knitting Lace and Net Industry
    Training Board
University of London AV Centre
Loughborough University CES
Management Games Ltd
Merchant Navy Training Board
National Audio Visual Aids Library
Open University Educational
    Enterprises Ltd
PIRA (Research Association for the
    Paper & Board Printing & Packaging
    Industries)
RTZ Services
SATRA (Shoe & Allied Trades Research
    Association)
Scientific Era Publications
Service Training Ltd
Sheffield City Polytechnic
Shell Film Library
Stewart Film Distributors Ltd
Timber Research & Development
    Association
Viscom Ltd
Wool, Jute & Flax Industry
    Training Board

41. Reading
Drake Educational Associates
Educational Media International
Hertfordshire County Council
    Programmed Learning Centre
Longman Group Ltd
Packman Research Ltd
Reading University Centre for the
    Teaching of Reading
Stewart Film Distributors Ltd

42. Environmental studies
Audio Learning Ltd
Hugh Baddeley Productions
Chiltern Consortium
Community Service Volunteers
Educational Media International
Looking & Seeing Filmstrips
Loughborough University CES
Ann & Bury Peerless
Viscom Ltd
Woodmansterne Ltd

43. Teaching and teacher training
Chiltern Consortium
ETV Films Ltd
Stewart Film Distributors Ltd

Part 2: Producers and Distributors' Names and Addresses

Acrofilms Ltd, Gate Studios,
Station Road, Boreham Wood, Herts

OHP transparencies, photos

Geography

Alcan Film Library, 303 Finchley
Road, London NW3 6DT

Film

Electricity and electronics, engineering,
industrial processes

*Allyn & Bacon, 1 Bedford Road,
London N1

*Programmed books, slide/tape materials,
OHP transparencies, games
and simulations, case studies*

Management and supervision, languages,
music, history, social studies

Edward Arnold (Publishers) Ltd,
41 Bedford Square,
London WC1B 3DQ

*Books, sound-tape, games and
simulations*

Office practice, management and
supervision, English language, English
literature, EFL, languages,
mathematics, health, nursing and
medicine, physiology, drama,
religion, history, economics and
politics, social studies, geography
and geology, general science, biology,
chemistry, physics, electricity and
electronics, computers and computing,
engineering, industrial safety, industrial
processes

Applied Data Education Services,
Suite 504, Albany House,
324 Regent Street,
London W1R 5AA

Sound-tape and text (self-instruction)

Computers and computing

E J Arnold & Sons Ltd,
Butterley Street,
Leeds LS10 1AX

*Sound-tapes, slide sets, OHP
transparencies, filmstrips*

Arts Council of Great Britain,
105 Piccadilly, London W1

Film

Art and architecture

Audio-Visual Library Services,
10-12 Powdrake Road, Grangemouth,
Stirlingshire FK3 9UT

*Slide-tape materials, filmstrips, sound-
tapes*

Audio Learning Ltd, Sarda House,
183-9 Queensway, London W2

Slide-tape materials, sound-tape

English literature, mathematics, art and
architecture, history, economics and
politics, social studies, geography and
geology, psychology, biology, chemistry,
physics, environmental studies

Audio-Visual Productions, Hocker Hill
House, Chepstow, Gwent NP6 5ER

*Slide/tape materials, sound-tape,
OHP transparencies, filmstrips*

English language, English literature,
EFL, French, mathematics, health,
physiology, art and architecture,
history, social studies, geography and
geology, general science, biology,
chemistry, physics, electricity and
electronics

**County of Avon Resources for
Learning Development Unit,**
Redcross Street,
Bristol BS2 0BA

*Programmed books, slide/tape materials,
sound-tape, games and simulations*

English language, English literature,
languages, mathematics, teaching and
learning: programmed instruction,
training, analysis; religion, history, social
studies, geography and geology, general
science, industrial safety

BBC English by Radio & Television,

PO Box 76, Bush House, The Strand,
London WC2B 4PH

Video, sound-tape, film

English language, EFL

BBC Enterprises,
c/o Guild Sound & Vision Ltd,
Woodston House, Oundle Road,
Peterborough PE2 9PZ

Video cassettes

BBC Publications, 35 Marylebone High
Street, London W1M 4AA

Filmstrips

**BLAT Centre for Health and Medical
Education,** BMA House, Tavistock
Square, London WC1H 9JP

*Slide/tape materials, sound-tape, film,
games and simulations, algorithms*

Health, nursing and medicine,
physiology

BNA Communications Europe
17 Dartmouth Street,
London SW1H 9BL

Video cassettes, film

Management and supervision,
salesmanship and marketing, industrial
safety

BP Educational Service,
Britannic House, Moor Lane,
London WC2Y 9BU

*Slide/tape materials, film, games and
simulations, case studies, wallcharts,
handbooks*

General crafts, hobbies, etc,
management and supervision,
salesmanship and marketing, teaching
and learning: programmed instruction,
training, analysis; geography and
geology, general science, biology,
chemistry, physics, electricity and
electronics, computers and computing,
engineering, industrial processes

BSIP ARS Magna Ltd,
12 Leeward Gardens, Wimbledon,
London SW19 7QR

*Videotape, slide-tape, sound-tape, film,
OHP transparencies, games and
simulations, case studies, consultancy,
purchasing*

Office practice, management and
supervision, salesmanship and
marketing, logic, health, nursing and
medicine, physiology, physical
education, psychology, general science,

biology, computers and computing

Hugh Baddeley Productions,
64 Moffats Lane, Brookmans Park,
Hatfield, Herts AL9 7RU

Films, filmstrips, slide-tape programmes

Languages (French), religion, history,
social studies, geography, biology,
physics, engineering, environmental
studies

Bell & Howell AV Ltd,
Alperton House,
Bridgewater Road,
Wembley, Middx HA0 1EG

Programmes (for card-reading machines)

English language, EFL, languages
(Welsh), logic, mathematics

Ivan Berg Associates, 35a Broadhurst
Gardens, London NW6 3QT

Sound-tapes

General crafts, hobbies, etc, English
language, English literature, languages,
mathematics, music, drama, history,
general science, biology, chemistry,
physics

*Clive Bingley Ltd,
Commonwealth House,
1-19 New Oxford Street,
London WC1A 1NG

Programmed books
Librarianship

The Bodleian Library, The Western
Manuscript Department, Oxford

Slides, filmstrips
Art and architecture, history

Boulton-Hawker Films Ltd, Hadleigh,
Ipswich, Suffolk IP7 5BG

Video, film

English language, languages,
mathematics, health, nursing and
medicine, physiology, art and
architecture, physical education,
religion, history, economics and politics,
social studies, geography and geology,
general science, biology, physics

British Gas Film Library – *see* Viscom
Ltd

British Insurance Association,
Aldermary House, Queen Street,
London EC4N 1TU

Film, games and simulations
Economics and politics (insurance)

British Productivity Council,
8 Southampton Row,
London WC1B 4AQ

Slide-tape materials, film

Office practice, management and
supervision, salesmanship and
marketing, engineering

British Telecom, Films Officer,
ME/PUB 1.2.5. Seal House, 1 Swan
Lane, London EC4R 3TH

Videotape, film
Office practice

*Brunel University Audio Visual Centre,
Uxbridge, Middx UB8 3PU

Videotape

Social studies, psychology, biology,
chemistry, physics, electricity and
electronics, computers and computing,
engineering

CST Training Resources Ltd,
78 High Street, Bushey, Herts WD2
3DE

Videotape, sound-tape, film

Accountancy, office practice,
management and supervision,
salesmanship and marketing, electricity
and electronics, engineering, industrial
safety

CTVC, Film Library, Foundation
House, 6 Walton Road, Bushey,
Watford WD2 2JS

Video, sound-tape, film

General crafts, hobbies, etc, religion,
social studies

Caedmon Spoken Word – *see* Teakfield
Publishing Co Ltd

Cambridge University Press (Publishing
Division), The Edinburgh Building,
Shaftesbury Road, Cambridge CB2 2RU

*Slide/tape materials, videotape,
sound-tape*

English as a second language

*Camera Talks Ltd, 31 North Row,
London W1R 2EN

Filmstrips, video-cassettes

The Carborundum Company Ltd,
c/o Cinephoto Film Library,
13 The Crescent, Salford,
Manchester M5 4PF

Film
Engineering (abrasives)

Careers and Occupational Information Centre, Manpower Services Commission, Moorfoot, Sheffield S1 4PQ
Slide-tape materials, OHP transparencies
Librarianship, careers

*Carwal Audio Visual Aids, PO Box 55, Wallington, Surrey
Filmstrips

Cassell Ltd, 35 Red Lion Square, London WC1E 4SG
Sound-tape, games and simulations, packs, kits and filmstrips, spirit duplicator masters
Accountancy, office practice, management and supervision, salesmanship and marketing, English language, EFL, languages, mathematics, health, nursing and medicine, physiology, religion, history, social studies, geography and geology, general science, biology, chemistry, physics, electricity and electronics, computers and computing, engineering, industrial safety, industrial processes

Cassette Teaching Services, 73 Chapel Street, Billericay, Essex CM12 9LR
Sound-tape
Office practice (shorthand/speed dictation)

Cement & Concrete Association, Films & Photographs Manager, Wexham Springs, Slough SL3
Slide materials, film
General crafts, hobbies, etc, architecture, engineering (civil)

Centre for World Development Education (CWDE), Parnell House, 25 Wilton Road, London SW1
Slides, filmstrips, printed materials
Economics and politics, social studies, geography

The Certified Accountants Educational Trust, 9 Museum House, Museum Street, London WC1A 1JT
Sound-tape
Accountancy

W & R Chambers Ltd, 11 Thistle Street, Edinburgh EH2 1DG
OHP transparencies
Mathematics

Chapman and Hall, 11 New Fetter Lane, London EC4P 4EE
Programmed books, games and simulations
Mathematics, nursing and medicine, biology, chemistry, physics, electricity and electronics, computers and computing, engineering, industrial safety, industrial processes

Chemical & Allied Products Industry Training Board, Staines House, 158-162 High Street, Staines, Middx TW18 4AT
Slide/tape materials, videotape sound-tape, film, OHP case studies
Management and supervision, salesmanship and marketing, teaching and learning: programmed instruction, training, analysis; industrial safety

Chiltern Consortium, Wall Hall, Aldenham, Watford, Herts
Slide-tape materials, videotape
Ofice practice, EFL, dance, physical education, teaching and learning: programmed instruction, training, analysis; religion, history, social studies, general science, computers and computing, teaching and teacher training

Christian Aid, PO Box 1, London SW9 8BH
Slide-tape materials, film, games and simulations
Religion, social studies, geography and geology

Church Army AV Resources, Independents Road, Blackheath, London SE3 9LG
Slide-tape materials, videotape, sound-tape
Religion

Church Missionary Society, 157 Waterloo Road, London SE1
Slide-tape materials, filmstrips
Religion

Ron Clements Associates (Training Consultants), 29 Paxton Gardens, Woodham Lane, Woking, Surrey GU21 5TS
Programmed books, slide-tape materials, OHP transparencies, packages and kits
Office practice, management and supervision, salesmanship and marketing

Colour Centre Slides Ltd, Hilltop, Hedgerley Hill, Hedgerley, Slough
Slide materials, filmstrips
History

Commonwealth Association of Architects, The Building Centre, 26 Store Street, London WC1E 7BT
Slide-tape materials, filmstrips
Architecture. building

Community Service Volunteers (Advisory Service), 237 Pentonville Road, London N1 9NJ
Slides, video, games and simulations, resource packs
Social studies, environmental studies

Consort Films, The Rig, Newmillerdam, Wakefield, Yorks WF2 6QF
Slide-tape materials, video, film
General crafts, hobbies, etc, nursing and medicine, industrial safety

*****Construction Industry Training Board,** Radnor House, London Road, Norbury, London SW16
Programmed books, slide-tape materials, film, training recommendations
Management and supervision, teaching and learning: programmed instruction, training, analysis; industrial safety

Council for Educational Technology, 3 Devonshire Street, London W1N 2BA
Programmed books, case studies, multi-media packages, print packages
Teaching and learning: programmed instruction, training, analysis

Creative Film Makers Ltd, Pottery Lane House, Pottery Lane, London W11 4LZ
Programmes (for machines), slide/tape materials, videotape, sound-tape, film
General crafts, hobbies, driving etc, physical education

*****Cybernetic Teaching Systems Ltd,** Park Lane, Castle Donington, Derby
Slide/tape materials, sound-tape, OHP transparencies, games and simulations, case studies, algorithms, CRI materials
Office practice, management and supervision, teaching and learning: programmed instruction, training, analysis; computers and computing

Fergus Davidson Associates Ltd, 1 Bensham Lane, Croydon, Surrey CR0 2RU

Video, sound-tape, film, OHP transparencies
Office practice, salesmanship and marketing, English language, English literature, languages (15), mathematics, health, nursing and medicine, physiology, music, drama, dance, art and architecture, physical education, teaching and learning: programmed instruction, training, analysis; religion, history, economics and politics, social studies, geography and geology, general science, biology, chemistry, physics, electricity and electronics, computers and computing, engineering, industrial safety, industrial processes

*****Joan Davies,** 21 Carlton Grange, Grove Road, Wrexham
Programmed books, sound-tape
General

Distributive Industry Training Board, MacLaren House, Talbot Road, Stretford, Manchester
Programmed books, slide/tape materials, videotape sound-tape, film, OHP transparencies
Management and supervision, salesmanship and marketing, industrial safety

Diversey (AV) Ltd, 33-35 New Bedford Road, Luton, Beds
Slide/tape materials, filmstrip-tape materials
Management and supervision, salesmanship and marketing, health (hygiene), industrial (hospital/catering) safety

Drake Educational Associates, 212 Whitchurch Road, Cardiff CF4 3XF
Programmes (for machines), slide/tape
English language, English literature, EFL, librarianship, mathematics, music, physical education, teaching and learning: programmes instruction, training, analysis; general science, reading

Dundee College of Education, Gardyne Road, Broughty Ferry, Dundee DD5 1NY
Programmed books, slide/tape materials, videotape, sound-tape, film, games and simulations, case studies
General crafts, hobbies, driving etc, accountancy, management and

supervision, English language, languages, librarianship, mathematics, health, physiology, music, drama, dance, art and architecture, physical education, teaching and learning: programmed instruction, training, analysis; religion, history, economics and politics, social studies, geography and geology, psychology, general science, biology, chemistry, physics, electricity and electronics, engineering, industrial processes

*Du Pont (UK) Ltd,
Applied Technology Department,
Du Pont House, 18 Bream's Buildings,
Fetter Lane, London EC4A 1HT
Programmed books

Management and supervision, mathematics, chemistry, engineering, industrial safety, industrial processes

EAV Ltd, c/o Mary Glasgow
Publications Ltd, Brookhampton Lane,
Kineton, Warwick CV35 0JB
Half frame 35 mm filmstrips – accompanying tapes or cassettes

English language, English literature, languages, music, drama, dance, art and architecture, religion, history, economics and politics, social studies, geography and geology, physics

EMI Films Ltd – *see* Viscom Ltd

*ESL Bristol, Waverley Road, Yate,
Bristol BS17 5RB
Programmes (for machines), programmed books, slide/tape materials, sound-tape, film

General crafts, hobbies, driving etc, accountancy, office practice, management and supervision, salesmanship and marketing, logic, mathematics, nursing and medicine, teaching and learning: programmed instruction, training, analysis; biology, chemistry, physics, electricity and electronics, computers and computing, engineering, industrial safety

ETV Films Ltd, 247A Upper Street,
Highbury Corner, London N1 1RU
Films (see 'Some Useful Catalogues' listing)

General crafts, hobbies, etc, languages, health, music, drama, dance, art and architecture, physical education, religion, social studies, geography and

geology, general science, teaching and teacher training

*Educational Audio Cassettes,
PO Box 59, Barnet, Herts EN5 4AF
Sound-tapes

Educational Media International,
25 Boileau Road, London W5 3AL
Slide/tape materials, videotape, film

General crafts, hobbies, etc, office practice, management and supervision, English language, English literature, librarianship, mathematics, health, nursing and medicine, physiology, music, drama, dance, art and architecture, physical education, teaching and learning: programmed instruction, training, analysis; religion, history, economics and politics, social studies, geography and geology, psychology, general science, biology, chemistry, physics, electricity and electronics, computers and computing, engineering, industrial safety, industrial processes

Educational Productions Ltd,
Bradford Road, East Ardsley,
Wakefield WF3 2JN
Slide/tape materials, videotapes, sound-tapes, OHP transparencies, games and simulations, filmstrips, wallcharts, study kits

General crafts, hobbies, driving etc, office practice, English language, English literature, languages, mathematics, health, nursing and medicine, physiology, music, drama, art and architecture, physical education, teaching and learning: programmed instruction, training, analysis; religion, history, economics and politics, social studies, geography and geology, general science, biology, chemistry, physics, electricity and electronics, engineering

Educational Tapes – *see* Institute of Tape Learning

*Educational Techniques Subject Group of The Chemical Society,
c/o Dr P J Hills, University of Surrey
IET, Guildford, Surrey
Sound-tape
Chemistry

*Edu-Tex, 85 St Germain's Lane,
Marske-by-Sea, Redcar,
Teesside TS1 1EL

OHP transparencies
Engineering

The Edutronics Division, McGraw-Hill
International Training Systems,
68 Sheen Lane, London SW4 8LP
Programmed books, videotape
Computers and computing

Employment Relations Ltd,
62 Hills Road,
Cambridge CB2 1LA
*Audiovisual, video and film,
simulations, case studies, OHP
transparencies, programmed instruction,
role-play exercises, training
recommendations*
Industrial relations; management and
supervision, collective bargaining,
negotiation, managing change, grievance
handling and industrial relations training

*****Engineering Industry Training Board,**
PO Box 176, 54 Clarendon Road,
Watford, Herts WD1 1LB
Training publications
Office practice, teaching and learning:
programmed instruction, training,
analysis; electricity and electronics,
engineering

English by Listening, 204 Raleigh
House, Dolphin Square, London SW1
Sound-tapes
EFL

Eothen Films Ltd, EMI Film Studios,
Shenley Road, Borehamwood,
Herts WD6 1JG
Slide/tape materials, videotape, film
Mathematics, health, nursing and
medicine, physiology, art and
architecture, general science, biology,
chemistry, physics, electricity and
electronics, computers and computing,
engineering

Exeter Tapes, University of Exeter
Language Centre, Queen's Building,
Queen's Drive, Exeter EX4 4YS
Sound-tapes
Languages

*****Feedback Instruments Ltd,** Park Road,
Crowborough, Sussex
*Laboratory equipment, simulators and
demonstrators for engineering
instruction*
Logic, electricity and electronics,

computers and computing, engineering,
industrial processes

Fire Protection Association, Aldermary
House, Queen Street, London EC4 1TJ
Slide/tape materials, sound-tape, film
Industrial safety

Focal Point Audio Visual Ltd,
251 Copner Road,
Portsmouth PO3 5EE
*Slide/tape materials, filmstrips, slide
books*
General crafts, hobbies, etc, ESL, health

**Food, Drink and Tobacco Industry
Training Board,** Barton House,
Barton Street, Gloucester GL1 1QQ
*OHP transparencies, case studies, 35mm
slides, course notes, exercises, handouts*
industrial safety

*****Fordigraph,** Ofrex House,
Stephen Street, London W1A 1EA
OHP transparencies
Languages, mathematics, nursing and
medicine, art and architecture, religion,
history, social studies, geography and
geology, general science, biology,
chemistry, physics, electricity and
electronics

*****Foundation for Teaching Aids at Low
Cost,** Institute of Child Health,
30 Guildford Street,
London WC1N 1EH
Slide/tape, slide sets·
Health care

W. H. Freeman & Co Ltd,
20 Beaumont Street,
Oxford OX1 2NQ
*Programmed books, slide/tape
materials, OHP transparencies*
Mathematics, geography and geology,
biology, chemistry

GP Systems Co Ltd, 138 Walsgrave
Road, Coventry CV2 4AX
*Telephone technique training equipment,
audio-typing equipment, typing/
shorthand/audio-typing desks*
Office practice

GRD Productions, 14 Elizabeth Court,
Collingham, Wetherby,
W Yorkshire LS22 5JL
Slide/tape materials
Industrial safety

Gateway Educational Media – *see* Viewtech AV Media

General Dental Council, 37 Wimpole Street, London W1M 8DQ

Slide/tape materials, film

Health (dentistry)

Geoslides, 4 Christian Fields, London SW16

Slide and filmstrip materials

Mary Glasgow Publications Ltd, Brookhampton Lane, Kineton, Warwicks

Programmed books, slide/tape materials, videotape, sound-tape, film

English language, English literature, EFL, languages, religion, social studies, geography and geology

Graves Medical Audio-Visual Library, 220 New London Road, Chelmsford, Essex

Videotapes

Nursing and medicine

Guardian Business Services, 119 Farringdon Road, London EC1R 3DA

Programmed books, slide/tape materials, sound-tape, videotape, OHP transparencies, games and simulations, case studies, algorithms

Office practice, management and supervision, English language, teaching and learning: programmed instruction, training, analysis; industrial safety, industrial processes

Guild Sound & Vision Ltd, Woodston House, Oundle Road, Peterborough PE2 9PZ

Slide/tape materials, videotape, film, OHP transparencies

General crafts, hobbies, driving etc, accountancy, office practice, management and supervision, salesmanship and marketing, mathematics, health, nursing and medicine, physiology, music, dance, art and architecture, physical education, teaching and learning: programmed instruction, training, analysis; religion, history, economics and politics, social studies, geography and geology, general science, biology, chemistry, physics, electricity and electronics, computers and computing, engineering, industrial safety, industrial processes

HLL Publications, 1 Westbourne Place, Hove, Sussex BN3 4GN

Programmed books, sound-tape

Languages

Harcourt Brace Jovanovich Ltd, 24-28 Oval Road, London NW1 7DU

Sound-tapes, film

EFL, languages, psychology

*****Harrap Didier,** 182-184 High Holborn, London WC1V 7AX

OHP transparencies, sound-tapes

Languages

Philip Harris Biological, Oldmixon, Weston-super-Mare, Avon BS24 9BJ

Slide/tape materials, OHP transparencies, games and simulations

Health, nursing and medicine, geography and geology, biology

Health Education Audio Visual, Neatham Mill, Lower Neatham Lane, Holybourne, Alton, Hants

Slide/tape materials, sound-tape

Health, social studies, biology

Helikon Imports (Hamonds AV Video Supplies), 60-62 Queen's Road, Watford, Herts WD1 2LW

Opticart strobed living diagrams

Office practice, management and supervision, health, nursing and medicine, physical education, teaching and learning: programmed instruction, training, analysis; geography and geology, general science, biology, chemistry, physics, electricity and electronics, engineering, industrial processes

Hertfordshire County Council, County Programmed Learning Centre, Hatfield Road, St Albans, Herts

Programmed books, sound-tape, OHP transparencies, structured print materials

English language, mathematics, health, nursing and medicine, teaching and learning: programmed instruction, training, analysis; general science, biology, chemistry, physics, reading

Heyden & Son Ltd, Spectrum House, Hillview Gardens, London NW4 2JQ

Programmed books, OHP transparencies, games and simulations

Chemistry, electricity and electronics, computers and computing

Hodder & Stoughton Educational,
PO Box 702, Mill Road,
Dunton Green, Sevenoaks,
Kent TN13 2YA

Programmed books, sound-tape, film

Accountancy, management and supervision, salesmanship and marketing, EFL, languages, mathematics, nursing and medicine, chemistry

Holdsworth Audio-Visual, 18 Malbrook Road, London SW15

Slide/tape materials, videotape, sound-tape, film, games and simulations, case studies

Office practice, management and supervision, psychology

Hotel & Catering Industry Training Board, Ramsey House, Central Square, Wembley, Middx HA9 7AP

Programmed books, slide/tape materials, videotape, film, OHP transparencies, case studies

Management and supervision, salesmanship and marketing, teaching and learning: programmed instruction, training, analysis; industrial safety

G Hubert White, 71 Norburn, Bretton, Peterborough PE3 8NT

Programmed books

Health, physical education, teaching and learning: programmed instruction, training, analysis

*Hulton Educational Productions Ltd,
Raans Road, Amersham, Bucks

Filmstrips

Nicholas Hunter Ltd, PO Box 22, Oxford OX1 2JT

Slide/tape materials

General crafts, hobbies, driving etc

Art and architecture, history, general science, biology, chemistry, physics

ICI Film Library, 15 Beaconsfield Road, London NW10 2LE (*See also:* Millbank Films Ltd)

Videotape

Teaching and learning: programmed instructional learning, analysis; economics and politics, general science, chemistry, physics, computers and computing, engineering

ICL-CES, 60 Portman Road, Reading, Berks RG3 1NR

Slide/tape materials, OHP transparencies, case studies, students' books and teachers' materials

Computers and computing

ILEA Learning Materials Service,
Publishing Centre, Highbury Station Road, London N1 1SB

Videotape (cassettes), sound-tape, games and simulations, resource packs

Office practice, languages, mathematics, health, music, drama, physical education, religion, history, economics and politics, social studies, general science, physics

ITL Vufoils Ltd, 10-18 Clifton Street, London EC2A 4BT

Slide/tape materials, film, OHP transparencies

Mathematics, health, physiology, teaching and learning: programmed instruction, training, analysis; history, geography and geology, general science, biology, chemistry, physics, electricity and electronics, industrial processes

The Industrial Society, 3 Carlton House Terrace, London SW1Y 5DG

Slide/tape materials, videotape, case studies, books

Office practice, management and supervision

The Institute of Chartered Accountants in England and Wales, PO Box 433, Chartered Accountants' Hall, Moorgate Place, London EC2P 2BJ

Packaged training courses (inc. video/audio material), OHP transparencies

Accountancy

The Institute of Chartered Accountants of Scotland, 27 Queen Street, Edinburgh EH2 1LA

Slide-tape materials, sound-tape

Accountancy

Institute of Grocery Distribution,
Grange Lane, Letchmore Heath, Watford WD2 8DQ

Slide materials, OHP transparencies, case studies

Salesmanship and marketing, economics and politics

The Institute of Supervisory Management, 22 Bore Street, Lichfield,

Staffs WS13 6LP

Slide/tape materials, games and simulations, case studies, kits

Management and supervision

Institute of Tape Learning, PO Box 4, Hemel Hempstead, Herts

Programmes (for machines), sound-tape (recorded)

Salesmanship and marketing, English language, EFL, languages, mathematics, teaching and learning: programmed instruction, training, analysis; economics and politics, geography, psychology, biology, chemistry, physics

Instructa, 225 Fort Austin Avenue, Plymouth PL6 5ST, Devon

Programmes (for machines), programmed books, sound-tape, OHP transparencies, games and simulations, case studies, audio-tutorial studies (cassette/workbook)

Management and supervision, salesmanship and marketing, English language, teaching and learning: programmed instruction, training, analysis

International Tutor Machines Ltd, 15 Holder Road, Aldershot, Hants

OHP transparencies, games and simulations

Office practice, management and supervision, salesmanship and marketing, physical education, teaching and learning: programmed instruction, training, analysis

Jordanhill College of Education,
A-V Media Dept,
76 Southbrae Drive,
Glasgow G13 1PP

Slide/tape materials, videotape, sound tape, film, OHP transparencies, games and simulations, case studies

English language, EFL, languages, librarianship, music, drama, dance, physical education, teaching and learning: programmed instruction, training, analysis; religion, history, economics and politics, social studies, geography and geology, psychology, biology, chemistry, physics, computers and computing

*Knitting, Lace and Net Industry Training Board, 4 Hamilton Road, Nottingham NG5 1AV

Slide/tape materials, games and simulations

Management and supervision, industrial processes

LAMSAC, 3 Buckingham Gate, London SW1E 6JH

Slide/tape materials

Office practice, computers and computing

*Larman Associates Ltd (Consultants in Human Resourcing), Tavistock House North, Tavistock Square, London WC1H 9HX

Programmed books, case studies

Management and supervision, teaching and learning: programmed instruction, training, analysis; industrial safety

Legal & General Assurance Society, 11 Queen Victoria Street, London EC4

Slide/tape materials, videotape

Management and supervision, teaching and learning: programmed instruction, training, analysis; economics and politics, industrial safety

*Lincolnshire Educational Television, Bishop Grosseteste College, Lincoln LN1 3DY

Film, video cassettes

General crafts, hobbies, driving etc, English language, mathematics, drama, physical education, teaching and learning: programmed instruction, training, analysis; psychology

*Linguaphone Institute Ltd, 207-209 Regent Street, London W1R 8AU

Home study language courses

EFL, languages

Local Government Training Board, 4th Floor, Arndale House, Arndale Centre, Luton LU1 2TS, Beds

Programmed books, slide/tape materials, videotape, sound-tape, film, OHP transparencies, games and simulations, case studies, algorithms

Management and supervision, teaching and learning: programmed instruction, training, analysis

University of London Audio-Visual Centre, 11 Bedford Square, London WC1B 3RA

Slide/tape materials, videotape, sound-tape, film

Management and supervision, English literature, languages – literature, mathematics, health, nursing and medicine, physiology, drama, teaching and learning: programmed instruction, training, analysis; history, social studies, geography and geology, psychology, biology, chemistry, physics, electricity and electronics, computers and computing, engineering, industrial safety, industrial processes

Longman Group Ltd, Longman House, Burnt Mill, Harlow, Essex

Slide/tape materials, videotape, sound-tape, film, OHP transparencies, games and simulations

Office practice, English language, English literature, EFL, languages, mathematics, health, nursing and medicine, music, art and architecture, religion, history, economics and politics, social studies, geography and geology, general science, biology, chemistry, physics

Longman Microsoftware, 33-35 Tanner Row, York YO1 1JP

Microsoftware

Mathematics, economics, geography, biology, chemistry, physics

Looking and Seeing Filmstrips, 81 Southway, London N20

Slide and filmstrip materials

Art and architecture, engineering, industrial processes (design), environmental studies

Loughborough University, Centre for Extension Studies, Loughborough, Leics LE11 3TU

Slide/tape materials, videotape, film

Engineering, industrial processes, environmental studies (pollution)

Lutterworth Press, Luke House, Farnham Road, Guildford, Surrey GU1 4XD

Programmed books

General crafts, hobbies, driving etc, accountancy

*Macdonald & Co (Publishers) Ltd, Holywell House, Worship Street, London EC2A 2E

Programmed books

General crafts, hobbies, driving etc, English literature, EFL, health, music, dance, art and architecture, teaching and learning, history, geography and geology, biology, chemistry, physics, computers and computing,

McGraw-Hill Book Co (UK) Ltd, Shoppenhangers Road, Maidenhead, Berks

Programmed books, slide/tape materials, videotape, sound-tape, film, OHP transparencies, games and simulations, case studies, slides

Office practice, management and supervision, salesmanship and marketing, mathematics, health, nursing and medicine, teaching and learning: programmed instruction, training, analysis; general science, biology, chemistry, physics, electricity and electronics, computers and computing, engineering

McMillan-LTR, 83 Parkgate, Knutsford, Cheshire WA16 8HF

Sound-tape, LP records

Languages (inc. Japanese)

Management Games Ltd, 2 Woburn Street, Ampthill, Beds MK45 2HP

Programmes (for machines), programmed books, games and simulations, case studies

Accountancy, office practice, management and supervision, salesmanship and marketing, EFL, nursing and medicine, teaching and learning: programmed instruction, training, analysis; economics and politics, social studies, computers and computing, engineering, industrial safety, industrial processes

Mathematical Pie, West View, Five Ways, Hatton, Warwicks

Filmstrips, charts, booklets

Mathematics

Melrose Film Productions Ltd, 8-12 Old Queen Street, London SW1H 9HP

Videotape, film

Accountancy, office practice, management and supervision, salesmanship and marketing, computers and computing

Merchant Navy Training Board,
30-32 St Mary Axe, London EC3A 8ET
Videotape, film, OHP transparencies
Management and supervision, industrial
processes

Middlesex Film Productions Ltd,
Shepperton Studio Centre, Post No 25,
Studios Road, Shepperton,
Middx TW17 0QD
Slide/tape materials, videotape, sound-tape, film, OHP transparencies
Office practice, management and
supervision, salesmanship and
marketing, health, industrial safety

Millbank Films Ltd, (a subsidiary
company of ICI Ltd), Thames House
North, Millbank, London SW1P 4QG
Film
Management and supervision, health,
industrial safety

Mobile Training Ltd, Imperial
Buildings, 56 Kingsway,
London WC2B 6DX
Slide/tape materials, sound-tape
Accountancy

Multimedia Publishing Ltd, 3 Lower
Camden, Chislehurst, Kent BR7 5HY
*Slide/tape materials, videotape, sound-tape, film, OHP transparencies, training
packs*
Accountancy, office practice,
management and supervision,
salesmanship and marketing, English
language

National Audio-Visual Aids Library,
2 Paxton Place, Gipsy Road,
London SE27
Slide/tape materials, videotape, sound-tape, OHP transparencies, case studies
General crafts, hobbies, driving etc,
accountancy, office practice,
management and supervision,
salesmanship and marketing, English
language, English literature, EFL,
languages, mathematics, health, nursing
and medicine, physiology, music,
drama, dance, art and architecture,
physical education, teaching and
learning: programmed instruction,
training, analysis; religious instruction,
history, economics and politics, social
studies, geography and geology, general
science, biology, chemistry, physics,
electricity and electronics, computers

and computing, engineering, industrial
safety, industrial processes, teacher
training

**National Centre for Developments in
Nurse Education,** NHS Learning
Resources Unit, 55 Broom Grove Road,
Sheffield S10 2NA
*Programmed books, slide/tape
materials, games and simulations*
Nursing, teaching and learning:
programmed instruction, training,
analysis; human biology

National Coal Board, Hobart House,
Grosvenor Place, London SW1X 7AE
*Programmed books, film, OHP
transparencies, books and pamphlets*
Management and supervision

The National Computing Centre Ltd,
Oxford Road, Manchester M1 7ED
*Programmes (for machines),
programmed books, slide/tape
materials, videotape, sound-tape, OHP
transparencies, games and simulations,
case studies*
Teaching and learning: programmed
instruction, training, analysis; computers
and computing

**Thomas Nelson & Sons/Nelson
Filmscan,** Nelson House, Mayfield
Road, Walton-on-Thames,
Surrey KT12 5PL
*Programmed books, slide/tape
materials, videotape, sound-tape, OHP
transparencies, games and simulations,
computer software*
EFL, languages, health, music, drama,
geography and geology, biology,
measurement and guidance

**University of Newcastle, Computing
Laboratory,** Newcastle-upon-Tyne
NE1 7RU
Slide/tape materials
Teaching and learning: programmed
instruction, training, analysis; computers
and computing

Oliver & Boyd, Robert Stevenson
House, 1-3 Baxter's Place, Leith Walk,
Edinburgh EH1 3BB
*Videotape, sound-tape, case studies,
resource packs*
English language, English literature,
languages, mathematics, music, teaching
and learning: programmed instruction,

training, analysis; religion, history, social studies, geography and geology, general science, biology, chemistry, physics, electricity and electronics, computers and computing

Olymp Training Ltd, 14-20 Station Road, West Croydon CR0 2RB
Programmed books, slide/tape materials, sound-tape
Accountancy, office practice, management and supervision, salesmanship and marketing

Open University Educational Enterprises Ltd, 12 Cofferidge Close, Stony Stratford, Milton Keynes MK11 1BY
Videotape, sound-tape, film
English literature, mathematics, physiology, music, drama, art and architecture, teaching and learning: programmed instruction, training, analysis; history, economics and politics, social studies, geography and geology, psychology, biology, chemistry, physics, electricity and electronics, computers and computing, engineering, industrial safety, industrial processes

*The Original Record & Tape Co, Biblios Road, Glenside Industrial Estate, Partridge Green, Horsham, Sussex
Sound-tapes

Oxford Educational Resources Ltd, 197 Botley Road, Oxford OX2 0HE
Programmes (for machines), slide/tape materials, videotape, sound-tape, film
Health, nursing and medicine, physiology, computers and computing, engineering, industrial safety

*Oxford University Press, Walton Street, Oxford
Sound-tapes

PIRA – The Research Association for the Paper and Board Printing and Packaging Industries, Randalls Road, Leatherhead, Surrey KT22 7RU
Programmed books, slide/tape materials, videotape
Industrial processes – printing and packaging industries

*Packman Research Ltd, Twyford, Reading, Berks
Programmes (for machines)
English language, reading

Edward Patterson Associates Ltd, 68 Copers Cope Road, Beckenham, Kent
Slide/tape materials, videotape, film
Management and supervision, English language, English literature, languages, mathematics, health, nursing and medicine, physiology, art and architecture, physical education, teaching and learning: programmed instruction, training, analysis; religion, history, social studies, geography and geology, psychology, general science, biology, chemistry, physics, industrial safety

*Pattison & Co, Newgate, Sandpit Lane, St Albans, Herts AL4 6BS
Programmed books, slide/tape materials
Mathematics, general science, biology, chemistry, physics, electricity and electronics, computers and computing, industrial safety

Pavic Productions – *see* Sheffield City Polytechnic

Anne & Bury Peerless, 22 King's Avenue, Minnis Bay, Birchington-on-Sea, Kent CT7 9QL
Slide sets and studies
Art and architecture, religion, history, social studies, geography, environmental studies

Pennant Audio-Visual Systems, King Alfred Way, Cheltenham, Glos GL52 6QP
'Opasym' animated OHP transparencies
Nursing and medicine, physics, electricity and electronics, computers and computing, engineering

*Pergamon Press Ltd, A Wheaton & Co, Hennock Road, Exeter EX2 8RP
OHP transparencies (Flipatran books)
History, geography and geology, chemistry, technical drawing

Pictorial Charts Educational Trust, 27 Kirchen Road, London W13 0UD
Educational wall charts
Office practice, English language, mathematics, health, music, art and architecture, religion, history, social studies, geography and geology, general science, biology, chemistry, physics, electricity and electronics, computers and computing

Pitman Correspondence College,
Worcester Road, London SW19 7QQ
Correspondence courses (tutor-assisted/self-study)
General crafts, hobbies, etc,
accountancy, office practice,
management and supervision,
salesmanship and marketing, English
language, EFL, teaching and learning:
programmed instruction, training,
analysis

*Pitman Publishing Ltd, 39 Parker
Street, London WC2B 5PB
OHP transparencies
Biology, physics, electricity and
electronics, computers and computing,
engineering

*Prentice-Hall International, 66 Wood
Lane End, Hemel Hempstead,
Herts HP2 4PG
*Programmed books, slide/tape
materials, film, OHP transparencies*
Health, nursing and medicine,
psychology

RTZ Services, Group Public Affairs
Dept, 6 St James' Square,
London SW1
Film
Industrial processes

*Random Film Library Ltd,
25 The Burroughs, Hendon,
London NW4 4AT
Videotape, film
Computers and computing

*Rank Audio Visual Ltd, PO Box 70,
Great West Road, Brentford, Middx
TW8 9HR
Programmes (for machines), film
Management and supervision,
salesmanship and marketing, English
literature, mathematics, health, nursing
and medicine, drama, religion, history,
economics and politics, social studies,
geography and geology, general science,
biology, physics, electricity and
electronics, industrial safety

Marian Ray, 36 Villiers Avenue,
Surbiton, Surrey
Filmstrips
Physiology, music, geography and
geology, general science, biology,
chemistry, physics

Reach-a-Teacha Ltd, 2 Hastings Court,
Collingham, Wetherby, West Yorkshire
LS22 5AW
*Programmes (for machines),
programmed books, slide/tape
materials, videotape, sound-tape, film*
Office practice, management and
supervision, teaching and learning:
programmed instruction, training,
analysis; engineering, industrial safety

**University of Reading, Centre for the
Teaching of Reading,** School of
Education, 29 Eastern Avenue, Reading
RG1 5RU
Slide/tape materials, videotape
English language, reading

*Resources for Learning Ltd,
41A Bowman Lane,
Leeds LS10 1JA
Slide/tape materials, case studies
Art and architecture, teaching and
learning: programmed instruction,
training, analysis; economics and politics

**Road Transport Industry Training
Board,** Capitol House, Empire Way,
Wembley, Middx
*Programmed books, slide/tape
materials, videotape, sound-tape, film,
OHP transparencies, games and
simulations*
Accountancy, office practice,
management and supervision,
salesmanship and marketing, teaching
and learning: programmed instruction,
training, analysis; industrial safety

**Royal Society for the Protection of
Birds,** The Lodge, Sandy, Beds
SG19 2DL
*Slide/tape materials, film, notes for
teachers on aspects of bird study in
schools*
General science, biology, environmental
studies

SAGSET (Society for Academic Gaming
and Simulation in Education and
Training), Centre for Extension Studies,
University of Technology,
Loughborough, Leics LE11 3TU
*Resource lists of gaming/simulation
materials in the following topics:*
Office practice, management training,
mathematics, health education,
economics, chemistry

SATRA – Shoe and Allied Trades Research Association, SATRA House, Rockingham Road, Kettering, Northants NN16 9JH

Programmes (for machines), slide/tape materials, sound-tape, algorithms, industrial processes

***St David's University College** (Department of Philosophy), Lampeter, Dyfed SA48 7ED

Programmed books

Logic

***Scientific Era Publications,** 4 St Mary's Place, Stamford, Lincs

Programmed books

Office practice, physics, electricity and electronics, industrial processes

Scottish & Newcastle Breweries Ltd, Group Training Department, Gilmore Park, Edinburgh EH3 9SB

Slide/tape materials, videotape, sound-tape, OHP transparencies

Office practice, management and supervision, salesmanship and marketing, teaching and learning, programmed instruction, training, analysis; industrial safety

Scripture Union, 130 City Road, London EC1V 2NJ

Slide/tape materials, filmstrips, sound-tapes

Religion, social studies

Selsdon Park Management Centre, Selsdon Park Hotel, Sanderstead, Surrey

Programmes (for machines), programmed books, slide/tape materials, OHP transparencies

Management and supervision, salesmanship and marketing, teaching and learning: programmed instruction, training, analysis

Seminar Cassettes Ltd, 218 Sussex Gardens, London W2 3UD

Programmes (for machines), programmed books, sound-tape

English language, English literature, EFL, nursing and medicine, physiology, religion, economics and politics, social studies, psychology, general science, biology, computers and computing

Service Training Ltd, 34 The Square, Kenilworth, Warwicks CV8 1EB

General crafts, hobbies etc, accountancy, office practice, management and supervision, salesmanship and marketing, logic, mathematics, health, nursing and medicine, physiology, art and architecture, teaching and learning: programmed instruction, training, analysis; economics and politics, geography and geology, psychology, general science, biology, chemistry, physics, electricity and electronics, computers and computing, engineering, industrial safety, industrial processes

Sheffield City Polytechnic, Pavic Productions, Instructional Technology Unit, Dept of Education Services, Collegiate Crescent, Sheffield S10 2BP

Programmed books, slide/tape materials, games and simulations, case studies

Management and supervision, nursing and medicine, teaching and learning: programmed instruction, training, analysis; social studies, geography and geology, electricity and electronics, industrial safety

***Shell Education Service,** Shell UK Ltd, Shell Mex House, Strand, London WC2R 0DX

Film

Geography and geology, general science, biology, chemistry

Shell Film Library, 25 The Burroughs, Hendon, London NW4 4AT

Videotape, film

General crafts, hobbies, driving etc, history, geography and geology, general science, biology, chemistry, physics, engineering, industrial processes

***The Slide Centre,** 143 Chatham Road, London SW11 6SR

Slide/tape materials, slide sets, filmstrips, filmstrip/tape packages

General crafts, hobbies, driving etc, accountancy, office practice, languages, mathematics, health, physiology, music, art and architecture, physical education, religion, history, economics and politics, social studies, geography and geology, general science, biology, chemistry, physics, electricity and electronics, computers and computing, engineering

Sound Education, 7 Grove Park, Liverpool L8 0TL

Sound-tape

English language, English literature, health, nursing and medicine, music, drama, history, economics and politics, social studies, geography and geology, psychology

*University of Southampton, Department of Teaching Media, Southampton SO9 5NH

16mm film, tape-slide, videotape, sound-tape, exhibitions and supporting written materials

Health: health education, medicine, nurse training, ambulance training; engineering (including careers), educational technology, biology, geography and geology, industrial archaelogy, industrial safety, language teaching

Space Frontiers Ltd, 30 Fifth Avenue, Havant, Hampshire PO9 2PL

Slide/tape materials, videotape, sound-tape, film

Space science, including aspects of: geography, general science

Stewart Film Distributors Ltd, 107-115 Long Acre, London WC2E 9NT

Slide/tape materials, videotape, film

Health, nursing and medicine, teaching and learning: programmed instruction, training, analysis; electricity and electronics, industrial safety, industrial processes, reading (dyslexia)

Stillitron Ltd, 72 New Bond Street, London W1

Sound-tapes

Languages

*Students' Recordings Ltd, 88 Queen Street, Newton Abbot, Devon

Sound-tapes, filmstrips

Studio Two Educational AV, 6 High Street, Barkway, Royston, Herts SG8 8EE

Slide/tape materials, sound-tape, OHP transparencies, wallcharts and tactile material

Mathematics, health, art and architecture, religion, history, economics and politics, social studies, geography

and geology, general science, biology, chemistry, physics, electricity and electronics, computers and computing

*Studytapes Ltd, 9 Chestnut Avenue, Haslemere, Surrey

Sound-tape

Supervisory Management Training Ltd, 21 Green Lane, London SE20 7JA

Slide/tape materials, games and simulations, case studies

Management and supervision

Sussex Tapes
(Educational Productions Group, *see* above)

Teakfield Publishing Co Ltd, Gower House, Croft Road, Aldershot, Hants GU11 3HR
(Distributors of Caedmon Spoken Word recordings and of Lyrichord Ethnic Music recordings)

Sound-tape, records

English literature, music, drama

The Technical Press Ltd, Freeland, Oxford OX7 2AP

Programmed books, games and simulations, books

General crafts, hobbies, driving etc, mathematics, chemistry, electricity and electronics, computers and computing, engineering, industrial processes

Tetradon Publications Ltd, 49 Hadzor Road, Oldbury, Warley, West Midlands B68 9LA

Slide/tape materials, sound-tape, OHP transparencies

General crafts, hobbies, driving etc, mathematics, teaching and learning: programmed instruction, training, analysis; chemistry, physics

Timber Research and Development Association, Hughenden Valley, High Wycombe, Bucks

Slide/tape materials, film, information sheets

Art and architecture, engineering, industrial processes

Town & Country Productions Ltd, 21 Cheyne Row, Chelsea, London SW3 5HP

Slide/tape materials, sound-tape, film

General crafts, hobbies, driving etc,

health (inc the disabled), nursing and medicine, art and architecture, physical education

Training Films International Ltd, 14 St Mary's Street, Whitchurch, Shropshire
London office: 159 Great Portland Street, W1
Slide/tape materials, videotape, film
Management and supervision, salesmanship and marketing, industrial safety

*****Transaid,** Francis Gregory & Son Ltd, Spur Road, Feltham, Middx TW14 0SX
OHP transparencies
Accountancy, mathematics, religion, geography and geology, biology

*****Transart Visual Products Ltd,** East Chadley Lane, Godmanchester, Cambs
OHP transparencies (Flipatran books)
Mathematics, history, geography and geology, technology, education sciences

*****Tutor Tape Co Ltd,** 2 Replingham Road, London SW18 5LS

*****Video Arts Ltd,** 2nd Floor, Dumbarton House, 68 Oxford Street, London W1N 9LA
Videotape, film
Accountancy, office practice, management and supervision, salesmanship and marketing, computers and computing, industrial safety

Viewtech AV Media, 122 Goldcrest Road, Chipping Sodbury, Bristol BS17 6XF
Slide/tape materials, videotape, sound-tape, film
Mathematics, health, nursing and medicine, music, history, social studies, geography and geology, general science, biology, chemistry, physics

Viscom Ltd, Unit B11, Parkhall Road, Dulwich, London SE21 8EL. (NB Viscom now incorporates the British Gas Film Library)
Videotape, film
General crafts, hobbies etc, accountancy, salesmanship and marketing, English language, health, nursing and medicine, physiology,

music, art and architecture, religion, history, economics and politics, social studies, geography and geology, general science, biology, chemistry, electricity and electronics, engineering, industrial processes, environment and conservation

Vistech, 74 Brodrick Road, London SW17 7DY
Slide/tape materials, filmstrips
Office practice

*****Visual Publications,** 197 Kensington High Street, London W8 6BB
Slide/tape materials, filmstrips
English literature, language, mathematics, drama, art and architecture, religion, history, social studies, geography and geology, general science, biology, physics

Walton Sound and Film Services, Walton House, 87 Richford Street, London W6
Slide, filmstrip materials

*****Ward Lock Educational,** 116 Baker Street, London W1
Programmed books, games and simulations
Mathematics, drama

Waterlow Publishers Ltd, Holywell House, Worship Street, London EC2A 2EN
Sound-tape
Accountancy, office practice, management and supervision, teaching and learning: programmed instruction, training, analysis; industrial safety

John Wiley & Sons Ltd, Baffins Lane, Chichester, Sussex PO19 1UD
Programmes (for machines), programmed books, film, games and simulations
General crafts, hobbies etc, teaching and learning: programmed instruction, training, analysis; biology, computers and computing

Woodmansterne Ltd, Holywell Industrial Estate, Watford WD1 8RD
Slide sets
Drama, dance, art and architecture, religion, history, geography and geology, environmental studies

Wool, Jute and Flax Industry Training Board, Butterfield House, Otley Road, Baildon, Shipley, West Yorkshire BD17 7HE

Slide/tape materials, film, OHP transparencies

Industrial processes

*****World of Learning Ltd,** 359 Upper Richmond Road West, East Sheen, London SW14 8QN

Programmed books, sound-tape

EFL, languages

Diana Wyllie Ltd, 1 Park Road, Baker Street, London NW1 6XP

Slide/tape materials, filmstrips

General crafts, hobbies, etc, art and architecture, history, social studies, geography and geology, general science, biology, computers and computing, meteorology

Producers of Audiovisual Hardware in North America

In the compilation of this section particular difficulty is always posed by distance and communications between the UK and the USA, and once again Dr Carl Hendershot has rendered great and dependable assistance. Much as previous editions have drawn heavily on his *Programmed Learning and Individually Based Instruction – Bibliography,* this edition also owes much to the generous provision of a preview copy of the revised publishers' listing in that publication. Readers wishing a fuller listing of the great wealth of American materials should consult the *Hendershot Bibliography,* for which the 6th Supplement is due to appear in March 1982.

Useful information can also be found in the fourteen *Indices to Educational Media* published by NICEM (*see* Centres of Activity – US):

Index to 16mm Educational Films
Index to 35mm Filmstrips
Index to Educational Overhead Transparencies
Index to Educational Records
Index to Educational Videotapes
Index to Educational Audio-tapes
Index to 8mm Motion Cartridges
Index to Educational Slides
Index to Producers and Distributors
Index to Psychology – Multimedia
Index to Health and Safety Education – Multimedia
Index to Vocational and Technical Education – Multimedia
Index to Environmental Studies – Multimedia
Index to Free Educational Material – Multimedia.

This Section is organized in the same manner as that outlined in the preface to the UK Section: the same subject categories give the names of producers/distributors in that area; and all producers/distributors are listed, with addresses, in the second part of this Section. Also, as in the UK listing, an asterisk(*) before a name indicates that the subsequent information is basically unaltered from 1980/1, no reply having been received to the invitation to update the entry. (A mention of the *Yearbook* as source when writing to producers might lead them more to value their entry therein. Unlisted or new producers, of course, are always welcome to notify the editor of their existence and of their products.)

As with the UK, this list does not specifically list micro-software although at least one producer (Science Research Associates Inc) now includes such materials in its products. Such materials will predictably be more numerous in the 1984/85 edition.

In the listing of producers in this section, acronyms have been placed at the beginning of each alphabetical group; when the letters 'US' (for 'United

States') are an integral part of such initials (eg USAAF) they have been retained, but when they merely preface a name they have been omitted.

Part 1: Index of Producers/ Distributors by Subjects

1. General crafts, hobbies, driving etc
Americal Educational Films
Paul S Amidon Associates Inc
Behavioral Research Laboratories Inc
University of California (EMC)
The Center for Applied Research in Education Inc
Educational Communications Inc
Educational Projections Corporation
Great Plains National Instructional Television Library (GPN)
Houghton Mifflin Co
Michigan State University Institutional Media Center
Pyramid Films & Video
Tab Books
Time-Life Multimedia
Van Nostrand Reinhold Co
World Book – Childcraft International Inc

2. Accountancy
Addison-Wesley Publishing Company
The American College
Continuing Education Systems Inc
Educational Communications Inc
Educational Methods
Grid Publishing Inc
Houghton Mifflin Co
Richard D Irwin Inc
Lansford Publishing Co
Learning Systems Company, Divn of Richard D Irwin Inc
NCR Corporation
National Association of Accountants
National A-V Center
Prentice-Hall Media Inc
Van Nostrand Reinhold Co

3. Office practice
Agency for Innovative Curriculum Inc
American Management Associations
Automated Instruction, Div of Random House Inc
Robert T Brady Co (Subsidiary of P-H Inc Routes)
Creative Universal Inc
Dartnell Corporation
Educational Communications Inc
Effective Learning Inc
Grid Publishing Inc
Houghton Mifflin Co
Richard D Irwin Inc
Lansford Publishing Co
Learn Incorporated
Learncom Inc
Learning & Information Inc
Michigan State University Instructional Media Center
NCR Corporation
National Association of Accountants
National A-V Center
Prentice-Hall Media Inc
Professional Development Inc
Quickhand Shorthand
Science Research Associates Inc
Today News Service Inc
Van Nostrand Reinhold Co

4. Management and supervision
ABC Wide World
Addison-Wesley Publishing Company
The American College
American Management Associations
Paul S Amidon & Associates Inc
BNA Communications Inc
Behaviordelia Inc
University of California (EMC)
Creative Universal Inc
Dartnell Corporation
Development Dimensions International
Development Digest
Development Publications
EFM Films
Education & Training Consultants Co
Educational Communications Inc
Educational Resources Foundation
Effective Learning Inc
Fearon Pitman Publishers Inc
General Cassette Corp
Grid Publishing Inc
Houghton Mifflin Co
Idea Development Associates
Richard D Irwin Inc
Lawford Publishing Co
Learncom Inc
Learning & Information Inc
Little, Brown & Co
Magnetic Video Corporation
Management Research Associates
Management Resources Inc
National Association of Accountants
National Audiovisual Center (GSA)
National Center for Research in Vocational Education
National Educational Media Inc
Organisational Tests
Prentice-Hall Media Inc
Professional Development Inc
Republic Education Publishing Co
Research Press Co

Roundtable Films Inc
Salenger Educational Media
Science Research Associates Inc
Society of Manufacturing Engineers
Springboard Associates
Telstar Inc
Teleometrics International
Today News Service Inc
Training House Inc
USC Broadcast Production
University Associates Inc
Van Nostrand Reinhold Co
Xicom Inc

5. Salesmanship and marketing
ABC Wide World
Addison-Wesley Publishing Company
American Management Associations
BNA Communications Inc
Bevin Enterprises
Continuing Education Systems Inc
Creative Universal Inc
Dartnell Corporation
Development Digest
EFM Films
Educational Communications Inc
Educational Resources Foundation
Effective Learning Inc
General Cassette Corp
Grid Publishing Inc
Richard D Irwin Inc
Lansford Publishing Co
Learncom Inc
Learning & Information Inc
Learning Systems Company, Division
   of Richard D Irwin Inc
Little, Brown & Co
Magnetic Video Corporation
National A-V Center
National Educational Media Inc
Prentice-Hall Media Inc
Professional Development Inc
Pyramid Film & Video
Republic Education Publishing Co
Roundtable Films Inc
Salenger Educational Media
Science Research Associates Inc
Springboard Associates
Teaching Systems Corporation
Teleometrics International
Training House Inc
Van Nostrand Reinhold Co
Xicom Inc

6. English language
AGS – American Guidance Service Inc
American Educational Films
Paul S Amidon & Associates Inc
Ann Arbor Publishers Inc
Audiotronics Corporation

Behavior Science Press (A division of
   Rehabilitation Research Foundation)
Behavioral Research Laboratories Inc
Book-Lab Inc
Robert J Brady Co
CTB/McGraw-Hill
Center for Educational Technology,
   Catholic University of America
The Center for Applied Research in
   Education Inc
University of Chicago Press
Communacad
The Continental Press
Continuing Educations Systems Inc
Ken Cook Co
Crane Publishing Company (Division
   of MLP)
Creative Curriculum Inc
Creative Publications
E-Z Grader Co
Educators Publishing Service Inc
Educulture Inc
Effective Learning Inc
Encyclopaedia Britannica Educational
   Corporation
Enrich Inc
Great Plains National Instructional
   Television Library
Houghton Mifflin Co
Howell Training Company
Instructional/Communications
   Technology Inc, Taylor Associates
Instructional Fair Inc
Lansford Publishing Co
Learning Corporation of America
Little, Brown & Co
Media Materials Inc
National A-V Center
New Readers Press (Division of
   Laubach Literacy International)
Ontario Institute for Studies in
   Education
Prentice-Hall Media Inc
Psychotechnics Inc
The Reading Laboratory Inc
Republic Education Publishing Co
Sargent-Welch Co, Tutorsystems
   Division
Science Research Associates Inc
Silver Burdett Company
Stanwix House Inc
Teachers College Press
Teaching Research Publications,
   Oregon
Telstar Inc
Ulrich's Books Inc
Van Nostrand Reinhold Co
WFF'N PROOF Publishers

World Book – Childcraft International Inc

7. English literature
ABC Wide World
University of California (EMC)
The Center for Applied Research in Education Inc
University of Chicago Press
Crane Publishing Company, Division of MLP
Creative Curriculum Inc
Effective Learning Inc
Encyclopaedia Britannica Educational Corporation
Great Plains National Instructional Television Library
Houghton Mifflin Co
Learning Corporation of America
Media Materials, Inc
Prentice-Hall Media Inc
Pyramid Film & Video
Science Research Associates Inc
Silver Burdett Company
USC Broadcast Production (comparative literature)

8. English as a second language (EFL)
AGS – American Guidance Service Inc
Addison-Wesley Publishing Company
Paul S Amidon and Associates Inc
Ann Arbor Publishers Inc
Audiotronics Corporation
Behavioral Research Laboratories Inc
Book-Lab Inc
Borg-Warner Educational Systems
The Center for Applied Research in Education Inc
Communacad
Crane Publishing Company – Division of MLP
EDL/McGraw-Hill
Educational Projections Corporation
Effective Learning Inc
Instructional/Communications Technology Inc – Taylor Associates
University of Michigan Press
Michigan State University Instructional Media Center
New Readers Press, Division of Lanbach Literacy International
Prentice-Hall Media Inc
Psychotechnics Inc
Republic Education Publishing Co
Science Research Associates Inc
Silver Burdett Company
Teachers College Press
Ulrich's Books Inc

9-13. Languages
Paul S Amidon & Associates Ltd

Audiotronics Corporation
Behavioral Research Laboratories Inc
Behrman House Inc
Borg-Warner Educational Systems
University of California (EMC)
University of Chicago Press
Crane Publishing Company – Division of MLP
Educational Projections Corporation
Encyclopaedia Britannica Educational Corporation
Great Plains National Instructional Television Library
Houghton Mifflin Co
Howell Training Company
Instructional/Communications Technology Inc
Learning Corporation of America
Loyola University Press
Marshfilm Enterprises Inc
University of Michigan Press
National AV Center (GSA)
Science Research Associates Inc

14. Librarianship
Center for Educational Technology, Catholic University of America
University of Chicago Press
Development Digest
Encyclopaedia Britannica Educational Corporation
Media Systems Inc
Mojave Books
National AV Center (GSA)
The Shoe String Press
Today News Service Inc

15. Logic
Addison-Wesley Publishing Company
Ann Arbor Publishers Inc
University of Chicago Press
Educational Communications Inc
Educulture Inc
Effective Learning Inc
Lansford Publishing Co
TPC Training Systems
USC Broadcast Production
Van Nostrand Reinhold Co
WFF'N PROOF Publishers

16. Mathematics
AGS – American Guidance Service Inc
Addison-Wesley Publishing Company
The American College
American Educational Films
Paul S Amidon & Associates Inc
Ann Arbor Publishers Inc
Audiotronics Corporation
Behavior Science Press
Behavioral Research Laboratories Inc
Benjamin/Cummings Publishing

Company
Borg-Warner Educational Systems
CTB/McGraw-Hill
University of Chicago Press
The Continental Press
Continuing Education Systems Inc
Creative Publications
EDL/McGraw-Hill
E-Z Grader Co
Educational Communications Inc
Educational Projections Corporation
Educulture Inc
Edu-Pac Publishing Co
Effective Learning Inc
Encyclopaedia Britannica Educational
    Corporation
Enrich Inc
Entelek Inc
Great Plains National Instructional
    Television Library
Houghton Mifflin Co
Instructional/Communications
    Technology Inc
Instructional Fair Inc
Learning Systems Company, Division
    of Richard D Irwin Inc
Media Materials Inc
National A-V Center
National Council of Teachers of
    Mathematics
National Tool, Die & Precision
    Machining Assn
Ontario Institute for Studies in
    Education
Prentice-Hall Media Inc
Pyramid Film & Video
Sargent-Welch Scientific Co,
    Tutorsystems Division
Science Research Associates Inc
Silver Burdett Company
TPC Training Systems
Tab Books
Technical Education Research Centers
University of Texas at Austin
Today News Service Inc
Ulrich's Books Inc
Van Nostrand Reinhold Co
WFF'N PROOF Publishers
World Book – Childcraft International
    Inc

17. Health: first aid, sex information,
    nutrition, dentistry, veterinary
    surgery
ABC Wide World
Abt Associates
Addison-Wesley Publishing Company
Benjamin/Cummings Publishing
Company

Robert J Brady Co, Subsidiary of
    PH Inc Routes
CEM Company
University of California (EMC)
Center for Educational Technology,
    Catholic University of America
The Center for Applied Research
    in Education Inc
Co-operative Extension Services
Docent Corp
Educational Communications Inc
Educational Projections Corporation
Edu-Pac Publishing Co
Effective Learning Inc
Encyclopaedia Britannica Educational
    Corporation
Farrall Instruments
Great Plains National Instructional
    Television Library
Health Sciences Consortium
Houghton Mifflin Co
Little, Brown & Co
Litton Educational Publishing Int'l
Marshfilm Enterprises Inc
Med Ed Projects Inc
Medical Examination Publishing Co Inc
Michigan State University, Instructional
    Media Center
Modern Talking Picture Service
National A-V Center
National Teaching Aids Inc
New Readers Press, Division of
    Lanbach Literacy International
Prentice-Hall Media Inc
Pyramid Film & Video
Republic Education Publishing Co
Salenger Educational Media
Silver Burdett Company
Teaching Research Publications,
    Oregon
Charles C Thomas, Publisher
Time-Life Multimedia
Today News Service Inc
USC Broadcast Production
Unipub
Van Nostrand Reinhold Co
Williams & Wilkins Co
Year Book Medical Publishers

18. Nursing and medicine
ABC Wide World
Addison-Wesley Publishing Company
Aerospace Education Foundation
Benjamin/Cummings Publishing
Company
Robert J Brady Co
University of California (EMC)
Center for Educational Technology,
    Catholic University of America

University of Chicago Press
Docent Corp
Educational Communications Inc
Edu-Pac Publishing Co
Effective Learning Inc
Farrall Instruments
Health Sciences Consortium
Houghton Mifflin Co
Ken-a-Vision
Little, Brown & Co
MCV School of Pharmacy
Med Ed Projects Inc
Medical Examination Publishing Co Inc
Michigan State University, Instructional
    Media Center
Modern Talking Picture Service
National AV Center (GSA)
National Center for Research in
    Vocational Education
National Teaching Aids Inc
Republic Education Publishing Co
Charles B Slack Inc
Springboard Associates
Springer Publishing Co Inc
Teachers College Press
Telstar Inc
Charles C Thomas, Publisher
Today News Service Inc
Van Nostrand Reinhold Co
Xicom Inc
Year Book Medical Publishers

19. Physiology
Addison-Wesley Publishing Company
Behavioral Research Laboratories Inc
Benjamin/Cummings Publishing
Company
Robert J Brady Co, Subsidiary of
    PH Inc Routes
Educational Communications Inc
Health Sciences Consortium
Houghton Mifflin Co
Little, Brown & Co
Medical Examination Publishing Co Inc
Michigan State University
National A-V Center
Prentice-Hall Media Inc
Republic Education Publishing Co
Stipes Publishing Co
World Book – Childcraft International
    Inc
Year Book Medical Publishers

20. Music
Behrman House Inc
The Center for Applied Research in
    Education Inc
Educational Projections Corporation
Encyclopaedia Britannica Educational
    Corporation

Great Plains National Instructional
    Television Library (GPN)
University of Illinois at Chicago Circle
Learning Corporation of America
National A-V Center
Prentice-Hall Media Inc
Pyramid Film & Video
Silver Burdett Company
Tab Books
USC Broadcast Production
Van Nostrand Reinhold Co
World Book – Childcraft International
    Inc

21. Drama
ABC Wide World
University of California (EMC)
Encyclopaedia Britannica Educational
    Corporation
Great Plains National Instructional
    Television Library (GPN)
Learning Corporation of America
Michigan State University
Prentice-Hall Media Inc
Pyramid Film & Video
Science Research Associates Inc
Silver Burdett Company
Time-Life Multimedia

22. Dance
University of California (EMC)
Center for Educational Technology,
    Catholic University of America
Encyclopaedia Britannica Educational
    Corporation
Learning Corporation of America

23. Art and architecture
Paul S Amidon & Associates Inc
Behrman House Inc
Robert J Brady Co
University of California (EMC)
The Center for Applied Research in
    Education Inc
University of Chicago Press
Educational Communications Inc
Educational Projections Corporation
Encyclopaedia Britannica Educational
    Corporation
Great Plains National Instructional
    Television Library (GPN)
Learning Corporation of America
Prentice-Hall Media Inc
Pyramid Film & Video
Tab Books
Unipub
Van Nostrand Reinhold Co

24. Physical Education
Addison-Wesley Publishing Company
Paul S Amidon & Associates Inc

Robert J Brady Co
The Center for Applied Research in
Education Inc
Encyclopaedia Britannica Educational
Corporation
Great Plains National Instructional
Television Library (GPN)
Learning Corporation of America
Marshfilm Enterprises Inc
Michigan State University
National A-V Center
National Center for Research in
Vocational Education
Pyramid Film & Video
Charles C Thomas, Publisher
Time-Life Multimedia
Van Nostrand Reinhold Co

25. *Teaching and learning: programmed*
instruction, training, analysis
AGS – American Guidance Service Inc
ASTD
Addison-Wesley Publishing Company
Aerospace Education Foundation
The American College
American Management Associations
Paul S Amidon & Associates Inc
Ann Arbor Publishers Inc
Association for Educational and
Communications Technology
Audiotronics Corporation
Automated Instruction, Division of
Random House Inc
Behavior Science Press
Behrman House Inc
Book-Lab Inc
Robert J Brady Co
Burgess Publishing Company
CEM Company
University of California (EMC)
Center for Educational Technology,
Catholic University of America
University of Chicago Press
Continuing Education Systems Inc
Creative Curriculum Inc
Creative Universal Inc
Development Digest
DuPont
EDL/McGraw-Hill
Education and Training Consultants Co
Educational Communications Inc
Edu-Pac Publishing Co
Effective Learning Inc
Electronic Data Systems Corp
Encyclopaedia Britannica Educational
Corporation
Enrich Inc
Entelek Inc
Health Sciences Consortium

Houghton Mifflin Co
University of Illinois at Chicago Circle
Industrial Training Inc
Instructional/Communications
Technology Inc
Instructional Fair Inc
Instructional Systems Engineering
Lansford Publishing Co
Learncom Inc
Learning & Information Inc
Mager Associates Inc
Management Research Associates
Media Materials Inc
Media Systems Inc
Michigan State University, Instructional
Media Centre
NCR Corporation
National Association for Accountants
National A-V Center
National Center for Research in
Vocational Education
National Council of Teachers
of Mathematics
National Tool, Die & Precision
Machining Assn
New Readers Press
Ontario Institute for Studies in
Education
Prentice-Hall Media Inc
Psychotechnics Inc
Republic Education Publishing Co
Research Press Co
Roundtable Films Inc
Salenger Educational Media
Science Research Associates Inc
Stipes Publishing Co
Technical Education Research Centers
University of Texas at Austin
Charles C Thomas, Publisher
Today News Service Inc
Ulrich's Books Inc
University Associates Inc
Van Valkenburgh, Nooger & Neville Inc
Vimcet Associates
WFF'N PROOF Publishers

26. *Religion*
Behrman House Inc
Center for Educational Technology,
Catholic University of America
Edu-Pac Publishing Co
Marshfilm Enterprises Inc
Media Materials Inc
Pyramid Film & Video
Silver Burdett Company
United Methodist Publishing House

27. *History*
ABC Associates

Paul S Amidon & Associates Inc
Behrman House Inc
The Center for Applied Research in
   Education Inc
University of Chicago Press
Educational Projections Corporation
Effective Learning Inc
Encyclopaedia Britannica Educational
   Corporation
Great Plains National Instructional
   Television Library (GPN)
Houghton Mifflin Co
Richard D Irwin Inc
Learning Corporation of America
Learning Systems Company
Little, Brown & Co
Michigan State University, Instructional
   Media Center
National Audiovisual Center
Ontario Institute for Studies in
   Education
Prentice-Hall Media Inc
Pyramid Film & Video
The Reading Laboratory Inc
Republic Education Publishing
   Company
Science Research Associates Inc
Silver Burdett Company
Time-Life Multimedia
Van Nostrand Reinhold Co

28. *Economics and politics*
ABC Wide World
Abt Associates
Addison-Wesley Publishing Company
American Educational Films
Behavioral Research Laboratories Inc
Benjamin/Cummings Publishing
Robert J Brady Co
University of Chicago Press
Co-operative Extension Services
Educational Communications Inc
Educational Projections Corporation
Educational Resources Foundation
Effective Learning Inc
Encyclopaedia Britannica Educational
   Corporation
The Ford Foundation
Great Plains National
   Instructional Television Library
Grid Publishing Inc
Houghton Mifflin Co
Richard D Irwin Inc
Lansford Publishing Co
Learning Systems Company
Little, Brown & Co
Management Resources Inc
Marshfilm Enterprises Inc
National A-V Center

Prentice-Hall Media Inc
Pyramid Film & Video
Republic Education Publishing
   Company
Science Research Associates Inc
Today News Service Inc
USC Broadcast Production
Van Nostrand Reinhold Co

29. *Social studies*
ABC Wide World
AGS – American Guidance Service Inc
Abt Associates
Paul S Amidon & Associates Inc
Audiotronics Corporation
Behrman House Inc
Robert J Brady Co
University of California (EMC)
The Center for Applied Research in
   Education Inc
Center for Educational Technology,
   Catholic University of America
University of Chicago Press
Educational Projections Co
Effective Learning Inc
Encyclopaedia Britannica Educational
   Corporation
Entelek Inc
The Ford Foundation
Great Plains National Instructional
   Television Library (GPN)
Houghton Mifflin Co
Learning Corporation of America
Learning Systems Company
Marshfilm Enterprises Inc
Media Materials Inc
National A-V Center
Ontario Institute for Studies in
   Education
Prentice-Hall Media Inc
Pyramid Film & Video
The Reading Laboratory Inc
Republic Education Publishing
   Company
Science Research Associates Inc
Silver Burdett Company
Charles C Thomas, Publisher
Time-Life Multimedia
Today News Service Inc
WFF'N PROOF Publishers
World Book – Childcraft International
   Inc

30. *Geography and geology*
Addison-Wesley Publishing Company
Benjamin/Cummings Publishing
   Company
Robert J Brady Co
The Center for Applied Research in
   Education Inc

Center for Educational Technology,
Catholic University of America
University of Chicago Press
Educational Communications Inc
Effective Learning Inc
Encyclopaedia Britannica Educational
Corporation
Great Plains National Instructional
Television Library (GPN)
Houghton Mifflin Co
Learning Corporation of America
National A-V Center
National Teaching Aids Inc
Prentice-Hall Media Inc
Pyramid Film & Video
Science Research Associates Inc
Silver Burdett Company
Time-Life Multimedia
Van Nostrand Reinhold Co

31. Psychology
Addison-Wesley Publishing Company
Behaviordelia Inc
Benjamin/Cummings Publishing
Company
Robert J Brady Co
University of California (EMC)
University of Chicago Press
Childhood Resources Inc
Development Digest
Educational Communications Inc
Educulture Inc
Edu-Pac Publishing Co
Effective Learning Inc
Great Plains National Instructional
Television Library (GPN)
Health Science Consortium
Houghton Mifflin Co
Richard D Irwin Inc
Lansford Publishing Co
Learning Systems Company
Little, Brown & Co
Magnetic Video Corporation
Marshfilm Enterprises Inc
National A-V Center
Prentice-Hall Media Inc
Pyramid Film & Video
Research Press Co
Republic Education Publishing
Company
Science Research Associates Inc
Springer Publishing Co Inc
Charles C Thomas, Publisher
Van Nostrand Reinhold Co

32. General science
Addison-Wesley Publishing Company
American Educational Films
Audiotronics Corporation
Benjamin/Cummings Publishing

Company
Robert J Brady Co
The Center for Applied Research in
Education Inc
Central Scientific Co Inc
University of Chicago Press
Educational Communications Inc
Edu-Pac Publishing Co
Effective Learning Inc
Encyclopaedia Britannica Educational
Corporation
Enrich Inc
Entelek Inc
Great Plains National Instructional
Television Library (GPN)
Houghton Mifflin Co
Instructional Systems Engineering
Jeppeson Sanderson
Ken-A-Vision
Learning Corporation of America
Media Materials Inc
National Audiovisual Center
Ontario Institute for Studies in
Education
Prentice-Hall Media Inc
Pyramid Film & Video
Silver Burdett Company
Technical Education Research Centers
Today News Service Inc
Van Nostrand Reinhold Co

33. Biology
Addison-Wesley Publishing Company
Paul S Amidon & Associates Inc
Behavioral Research Laboratories Inc
Benjamin/Cummings Publishing
Company
Robert J Brady Co
University of California (EMC)
The Center for Applied Research in
Education Inc
Central Scientific Co Inc
University of Chicago Press
Co-operative Extension Services
Educational Communications Inc
Educational Methods
Effective Learning Inc
Encyclopaedia Britannica Educational
Corporation
Entelek Inc
Houghton Mifflin Co
Ken-A-Vision
Little, Brown & Co
Management Research Associates
University of Michigan Press
National A-V Center
National Teaching Aids Inc
Prentice-Hall Media Inc
Pyramid Film & Video

Silver Burdett Company
Technical Education Research Centers
Time-Life Multimedia
Today News Service Inc
USC Broadcast Production
Van Nostrand Reinhold Co

34. Chemistry
Addison-Wesley Publishing Company
Paul S Amidon & Associates Inc
Behavioral Research Laboratories Inc
Benjamin/Cummings Publishing
Company
The Center for Applied Research in
Education Inc
Central Scientific Co Inc
University of Chicago Press
Educational Communications Inc
Educational Projections Corporation
Educulture Inc
Effective Learning Inc
Encyclopaedia Britannica Educational
Corporation
Entelek Inc
Houghton Mifflin Co
University of Illinois at Chicago
Circle
Little, Brown & Co
Management Research Associates
Mojave Books
National A-V Center
Prentice-Hall Media Inc
Silver Burdett Company
Stipes Publishing Co
Technical Education Research Centers
Van Nostrand Reinhold Co

35. Physics
Addison-Wesley Publishing Company
Benjamin/Cummings Publishing
Company
University of California (EMC)
The Center for Applied Research in
Education Inc
Central Scientific Co Inc
University of Chicago Press
Educational Communications Inc
Educational Projections Corporation
Effective Learning Inc
Encyclopaedia Britannica Educational
Corporation
Entelek Inc
Houghton Mifflin Co
Instructional Systems Engineering
Little, Brown & Co
Michigan State University, Instructional
Media Center
National A-V Center
Prentice-Hall Media Inc
Pyramid Film & Video

Silver Burdett Company
Technical Education Research Centers
Van Nostrand Reinhold Co

36. Electricity and electronics
Addison-Wesley Publishing Company
Aerospace Education Foundation
Behavior Science Press
Robert J Brady Co
Educational Communications Inc
Educational Projections Corporation
Effective Learning Inc
Industrial Training Inc
Instructional Systems Engineering,
Sperry Gyroscope
LabVolt Systems
NCR Corporation
National Audiovisual Center
National Laboratory for Advancement
of Education, Aerospace Education
Foundation
National Services Inc
Power Transmission Design
Prentice-Hall Media Inc
Science Research Associates Inc
Silver Burdett Company
TPC Training Systems
Tab Books
Technical Education Research Centers
USC Broadcast Production
Van Nostrand Reinhold Co
Van Valkenburgh, Nooger & Neville
Inc

37. Computers and computing
Addison-Wesley Publishing Company
Aerospace Education
Foundation
The American College
Benjamin/Cummings Publishing
Company
Boeing Computer Services
Robert J Brady Co
Center for Educational Technology,
Catholic University of America
Continuing Education Systems Inc
Creative Publications
Education and Training Consultants Co
Educational Communications Inc
Edu-Pac Publishing Co
Edutronics
Effective Learning Inc
Electronic Data Systems Corp
Entelek Inc
Great Plains National Instructional
Television Library
Grid Publishing Inc
Honeywell Information Systems
Houghton Mifflin Co
Instructional Systems Engineering

Sperry Gyroscope
Richard D Irwin Inc
Learncom Inc
Learning Systems Company
Michigan State University Instructional
    Media Center
NCR Corporation
National Association of Accountants
National Audiovisual Center
National Council of Teachers of
    Mathematics
Prentice-Hall Media Inc
Pyramid Film & Video
Republic Education Publishing Co
Tab Books
Technical Education Research Centers
Today News Service Inc
TPC Training Systems
Van Nostrand Reinhold Co
Van Valkenburgh, Nooger & Neville Inc
Xicom Inc

Engineering
Addison-Wesley Publishing Company
Robert J Brady Co
Co-operative Extension Services
Education and Training Consultants Co
Educational Communications Inc
Effective Learning Inc
Grid Publishing Inc
Houghton Mifflin Co
University of Illinois of Chicago Circle
Roy Jorgensen Associates Inc
National Audiovisual Center
Power Transmission Design
Tab Books
Technical Education Research Centers
Today News Service Inc
Van Nostrand Reinhold Co

39. Industrial safety
BNA Communications Inc
Robert J Brady Co
University of California (EMC)
Continuing Education Systems Inc
Creative Universal Inc
DCA Educational Products
DuPont
Educational Communications Inc
Educational Projections Corporation
Educational Resources Foundation
Effective Learning Inc
Grid Publishing Inc
Industrial Training Inc
Richard D Irwin Inc

Learncom Inc
Learning & Information Inc
Management Research Associates
Management Resources Inc
National Audiovisual Center
Power Transmission Design
Prentice-Hall Media Inc
Pyramid Film & Video
Salenger Educational Media
Today News Service Inc
TPC Training Systems
Ulrich's Books Inc
Van Nostrand Reinhold Co

40. Industrial processes
American Machinist/Beckwith Training
    Programs Inc
Robert J Brady Co
Ken Cook Co
Creative Universal Inc
DCA Educational Products
Educational Communications Inc
Edu-Pac Publishing Co
Effective Learning Inc
Grid Publishing Inc
Hobart School of Welding Technology
Howell Training Company
Richard D Irwin Inc
Learncom Inc
Learning & Information Inc
National A-V Center
Power Transmission Design
Prentice-Hall Media Inc
Society of Manufacturing Engineers
Today News Service Inc
TPC Training Systems
Ulrich's Books Inc
Unipub
Van Nostrand Reinhold Co

41. Reading
Educators Publishing Service Inc
Learn Incorporated
Science Research Associates Inc
Teaching Research Publications

42. Environmental studies
Pyramid Film & Video

43. Teaching and teacher training
Paul S Amidon and Associates Inc
University of Chicago Press
Childhood Resources Inc
Graduate School Press
Learncom Inc (training)
Pyramid Film & Video

Part 2: Producers' and Distributors' Names and Addresses

ABC Wide World of Learning, 825 7th Avenue, New York, NY 10019

Programmes (for machines, videotape)

Management and supervision, salesmanship and marketing, English literature, health, nursing and medicine, drama, history, economics and politics, social studies

AGS American Guidance Service, Publishers' Building, Circle Pines, Minnesota 55014

Programmed books, instructional programmes, tests

English language, EFL, mathematics, teaching and learning: programmed instruction, training, analysis; social studies

*ASTD – International Federation of Training and Development Organizations, PO Box 5664, Madison, WI 53705

Resource referrals

Teaching and learning: programmed instruction, training, analysis

*Abt Associates, 55 Wheeler Street, Cambridge, Massachusetts 02138

Games, kits, lesson sheets
Careers, economics, social studies, health, history

*Addison-Wesley Publishing Company, Reading, Massachusetts 01867

Programmed books, sound-tape, OHP transparencies, case studies, algorithms, textbooks

Accountancy, management and supervision, salesmanship and marketing, EFL, logic, mathematics, health, nursing and medicine, physiology, physical education, teaching and learning: programmed instruction, training, analysis; economics and politics, geography and geology, psychology, general science, biology, chemistry, physics, electricity and electronics, computers and computing, engineering

Aerospace Education Foundation, 1750 Pennsylvania Avenue NW, Washington, DC 20006

Programmed books, slide/tape materials, videotape, sound-tape

Nursing and medicine, teaching and learning: programmed instruction, training, analysis; electricity and electronics, computers and computing

*Agency for Innovative Curriculum Inc, Division of Random House Inc, 580 Sylvan Avenue, Englewood Cliffs, NJ 07632

Programmes (for machines), videotape, film, games and simulations

Office practice

Agency for Instructional Television, Box A, Bloomington, IN 47402

Film, videotapes

All subjects

*The American College, Bryn Mawr, Pennsylvania 19010

Programmes (for machines), programmed books, slide/tape materials, videotape, sound-tape, film, OHP transparencies, case studies, algorithms

Accountancy, management and supervision, mathematics, teaching and learning: programmed instruction, training, analysis; computers and computing.

*American Educational Films, 132 Lasky Drive, Beverly Hills, CA

Film

General, health, mathematics, general science, politics, English language

*American Machinist/Beckwith Training Programs Inc, 3620 Walnut Hills, Cleveland, Ohio 44122

Programmed books

Industrial processes

American Management Associations, 135 West 50th Street, New York, NY 10020

Programmed books, videotape, sound-tape, film, games and simulations, multi-media packages, assessment center

Office practice, management and supervision, salesmanship and marketing, teaching and learning: programmed instruction, training, analysis

Paul S Amidon & Associates Inc, 1966 Benson Avenue, St Paul, Minnesota 55116

Games and simulations, case studies, supplementary printed teaching materials for schools, teacher education (pre- and in-service)

Management and supervision, Spanish, mathematics, teaching and learning: programmed instruction, training, analysis; history, social studies, biology, chemistry, teaching and teacher training

Ann Arbor Publishers Inc, PO Box 7249, Naples, Fla 33940

Programmed books, sound-tape

English language, EFL, logic, mathematics, teaching and learning: programmed instruction, training, analysis

Association Films Inc *see:* Modern Talking Picture Service Inc

*Association for Educational & Communications Technology, Publications Department A-23, 1126 16th Street NW, Washington, DC 20036

Books, filmstrips, magazines

Teaching and learning: programmed instruction, training, analysis

Audiotronics Corporation, Box 3997, North Hollywood, California 91609

Programmes (for machines), film, games and simulations, case studies

English language, EFL, language, French, Spanish, mathematics, teaching and learning: programmed instruction, training, analysis; social studies, general science

*Audio Visual Publications, Box 2576, Station A, Champaign, Illinois 61820

Individualized materials

Languages

*Automated Instruction, Division of Random House Inc, 400 Hahn Road, Westminster, MD 21157

Programmed books, sound-tape, film

Office practice, teaching and learning: programmed instruction, training, analysis

BNA Communications Inc, 9417 Decoverly Hall Road, Rockville, Maryland 20850

Videotape, film, case studies, multimedia learning packages (film/video and programmed workbooks)

Management and supervision, salesmanship and marketing, industrial safety

*Behaviordelia Inc, PO Box 1044, Kalamazoo, MI 49005

Programmed books, slide/tape materials

Management and supervision, psychology

Behavioral Research Laboratories Inc *see* The Learning Line

*Behavior Science Press, Division of Rehabilitation Research Foundation, PO Box A, University, AL 35486

Programmed books

English language, mathematics, teaching and learning: programmed instruction, training, analysis; electricity and electronics

*Behrman House Inc, 1261 Broadway, New York, NY 10001

Programmed books, film, games and simulations, textbooks

Other languages – Hebrew, music, art and architecture, teaching and learning: programmed instruction, training, analysis; religion, history, social studies

Benjamin/Cummings Publishing, 2727 Sand Hill Road, Menlo Park, California 94025

Textbooks

Mathematics, health, nursing and medicine, physiology, economics and politics, psychology, general science, biology, chemistry, physics, computers and computing

*Bevin Enterprises, PO Box 85, Moraga, CA 94556

Programmed books, slide/tape materials, sound-tape, OHP

transparencies, case studies

Salesmanship and marketing

*Bobbs-Merrill Co, Subsidiary of Howard W Sams & Co, 4300 West 62nd Street, PO Box 558, Indianapolis, IN 46268

Boeing Computer Services Company, Education and Training Division, PO Box 24346, Mail Stop 9A-90, Seattle, WA 98124

Videotape

Computers and computing

*Book-Lab Inc, 1449 37th Street, Brooklyn, NY 11218

Educational material geared to special education, one-to-one tutoring, remedial reading

English language, EFL, teaching and learning: programmed instruction, training, analysis

*Borg-Warner Educational Systems, 7450 North Matchez Avenue, Niles, Illinois 60648

Programmes (for machines), sound-tape, System 80(R), individualized instruction in basic academic skills, System 80 audiovisual unit and System 80 instructional materials

EFL, mathematics

*Robert J Brady Co, Subsidiary of P-H Inc Routes, 197 and 450; Bowie, MD 20715

Programmed books, slide/tape materials, videotape, film, OHP transparencies, case studies

Office practice, English language, health, nursing and medicine, physiology, art and architecture, physical education, teaching and learning: programmed instruction, training, analysis; economics and politics, social studies, geography and geology, psychology, general science, biology, electricity and electronics, computers and computing, engineering, industrial safety, industrial processes

*CEM Company, 3154 Coventry Drive, Bay City, MI 48706

Structured books

Health: sex information; teaching and learning: programmed instruction, training, analysis

*CTB/McGraw-Hill, Del Monte Research Park, Monterey, CA 93940

Programmes (for machines), programmed books

English language, mathematics

University of California, Extension Media Center, 2223 Fulton Street, Berkeley, CA 94720

Videotape, film

General crafts, hobbies, etc, management and supervision, English literature, French, health, nursing and medicine, drama, dance, art and architecture, teaching and learning: programmed instruction, training, analysis; social studies, psychology, biology, physics, industrial safety

*The Center for Applied Research in Education Inc, PO Box 130, West Nyack, New York, NY 10995

Games and simulations, instructional aids for in-service educators – K12

General crafts, hobbies, driving etc, English language, English literature, EFL, mathematics, health, music, art and architecture, physical education, history, social studies, geography and geology, general science, biology, chemistry, physics

*Center for Educational Technology, School of Education, Catholic University of America, Washington, DC 20017

Programmed books, slide/tape materials, videotape, sound-tape, games and simulations, algorithms

English language, librarianship, health, nursing and medicine, dance, teaching and learning: programmed instruction, training, analysis; religion, social studies, geography and geology, computers and computing

*Central Scientific Co Inc, 2600 S Kostner, Chicago, IL 60623

Teaching aids and hardware

General science, biology, chemistry, physics

University of Chicago Press, 5801 Ellis Avenue, Chicago, IL 60637

Microfiche with text

English language, English literature, Spanish, librarianship, logic, mathematics, nursing and medicine, art and architecture, history, economics and politics, social studies, geography and geology, psychology, general science, biology, chemistry, physics, teaching and teacher training

Childhood Resources Inc, PO Box 561, 4017 Williamsburg Square, Fairfax, Virginia 22030

Video cassettes

Psychology, teaching and teacher training (ie tapes on early childhood and early education)

*Communacad, Box 541, Wilton, CT 06897

Programmes (for machines), sound-tapes, games and simulations

English language, EFL

The Continental Press Inc, Elizabethtown, PA 17022

English language, mathematics

Continuing Education Systems Inc, 112 South Grant Street, Hinsdale, IL 60521

Programmes (for machines), programmed books, slide-tape materials, sound-tape, case studies

Accountancy, salesmanship and marketing, English language, mathematics, teaching and learning: programmed instruction, training, analysis; computers and computing, industrial safety

*Ken Cook Co, 9929 W Silver Spring Road, Milwaukee, Wisconsin 53225

Programmed books, slide/tape materials

English language, industrial processes

*Cooperative Extension Services, Colo State 11, Fort Collins, Co 80523

Slide/tape materials, videotape, sound-tape, film

Health, economics and politics, biology, engineering

Crane Publishing Company, Division of MLP, 1301 Hamilton Avenue, PO Box 3713, Trenton, NJ 08629

Programmed books, elementary textbooks

English language, English literature, EFL, Spanish

*Creative Curriculum Inc, 15681 Commerce Lane, Huntington Beach, CA 92649

Programmes (for machines)

English language, English literature, teaching and learning: programmed instruction, training, analysis

Creative Publications, PO Box 10328, Palo Alto, CA 94303

Models, posters, kits, games, workbooks

English language, mathematics, computers and computing

*Creative Universal Inc, Suite 1200, 21700 Northwestern Highway, Southfield, Michigan 48705

Programmed books, slide/tape materials, videotape, sound-tape, film, OHP transparencies, games and simulations, case studies, algorithms

Office practice, management and supervision, salesmanship and marketing, teaching and learning: programmed instruction, training, analysis; industrial safety, industrial processes

DCA Educational Products, 424 Valley Road, Warrington, PA 18976

Slide/tape materials, OHP transparencies

Industrial safety, industrial processes

The Dartnell Corporation, 4660 Ravenswood Avenue, Chicago, IL 60640

Videotape, film

Office practice, management and supervision, salesmanship and marketing

Development Digest, PO Box 49938, Los Angeles, CA 90049

Sound-tape, case studies

Management and supervision, salesmanship and marketing, librarianship, teaching and learning: programmed instruction, training, analysis; psychology

Development Dimensions International, 1225 Washington Pike, Box 13379, Pittsburgh, PA 15243

Videotape, film, games and simulations

Management and supervision

Development Publications, 5605 Lamar Road, Washington DC 20016

Books and films

Management and training

DuPont de Nemours & Co, 1007 Market Street, Wilmington, Delaware 19898

Programmed books

Teaching and learning: programmed instruction, training, analysis; industrial safety

*EDL/McGraw-Hill, 1221 Avenue of the Americas, New York, NY 10020

Programmes (for machines), programmed books, sound-tape, film, algorithms, EFL

Mathematics, teaching and learning: programmed instruction, training, analysis

EFM Films, 85 Main Street, Watertown, MA 02172

Videotape, film

Management and supervision, salesmanship and marketing

E-Z Grader Co, PO Box 24040, Cleveland, Ohio 44124

Games and simulations, instructional teacher and teaching aid slide charts

English language, mathematics

Edmark Associates, PO Box 3903, Bellevue, Washington 98009

Special education materials

Education & Training Consultants Co, Box 2085, Sedona, Arizona 86336

Programmed books, slide/tape materials, simulations

Management and supervision, teaching and learning: programmed instruction, training, analysis; computers and computing, engineering

Educational Communications Inc, 761 Fifth Avenue, King of Prussia, 19406 PA

General crafts, hobbies, etc, accountancy, office practice, management and supervision, salesmanship and marketing, logic, mathematics, health, nursing and medicine, physiology, art and architecture, teaching and learning: programmed instruction, training, analysis; economics and politics, geography and geology, psychology, general science, biology, chemistry, physics, electricity and electronics, computers and computing, engineering, industrial safety, industrial processes

*Educational Methods, 500 N Dearborn Street, Chicago, IL 60610

Programmed books

Accountancy, biology

*Educational Projections Corporation, 224 North First Street, PO Box 50276, Jacksonville Beach, Florida 32750

Programmes (for machines)

General crafts, hobbies, driving etc, EFL, Spanish, mathematics, health, music, art and architecture, history, economics and politics, social studies, chemistry, physics, electricity and electronics, industrial safety

Educational Resources Foundation, PO Drawer L, 2712 Millwood Avenue, Columbia, SC 29250

Videotape and film backed up by written materials, case studies

Management and supervision, salesmanship and marketing, economics and politics, industrial safety

Educators Publishing Service Inc, 75 Moulton Street, Cambridge, Massachusetts 02138

Programmed books, sound-tape materials, workbooks, spirit duplicating masters

English language, reading

Educulture Inc, 1 Dubuque Plaza, Suite 150, Dubuque, Iowa 52001

Audio-tutorial learning programmes

English language, logic, mathematics, psychology, chemistry

*Edu-Pac Publishing Co, PO Box 27101, Minneapolis, MN 55427

*Programmed books, games and
simulations*

Mathematics, health, nursing and
medicine, teaching and learning:
programmed instruction, training,
analysis; religion, social studies,
psychology, general science, computers
and computing, industrial processes

Edutronics/McGraw-Hill, 55 Corporate
Woods, 9300W 110th Street, Overland
Park, Kansas 66210

Programmed books, videotape

Computers and computing

***Effective Learning Inc,** 7 North
McQuesten Parkway, Mount Vernon,
NY 10550

*Programmes (for machines),
programmed books, slide/tape
materials, videotape, sound-tape, film,
games and simulations, case studies,
algorithms*

Office practice, management and
supervision, salesmanship and
marketing, English language, English
literature, EFL, logic, mathematics,
health, nursing and medicine, teaching
and learning: programmed instruction,
training, analysis; history, economics
and politics, social studies, geography
and geology, psychology, general
science, biology, chemistry, physics,
electricity and electronics, computers
and computing, engineering, industrial
safety, industrial processes

Electronic Data Systems Corporation,
14580 Midway Road, Dallas, TX 75234

*Programmes (for machines),
programmed books, videotape*

Teaching and learning: programmed
instruction, training, analysis; computers
and computing

**Encyclopaedia Britannica Educational
Corporation,** 425 North Michigan
Avenue, Chicago, IL 60611

*Slide/tape materials, videotape, sound-
tape, film, OHP transparencies, books*

English language, English literature,
languages, librarianship, mathematics,
health: first aid, sex information,
nutrition, dentistry, veterinary surgery;
music, drama, dance, art and
architecture, physical education,

teaching and learning: programmed
instruction, training, analysis; history,
economics and politics, social studies,
geography and geology, general science,
biology, chemistry, physics, electricity
and electronics, engineering

***Enrich Inc,** 2325 Paragon Drive, San
Jose, CA 95131

*Programmes (for machines), TELOR
individualized teaching aid*

English language, mathematics, teaching
and learning: programmed instruction,
training, analysis; general science

Entelek Inc, Ward Whitton House,
The Hill, PO Box 1303, Portsmouth,
NH 03801

*Programmes (for machines),
programmed books*

Mathematics, teaching and learning:
programmed instruction, training,
analysis; social studies, general science,
biology, chemistry, physics, computers
and computing

Farrall Instruments, PO Box 1037,
Grand Island, Nebraska 68801

Slide/tape materials

Health, psychology

***Fearon Pitman Publishers Inc,** 6 Davis
Drive, Belmont, CA 94002

Programmed books

Management and supervision

***The Ford Foundation,** 320 East 43rd
Street, New York, NY 10017

Film

Economics and politics, social studies

General Cassette Corporation, 2311 N
35th Avenue, Phoenix, AZ 85005

Videotape, sound-tape

Management and supervision,
salesmanship and marketing

General Motors Corp, 1700 W 3rd
Avenue, Flint, Michigan 48502

*Slide/tape materials, videotape, sound-
tape, film*

Office practice, management and
supervision, industrial safety

Graduate School Press, USDA, Room
6847, South Agriculture Building,
Washington DC 20250

Video cassettes

Teaching and teacher training (theme of 'Learning')

Great Plains National Instructional Television Library (GPN), Box 80669, Lincoln, Nebraska 68501

Videotape, film

General crafts, hobbies, etc, English language, English literature, languages, mathematics, health, music, drama, art, physical education, history, economics and politics, social studies, geography and geology, psychology, general science, computers and computing

*Grid Publishing Inc, 4666 Indianola Avenue, Columbus, Ohio 43214

Programmed books, games and simulations, case studies

Accountancy, office practice, management and supervision, salesmanship and marketing, economics and politics, computers and computing, engineering, industrial safety, industrial processes

Health Sciences Consortium, 200 Eastowne Drive, Suite 213, Chapel Hill, NC 27514

Programmed books, slide/tape materials, videotape, sound-tape, case studies

Health, nursing and medicine, physiology, teaching and learning: programmed instruction, training, analysis; psychology

Hobart School of Welding Technology, Trade Square East, Troy, Ohio 45373

Programmed books, Super 8 film with sound-tape, workbooks and manuals

Industrial processes

*Honeywell Information Systems, Education Systems, 110 Cedar Street, Wellesley Hills, Masachusetts 02181

Programmes (for machines), programmed books, slide/tape materials, videotape, sound-tape, simulations

Computers and computing

*Houghton Mifflin Co, 110 Tremont Street, Boston, Massachusetts 02107

Programmes (for machines),

programmed books, games and simulations

General crafts, hobbies, driving etc, accountancy, office practice, management and supervision, salesmanship and marketing, English language, English literature, EFL, French, German, Spanish, Italian, mathematics, health, nursing and medicine, physiology, teaching and learning: programmed instruction, training, analysis; history, economics and politics, social studies, geography and geology, psychology, general science, biology, chemistry, physics, computers and computing

*Howell Training Company, 5201 Langfield Road, Houston, Texas 77040

Programmed books, slide/tape materials, videotape

English language, French, industrial processes

Idea Development Associates, PO Box 167, Palo Alto, California

Multimedia kits (slide/tape, filmstrip/tape plus workbooks)

Management and supervision (problem-solving, decision-making)

University of Illinois at Chicago Circle, Instructional Resources, Box 4348, Chicago, Illinois 60680

videotape, film

Music, teaching and learning: programmed instruction, training, analysis; chemistry, engineering

Industrial Training Inc, 2023 Eastern Avenue SE, Grand Rapids, MI 49510

Slide/tape materials, videotape

Teaching and learning: programmed instruction, training, analysis; electricity and electronics, computers and computing, industrial safety

*Information Resources Inc, PO Box 417, Lexington, Massachusetts 02173

Instructional/Communications Technology Inc – Taylor Associates, 10 Stepar Place, Huntington Station, NY 10746

Programmes (for machines), programmed books, sound-tape

English language, EFL, languages, mathematics, teaching and learning: programmed instruction, training, analysis

*Instructional Fair Inc, 4153 Lake Michigan Drive, Grand Rapids, MI 49504

General

English language, mathematics, teaching and learning: programmed instruction, training, analysis

Instructional Systems Engineering, Sperry Gyroscope, Sperry Division, Sperry Rand Corporation, Great Neck, New York, NY 11020

Programmes (for machines), programmed books, slide/tape materials, videotape, sound-tape, film, OHP transparencies, computer based simulation and maintenance trainers using video discs, performance guides

Teaching and learning: programmed instruction, training, analysis; general science, physics, electricity and electronics, computers and computing

Richard D Irwin Inc, 1818 Ridge Road, Homewood, IL 60430

Programmed books, case studies

Accountancy, office practice, management and supervision, salesmanship and marketing, history, economics and politics, psychology, computers and computing, industrial safety, industrial processes

Jeppesen Sanderson, Education Department, 55 Inverness Drive East, Englewood, CO 80112

Programmed books, slide/tape materials, sound-tape, film, OHP transparencies, textbooks, workbooks, instructor guides, student materials

Aviation/aerospace education, general science

*Roy Jorgensen Associates Inc, PO Box 575, Gaithersburg, Maryland 20760

Programmed books, slide/tape materials, case studies, algorithms

Management and supervision, engineering

Ken-A-Vision, 5615 Raytown Road, Kansas City, Missouri 64133

Programmes (for machines), microprojectors

Nursing and medicine, general science, biology

Lab-Volt Systems Division/Buck Engineering Co, Inc, PO Box 686, Farmingdale, NJ 07727

Slide/tape materials

Electricity and electronics

Lansford Publishing Co, PO Box 8711, San Jose, CA 95155

Slide/tape materials, sound-tape, OHP transparencies, games and simulations, statistical demonstrators

Accountancy, office practice, management and supervision, salesmanship and marketing, English language, logic, teaching and learning: programmed instruction, training, analysis; economics and politics, psychology

Learn Incorporated, 113 Gaither Drive, Mount Laurel, New Jersey 08054

Programmes (for machines), programmed books, videotape, sound tape, film

Office practice (business writing), reading (adult/advanced)

Learncom Inc, 113 Union Wharf East, Boston, MA 02109

Programmed books, slide/tape materials, videotape, sound-tape, OHP transparencies, games and simulations, case studies

Office practice, management and supervision, salesmanship and marketing, teaching and learning: programmed instruction, training, analysis; computers and computing, industrial safety, industrial processes, teaching and teacher training

*Learning & Information Inc, 315 Central Park West, New York, NY 10025

Programmes (for machines), programmed books, film

Office practice, management and supervision, salesmanship and marketing, teaching and learning: programmed instruction, training, analysis; industrial safety, industrial processes

Learning Corporation of America, 1350 Avenue of the Americas, New York, NY 10019

Videotape, film

English language, English literature, French, Spanish, music, drama, dance, art and architecture, physical education, history, economics and politics, social studies, geography and geology, general science

The Learning Line, PO Box 1200, Palo Alto, CA 94302 (*inc* Behavioral Research Labs.

Inc)

Programmed books, sound-tape

English language, languages (French, German, Spanish), mathematics, health, biology, chemistry

Learning Systems Company, Division of Richard D Irwin Inc, 1818 Ridge Road, Homewood, IL 60430

Programmed books

Accountancy, management and supervision, salesmanship and marketing, mathematics, history, economics and politics, social studies, psychology, computers and computing

*Life Insurance Marketing & Research Association, 170 Sigourney Street, Hartford, Connecticut 06105

Programmed books

Life insurance (various policies and how they are constructed)

*Little, Brown, & Co, 34 Beacon Street, Boston, Massachusetts 02106

Management and supervision, salesmanship and marketing, English language, health, nursing and medicine, physiology, history, economics and politics, psychology, biology, chemistry, physics

Litton Educational Publishing International – *see* Van Nostrand Reinhold Co

Loyola University Press, 3441 N Ashland Avenue, Chicago, Ill 60657

Programmed books

French, other languages – Greek

MCV School of Pharmacy, MCV Station, Box 581, Richmond, VA 23298

Programmed books

Nursing and medicine (pharmacy education)

*Macmillan Inc, 866 Third Avenue, New York, NY 10022

Instructional materials

Mager Associates Inc, 13245 Rhoda Drive, Los Altos Hills, CA 94022

Programmed books, slide/tape materials, videotape, film

Teaching and learning: programmed instruction, training, analysis

Magnetic Video Corporation, 23705 Industrial Park Drive, Farmington Hills, MI 48024

Videotape

Management and supervision, salesmanship and marketing, psychology

Management Research Associates, R R 25, Box 26, Terre Haute, Indiana 47802

Programmed books, film

Management and supervision, teaching and learning: programmed instruction, training, analysis; biology, industrial safety

Management Resources Inc, 757 Third Avenue, New York, NY 10017

Programmed books, case studies

Management and supervision, economics and politics, industrial safety

Marshfilm Enterprises Inc, PO Box 8082, Shawnee Mission, Kansas 66208

35mm filmstrips with cassette or record

Spanish, health, physical education, religion, economics and politics, social studies, psychology

*Med Ed Projects Inc, 292 Cox Street, Roselle, NJ 07203

Programmes (for machines), programmed books, slide/tape materials, videotape, sound-tape, film, case studies, health, nursing and medicine

*Media Materials Inc, 409 West Cold Spring, Baltimore, Maryland 21210

Programmes (for machines), programmed books, slide/tape materials – sound filmstrips, sound-tapes

English language, English literature – fairytales; mathematics, teaching and learning: programmed instruction, training, analysis; religion, social studies, general science

*Media Systems Corp, Affiliate of Harcurt Brace Jovanovich Inc, 250 West Main Street, Moorestown, NJ 08057

*Media Systems Inc, 3637 East 7800 South, Salt Lake City, Utah 84121

Sound-tape, OHP transparencies, sound filmstrip

Librarianship, teaching and learning: programmed instruction, training, analysis

Medical Examination Publishing Co Inc, (an Excerpta Medica company), 969 Stewart Avenue, Garden City, NY 11530

Case studies, textbooks, handbooks, examination review books, health, nursing and medicine, physiology

*The Merritt Company, 1661 Ninth Street, PO Box 955, Santa Monica, CA 90406

Programmed books, slide/tape materials, sound-tape, film

Industrial processes (insurance)

*Michigan State University, Instructional Media Center, East Lansing, Michigan 48824

Programmes (for machines), programmed books, slide/tape materials, videotape, sound-tape, film

General crafts, hobbies, driving etc, office practice, EFL, health, nursing and medicine, physiology, drama, physical education, teaching and learning: programmed instruction, training, analysis; history, physics, computers and computing

*University of Michigan Press, 839 Greene Street, Ann Arbor, Michigan 48106

Programmed books

EFL, languages, biology,

Modern Talking Picture Service Inc, 5000 Park Street North, St Petersburg, Florida 33907

Distributors for the US National Medical AV Center Loan Programme

Health, nursing and medicine

*Mojave Books, 7040 Darby Avenue, Reseda, CA 91335

Programmed books

Librarianship, chemistry

*NCR Corporation, Educational Development, Education Center – Sugar Camp, Dayton, Ohio 45409

Programmes (for machines), sound-tape, case studies

Accountancy, office practice, teaching and learning: programmed instruction, training, analysis; electricity and electronics, computers and computing

*National Association of Accountants, 919 Third Avenue, New York, NY 10022

Slide/tape materials, sound-tape

Accountancy, office practice, management and supervision, teaching and learning: programmed instruction, training, analysis; computers and computing

National Audiovisual Center, General Services Administration, AHN: Reference Section, Washington DC 20409

Slide/tape materials, videotape, sound-tape, film, videodisc, filmstrip

Accountancy, office practice, management and supervision, salesmanship and marketing, English language, languages (French, German, Spanish, etc), librarianship, mathematics, health, nursing and medicine, physiology, music, physical education, teaching and learning: programmed instruction, training, analysis; history, economics and politics, social studies, geography and geology, psychology, general science, biology, chemistry, physics, electricity and electronics, computers and computing, engineering, industrial safety, industrial processes

National Center for Research in Vocational Education (c/o Ohio State University), 1960 Kenny Road, Columbus, Ohio 43210

Programmed books, slide/tape materials, games and simulations

Management and supervision, nursing

and medicine, physical education, teaching and learning: programmed instruction, training, analysis

National Council of Teachers of Mathematics, 1906 Association Drive, Reston, Virginia 22091

Videotapes, books and journals

Mathematics, teaching and learning: programmed instruction, training, analysis; computers and computing

*National Education Association, 1201 16th Street NW, Washington, DC 20036

Videotape, film, OHP transparencies

Teaching and learning: programmed instruction, training, analysis

National Educational Media Inc, 21601 Devonshire Street, Chatsworth, California 91311

Slide/tape materials, sound-tape, film, printed study materials for each film

Management and supervision, salesmanship and marketing

National Medical AV Center Loan Programme – *see* Modern Talking Picture Service Inc

*National Services Inc, PO Box 1031, Montgomery, Alabama 36102

Programmed books

Electricity and electronics

National Teaching Aids Inc, 120 Fulton Avenue, Garden City Park, NY 11040

Individualized materials

Health, geography and geology, biology, life science

*National Tool, Die & Precision Machining Association, 8300 Livingston Road, Washington, DC 20022

Programmes (for machines), sound-tape, filmstrip

Mathematics, teaching and learning: programmed instruction, training, analysis for machinists

*New Readers Press, Division of Laubach Literacy International, Box 131, Syracuse, NY 13210

Programmed books

English language, EFL, health, teaching

and learning: programmed instruction, training, analysis

*W W Norton & Co Inc, 500 Fifth Avenue, New York, NY 10036

Ohio State University – *see* National Center for Research in Vocational Education

*Ontario Institute for Studies in Education, 252 Bloor Street West, Toronto, Ontario M5S 1V6

Curriculum resource kits, film

English language, mathematics, teaching and learning: programmed instruction, training, analysis; history, general science, social science, thinking

*Organisational Tests, PO Box 324, Fredericton, New Brunswick, Canada E3B 4Y9

Management and supervision

*Power Transmission Design Magazine, 614 Superior Avenue West, Cleveland, Ohio 44113

Programmed books

Electricity and electronics, engineering, industrial safety, industrial processes

Prentice-Hall Media Inc, 150 White Plains Road, Tarrytown, NY 10591

Slide/tape materials, videotape, sound-tape, film, sound-filmstrip materials, textbooks

Accountancy, office practice, management and supervision, salesmanship and marketing, English language, English literature, EFL, mathematics, health, physiology, music, drama, art and architecture, teaching and learning: programmed instruction, training, analysis; history, economics and politics, social studies, geography and geology, psychology, general science, biology, chemistry, physics, electricity and electronics, computers and computing, industrial safety, industrial processes, all vocational subjects

Professional Development Inc, 2915 Terminal Tower Building, Cleveland, Ohio 44113

Videotape, film

Office practice, management and supervision, salesmanship and marketing

*Psychotecnics Inc, 1900 Pickwick Avenue, Glenview, IL 60025

Programmes (for machines), film, projectors, reading pacer, tape cassette programmes, films and books for reading training

English language, EFL, teaching and learning: programmed instruction, training, analysis

Pyramid Film & Video, Box 1048, Santa Monica, CA 90406

Videotape, film

General crafts, hobbies, etc, salesmanship and marketing, English literature, mathematics, health, music, drama, art and architecture, physical education, religion, history (inc archaeology), economics and politics, social studies, geography and geology, psychology, general science, biology, physics, computers and computing (inc computer graphics), industrial safety, environmental studies, teaching and teacher training

*Quickhand Shorthand, 2445 Lyttonsville Road, Silver Spring, Maryland 20910

Programmed books, sound-tape

Office practice

The Reading Laboratory Inc, 55 Day Street, S Norwalk, CT 06854

35mm sound filmstrips (filmstrip and cassette) and coordinated workbooks

English language, history, social studies

*Redgrave Publishing Company (A Division of Docent Corp), PO Box 67, South Salem, NY 10590

Programmed books

Nursing and medicine, economics and politics

Republic Education Publishing Company, 3110 North Arlington Heights Road, Arlington Heights, Illinois 60004
Also office at: 645 East 6th Street, St Paul, Minnesota 55101

Programmes (for machines), programmed books, computer-based education software, textbooks

Management and supervision, salesmanship and marketing, English language, EFL, health, nursing and medicine, physiology, teaching and learning: programmed instruction, training, analysis; history, economics and politics, social studies, psychology, computers and computing

Research Press Co, 2612 North Mattis Avenue, Champaign, IL 61820

Programmed books, videotape, sound-tape, film

Management and supervision, teaching and learning: programmed instruction, training, analysis; psychology

Roundtable Films Inc, 113 North San Vicente Boulevard, Beverly Hills, California 90211

Videotape, film

Management and supervision, salesmanship and marketing, teaching and learning: programmed instruction, training, analysis

Salenger Educational Media, 1635 12th Street, Santa Monica, California 90404

Videotape, film, supplementary print materials to accompany film and video programs

Management and supervision, salesmanship and marketing, health, teaching and learning: programmed instruction, training, analysis; industrial safety

*Sargent-Welch Scientific Co, (Tutorsystems Division), 7300 Linder Avenue, Skokie, IL 60076

Programmes (for machines)

English language, mathematics

Science Research Associates (SRA), Inc 155 North Wacker Drive, Chicago, IL 60606

Programmes (for microcomputers), slide/tape materials, videotape, sound-tape, film, case studies

Office practice, management and supervision, salesmanship and marketing, English language, English literature, EFL, Spanish, mathematics, drama, teaching and learning: programmed instruction, training, analysis; history economics and politics, social studies, geography and geology, psychology, electricity and electronics, computers and computing, engineering, reading

*The Shoe String Press, PO Box 4327, Hamden, CT 06514

Programmed books

Librarianship

*Silver Burdett Company, 250 James Street, Morristown, NJ 07960

Programmed books, sound-tape, film, games and simulations, records (LP), main kits (Metrilab), science kits (Lab Program), musical instruments, Disney Youth Musical packages, picture packets

English language, English literature, EFL, mathematics, health, music, drama, religion, history, social studies, geography and geology, general science, biology, chemistry, physics, electricity and electronics

*Charles B Slack Inc, 6900 Grove Road, Thorofare, NJ 08086

Sound-tape

Nursing and medicine

Society of Manufacturing Engineers, 1 SME Drive, PO Box 930, Dearborn, Michigan 48128

Programmed, self-study and correspondence courses, videotape, sound-tape, reference, text and hand-books, technical papers

Management, industrial processes (topics covered: manufacturing management, industrial robots, automated systems, metalworking, quality control, assembly, and tool engineering)

University of Southern California – *see USC Broadcast Production*

Springboard Associates, 2767 Scott Avenue, Lincoln, Nebraska 68506

Programmed books, slide/tape materials, videotape, sound-tape

Management and supervision, salesmanship and marketing, nursing and medicine

Springer Publishing Co Inc, 200 Park Avenue South, New York NY 10003

Programmed books, tests

Nursing and medicine, psychology

*Stanwix House Inc, 3020 Chartier's Avenue, Pittsburgh, Pennsylvania 15204

Programmed books, games and simulations

English language

*Stipes Publishing Co, 10-12 Chester Street, Champaign, IL 61820

Programmed books

Physiology, teaching and learning: programmed instruction, training, analysis; chemistry

TPC Training Systems, 1301 S Grove Avenue, Barrington, IL 60010

Programmed books, slide/tape materials, videotape

Logic, mathematics, electricity and electronics, industrial safety, industrial processes

Tab Books, Blue Ridge Summit, PA 17214

Programmes (for machines), games and simulations

General crafts, hobbies, driving etc, mathematics, music, art and architecture, electricity and electronics, computers and computing, engineering

Teachers College Press, 1234 Amsterdam Avenue, New York, NY 10027

Programmed books

English language, EFL, nursing and medicine

*Teaching Research Publications, Division of the Oregon State System of Higher Education, Monmouth, Oregon 97361

Programmed texts, films, student manuals

Health, reading

*Teaching Systems Corporation, 100 Boylston Street, Boston, MA 02116

Programmed books, correspondence course

Salesmanship and marketing

*Technical Education Research Centers, 44 Brattle Street, Cambridge, MA 02139

Programmes (for machines), laboratory equipment

Mathematics, teaching and learning: programmed instruction, training, analysis; general science, biology, chemistry, physics, electricity and electronics, computers and computing, engineering

*Technical Publishing Co, 1301 S Grove Avenue, Barrington, IL 60010

Programmed books

Electricity and electronics, industrial safety, industrial processes

Teleometrics International, 1755 Woodstead Court, The Woodlands, Texas 77380

Slide/tape materials, film

Management and supervision, salesmanship and marketing

Telstar Inc, 336 North Prior Avenue, St Paul, MN 55104

Videotape, sound-tape

Management and supervision, English language, nursing and medicine

University of Texas at Austin, Film Library, Box W, Austin Texas 78712

Film, books

Librarianship, teaching and learning: programmed instruction, training, analysis

Charles C. Thomas, Publisher, 2600 S First Street, Springfield, IL 62717

Programmed books

Health, nursing and medicine, physical education, teaching and learning: programmed instruction, training, analysis, social studies, psychology

*Time-Life Multimedia, Time & Life Building, New York NY 10020

Film, video

General crafts, hobbies, driving etc, health, drama, physical education – sport, history, social studies, geography and geology, biology

Today News Service Inc, National Press Building, Washington, DC 20045

Programmes (for machines), programmed books, slide-tape materials, games and simulations, case studies, algorithms, printed materials/manuals

Office practice, management and

supervision, librarianship, mathematics, health, nursing and medicine, teaching and learning: programmed instruction, training, analysis; economics and politics, social studies, general science, biology, computers and computing, engineering, industrial safety, industrial processes

Training House Inc, Box 3090, Princeton NJ 08540

Slide-tape materials, sound-tape, games and simulations, case studies, learning kits (tape plus workbook)

Management and supervision, salesmanship and marketing

US...*Note:* the prefix 'US' for 'United States', other than when an organization is best known by initials alone (eg USAAF), has been omitted in all cases – organizations are listed under the remainder of their title

USC Broadcst Production (University of Southern California), Davidson Conference Center, Los Angeles, California 90007

Videotape

Management and supervision, comparative literature, logic, health, music, economics, biology, electricity and electronics

Ulrich's Books Inc, 549 E University Avenue, Ann Arbor, MI 48104

Programmed books

English language, EFL, mathematics, teaching and learning: programmed instruction, training, analysis

Unipub, 345 Park Avenue South, New York NY 10010

Slide/tape materials, OHP transparencies

Health, art and architecture, industrial process, agriculture

*United Methodist Publishing House, Cokesbury Division, 201 Eighth Avenue South, Nashville, Tennessee 37202

Slide/tape materials, sound-tape, film, OHP transparencies

Religion

Van Nostrand Reinhold Company, 135 West 50th Street, New York NY 10020

(Incorporates Litton Educational Publishing International)

Books (and AV materials?)

General crafts, hobbies, driving, etc, accountancy, office practice, management and supervision, salesmanship and marketing, English language, logic, mathematics, health, nursing and medicine, music, art and architecture, physical education, economics and politics, history, geography and geology, psychology, general science, biology, chemistry, physics, electricity and electronics, computers and computing, engineering, industrial safety, industrial processes

*Van Valkenburgh, Nooger & Neville Inc, 15 Maiden Lane, New York NY 10038

Programmed books, games and simulations, adjunctive and programmed texts, student instant response systems

Teaching and learning: programmed instruction, training, analysis; electricity and electronics, computers and computing

*Vimcet Associates, PO Box 27414, Los Angeles, California 90024

Sound-tape, film

Teaching and learning: programmed instruction, training, analysis

WFF'N PROOF Publishers, 1940 South Boulevard, Ann Arbor, Michigan 48104

Programmes (for machines), programmed books, games and simulations

English language, logic mathematics, teaching and learning, programmed instruction, training, analysis; social studies

*Williams & Wilkins Co, 428 East Preston Street, Baltimore, Maryland 21202

Slides, microfiche

Health

*World Book – Childcraft International Inc (formerly Field Enterprises Educational Corp), Merchandise Mart Plaza, Chicago, IL 60654

Programmes (for machines) – cycloteacher learning aid

General crafts, hobbies, driving etc, English language, mathematics, physiology, music, social studies

Xicom Inc, Sterling Forest, Tuxedo, NY 10910

Videotape, sound-tape, film, games and simulations

Management and supervision, salesmanship and marketing, nursing and medicine, computers and computing

*Year Book Medical Publishers, 35 East Wacker Drive, Chicago, Il 60601

Programmed books, slide/tape materials

Health, nursing and medicine, physiology

Some Useful Catalogues

The following list gives the addresses of organizations which produce catalogues of their audiovisual products, and indicates the media in which they specialize. Most of the listed organizations feature in the earlier parts (UK, USA) of Section 5, where indications of subject coverage can be obtained.

University of Aberdeen, *Catalogue of Videotape recordings,* University of Aberdeen Television Service, King's College, Aberdeen AB9 2UB

Alcan Film Library,
303 Finchley Road, London NW3
(Films – industrial themes)

American Educational Films,
162 Fourth Avenue North – Suite 123, Nashville, Tennessee 32719, USA
(Film, video)

Ashridge Management College,
see Employment Relations Ltd

Association for Liberal Education, *Films for General Studies* (1971) and *Supplement* (1973), EFVA, Paxton Place, Gipsy Road, London SE27 9SR

Audio Visual Productions, Hocker Hill House, Chepstow, Gwent NP6 5ER
(Slide programmes)

BBC Enterprises, *BBC Enterprises Film & Video Catalogue* (for purchase), Room 503, Villiers House, The Broadway, London W5 2PA

BBC TV Film Enterprises Film Hire, *see* Guild Sound & Vision Ltd

BFI, *The British National Film Catalogue; Catalogue of Viewing copies* (1971) and *Supplement* (1974); *Catalogue of Viewing copies (fiction)* (1977), British Film Institute, 81 Dean Street, London W1V 6AA

BFI Education, British Film Institute, 81 Dean Street, London W1V 6AA
(Film – education)

BMA/BLAT Film Library,
BMA House, Tavistock Square, London WC1
(Over 900 films and video – health, medicine)

British Gas Film Library, *see* Viscom Ltd (Film, video)

The British Library, *British Catalogue of Audio Visual Materials,* The British Library, Bibliographic Services Division, 2 Sheraton Street, London W1V 4BH

British Productivity Council,
8 Southampton Row, London WC1B 4AQ
(Film, tape-slide – industrial themes)

British Transport Film Library, *see* Central Film Library

British Universities Film Council, *Catalogue of Higher Education Film and Video Library; HELPIS – Audio-Visual Materials For Higher Education,* BUFC, 81 Dean Street, London W1V 6AA

Brunel University, *Catalogue of Videotape recordings,* Brunel University, AV Centre, Uxbridge UB8 3PH

CTVC Film Library, Hillside, Merryhill Road, Bushey, Watford WD2 1DR

Central Film Library, *CFL Catalogue* (over 1200 films – costs £2); *ILEA Catalogue of Educational Films* (free); *Free to Schools and Colleges; Industrial and Management Training* (free), Central Film Library, Chalfont Grove, Gerrards Cross, Bucks SL9 8TN

Chiltern Consortium, *Chiltern Resources Library Catalogue,* Wall Hall, Aldenham, Watford, Herts
(Wide range of media and subjects)

Christian Aid, Films & Publications Dept, PO Box 1, London SW9 8BH

Church Army AV Resources, *Filmstrips Catalogue,* Independents Road, London SE3 9LG
(Filmstrips, video, audio-tape – religion)

Concord Films Council, 201 Felixstowe Road, Ipswich, Suffolk IP3 9BJ
(Films – very wide subject range)

Concordia Films, Viking Way, Bar Hill, Cambridge CA3 8EL

Connoisseur Film Library, c/o Harris Films, Glenbuck Road, Surbiton, Surrey KT6 6BT

Contemporary Films Ltd, 55 Greek Street, London W1V 6DB

Council for Educational Technology, 3 Devonshire Street, London W1 *Publications List* (includes details of USPEC's user specifications for AV hardware)

Walt Disney Educational Media Company, 83 Pall Mall, London SW1

Dundee College of Education, *Catalogue of Self-Instructional and other Learning Materials,* Learning Resources Department, Dundee College of Education, Gardyne Road, Broughty Ferry, Dundee DD5 1NY

EAV Ltd, c/o Mary Glasgow Publications Ltd, Brookhampton Lane, Kineton, Warwick CV35 0JB
(Slide-tape materials)

EMI Film Distributors, *see* Viscom Ltd, Educational and Television Films Ltd (ETV), 247a Upper Street, London N1 1RU
(Films – feature, cartoon, documentary – mostly from USSR and Eastern Europe)

Educational Foundation for Visual Aids, *Catalogues of Audio Visual Aids, Films, Filmstrips, Transparencies, Wallsheets and Recorded sound, Parts 5-8 Filmstrips, Slides, Kits, OHPs; Filmstrips for Regional Geography; Catalogue of Films for General studies* (1971) and *Supplement* (1973);

Catalogue of 16mm films in the National Audio Visual Aids Library and Supplements, EFVA, Paxton Place, Gipsy Road, London SE27 9SR

Educational Productions Ltd, Bradford Road, East Ardsley, Wakefield WF3 2JW
(Slides, video, audio – wide subject range)

Educational Resources Foundation, PO Drawer L, Columbia, South Carolina 29250, USA
(Film, video, audio – industrial training)

Electricity Council Film Library, 30 Millbank, London SW1P 4RD

Employment Relations Ltd, *Catalogue of Audio-Visual Training Material for Industrial Relations Training,* Employment Relations Ltd, 62 Hills Road, Cambridge, CB2 1LA

Encyclopaedia Britannica International Ltd, Fergus Davidson Associates, 376 London Road, West Croydon, Surrey CR0 8RJ

Eothen Films Ltd, EMI Film Studios, Shenley Road, Borehamwood, Herts WD6 1JE

Gateway Educational Films Ltd, Waverley Road, Yate, Bristol BS17 5RB

Golden Films, Stewart House, Frances Road, Windsor, Berks
(Film)

Graves Medical Audio-Visual Library, PO Box 99, Chelmsford, Essex

Guild Sound & Vision Ltd, Woodston House, Oundle Road, Peterborough PE2 9PZ

Health Sciences Consortium, 200 Eastowne Drive, Suite 213, Chapel Hill, North Carolina 27514 USA
(Film, video, tape-slide – medicine, nursing, health)

Higher Education Film & Video Library, *Catalogue of Films and Videocassettes for Degree-Level Use,* BUFC, 81 Dean Street, London W1V 6AA

ICI Film Library, 15 Beaconsfield Road, London NW10 2LE
(Film, video – science and industry themes)

ILEA Films, *see* Central Film Library)

ILEA Learning Materials Service, two catalogues of publications and videocassettes – *Primary* or *Secondary/Special/FHE* level, ILEA Learning Materials Service, Publishing Centre, Highbury Station Road, London N1 1SB

Kogan Page Ltd, *The Industrial Film Guide,* Kogan Page Ltd, 120 Pentonville Road, London N1 9JN

University of London, *Catalogue of Videotapes, Films, Sound Recordings, etc,* University of London AV Centre, 11 Bedford Square, London WC1B 3RA

McGraw-Hill Publishing Co Ltd, AV Department, Shoppenhangers Road, Maidenhead, Berks, SL6 2QL (Attention: Mr Hugh Murray, Training and Development Manager) (Film)

Millbank Films, Thames House North, Millbank, London SW1P 4QG (Film)

National Audio Visual Aids Centre (NAVAC), *Audio-Visual and Video Equipment Survey,* EFVA, Paxton Place, Gipsy Road, London SE27 9SR

National Audio-Visual Aids Library (NAVAL), *see* Educational Foundation for Visual Aids

National Film Board of Canada, 1 Grosvenor Square, London W1X 0AB (Film)

North Staffordshire Polytechnic, *Computers in Economics – Program Index,* Economics Department, North Staffordshire Polytechnic, College Road, Stoke-on-Trent ST4 2DE

University of Nottingham, *Materials bulletin* (published biennially), Department of Linguistics, University of Nottingham, University Park, Nottingham NG7 2RD

Open University, *Film Library,* c/o Guild Sound & Vision Ltd, Woodston House, Oundle Road, Peterborough PE2 9PZ

Other Cinema, 12/13 Little Newport Street, London WC2 7JJ (Film)

Edward Patterson Associates Ltd 68 Copers Cope Road, Beckenham, Kent (Various media and subjects)

Pyramid Film & Video, PO Box 1048, Santa Monica, California 90406, USA (Film, video – wide subject coverage)

Random Film Library, 25 The Burroughs, Hendon, London NW4 4AT (Film – general)

Rank Aldis Audio Visual Ltd, PO Box 70, Great West Road, Brentford, Middlesex TW8 9HR (Film)

Roundtable, 113 North San Vicente Boulevard, Beverly Hills, California, CA 90211 (Film, video, multimedia – industrial training)

SAGSET, Centre for Extension Studies, University of Technology, Loughborough, Leics LE11 3TU *(Resource Lists* of games and simulation kits available in various subjects)

Scottish Central Film Library, *Catalogue,* 74 Victoria Crescent Road, Glasgow G12 9JN

Seminar Cassettes, 218 Sussex Gardens, London W2 3DU (Audio-tapes – general subjects)

Sheffield City Polytechnic, Instructional Technology Unit, *Register of learning resources for management education,* ITU, Sheffield City Polytechnic, Collegiate Crescent, Sheffield

Shell Film Library, 25 The Burroughs, Hendon, London NW4 4AT (Film)

Stewart Film Distributors Ltd, 107-115 Long Acre, London WC2E 9NU

Sussex Tapes, *see* Educational Productions Ltd

TFI (Training Films International), St Mary's Street, Whitchurch, Shropshire

Trent Polytechnic, *Directory of resource materials for teachers of technology in schools,* National Centre for School Technology, Trent Polytechnic, Burton Street, Nottingham

US National Audio-Visual Center, *Media For Government by Government,* National AV Center, National Archives & Records Service, General Services Administration, Reference Section EG,

Washington DC 20409
(Office training – various media)

Video Arts, Dumbarton House,
68 Oxford Street, London W1N 9LA

Viscom Ltd, *Catalogue of 16mm films and Video Cassettes,* Viscom Ltd, Parkhall Road Trading Estate, Dulwich, London SE21 8EL
(Wide subject range)

Welsh Office Film Library
Oxford House, Hills Street,
Cardiff CF1 2XG

Woodmansterne Ltd, Holywell Industrial Estate, Watford, Herts WD1 8RD
(Slides – educational and general)

Section 6: A Guide to Audiovisual Hardware on the Market

Introduction

This section has been restructured and identifies manufacturers of particular categories of hardware (including microcomputers), followed by a cumulative producers list. It is felt that this will be more useful to readers since the pace of change in equipment and technology rapidly renders description of particular models of equipment out-of-date, while the formats in any category are now well-known (if not actually standardized).

For those seeking more detailed information, the National Audio Visual Aids Council produces an *Audio Visual and Video Equipment Survey* (see entry in Section 4: Educational Foundation for Visual Aids); similarly, the SCET produces the *Audio Visual Handbook,* edited by John Henderson and Fay Humphrys (published by Kogan Page). Both these sources include descriptions of specific items of equipment. For a detailed technical report on a particular item, however, the reader is advised to contact The Training and Educational Systems Testing Bureau (The Test Bureau, see Section 4). A fee may be charged for this service.

The categories of equipment listed here are:

1. Language laboratories and supplementary equipment
2. Teaching machines
3. Cine projectors (16mm)
4. Cine projectors (8mm)
5. Slide and filmstrip projectors and viewers
6. OHPs and episcopes
7. Videotape recorders
8. Audio-tape recorders and players
9. Microfiche viewers
10. Microcomputers

Audiovisual equipment producers listed by product

1. Language laboratories and supplementary equipment

Two main systems of language laboratory are in common use in educational systems, and are indicated in this list by the abbreviations shown here:

AA *Audio-Active Language Laboratory:* equipment where each individual student has only LISTEN and RESPOND facilities, but no personal recording facilities for comparing his own attempts with the master version. The teacher's console may have facilities for recording the attempts of individual students selected by the teacher.

AAC *Audio-Active-Comparative Language Laboratory:* equipment where each student not only has LISTEN and RESPOND facilities, but also has full personal RECORD facilities for recording his own attempts.

APT Radar Systems Ltd (AA;AAC)
Aiwa (UK) Ltd (AAC)
Amos of Exeter Ltd (ancillary
 equipment)
Avcom Systems Ltd (Telex) (AAC)
F W O Bauch Ltd (AAC)
W J & M Baylis Ltd (AA; AAC)
Clarke & Smith Manufacturing Co Ltd
 (AA; AAC)
ESL Bristol Ltd (AA; AAC)
Force Ten Co Ltd (AA; AAC)
R W Friedel & Co Ltd (AA; AAC)
Goodsell Ltd (AAC)
Hanimex (UK) Ltd (supplementary
 equipment)
Leevers-Rich Equipment Ltd
 (supplementary equipment)
Linguaphone Institute Ltd
Philips Electrical Ltd (mini-labs and
 supplementary equipment)
Revox (AA; AAC)
Sign Electronics Ltd (AA; AAC)
Smiths (Electrical Engineers) Ltd (AA;
 AAC)
Sony Ltd (AA; AAC)
Specialist Audio-Visual Co
 (supplementary equipment)
Stereoscopic Television Ltd (AAC)
Stillitron (AAC)
Tandberg Ltd (AA; AAC)
Uher Ltd (AAC)
World of Learning Ltd

2. Teaching machines

E J Arnold & Sons Ltd
Bell & Howell AV Ltd
ESL Bristol Ltd
Packman Research Ltd
Rank Aldis Audio Visual Ltd
Stillitron

3. Cine projectors (16mm)
(all with sound)

AV Distributors London Ltd

AV8
Bell & Howell AV Ltd
Bolex
CZ Scientific Instruments Ltd
ESL Bristol Ltd
Elf Audio Visual Ltd
Elmo
Fumeo
Gordon Audio-Visual Ltd
Goring-Kerr Ltd
Interphoto Ltd
Kem Electronic Mechanisms Ltd
Lara (UK) Ltd
Lee's Cameras (Holborn) Ltd
E Leitz (Instruments) Ltd
Microtecnia
Photax (London) Ltd
Rank Aldis Audio Visual Ltd
Singer
Viewlex AV Inc

4. Cine projectors (8mm)

The following abbreviations are used:
 C – cassetted (silent)
 Cs – cassetted (with sound)
 S – silent
 WS – with sound

AV Distributors London Ltd
AV8
Bauer
Beaulieu
Braun Electric (UK) Ltd
CZ Scientific Instruments Ltd
ESL Bristol Ltd
Elmo
Eumig (UK) Ltd
Fairchild
Fumeo (WS)
Gordon Audio-Visual Ltd
Goring-Kerr Ltd
Kem Electronic Mechanisms Ltd
Lara (UK) Ltd
Lee's Cameras (Holborn) Ltd
E Leitz (Instruments) Ltd

Minolta (UK) Ltd (WS)
Photax (London) Ltd
Sanyo Marubeni (UK) Ltd (WS)
THD Manufacturing Ltd
Technicolor Ltd (C; CS)

5. Slide and filmstrip projectors and viewers

Abbreviations used:
S – Slide projector
S/FS – Slide and filmstrip projector
F/S – Filmstrip projector
V – Slide and/or filmstrip viewer
VS – Slide and/or filmstrip viewer with sound

Agfa-Gevaert Ltd (S; V)
Avcom Systems Ltd (FS; S; VS)
Avtec Audio-Visual Ltd (V)
Bell & Howell AV Ltd (S/FS; VS)
Braun Electric (UK) Ltd (S)
CZ Scientific Instruments Ltd (S/FS)
Clear Light (VS)
Dukane (S/FS; VS)
ESL Bristol Ltd (S/FS; V)
Edric Audio-Visual Ltd (V; VS)
Elf Audio Visual Ltd (VS)
George Elliott & Sons Ltd (S)
Elmo (S/FS; VS)
Fairchild (VS)
GAF (GB) Ltd (S)
Gnome Photographic Products Ltd (S)
Gordon Audio-Visual Ltd (S; V)
Hanimex (UK) Ltd (S/FS; S)
Highgate-Dufay Ltd (S)
Imatronic Ltd (S)
International Tutor Machines Ltd (S/FS)
Johnsons of Hendon Ltd (S)
Kindermann (SR; S; VS)
Kodak Ltd (S; VS)
La Belle Industries (Canada) Ltd (VS)
Lee's Cameras (Holborn) Ltd
E Leitz (Instruments) Ltd (S/FS; S)
Liesegang (S/FS; S)
Malinverno (S/FS; V)
Philips Electrical Ltd (S)
Prestinox (S/FS; S)
Prima (FS; S; V; SR)
Rank Aldis Audio Visual Ltd (FS/S; S; V)
Rollei (UK) Ltd (S)
J J Silber Ltd (S; V)
Simda (S; VS)
Singer (VS)
Specialist Audio Visual Co (S/FS; S; V)
THD Manufacturing Ltd (S/FS)
Technicolor Ltd (VS)

6. OHPs and episcopes

E J Arnold & Sons Ltd

Bell & Howell AV Ltd
Braun Electric (UK) Ltd
CZ Scientific Instruments Ltd
Clarke & Smith Manufacturing Co Ltd
Dixons Professional
Demolux
Elf Audio Visual Ltd
Elite Optics Ltd
George Elliott & Sons Ltd
Elmo
Erskine-Westayr (Engineering) Ltd
Fordigraph
Gordon Audio-Visual Ltd
Ilado
International Tutor Machines Ltd
Kindermann
E Leitz (Instruments) Ltd
Liesegang
Lumatic
Ofrex Ltd
Ormig
Ozalid (UK) Ltd
Paul Plus
Projection Optics Co Inc
Rank Aldis Audio Visual Ltd
Specialist Audio-Visual Co
THD Manufacturing Ltd
3M United Kingdom Ltd
Weyel

7. Video tape recorders

Various videocassette formats currently exist, and are indicated after each manufacturer's name as appropriate:

Betamax (Sony system)
U-matic
VCC (Video compact cassette – Philips)
VCR
VHS

Akai (VHS)
Ampex (GB) Ltd
Bell & Howell AV Ltd
Dixons Professional
Ferguson (VHS)
J O Grant & Taylor (London) Ltd
Grundig International Ltd (VCR; VCC)
Hitachi Sales (UK) Ltd (U-matic; VHS)
IVC – International Video Corporation (UK) Ltd
JVC (UK) Ltd (U-matic; VHS)
Mitsubishi Corporation (VHS)
National Panasonic (UK) Ltd (VHS; U-matic)
Normende (VHS)
Philips Electrical (VCR; VCC)
Pye Business Communications Ltd
Radio Rentals Contracts Ltd

Rank Aldis Audio Visual Ltd
  VCR; VHS)
Sanyo Marubeni (UK) Ltd (Betamax)
Sharp Electronics (UK) Ltd (VHS)
Sony Ltd (U-matic; Betamax)
Technicolor Ltd (VCC)
Toshiba (Betamax)

8. Audio-tape players and recorders

Abbreviations used below indicate:

CP – Cassette player
CR – Cassete recorder
R – Radio only
RC – Radio cassette recorder
RR – Reel-to-reel

Aiwa (UK) Ltd (CR)
Akai (CR; RR)
Ampex (GB) Ltd
Avcom Systems Ltd (CP; CR)
F W O Bauch Ltd (RR; CR)
Bell & Howell AV Ltd (CR)
Clarke & Smith Manufacturing Co Ltd
  (CP; R; RC)
Coomber Electronic Equipment Ltd
  (CP; CR; R; RC)
Farnell AV Ltd (CR; RC)
Ferguson (CR; RC; RR)
Ferrograph (CR; RR)
Goodsell Ltd (CP; CR; RC; R)
Grundig International Ltd (CR; RR;
  RC)
Hacker Sound Ltd (RC; R)
Hanimex (UK) Ltd (CR)
Hitachi Sales (UK) Ltd (CR; RC)
ITT Consumer Products Ltd (CR; RC)
JVC (UK) Ltd (CR; RC; RR)
Marantz Audio Ltd (CR; RC)
National Panasonic (UK) Ltd (CR; RR)
Philips Electrical Ltd (CR; RR; RC)
Pioneer (GB) Ltd (RR)
Rank Aldis Audio Visual Ltd (CP; CR;
  RR)
Revox (CR; RR)
Sanyo Marubeni (UK) Ltd (CR; RC)
Sony Ltd (CR; RR)
Tandberg Ltd (CR; RR)
Technics (CR; RR)
Uher Ltd (RR)
3M United Kingdom Ltd (CR)
Variable Speech Control (RR; CR)
Wollensak (CR)

9. Microfiche viewers

W O Bauch Ltd
Graphic Data
Microphax Ltd
Microscot Ltd
THD Manufacturing Ltd

10. Microcomputers

Acorn Computers Ltd – 'Atom'
Altos Computer Systems
Apple Computer Inc
Atari Consumer Division
Commodore Business Machines   (Pet)
Compucolor Corp
Cromenco Inc
Exidy
Hewlett-Packard Ltd (HP5036,
  HP85)
ITT Consumer Products Ltd
Industrial Microsystems Inc
L J Electronics Ltd (micro
  equipment and ancillaries)
Newbury Laboratories Ltd
North Star Computers Inc
Rair Computers
Research Machines Ltd (380Z)
Rockwell International AIM 65
Sharp Electronics (UK) Ltd
Sinclair Research Ltd
Tandberg Ltd
Tandy Corporation (UK) Ltd
Tangerine Computer Systems Ltd
Texas Instruments Ltd

Addresses of producers of audiovisual hardware

APT Radar Systems Ltd
Cybervox Language Laboratory Ltd,
Sprint Industrial Estate,
Chertsey Road,
Byfleet,
Surrey

AV Distributors London Ltd
26 Park Road,
Baker Street,
London NW1 4SH

AV8
19 Garway Road,
London W2

Acorn Computers Ltd
4a Market Hill,
Cambridge CB2 3NJ

Agfa-Gevaert Ltd
27 Great West Road,
Brentford,
Middx TW8 9AX

Aiwa (UK) Ltd
30-32 Concorde Road,
Westwood Park Trading Estate,
Western Avenue,
London W3 0TH

Akai – *see* Rank Audio Visual

Altos Computer Systems
Sunnyvale,
CA 94086,
USA

Amos of Exeter Ltd
2 Barnfield Crescent,
Exeter EX1 1QT

Ampex (GB) Ltd
Acre Road,
Reading,
Berks RG2 1QR

Apple Computer Inc
10260 Blondley Drive,
Cupertino,
CA 95014,
USA
UK Distributors:
Microsene Computers Ltd
Finway Road,
Hemel Hempstead,
Herts HP2 7PS

E J Arnold & Sons Ltd
Butterley Street,
Leeds LS10 1AX

Atari Consumer Division
1265 Borregas Avenue,
PO Box 427,
Sunnyvale,
CA 94086,
USA
UK Distributors:
Ingersoll Ltd
202 New North Road,
London N1

Audio Visual Media Ltd
AVM House,
1 Alexandra Road,
Farnborough,
Hants GU14 6BU

Audio-Visual Methods Ltd – *see* Elf
Audio Visual Ltd

Avcom Systems Ltd
Newton Works,
Stanlake Mews,
Stanlake Villas,
London W12 7HS

Avtec Audio-Visual Ltd
Sherbourne House,
247 Humber Avenue,
Coventry

F W O Bauch Ltd
49 Theobald Street,
Borehamwood,
Herts WD6 4RZ
(distributor for Revox)

Bauer – *see* E Leitz Instruments Ltd

W J & M Baylis Ltd
611 Gorton Road,
Reddish,
Stockport,
Cheshire

Beaulieu
Maison Brandt Freres,
16 Rue de la Cerisaie,
94220 Charenton le Pont,
France

Bell & Howell AV Ltd
Alperton House,
Bridgewater Road,
Wembley,
Middx HA0 1EG

Bergen Expo Systems Inc
1088 Main Avenue,
Clifton,
NJ 07011,
USA

Bolex
14 Priestley Way,
London NW2 7TN

Braun Electric (UK) Ltd
Dolphin Estate,
Windmill Road,
Sunbury-on-Thames,
Middx

CZ Scientific Instruments Ltd
2 Elstree Way,
Borehamwood,
Herts WD6 1LD
(Distributor for Elmo)

Clarke & Smith Manufacturing Co Ltd
Melbourne House,
Melbourne Road,
Wallington,
Surrey

Clear Light,
Mynad AV Sales Ltd,
10-11 Great Newport Street,
London WC2

Commodore Business Machines
818 Leigh Road,
Slough,
Berks

Compucolor Corp
Intecolour D,
Norcross,
CA 30092,
USA

Coomber Electronic Equipment Ltd
58 The Tything,
Worcester WR1 1JT

Cromenco Inc
280 Bernardo Avenue,
Mountain View,
CA 94043,
USA
UK Distributor:
Comart,
PO Box 2,
St Neots,
Cambs PE19 4NY

Dixons Professional
7 Dean Street,
London W1V 5DE

Demolux – *see* Audio Visual Media Ltd

Dukane
Cintron Group,
Grove House,
551 London Rd,
Isleworth,
Middx TW7 4DS

ESL Bristol Ltd
Waverley Road,
Yate,
Bristol BS17 5RB

Edric Audio-Visual Ltd
34 Oak End Way,
Gerrards Cross,
Bucks SL9 8BR

Elf Audio Visual Ltd
836 Yeovil Road,
Trading Estate,
Slough,
Berks

Elite Optics Ltd
354 Caerphilly Road,
Cardiff CF4 4XJ

George Eliott & Sons Ltd
Ajax House,
Hertford Road,
Barking,
Esex 1G11 8BA
(Distributors for Liesegang)

Elmo – distributed by CZ Scientific
Instruments Ltd

Erskine-Westayr (Engineering) Ltd
PO Box 16,
Irvine,
Ayrshire KA12 8JL

Exidy
390 Java Drive,
Sunnyvale,
CA 94086,
USA
(UK distributors: various, see journals)

Fairchild – *see* Gordon AV Ltd

Farnell AV Ltd,
Kenyon Street,
Sheffield S1 48D

Ferguson,
Thorn EMI Ltd,
Thorn House,
Upper St Martin's Lane,
London WC2H 9ED

Ferrograph
c/o Audio Video Marketing Ltd,
Unit 21,
Royal Industrial Estate,
Jarrow,
Tyne & Wear NE32 9XX

Force Ten Co Ltd
20 Honeypots Road,
Mayford,
Woking,
Surrey

Fordigraph
Ofrex House,
Stephen Street,
London W1A 1EA

Fraser Peacock Associates (FPA) Ltd,
94 High Street,
Wimbledon Village,
London SW19 5EG

R W Friedel & Co Ltd
6 Frogmore Road,
Hemel Hempstead,
Herts HP3 9RW

Fumeo – *Distributed by:*
John King Films Ltd,
Film House,
71 East Street,
Brighton, Sussex BN1 1NZ

GAF (GB) Ltd
PO Box 70,
Blackthorne Road,
Colnbrook,
Slough, Berks

Gateway Educational Media – *see*
Viewtech Audio Visual Media

Gnome Photographic Products Ltd
Gnome Corner,
354 Caerphilly Road,
Cardiff CF4 4XJ

Goodsell Ltd
New England House,
New England Street,
Brighton,
Sussex BN1 4GH

Gordon Audio-Visual Ltd
Symes Mews,
37 Camden High St,
London NW1
(Distributors for Fairchild Ilado)

Goring-Kerr Ltd,
Hanover Way,
Windsor,
Berks

J O Grant & Taylor (London) Ltd
Arlingham House,
Bridgewater Road,
Wembley, Middx

Graphic Data
82 Edgeley Lane,
Clapham,
London SW4

Grundig International Ltd
42 Newlands Park,
London SE26 5NQ

Hacker Sound Ltd
St James' House,
Roman Road,
Blackburn, Lancs

Hanimex (UK) Ltd
Hanimex House,
Faraday Road,
Dorcan,
Swindon,
Wilts SN3 5HW

Hewlett-Packard Ltd
King Street Lane,
Winnersh,
Wokingham,
Berks

Highgate-Dufay Ltd
38 Jamestown Road,
London NW1 7ES

Hitachi Sales (UK) Ltd
Hitachi House,
Station Road,
Hayes, Middx UB3 4DR

ITT Consumer Products Ltd
Chester Hall Lane,
Basildon,
Essex

IVC-International Video Corporation (UK) Ltd
10 Portman Road,
Reading RG3 1JR

Ilado – *see* Gordon AV

Imatronic Ltd
Dorian House,
Rose Street,
Wokingham,
Berks

Industrial Microsystems Inc
628 N Eckhoff,
Orange,
California CA 92668,
USA
UK Distributors:
Equinox Computer Systems Ltd
Kleeman House,
16 Anning Street,
New Inn Yard,
London EC2A 3HB

International Tutor Machines Ltd
15 Holder Road,
Aldershot,
Hants GU12 4PU

Interphoto Ltd
11 Castle Street,
High Wycombe,
Bucks

JVC (UK) Ltd
Eldonwall Trading Estate,
6-8 Priestley Way,
Staples Corner,
London NW2 7AF

Johnsons of Hendon Ltd
Priestley Way,
London NW2 7TN

Kem Electronic Mechanisms Ltd
24 Vivian Avenue,
Hendon,
London NW11

Kindermann – *see* J J Silber Ltd

Kodak Ltd
PO Box 66,
Kodak House,
Station Road,
Hemel Hemstead,
Herts

L J Electronics Ltd
Francis Way,
Bowthorpe Industrial Estate,
Norwich NR5 9JA

La Belle Industries (Canada) Ltd –
distributed by Fraser Peacock Associates
Ltd

Lara (UK) Ltd
34 Oak End Way,
Gerrards Cross,
Bucks

Lee's Cameras (Holborn) Ltd
58 Holborn Viaduct,
London EC1A 2FD

Leevers-Rach Equipment Ltd
319 Trinity Road,
Wandsworth,
London SW18 3SL

E Leitz (Instruments) Ltd
48 Park Street,
Luton,
Beds LU1 3HP

Liesegang – see George Elliott & Sons
Ltd

Linguaphone Institute Ltd
Business Services Division,
108 Cromwell Road,
London SW7

Lumatic
Associated Visual Products,
Prospect House,
14-20 Prospect Place,
Welwyn, Herts AL6 9EN

Malinverno – distributed by Specialist
AV Co

Marantz Audio Ltd
193 London Road,
Staines,
Middx

Microphax Ltd
Canterbury House,
393 Cowley Road,
Oxford

Microscot Ltd
Merit House,
Edgware Road,
Colindale,
London NW9

Microtecnia
Pulse Ltd,
The Laboratory,
Romsey Road,
Cadnam,
Southampton SO4 2NN

**Minnesota Mining & Manufacturing
Co** – see Three M

Minolta (UK) Ltd
1-3 Tanners Drive,
Blakelands,
Milton Keynes MK14 5EW

Mitsubishi Corporation
Otterspool Way,
Watford,
Herts WD2 8LD

National Panasonic (UK) Ltd
300-318 Bath Road,
Slough,
Berks SL1 6JB

Newbury Laboratories Ltd
King Street,
Odiham,
Hants RG25 1NN

Nordmende
Unit 4,
Blackwater Way,
Ash Road,
Aldershot,
Hants GU12 4DL
or Postfach 448360,
2800 Bremen 44,
W Germany

North Star Computers Inc
1440 Fourth Street,
Berkeley,
CA 94710,
USA
(*UK distributors:* various, see journals)

Ofrex Ltd – see Fordigraph

Ormig
Werk Oeynhausen,
497 Bad Oeynhausen,
Brunhildestrasse 18,
W Germany

Ozalid (UK) Ltd
Langston Road,
Loughton,
Essex IG10 3TH

Packman Research Ltd
Twyford,
Reading RG10 9BB
Berks

Paul Plus – distributed by Photopia
International Ltd

Philips Electrical Ltd
City House,
420-430 London Road,
Croydon CR9 3QR

Photax (London) Ltd
Hampden Park Industrial Estate,
Eastbourne,
Sussex BN22 9BG

Photopia International Ltd
Hempstalls Lane,
Newcastle-under-Lyme,
Staffs ST5 0SW

Pioneer (GB) Ltd
The Ridgeway,
Iver,
Bucks SL0 9JL

Prestinox
Aico (UK) Ltd,
Aico House,
Faraday Road,
London Road Estate,
Newbury,
Berks RG13 2AD

Prima – distributed by Viewtech Audio
Visual Media

Projection Optics Co Inc
Florham Park,
NJ 07932,
USA

Pye Business Communications Ltd
Northfield Industrial Estate,
Beresford Avenue,
Wembley,
Middx

Radio Rentals Contracts Ltd
Apex House,
Twickenham Road,
Feltham,
Middx

Rair Computers,
30-32 Neal Street,
London WC2H 9PS

Rank Aldis Audio Visual Ltd
PO Box 70,
Great West Road,
Brentford,
Middx TW8 9HR

Research Machines Ltd
209 Cowley Road,
Oxford

Revox
c/o F W O Bauch Ltd

Rockwell International
Microelectronic Devices,
PO Box 3669,
Anaheim,
CA 92803,
USA

UK Distributor:
Pelco (Electronics) Ltd,
26-27 Regency Square,
Brighton,
Sussex BN1 2FH

Rollei (UK) Ltd
Dennington Industrial Estate,
Wellingborough,
Northants NN8 2RG

Sanyo Marubeni (UK) Ltd
8 Greycaine Road,
Watford WD2 4UQ

Sharp Electronics (UK) Ltd
Thorp Road,
Newton Heath,
Manchester M10 9BE

Sign Electronics Ltd
Lakedale Road,
London SE18 1PW

J J Silber Ltd
Engineers Way,
Wembley,
Middx HA9 0EA

Simda
c/o Programmed Presentations
(Hardware) Ltd,
10 St Martin's Court,
London WC2N 4AJ

Sinclair Research Ltd
6 Kings Parade,
Cambridge CB2 1SN

Singer – *see* Rank Aldis Audio Visual
Ltd

Smiths (Electrical Engineers) Ltd
Baldwin Street,
Bamber Bridge,
Preston PR5 6SR
Lancs

Sony Ltd
Commercial & Industrial Division,
Pyrene House,
Sunbury-on-Thames,
Middx TW16 7AT

Specialist Audio-Visual Co
127 Trafalgar Road,
Greenwich,
London SE10 9TX

Stereoscopic Television Ltd
41-43 Charlbert Street,
St John's Wood,
London NW8 6JN

Stillitron
72 New Bond Street,
London W1Y 0QY

THD Manufacturing Ltd
South Coast Road,
Peacehaven,
Sussex

Tandberg Ltd
81 Kirkstall Road,
Leeds LS3 1HR

Tandy Corporation (UK) Ltd
Bilston Road,
Wednesbury,
W Midlands WS10 7JN

Tangerine Computer Systems Ltd
Forehill,
Ely,
Cambs

Teaching Wall Systems Ltd
185 Walton Summit Centre,
Bamber Bridge,
Preston,
Lancs PR5 8AJ

Technicolor Ltd
Bath Road,
Harmondsworth,
West Drayton,
Middx

Technics – *see* National Panasonic

Texas Instruments Ltd
Manton Lane,
Bedford

3M United Kingdom Ltd
PO Box 1,
Bracknell,
Berks RG12 1JU

Toshiba (UK) Ltd
Toshiba House,
Frimley Road,
Frimley,
Camberley,
Surrey GU16 5JJ

Uher Ltd
28 Spencer Street,
St Albans AL3 5EG
Herts

Variable Speech Control (Tape Recorders) – *see* Audio Visual Media Ltd

Viewlex AV Inc
c/o Lees Cameras (Holborn) Ltd
58 Holborn Viaduct,
London EC1A 2FD

Viewtech Audio Visual Media
122 Goldcrest Road,
Chipping Sodbury,
Bristol BS17 6XF

Weyel c/o Teaching Wall Systems Ltd

Wollensak – *see* 3M United Kingdom Ltd

World of Learning Ltd
359 Upper Richmond Road West,
East Sheen,
London SW14 8QN

Producers of Audiovisual Hardware Marketed in the United Kingdom

The following list is based on the one which appeared in the 1978/79 Yearbook with the generous permission of the National Audio-Visual Association Inc of the United States. NAVA is the trade association for the audio visual industry in the US. It serves a diverse international membership, including dealers, manufacturers and producers of AV equipment and materials, and also many individuals who use AV products but are not engaged in the AV industry commercially. NAVA celebrated its 40th anniversary in 1979. It has an extensive programme of activities and publications; readers interested in membership should write to:

National Audio Visual Association Inc
3150 Spring Street, Fairfax, Virginia 22031, USA

NAVA's Audio Visual Equipment Directory is the most helpful source of information about AV equipment in the USA. All items are listed with full details and photographs, and lists include the full range of technicians' equipment, classroom equipment etc, as well as the presentation services listed here.

This section does not include a section for *microcomputers;* but, as these are marketed internationally, the addresses for most major manufacturers can be found in the UK listing.

Audiovisual equipment manufacturers listed by product

1. 16mm sound motion picture projectors

Front projection:
Atlantic Audio Visual Corp
Audio Visual Devices
Bell & Howell Co
Bergen Expo Systems Inc
Berrey Marketing Companies
Carbons Inc
Eastman Kodak Co
Eiki International Inc
Elmo Mfg Corp
Kalat Victor Corp
Mackenzie Laboratories
Optical Radiation Corp
Rangertone Research Inc
Singer Education Systems
Viewtex Audio Visual

16mm analysis projectors:
Eastman Kodak Co
Kalart Victor Corp
Lafayette Instrument Co
L-W International
Visual Instrumentation Corp

16mm interlock projectors:
Berrey Marketing Companies
W A Palmer Films Inc

2. 8mm sound motion picture projectors

8mm front projection:
AIC Photo Inc
Atlantic Audio Visual Corp
Bell & Howell Co
Buhl Inc
Canon USA Inc
Chinon Corp of America Inc
Elmo Mfg Corp
Eumig/Bolex (USA)
General Audio-Visual Inc
Sankyo Seiki (America) Inc
Technicolor Audio-Visual Systems

*8mm sound motion picture projectors
with built-in screen:*
AIC Photo Inc
A/V Concepts Corp
Chinon Corp of America Inc
Eastman Kodak Co
Eumig/Bolex (USA)
Fairchild Industrial Products Division
La Belle Industries Inc
MFO Videotronic Projector Corp
Technicolor Audio-Visual Systems

8mm analysis projectors:
Lafayette Instrument Co

3. Filmstrip projectors and viewers – silent

Front projection:
A/V Concepts Corp
Audio Visual Accessories & Supplies
  Corp
Dukane Corp
Prima Education Products
Singer Education Systems
Standard Projector & Equipment Co
Viewlex Audio Visual

*Silent filmstrip projectors with built-in
screen:*
Audio Visual Dynamics
General Audio Visual Inc
Singer Education Systems

*Filmstrip viewers –
magnification type:*
Prima Education Products
Standard Projector & Equipment Co
Viewlex Audio Visual

4. Sound filmstrip projectors

Front projection:
Audiscan Products Corp
Dukane Corp
Elmo Mfg Corp
La Belle Industries Inc
McLure Projectors Inc
Radmar Inc
Singer Education Systems
TM Visual Industries Inc

With built-in screen:
Audiscan Products Corp
Bell & Howell
Charles Beseler Co
Dukane Corp
Hitachi Sales Corp of America
La Belle Industries Inc
Singer Education Systems

With both front and rear capability:
Audiscan Products Corp
Fairchild Industrial Products Division

La Belle Industries Inc
RCS Division, Buhl Inc

5. Silent slide projectors

2x2" – front projection:
AV Services Inc
Atlantic Audio Visual Corp
Bergen Expo Systems Inc
Buhl Inc
Buhl Optical Co
Eastman Kodak Co
Eiki International Inc
General Audio-Visual Inc
Hanimex (USA) Inc
E Leitz Inc
Mackenzie Laboratories
Optical Radiation Corp
Range-tone Research Inc
Singer Education Systems
Sirtage Inc
George R Snell Associates Inc, Genarco
  Division
Spindler & Sauppe Inc
Tempo Audivision Inc
TM Visual Industries Inc
Viewlex Audio Visual

2x2" with built-in screen:
Atlantic Audio Visual Corp
Hoppmann Corp

3¼x4" and larger – front projection:
Charles Beseler Co
Hoppmann Corp
Kalart Victor Corp
Kliegl Bros
George R Snell Associates Inc, Genarco
  Division

6. Sound slide projectors

Front projection:
Creatron Inc
Fairchild Industrial Products Division
Radmar Inc
Singer Education Systems
Tiffen Manufacturing Corp
3M Co, Visual Products Division

With built-in screen:
Eastman Kodak Co
Singer Education Systems
Slide-o-Motion

With front and rear capability:
AVSP Inc
Audio Visual Contractors
Bell & Howell Co
Creatron Inc
Eastman Kodak Co
Fairchild Industrial Products Division
General Audio-Visual Inc

Singer Education Systems
Technicolor Audio-Visual Systems

7. Random access projectors

Atlantic Audio Visual Corp
Buhl Optical
Computronic Inc
Daystar Audio Visual Inc
Eastman Kodak Co
Hoppman Corp
Imagimation Inc
Mast Development Co
Optical Radiation Corp
George R Snell Associates Inc, Genarco
  Division
Spindler & Sauppe Inc
Tempo Audiovision Inc

8. Overhead projectors

Advanced Office Systems
Bell & Howell Co, Audio Visual
  Products Division
Charles Beseler Co
Buhl Inc
Buhl Optical
Demolux Inc
Elmo Mfg Corp
Hoppmann Corp
Kalart Victor Corp
Projection Optics Co Inc
George R Snell Associates Inc, Genarco
  Division
TM Visual Industries Inc
3M Co, Visual Products Division

9. Opaque projectors

Charles Beseler Co
Buhl Inc
Kalart Victor Corp
Luminos Photo Corp
Projection Optics Co
George R Snell Associates Inc, Genarco
  Division
Squibb-Taylor Inc
Standard Projector & Equipment Co
Testrite Instrument Co Inc
Weiser/Robodyne Corp

10. Micro-projectors and viewers (microscopic)

Audio Visual Accessories & Supplies
Bioscope Manufacturing Co
Ken-a Vision Manufacturing Co Inc
G Leitz Inc
Nikon Inc

11. Microform projectors and readers

DO Industries Inc

Dukane Corp
Alan Gordon Enterprises Inc
Karl Heitz Inc
Library Microfilms & Materials Co
Revox Systems
Taylor Merchant Corp
3M Co

12. Portable video equipment

Akai America
Javelin Electronics
Panasonic Co
Sanyo Electric Inc

13. Videotape recorders and players

Reel-to-reel:
Ampex Corp
Panasonic Co, Video Systems Division
Sanyo Electric Inc
Sony Corp of America

Cassette and cartridge:
Cinema Products Corp
JVC Professional Video Division US,
  JVC Corp
Javelin Electronics
Knox Manufacturing Co
Mini Base Systems Inc
NEC America Inc
Panasonic Co
Sanyo Electric Inc
Sony Corp of America
Toshiba America Inc
Videodetics Corp

14. Video cameras

Cinema Products Corp
Cohu Inc
JVC Professional Video Division
Javelin Electronics
Knox Manufacturing Co
NEC America Inc
Panasonic Co
Philips Broadcast Equipment Corp
Sanyo Electric Inc
Sharp Electronics Corp
Sony Corp of America
Thomson CSF Laboratories
Toshiba America Inc

15. Video receivers and monitors

Audiotronics
Electrohome Ltd
Hitachi Denshi Ltd
JVC Professional Video Division
NEC America Inc
Panasonic Co
Sanyo Electric Inc
Sharp Electronics Corp

Sony Corp of America
Videcom

16. Video projectors

Conrac Corp
General Electric Co
Image Magnification Inc
Kalart Victor Corporation

17. Video projection systems

Advent Corp
Fryan Audio Visual Equipment Co Inc
Keyser Video Inc
Knox Manufacturing Co
Panasonic Co
Sony Corp of America
United Ventures Inc

18. Record players

Monaural:
Audio Visual Accessories & Supplies
  (AVAS)
Audio Visual Devices
Audiotronics Corp
Califone International Inc
Dealers Audio-Visual Supply Corp
Hamilton Electronics Corp
McClure Projectors Inc
MPC Educational Systems Inc
Newcomb Audio Products Co

Stereo:
Audiotronics Corp
Califone International Inc
Dealers Audio-Visual Supply Corp
Hamilton Electronics Corp
MP Audio Corp
Newcomb Audio Products Co
Radio-Matic of America Inc

19. Audio-tape recorders and players

Reel-to-reel:
Ampex Corp, Audio Video Systems
  Division
GEL Systems Inc
Otari Corp
Rangertone Research Inc
Studer Revox America Inc
Tandberg of America Inc
Teac Corp of America
Telex Communications Inc
Wollensak/3M Co

Cassette/AG operated:
Audio Visual Devices
Audiotronics Corp
Avedex Inc
Califone International Inc
Hamilton Electronics Corp

MP Audio Corp
Newcomb Audio Products
Palca Inc
Sharp Electronics Corp
Sony Learning Systems
Tandberg of America Inc
Telex Communications Inc
Wollensak/3M Co

Cassette/battery only or battery/AC:
Audiotronics Corp
Audio Visual Accessories & Supplies
  Corp (AVAS)
Bell & Howell Co, Audio Visual
  Products Division
Califone International Inc
Cinema Sync Systems Inc
Hamilton Electronics Corp
Hitachi Sales Corp of America
Hochiyo Electric Sound Co Ltd
Instructional/Communications
  Technology Inc
MPC Educational Systems Inc
RMF Products Inc
Sharp Electronics Corp

Continuous loop:
Mackenzie Laboratories Inc

Rate controlled speech recorders:
Lexicon Inc
Teknicon Industries Ltd
The VSC Co

Audio-tape recorders and players with built-in synchronizers:
Audio Tutorial Systems
Audiotronics Corp
Audio Visual Dynamics Inc
Buhl Inc
Califone International Inc
Dukane Corp
Electronic Designers Inc
General Exhibits & Displays Inc
La Belle Industries Inc
Mackenzie Laboratories Inc
Optisonics HEC Corp
Radmar Inc
Sharp Electronics Corp
Sirtage Inc
Sync-Master Group
Telex Communications Inc
Tiffen Manufacturing Corp
Wollensak/3M Co

20. Learning systems including language laboratories

Fixed installations:
Avedex Inc
Califone International Inc

Educational Media Division Inc
Educational Technology Inc
Fleetwood Inc
GEL Systems Inc
Group Communication Systems Inc
J-Tec Associates Inc
Radio-Matic of America Inc
Sony Learning Systems
Tandberg of America Inc
Telex Communications Inc
Wollensak/3M Co

Mobile and portable equipment:
Avedex Inc
AVID Corporation
Califone International Inc
Earmark Inc
Educational Technology Inc
Fleetwood Inc
GEL Systems Inc
Interand Corp, Subsidiary of
   Instructional Dynamics Inc
McClure Projectors Inc
P/H Electronics
R-Columbia Products Co Inc
Sony Learning Systems
Telex Communications Inc
University Research Co
3M Co, Visual Products Division
Voxcom Division
Zeecraft Inc

Magnetic card readers:
Audiotronics Corp
Bell & Howell Co, Audio Visual
   Products Division
Califone International
Voxcom Division

Hearing handicapped:
Earmark Inc
Eckstein Bros Inc

21. Reading and tachistoscopic devices

Tachistoscopes:
A/V Concepts Corp
Califone International Inc
Educational Developmental Laboratories
Ralph Gerbrands Co Inc
Instructional/Communications
   Technology Inc
Lafayette Instrument Co

Controlled reading devices:
A/V Concepts Corp
Creative Curriculum Inc
Educational Developmental
   Laboratories
Instructional/Communications
   Technology Inc

Keystone View Division, Mast
   Development Co
Learning Systems Inc

Pacing devices:
AV Concepts Corp
Educational Developmental
   Laboratories

22. Programmed instruction equipment

With built-in screen:
Basic Education Computers Inc
Behavioral Controls Inc
Bell & Howell Co, Audio Visual
   Products Division
Borg-Warner Educational Systems
Ken Cook Education Systems
Dorsett Educational Systems Inc
Dukane Corp
Gould Inc
Instructional Industries Inc
Keystone View Division, Mast
   Development Inc
Mast Development Co
McMahon Electronic Engineering
Response Systems Corp
Tutorsystems, Division of Sargent-
   Welch Scientific Co

Digital/manual response:
Centurion Industries Inc
Educational Insights
Educational Technology Inc
Enrichment Reading Corp of America
Instructional Industries Inc
Response Systems Corp
Synsor Corp
TM Visual Industries Inc
Visual Horizons

Direct view:
Dorsett Educational Systems Inc
Educational Projections Co

Variable speed projectors:
Charles Beseler Co
La Belle Industries Inc

Alphabetical list of audiovisual equipment manufacturers

Advanced Office Systems
590 River Valley Road NW,
Atlanta,
GA 30328

Advent Corp
195 Albany Street,
Cambridge,
MA 02139

AIC Photo Inc
30 Montauk Boulevard,
Oakdale,
NY 11769

Akai America Ltd
2139 E DelAmo Boulevard,
Compton,
CA 90220

Ampex Corp
401 Broadway,
MS 11-13, Redwood City,
CA 94063

Atlantic Audio Visual Corp
630 Ninth Avenue,
New York,
NY 10036

Audiotronics Corp
PO Box 3997,
7428 Bellaire Avenue,
North Hollywood, CA 91609

Audiotronics Video Display Division
530 Fifth Avenue NW,
New Brighton, MN 55712

Audio Tutorial Systems
Division of Deckmar Design Specialists,
PO Box 1306,
1440 Canal Street,
Auburn, CA 95603

Audio-Visual Accessories & Supplies Corp (AVAS)
196 Holt Street,
Hackensack, NJ 07602

Audio Visual Contractors Co
6875 E Evans,
Denver, CO 80222

Audio Visual Devices
Division of Wolsten's Projector
House Inc,
38 Smith Street,
Irvington, NJ 07111

Audio Visual Dynamics Inc
92 Stuyvesant Avenue,
Newark, NJ 07106

Audio Visual Specialty Products
5888A Smiley Drive,
Culver City, CA 90230

Audiscan Products Corp
Advanced Communications Systems,
PO Box 1456,
1414 130th Avenue NE,
Bellevue, WA 98006

AV Concepts Corp
30 Montauk Boulevard,
Oakdale, NY 11514

Avedex Inc
PO Box 184,
7326 N Niles Center Road,
Skokie, IL 60076

AVID Corp
10 Tripps Lane,
East Providence, RI 02914

AV Services Inc
2 W 45th Street,
New York, NY 10036

AVSP (*see* Audio Visual Specialty
Products)

Basic Education Computers Inc
2772 S Randolph Street,
Arlington, VA 22206

Behavioral Controls Inc
PO Box 480,
1506 W Pierce Street,
Milwaukee, WI 53201

Bell & Howell Co
Audio Visual Products Division,
7100 McCormick Road,
Chicago, IL 60645

Bergen Expo Systems Inc
1088 Main Avenue,
Clifton, NJ 07011

Berrey Marketing Companies
Bauer Division,
Brooklyn-Queens Expressway West,
Woodside, NY 11377

Charles Beseler Co
8 Fernwood Road,
Florham Park, NJ 07932

Bioscope Manufacturing Co
PO Box 1492,
220 W Archer Street,
Tulsa, OK 74101

Borg-Warner Educational Systems
600 W University Drive,
Arlington Heights, IL 60004

Buhl Inc
5 Paul Kohmer Place,
Elmwood Park, NJ 07407

Buhl Optical Co
1009 Beech Avenue,
Pittsburgh, PA 15233

Califone International Inc
5922 Bowcroft Street,
Los Angeles, CA 90016

Canon USA Inc
10 Nevada Drive,
Lake Success, NY 11040

Carbons Inc
Xetron Division,
10 Saddle Road,
Cedar Knolls, NJ 07927

Centurion Industries Inc
167 Constitution Drive,
Menlo Park, CA 94025

Chinon Corp of America Inc
43 Fadem Road,
Springfield, NJ 07081

Cinema Products Corp
2037 Granville Avenue,
Los Angeles, CA 90025

Cinema Sync Systems
14261 Avenue,
Mendocine,
Irvine, CA 94107

Cohu Inc
Electronics Division
PO Box 623,
5725 Kearny Villa Road,
San Diego, CA 92112

Computronic Inc
1801 Century Park East 1221,
Los Angeles, CA 90067

Conrac Corp
Systems-East Division,
32 Fairfield Place,
West Caldwell, NJ 07006

Ken Cook Education Systems
12855 W Silver Spring Drive,
Butler, WI 53007

Creative Curriculum Inc
15681 Commerce Lane,
Huntington Beach, CA 92649

Creatron Inc
32 Cherry Lane,
Floral Park, NY 11001

Daystar Audio Visual Inc
3 Inverness Drive East,
Englewood, CO 80112

Dealers Audio-Visual Supply Corp
PO Box 105,
1 Madison Street,
East Rutherford, NJ 07073

Demolux
1 Madison Street,
East Rutherford, NJ 07073

DO Industries Inc
Kowa Optical Division,
317 E Chestnut Street,
Summit, NJ 14445

Dorsett Educational Systems Inc
PO Box 1226,
Norman, OK 73070

Dukane Corp
2900 Dukane Drive,
St Charles, IL 60714

Earmark Inc
449 Putnam Avenue,
Hamden, CT 06517

Eastman Kodak Co
343 State Street,
Rochester, NY 14650

Eckstein Bros Inc
4807 West 118th Place,
Hawthorne, CA 90205

Educational Developmental Laboratories
Division of McGraw-Hill Inc
1221 Avenue of the Americas,
New York, NY 10020

Educational Insights
20435 S Tilman Avenue,
Carson, CA 90746

Educational Media Division Inc
PO Box 20604,
2812 Quail Plaza,
Oklahoma City, OK 73120

Educational Projections Co
Division of Standard Projector &
Equipment Co Inc,
1911 Pickwick Avenue,
Glenview, IL 60025

Educational Technology Inc
2224 Hewlett Avenue,
Merrick, NY 11566

Eiki International Inc
27882 Camino Capistrano,
Laguna Niguel, CA 92677

Electrohome Ltd
809 Wellington Street North,
Kitchener,
Ontario

Electronic Designers Inc
372 Vanderbilt Motor Parkway,
Hauppage, NY 11787

Elmo Mfg Corp
70 New Hyde Park Road,
New Hyde Park, NY 11040

Enrichment Reading Corp of America
Iron Ridge, WI 53035

Eumig/Bolex USA
Lake Success Business Park,
225 Community Drive,
Great Neck, NY 11020

Fairchild Industrial Products Division
75 Mall Drive,
Commack, NY 11725

Fleetwood Inc
Electronics Division,
PO Box 58,
25 E Washington,
Zeeland, MI 49464

Fryan Audio Visual Equipment Co Inc
4369 Hamann Parkway,
Willoughby, OH 44094

GEL Systems Inc
1085 Commonwealth Avenue,
Boston, MA 02215

General Audio Visual Inc
333 West Merrick Road,
Valley Stream, NY 11580

General Electric Co
Video Display Equipment Operation,
Electronics Park 6-205,
Syracuse, NY 13201

General Exhibits & Displays Inc
2100 N Racine Avenue,
Chicago, IL 60614

Ralph Gerbrands Co Inc
8 Beck Road,
Arlington, MA 02174

Alan Gordon Enterprises
PO Box 3914,
5362 Cahuenga Boulevard,
North Hollywood, CA 91601

Group Communication Systems Inc
Subsidiary of Simons Office Systems Inc,
1801 Century Park East,
Suite 1221,
Los Angeles, CA 90067

Gould Inc
Educational Systems Division,
4423 Arden Drive,
El Monte, CA 91731

Hachiyo Electric Sound Co Ltd
43 W 61st Street,
New York, NY 10023

Hamilton Electronics Corp
2003 W Fulton Street,
Chicago, IL 60612

Hanimex (USA) Inc
1801 W Touhy Avenue,
Elk Grove Village, IL 60007

Karl Heitz Inc
979 Third Avenue,
New York, NY 10022

Hitachi Denshi America Ltd
Brooklyn-Queens Expressway,
Woodside, NY 11377
Also 21015-19 S Figueroa,
Carson, CA 90745

Hitachi Sales Corp of America
401 W Artesia Boulevard,
Compton, CA 90220

Image Magnification Inc
739 Airway Circle,
New Smyrna Beach, FL 32069

Imagimation Inc
233 Harvard Street,
Brookline, MA 02146

Instructional/Communications Technology Inc
10 Stepar Place,
Huntington Station, NY 11746

Instructional Industries Inc
Executive Park,
Ballston Lake, NY 12019

Interand Corp
Telestrator Division,
666 N Lakeshore Drive,
Chicago, IL 60611

Javelin Electronics
Apollo Lasers Inc,
PO Box 45002,
6357 Arizona Circle,
Los Angeles, CA 90045

J-Tec Associates Inc
317 Seventh Avenue SE,
Cedar Rapids, IA 52401

JVC Professional Video Division
58-75 Queens-Midtown Expressway,
Maspeth, NY 11378

Kalart Victor Corp
PO Box 112,
Hultenius Street,
Plainville, CT 06062

Ken-a-Vision Manufacturing Co Inc
5615 Raytown Road,
Raytown, MO 64133

Keyser Video Inc
2537 Wilmington Pike,
Dayton, OH 45419

Keystone View
Division, Mast Development Co,
2212 E 12th Street,
Davenport, IA 52803

Kliegl Bros
32-32 48th Avenue,
Long Island City, NY 11100

Knox Mnufacturing Co
111 Spruce Street,
Wood Dale, IL 60191

La Belle Industries Inc
PO Box 128,
510 Worthington Street,
Oconomowoc, WI 53066

Lafayette Instrument Co
PO Box 1279,
Lafayette, IN 47902

Learning Systems Inc
1535 Fen Park Drive,
Fenton, MO 63026

E Leitz Inc
Link Drive,
Rockleigh, NJ 07647

Lexicon Inc
60 Turner Street,
Waltham, MA 02154

Library Microfilms & Materials Co
707 Augusta Street,
Inglewood, CA 90302

Luminos Photo Corp
25 Wolffe Street,
Yonkers, NY 10705

L-W International
6416 Variel Avenue,
Woodland Hills, CA 91364

Mackenzie Laboratories Inc
PO Box 3029,
5507 N Peck Road,
Arcadia, CA 91006

Mast Development Co
2212 E 12th Street,
Davenport, IA 52803
See also Keystone View Co

McClure Projectors Inc
PO Box 7,
1215 Washington Avenue,
Wilmette, IL 60091

McMahon Electronic Engineering
381 W Seventh Street,
San Pedro, CA 90731

MP Audio Corp
Fairfield, CT 06430

MPC Educational Systems Inc
35 Fulton Street,
New Haven, CT 06512

MPO Videotronic Projector Corp
305 E 46th Street,
New York, NY 10017

NEC America Inc
130 Martin Lane,
Elk Grove Village, IL 60007

Newcomb Audio Products Co
12881 Bradley Avenue,
Sylmar, CA 91342

Nikon Inc
623 Stewart Avenue,
Garden City, NY 11530

Optical Radiation Corp
6352 N Irwindale Avenue,
Azusa, CA 91702

Optisonics HEC Corp
1802 W Grant Road,
Tucson, AZ 85705

Otari Corp
981 Industrial Road,
San Carlos, CA 94070

Palca Inc
c/o Avedex Inc (*qv*)

W A Palmer Films Inc
611 Howard Street,
San Francisco, CA 94105

Panasonic Co
Video Systems Division
1 Panasonic Way,
Secaucus, NJ 07094

P/H Electronics
117 E Helena Street,
Dayton, OH 45404

Philips Broadcast Equipment Corp
PO Box 618,
91 McKee Drive,
Mahwah, NJ 07430

Prima Education Products Division
Hudson Photographic Industries Inc,
2 S Buckhout Street,
Irvington, NY 10533

Projection Optics Co Inc
8 Fernwood Road,
Florham Park, NJ 07932

Radio-Matic of America Inc
760 Ramsey Avenue,
Hillside, NJ 07205

Radmar Inc
1282 Old Skokie Road,
Highland Park, IL 60035

Rangertone Research Inc
509 Madison Avenue,
New York, NY 10022

R-Columbia Products Co Inc
2008 St Johns Avenue,
Highland Park, IL 60035

RCS Division Buhl Inc
5 Paul Kohner Place,
Elmwood Park, NJ 07407

Response Systems Corp
PO Box 95,
Edgemount, PA 19028

Revox Systems Inc
2224 Hewlett Avenue,
Merrick, NY 11566

RMF Products Inc
PO Box 413,
Batavia, IL 60510

Sankyo Seiki (America) Inc
149 Fifth Avenue,
New York, NY 10010

Sanyo Electric Inc
1200 Artesia Boulevard,
Compton, CA 90220

Sharp Electronics Corp
PO Box 588,
10 Keystone Place,
Paramus, NJ 07652

Singer Education Systems
3750 Monroe Avenue,
Rochester, NY 14603

Sirtage Inc
PO Box 30691,
Umstead Industrial Park,
Raleigh, NC 27612

Slide-o-Motion Ltd
102-545 West 10th Avenue,
Vancouver, BC V5Z 1K9

George R Snell Associates Inc
155 US Route 22 East,
Springfield, NJ 07081

Sony Corp of America
VTR Division
9 W 57th Street,
New York, NY 10019

Sony Learning Systems
Educational Electronics Corp
213 N Cedar Avenue,
Inglewood, CA 90301

Spindler & Sauppe Inc
13034 Saticoy Street,
North Hollywod, CA 91605

Squibb-Taylor Inc
PO Box 20158,
10807 Harry Hines Boulevard,
Dallas, TX 75220

Standard Projector & Equipment Co Inc
1911 Pickwick Avenue,
Glenview, IL 60025

Studer Revox America Inc
1819 Broadway,
Nashville, TN 37203

Sync-Master Group, EEC Inc
213 N Cedar Avenue,
Inglewood, CA 90301

Synsor Corp
Building 501,
2927 112th Street SW,
Paine Field,
Everett, WA 98204

Tandberg of America Inc
Labriola Court,
Armonk, NY 10504

Tandom Division, United Ventures Inc
2323 Bluemound Road,
Waukesha, WI 53186

Taylor Merchant Corp
25 W 45th Street,
New York, NY 10036

TEAC Corp of America
PO Box 750,
7733 Telegraph Road,
Montebello, CA 90640

Technicolor Audio-Visual Systems
299 Kalmus Drive,
Costa Mesa, CA 92626

Teknicon Industries Ltd
305 Seventh Avenue,
New York, NY 10001

Telex Communications Inc
9600 Aldrich Avenue South,
Minneapolis, MN 55420

Tempo Audivision Inc
290 Larkin Street,
Buffalo, NY 14210

Testrite Instrument Co Inc
135 Monroe Street,
Newark, NJ 07105

Thomson-CSF Laboratories
37 Brownhouse Road,
Stamford, CT 06902

Tiffen Manufacturing Corp
90 Oser Drive,
Haupauge, NY 11787

TM Visual Industries Inc
25 W 45th Street,
New York, NY 10036

Toshiba America Inc
280 Park Avenue,
New York, NY 10017

Tutorsystems
Division of Sargent-Welch Scientific Co
7300 N Linder Avenue,
Skokie, IL 60076

United Ventures Inc
(*See* Tandom Division)

University Research Co
7581 Palos Verdes Drive,
Goleta, CA 93017

Videcom
Division of General Technical
Products Inc,
328 Maple Avenue,
Industrial Park,
Horsham, PA 19044

Viewlex Audio Visual Inc
3 Broadway Avenue,
Holbrook, NY 11741

Visual Horizons
208 Westfall Road,
Rochester, NY 14620

Visual Instrumentation Corp
903 N Victory Boulevard,
Burbank, CA 91502

Voxcom Division, Tapecon Inc
PO Box 2520,
100 Clover Green,
Peachtree City, GA 30269

The VSC Corp
Variable Speech Control Company
185 Berry Street,
Suite 3850,
San Francisco, CA 94107

Weiser/Robodyne Corp
949 Bonifant Street,
Silver Spring, MD 20910

Wollensak/3M Co
3M Center, Building 223-5E,
St Paul, MN 55101

Zeecraft Inc
PO Box 7,
West Midland Drive,
Norwich, NY 13815

3M Co
Magnetic A/V Products Division,
3M Center, Building 225-5N,
St Paul, MN 55101
Microfilm Products Division
3M Center, Building 220-9E,
St Paul, MN 55101
Visual Products Division
3M Center, Building 220-10W,
St Paul, MN 55101
(*See also* Wollensak/3M Co)